White
The king's good servant

THE KING'S GOOD SERVANT

THE MACMILLAN COMPANY
NEW YORK · BOSTON · CHICAGO · DALLAS
ATLANTA · SAN FRANCISCO

MACMILLAN & CO., Limited
LONDON · BOMBAY · CALCUTTA
MELBOURNE

THE MACMILLAN COMPANY
OF CANADA, Limited
TORONTO

The King's Good Servant

By

Olive B. White

NEW YORK

THE MACMILLAN COMPANY

1936

Published April, 1936 Reprinted November, 1936.

Printed in the United States of America, by the National Process Company, Inc., New York, N. Y.

To My Mother

CONTENTS

I

"COMPASSED ALL ROUND"

CHAPTER I

THE most splendid day the old city had ever known! Already Thomas More had heard that boast a dozen times since his return from the cathedral. He had listened to the cheering in the narrow road before the abbey gate, the heroic effort at congratulation of the most timorous scullion imaginable—how some one must have beaten that child!—the school-boy murmuring of a little clump of novices waiting for him in the cloister, and but a moment since the quiet words of the Prior, who was a man old enough and thoughtful enough to see more than pageantry and largesse in this crowning of the excitement that had kept Cambrai ecstatic through these midsummer weeks of negotiation. From bits of the Prior's autobiography spoken casually during the past week—"in my father's hall at Tournai" and "those evil days when we besieged Thérouanne"—More had pieced out the picture of this man's life. It was little wonder that one who had grown to manhood in these fair, bloody provinces of Artois and Picardy, who had ridden in arms himself, and had in his middle years renounced a seigneury that meant always war and the soul-destroying alarms of war, should speak of this new peace more sadly than those who delighted in the full panoply of war, disguised now for a little while in the triumphal procession of a treaty. Strange that men made peace to the accompaniment of martial music, that they looked up from their deliberations to their rival badges and ensigns against the gray walls, that no light fell on them in their councils that did not glint on temporarily idling pikes and battle-axes. The swords were sheathed;

the cannon were too ugly for a pageant; but otherwise men came to treat of peace as if they might stay to fight.

God willing, though, this peace that they had made might last a lifetime. And if England, France, and the Empire could keep the peace for a lifetime, More thought, its pleasant ways might so insinuate themselves in men's gratitude that the children of those who had known war and their children's children would find it hard to believe that men had ever thought resort to arms an honorable way to settle the quarrels of princes. Always the settling was done afterwards, as in these days that had turned the head of Cambrai. Men sat down to write and talk and count their treasure and their land; they yielded a point here and demanded one there in return; and at the end they sang *Te Deum* and came bewildered from the glory of the cathedral to face the shouting, cheering populace. This morning the apprentices among the chimney-stacks had added their treble to the chant of their angelic brothers in the choir before the high altar. God willing, this peace would endure.

The people of Cambrai were right to exult, for to few cities come those undimmed high hours when men unite in a great enthusiasm. Soon enough the exaltation drifts to earth like a wounded bird, for policy and suspicion are shrewd falcons. But now one could bless his fellows and admit mankind to the praising company of all the rest of creation, from which sin seemed too often to exclude it. Now one could think of amity and peace, and welcome them, thrice-prayed for. More smiled to catch himself remembering the phrase from Homer to serve the modern turn. But so golden a day as this made the human fellowship of pagan and Christian as natural as the accord between France and Austria, for on the most gracious days that the time of man knows the mere illusory nature of time comes most sharply home to him.

Before the smiling mood with its little train of memories—

especially of his father's mistrust thirty years before of how well the pagan poets would consort with sensible English law—had passed from the forecourt of his musing, More heard a fresh huzzahing in the street. The sound clapped merrily in the tiles across the narrow way from his high chamber in the guest house; so he listened for a moment before he strained atip-toe to look from his dormer window towards the gate of the abbey. At best it was a crooked, sidelong view he could get of anyone approaching, and now the glare of the sunlight on stone and tile confused his vision. But the cheer was such a one as the town had been spending on the foreign ambassadors, and one glimpse of gold flashing in the cap of him who bowed in the gateway reminded the watcher: this was not the Bishop of London come back from the episcopal palace nor any other of their English embassy, but the Venetian who, accosting him yesterday with great courtliness, had asked a few moments' audience. Here he had come prompt to his appointment, for the bells were sounding the first soft, tentative notes of their summons of the monks to chapel. Half-reluctant to abandon his day-dream, More turned from the window and stepped from the triangle of sunlight on the stone floor back into the coolness of the room. The change reanimated his sense of business; so he gave his apartment a hasty glance to see that it was reasonably tidy for the reception of his unknown guest. He had been here just long enough, he reflected, to feel a certain proprietorship in the cumbrous, dark furniture which—to judge by the medley of carved insignia on the chests and wardrobes that lined the room—must have come to the abbey in many different bequests.

A two-paced clicking down the long gallery took him out to the head of the stairway, for he would save the lame lay-brother, who was coming to announce the visitor, some steps on his errand. Lamed in the wars, the man had told him and had added, gayly indeed for one forty years hobbled, "And that was once, your worship, that the devil did the Lord's work, for in a manner of speaking he drove me to serve God and His blessed saints." A pretty piece of theology, More thought, as he listened to the receding steps and then their returning volume, this time with the obbligato of a light, confident step, along the gallery below and up the dark well of the stairway.

Though they exchanged salutations at the head of the stairs, More could see his guest only in dim bulk until they came into the light of his chamber. The man was taller than he, poised in bearing and speech, well-versed in the amenities of cosmopolitan intercourse. So much of an appraisal More had been able to make in the twilight of the corridor; the fuller light into which they came confirmed the good impression, and added to it the challenging recognition of half familiarity in the eager dark face that seemed to be searching his own in recollection.

"You must have wondered at me, sir, that I was so bold as to pluck your sleeve in the throng yesterday and call you by name." The voice was rich and warm even through the little strain put upon it by the long stairs; not quite Venetian in accent, however. "What my kinsman, Antonius Bonvisi, has—"

"Antonius! Welcome indeed. Had his kinsman not spoken to me, I should have been sorry. Suppose he had asked me about you?"

"I should have written him that I had seen you at a distance but been afraid to address you."

"And he would have laughed at you for your pains. Afraid of Thomas More, lawyer of London!" More saw the laughter in his own voice answered merrily in the brown, quick eyes of his visitor.

They sat down in the stiff, high-backed settle, put at ease by the name of a kinsman and a friend as if they were old acquaintances.

"Perhaps not of the lawyer of London, for I have heard much of him," the Italian corrected, "but of the great King's envoy."

"Does the rôle so mar the man?" But More was sorry for the half sigh he had let play through the words, for the candid face clouded in uncertainty of interpretation. It takes time for men to be so sure of each other's tempers that words run no risk of being false counters. And he did not even know his guest's name. "Are you a Bonvisi also?"

"Yes, his cousin Piero. We are both far-wandered from Lucca, for I have been in Venice nearly as long as he has been in London."

"But that is more than thirty years." Though this brown, lean face could never have looked very young, it was such a one as lingers for years in the middle range, keeping firm while fleshier ones sag and crease. The smiling eyes made a slight admission.

"I am a little younger. Not much, though."

"You are very like him in voice and manner, the subtle things that are family ways. When you came in, I felt I ought to recognize you."

"Mannerisms are tenacious, aren't they?" The pride and pleasure that this man had in his cousin were sweet to More's observation. "And you, sir, if I may venture, are very like—" But the boldness broke off in awe.

"Like what?"

"The pictures of you that Antonius has given, and the one in Erasmus's letter to Ulrich von Hutten."

More wanted to laugh again, but it was not easy with this earnestness that sat a little stiffly behind the grace of a man at ease more because he had been much abroad than because he had innate facility. Here was really a shy nature that wanted to be confident.

"Though Antonius is a conscientious man, I fear he is partial, too. And surely, you can understand that Erasmus not only made generous allowances for my faults, but also wrote with some thought to the whole effect in print. That is the liberty of letters that we cannot grudge even when it puts a strain on poor nature. It is a sound prayer that asks that we be made worthy of the good opinion of our friends. But are you a scholar?"

"No, trade is in the blood. Ever since I went to Venice, though, I have met scholars in the house of Aldus, who has been a good friend. Again and again the Englishmen have spoken of you."

"Who are some of them? The house of Aldus has certainly been a temple of the Muses for northern scholars, and those I have known always speak enthusiastically of all his friends."

"Only last summer we had your ambassador, Dr. Stephen."

"Stephen Gardiner? Yes, he is an able man—more at home in law, I suspect, than in the humanities."

"But years ago, the very first northerner I met in Venice was Linacre."

"How fortunate England was in that! He showed you our scholarship at its best."

"And more than that. Some great mockers I knew used to scoff at the English as barbarians; and his courtliness and urbanity put even them to silence."

"That is as fine a tribute to a friend as I ever heard."

"Then would you not have me believe what he said of you?"

More smiled, as much at the adroitness with which Bonvisi had netted him in the compliment as with pleasure in the recollection of an old friend.

"Ah, but we know that it was what Linacre was and did, rather than what he said of people he liked, that silenced the scoffers. I am by no means ungrateful to the dead, but I know he was always generous. He would not have judged any man meanly." He could not speak to this near-stranger—kind as he was—the sequent thought flooding through the opened gate of feeling. In that moment, remembering the devotion that had bound Linacre to King Henry, More was glad that he had not lived to know with mortal limitations the change of the last few years. In this world it is very hard for men not to judge, yet not by their silence to condone. As he had done for months, he forced the chilling thought away. This was small courtesy to his guest. The latter, he noticed gratefully, sat musing too—on a happier theme than his had been if the even brows spoke truly of what passed behind them. When their eyes met again, Bonvisi smiled apologetically.

"Since I am no scholar," he said, "you must forgive me. I did not force myself upon you just to talk like a gawking schoolboy. You did me a service once, Sir Thomas, for which I can say 'Thank you,' straightforwardly."

"A service? From compliments you turn to riddles."

"No, really. A dozen years ago you saved an agent of mine in the rioting on—what have I heard it called?—'Evil May Day.' "

"Oh! Again, though, I think I must be getting the credit of other men's good deeds."

"No, this time I am sure of what I say. It was the poor fellow's first day in London; so every detail of his experience took hold. He has talked of it often enough at home for me to tell it almost as well as he would—if not so feelingfully. Just by some gate the apprentices ran full tilt into him and were hustling him along with some Dutchmen they had seized when Saint George—his very epithet—rode up and reasoned with them and won their prisoners away from them. Of course, he could not understand what you said, but he swears you were eloquent as Saint Anthony of Padua himself."

"I'm grateful he didn't say Lucifer. And may my enemies hear some day that I was once taken for a saint. I remember that the men who rode into the city with me were able to save some foreigners the apprentices had attacked. We escorted them out of the district with us. Surely your agent did not mention you or your cousin, or I should have remembered him."

"He was so frightened he could say no more than that he was a Venetian, and one of your retainers helped him to sanctuary. Afterwards I meant to write you through my cousin; but such resolutions fail all too easily."

"I know." These decent, generous intentions, with which time has such work to keep pace, More recognized as tormenting familiars: there was always one more letter than leïsure allowed that it would be pleasant to write. "It was a little thing, though, small credit to me."

"Yet was it not debt enough in conscience to justify my accosting you yesterday?"

They laughed together at the swing of thought back to Bonvisi's compliments.

"I should have been sorry," More commented, "had you let me pass for lack of a reason for speaking. And your reason is not inappropriate, Master Bonvisi, with all this shouting of the apprentices to-day to remind us. This morning, as we entered the cathedral, I thought of the last such crowd I had seen—that very mob of boys and journeymen in Saint Nicholas' Shambles. With a difference, though." For an instant recollection dwelt on the melancholy sequel to that riot; and he saw again in his mind's eye not only the gallows erected at strategic points in the city, but also the lamentable picture of four hundred and more men and women, roped together and haltered, trudging into Westminster Hall to sue for their pardon before the King. It was a strange picture to be remembering now in the midst of festivity; so he added quickly, "Have you ever seen people more merry than these citizens of Cambrai?"

"They seem almost good Latins."

"True, Master Bonvisi. I was forgetting how natural this temper must seem to you."

"It's not common, however, in this intensity. Think what a month these people have had. Not much over a month ago, the porter at my lodgings says, the Archbishop made his first grand entry into the town. And since then, a queen, two princesses, three cardinals, two archbishops, six bishops—enough to make any city delirious."

"And in their delirium the people have been seeing some of their notables more than twice over. One of the novices here asked me the other day about the eight cardinals he had heard were in Cambrai."

Bonvisi laughed a deep, throaty chortle. "I have heard the whole census read more lavishly still. The six bishops have become thirty-three, and all the rest of us have multiplied in proportion. The plain truth is a distinguished company enough; so the populace should drink Madame the Princess's wine heartily and cheer the peace. But I delay you, for you must be going to the banquet."

"In a little while," More reassured him. "When the Bishop of London returns, it will be time for us to set out. I'm sorry, however, for our feasting. The money would be better laid out on plain fare for the people; wine is scanty largesse for hungry men."

"Hungry? Surely, there is not famine in this green land? We have been too generously entertained for that."

"The fear of famine, if not yet the reality, is dark upon them, the Prior tells me. Last year the harvest was very lean, and a warm, dry winter let the insects thrive till it seems as though the plagues of Egypt were loosed upon the fields. Some of these genial shouters will be silent with hunger before this winter is over."

"That is a shocking thought." The Italian's lips were drawn by the pain of pitifully imagining what one cannot avert.

"Yes, but it has some beauty in it, too." The cluttered permanence of gabled roofs and chimney-stacks on which they gazed conjured up for More thought of the restless, swiftly wasting lives beneath them—hopes and dreams, charity and thrift and covetousness, and above all courage to go on. "Being men, they know what lies before them; yet they cheer us who are eating up what little fat there is in the land."

Bonvisi rose abruptly. The filming of the warm brown eyes, however, robbed the movement of its brusqueness. "Sir, those who love you have called you a philosopher and a poet. I shall remember you as such."

"I thank God for my generous friends, and I pray I may some day attain the evenness of spirit that is the philosopher's." The catch in his own voice startled More. "But the title of poet I'm afraid I owe to the heretics, who dislike my style. Have you been reading them, Master Bonvisi?"

"Heaven forbid!" The exculpatory shrug was delightful. "I would not fall in danger of your bishop's inquisition."

"We are in neutral territory. And haven't you diplomatic immunity, anyway? But, seriously, do you think my Lord of London likely to be a harsh inquisitor?"

"Is this he of whom the talk has been? I meant to congratulate you on his address the other day. People have been praising the English ambassadors' candor and fairness. And your bishop's address had a splendid eloquence. He must be a scholar and a very sensitive man."

"Both. Yet he has been much railed at because he is conscientious and zealous for the good of his people."

"Some months ago, I know, I went a day's journey with a printer from Saxony, a fiery Lutheran, who harangued me on the grievances of his brothers, as he called them, in England. He said that London was terrorized by the cruelties of its bishop; so I had in mind a picture of a fierce, haughty prelate. Why, this man—" Amazement and admiration so mingled in

Bonvisi's expression that More wondered at the frank impetuosity that years of trading had not schooled to a sleek fashion.

"He is loved. And what he is cries down the calumny of his detractors. London, you know, is a great port, an easy place for strange men and strange ideas and, in these recent years, pestilential books to find harborage. It is a difficult see."

"Indeed, I can believe that a mere merchant sleeps more comfortably than a magistrate or a bishop in such a city. And abroad we hear so many different tales that it is hard to sift out the truth in them. For example, there is constant disagreement—as many opinions as men—about your King and his suit to His Holiness."

More glanced sharply at his visitor. Was he trying to sound him? But the kindly face bore no shadow of shrewdness or disingenuous confidence. "I am the servant of the King's Majesty," he contented himself with saying; while he could freely defend Bishop Tunstall, he could not enter at all into discussions of Henry's policies and motives.

Bonvisi smiled in frank recognition of the barrier. "Yes, of course. I did not think of how I was trespassing. Again, sir, I must go. How gladly I shall write my cousin of our meeting!"

"I shall have the advantage of telling him in person. He must invite you to England soon. And if you come to England without my seeing you—"

"But, Sir Thomas, how could that be?"

Yes, More liked this man who spoke whole-heartedly. As they passed by corridors and stairs to the great gate of the abbey, their last talk, like their first, was rightly of Antonius Bonvisi. And they parted in a warmth of good will that was the little personal echo of this festal graciousness imbuing all Cambrai.

Even after his visitor had stridden out of the sunny close, More stood in the gateway, glad for the beauty of this August noon. Across the far end of a mere crevice of an alley before him scarlet pennants streaked, and the houses were gray again. Wine from an ill-broached cask in some neighboring square flashed and cascaded among the cobbles at his feet. The now distant shouting sounded well wetted; but the sudden lifting of trumpets that sang beyond the close-set houses was as clear and sweet as in the morning. He must be ready for the banquet and for his speech of thanks on behalf of the English embassy. And in a few days they would ride homeward. In the moment of that thought he breathed the blended scents of the abbey garden in its midsummer blooming and knew that he was homesick for his own garden by the river. He would be hard to lure away again, could he once persuade the King to smile on his retirement from these affairs of state.

CHAPTER II

"Now we might think ourselves pilgrims instead of ambassadors," Bishop Tunstall said as they set out from Faversham in a raw morning mist such as makes August the outrider of autumn.

"And out of season at that," laughed More, pulling his gown straight across his chest. "We must be great sinners to have deserved this penance."

The nearest riders had laughed with their chiefs and settled as comfortably as they could into the cold leather of their saddles. Close as they were to home and discharge from their mission, they took the discomfort of the early start with but half regret for the warmth of another hour or two abed. But they rode quietly for a while until the steady jog of their horses and the brisk wind, whipping the smell of the sea across the Kentish fields, had warmed the blood in their veins. Then it seemed good to be astir while the smoke from morning hearths blew roadward on the right or streamed through orchards on the left and church bells spoke back and forth along their way. And since August gives only warning of autumn, the sun was soon hot enough to loose tongues without danger from chattering teeth. Already, the whole population of hamlet after hamlet, it seemed, was in the fields, for the premonition of frost was unmistakable.

"At least, London may be a healthier place if it turns cool," Tunstall remarked as they topped a rise that brought them a brief glimpse of the Swale and the misty coast of the Isle of

Sheppey. "August and September are bad months in the city when the sultriness lingers. I don't like what the Abbot told us last evening about the plague."

"Probably exaggerated," said Hugh Marchaunt in the quiet, inconsequential manner that made no difference between weighty and trivial utterance. "He seemed to me a nervous sort. He's seen plagues enough, the Lord knows, to take rumors more casually than he evidently does."

More turned a little in his saddle. "Granted that rumor grows with the square of the distance, do you think many men ever take news of the plague with ideal calm? It's hard for reason and fear, which is a kind of imagination, to keep their nags apace."

"Besides," Tunstall broke in, "the Abbot feels his responsibility. He is not just a man afraid for himself or a few others, as we might be. He has the welfare of his house to consider; and with plague in London, he cannot be sure that the chance guest does not bring another with him unseen."

"I like your figure," mused More. Then he added gayly, "No wonder my Lord Abbot welcomed travelers fresh from the purgation of the sea."

"Well, if the King is keeping north of London because of the plague, as they say," remarked Marchaunt, as if he thought the first phase of the subject had been pursued to the end of its profit, "we have more riding ahead than we counted on."

"True," said More, "if you're going to join the Court."

"Aren't we all?" Marchaunt asked in unguarded amazement.

"I hadn't intended to. At this season the Court is too much occupied with hunting and feasting for my own mean taste. I have been counting on going home to Chelsea."

"I don't see why you shouldn't," added Tunstall. "Our report to the Cardinal ends this business."

Marchaunt held to his point with so precise an upward jerk

of his jaw that More listened for the snap of his teeth as he said, "Suppose the Cardinal be at Court?"

"I'm afraid he's not," said the Bishop slowly, "if the rest of what the Abbot was telling us is true. I'm sorry for this whispering, this getting ready to be glad if disgrace befalls the Cardinal, that we have met in the last few days."

"Nobody loves him," sneered Marchaunt.

"Even if that be granted, he has loved the King and served his interests," More remonstrated.

"Better than his own?" There was so studied an indifference in the tone of the question that More wondered suddenly what this courtier had heard and whether the openness of his attack on Wolsey were due merely to trust in his fellow-ambassadors.

"Yes, he has served the King better than himself, I dare maintain, for otherwise he would have paid more heed to his duties as a prince of the Church."

"You pretend to be simple, Sir Thomas," snorted Marchaunt. "You know as well as I that the Cardinal loves Court and cares little for the duties of a churchman, prince or curate. And if he is not at Court, as they say, then—mark my word!—he is out of favor."

"Your contentions hardly hang together, Master Marchaunt," said More in his most judicial tone. "According to your first premise, he might be holding a rival court of his own."

"A shrewd hit," laughed Marchaunt. "At any rate, we must ride farther than we planned, for I dare maintain that we'll not find the Cardinal in the same city with the plague."

More had already noticed Tunstall's pulling back as if the critical talk offended him, and he had been thinking appreciatively of the stubborn power of loyalty that had been his first impression of Cuthbert Tunstall years before. But in a moment, too, he was glad that Marchaunt had turned with a certain insistence that the Bishop hear that last remark.

"There I think you are wrong, Master Marchaunt," Tunstall said with the levelness that men feared and respected in him. "The Cardinal is no coward."

A sullen interlude might have followed had not one of the outriders wheeled back to the group with news of a fire ahead. Almost as he spoke, the main party could see heavy smoke and a burst of flame on the very road, it seemed, a mile or so before them.

One of the young men, an inexperienced traveler, cried, "Is it a plot, a trap?"

"Hardly in daylight on this road," the Bishop reassured him. Then he added, after a glance to his colleagues for their assent, "We'll see what's the matter when we come up with it."

"That smoke is from thatch, or I miss my guess," said More.

Spurred by the thought behind those words, the younger men broke their mounts from the decorum of an embassy, and even the older men, less daring riders, kept to a good trot. On the edge of a cluster of cottages, they halted a moment to make the horses safe, for now they could see that the farthest cottage in the group burned beyond hope of saving it. From the fields of the manor at the left the workers came running with their implements. Tunstall and Marchaunt, as well as some of the older men of their train, stayed with the horses; but More cast off his riding gown and hurried after the others. So close-set were the cottages that almost everyone was needed to save the rest of the hamlet, for the low hills lipping the saucerlike valley hardly broke the morning wind. Already, men were clambering to the thatched roofs with their spades in hand to beat out the sparks that showered them; others had formed a bucket-line from a brook four or five rods beyond the burning house. One man, who seemed to be a bailiff, was assigning posts to every available man, woman, or child. After a glance that comprehended the travelers' willingness to help, with panicky courtesy he included them in his directions; hence, More found himself tipping the water from a great well-bucket into the pails with which a steady round of boys and girls came running. Again and again the chains clanked on the stone-work of the well and the bucket splashed deep in the water, and as it came groaningly up, More remembered that there was drought around Cambrai. Here, by God's mercy, there was water for poor men's needs.

A sudden cracking, louder than the chatter of the flames, and a low, heavy sigh—"like the sigh of the damned," whispered a man at More's elbow—stayed every hand for the sad minute in which the walls of the cottage buckled and the burning thatch sank into the pit thus dug. A great shout from the toilers caught up the voice of destruction in a triumphant echo; for though the fighting would have to continue, the worst of it was over and the hamlet was rescued. Clearly the travelers could leave the labor to the villagers.

As More rubbed the rust from well chains and bucket-rim on some burdock leaves and then wiped his hands with his handkerchief, he saw the woman who had been working most fiercely to save the next cottage crumple on its doorstep. The other women ran to her aid and bore her out of sight. "Poor soul!" he thought. "But at least, she had a good hand in saving her house."

At the same moment the man who had been giving directions ducked a little breathlessly before him. "Will your honor forgive me? I was thinking of putting out the fire and nothing else, and so many men to help seemed heaven-sent."

"Then we must all thank heaven," said More gravely. He felt sorry that their state should embarrass the bailiff. "We couldn't have ridden by and not helped. But how did it happen? That's the question we always ask."

The man looked around as nervously as though he held some

guilty secret; then he dropped his voice to a whisper. "Did you notice the woman who just fainted? It was her house. A widow —the most charitable soul in the world. The other night a beggar came to her door. He was nearly dropping, probably with fever, though he said it was hunger. So she gave him bread and broth, and let him sleep in a shed, cleaner and tighter than many a house. And she took him water and food yesterday, and didn't tell anyone about him. But last night he was so sick, she called the priest. It was the plague. The poor fellow died about midnight, and the priest had him buried before daybreak. He didn't want to frighten the people. Then he said she'd better burn the shed for fear of the contagion, and she called me to help her. I don't know what happened, but before we knew it the other out-buildings had caught fire, and then the cottage." The strain of whispering had dried his voice. He coughed. "Poor soul! That's what she got for her charity—lost everything."

More was touched by the starkness of the bailiff's narrative, the tragedy of the humble, who take misfortune with the white, pitiful restraint that he remembered noticing on that woman's face in the time when his own hands and back strained at the well. He was, however, glad that he alone of their company was hearing of the plague while they lingered in the village. He felt in his purse for some coins.

"This will help her a little." And he saw with deep satisfaction that the rest of their train, who had come up in the road, were reaching for their purses. The embassy had put them all to great expense, but now almost within sight of home they could spare something in charity.

The bailiff, thus constituted their almoner, walked with him towards the road. As they stepped through the gateway in the blackened hedge, shriveled in the fierce, premature frost of the blaze, More could hear the sobbing of women, exhausted not hysterical, in the cottage where they had taken the widow. He hoped that she could weep, too, but he feared that she was still staring before her, white, tense, perhaps mercifully benumbed. Bishop Tunstall was waiting for them, and the villagers had gathered in awe about him. At his "Let us pray" they all knelt in dust or mud or trampled grass.

Slowly as at his high altar the Bishop spoke their prayer, "Almighty God, we thank Thee for the deliverance of Thy children from the terror of this destruction which we have seen stayed by the strength that Thou gavest them. May it be for us all a reminder of the destructions that waste the soul of man unless he come to Thee through the grace of Thy son, Jesus Christ. And may that grace comfort those who are distressed by this calamity and give us all a livelier sense of the binding power of charity between man and man and so between man and Thee. If it be Thy will, keep us from all evil henceforth and forever. Amen."

Then he gave the little congregation his blessing with as spacious meaning as More had ever heard the noble words pour upon the heads bowed before a bishop. As the men and women rose from their knees and the children crowded wide-eyed against the hedges, the silence of the prayer-time was prolonged. Slowly, as if they had been timed to make a pattern of activity again, the stirrings of these many people trickled together, and men remembered the things that were to have filled their day. The children were still living in their wonder. Surely, thought More, these youngsters had seen many gayer companies than this ride back and forth on busy Watling Street. To be sure, theirs was no town for merchants, ambassadors, and pilgrims to stop in; so perhaps they had most often merely peeped through gate-bars or over hedges to watch the passing pageant. To-day they had seen it halt and had timidly stroked the fur of a gown, some bright piece of harness within arm-reach, or the glossy heads of the horses sniffing the roadside weeds. The whispering of a freckled ten-year-old—"Maybe he's an archbishop"—and the stir of the men as they slapped smartly at the dust on their knees and the tentative stepping of the horses called More back to his business.

With him in the saddle again, the company took shape and, hampered as a procession is till it has spaced itself and found the rhythm of the long road, moved awkwardly away from the awe of the hamlet and the smoky air, suggestive of innocent autumn fires. Though a jest or two rose from the ambassadors about the propriety of private enterprise during their official service and about the blackness of their soft hands, throats had been too much rasped by smoke and unused muscles were too sore for much exertion beyond that of riding. After a few miles, however, some one asked the inevitable question: "How do you suppose that fire started?"

The question hung among them for a ponderable moment before More answered quietly, "Plague." Panic echoed the word forward and back through the train. Of the hands that moved in a forfending blessing, the first and the swiftest, More noted with a flash of pity for the man's earlier words, was Hugh Marchaunt's.

Whether the portent they had seen or the increasing warmth of an August noon that made dawn-risen men sleepy was responsible for their silence, it continued even for miles beyond Sittingbourne, where they had paused for a rest. Over their meager dinner More had told the bailiff's tale of the fire, and after that they had held only a desultory, soon-lapsed conversation. Now, though the dejected backs ahead of him drew More's compassion for the weariness that can make men merely dull, that has neither beauty nor dignity in it, as has exhaustion after fierce spending of body, mind, or spirit, he was glad of this quiet riding, perhaps the last this business would afford.

The days of riding and sailing and riding again were nearly over, for the road to London lay through such familiar territory that homesickness was already half-assuaged. At the end of a few miles the formal pageantry of ambassadorship would close as abruptly as the Christmas miming at Lambeth years before: they would all be still on the scene, but their parts played, they would have stepped back into their routine personalities. The days in the saddle, leisurely days consistent with the dignity of their mission, had meant genial conversations and long, friendly debates on the level roads of Flanders. Sometimes Tunstall and he had talked of their books and the men they loved; sometimes they had made the opulent beauty of the roadside incongruous by discourse of their common vexation, the perverse works that crept into the country to spread spiritual and social confusion among the people and to create discord in the state; sometimes one or another of the young men had sparred proudly with these elders in a disputation that he would rehearse with his peers in months to come. Sometimes they had ridden with such pleasure in the motion, the drumming of hoofs, and the cut of the wind, that speech had seemed an intrusion. For nearly three weeks life had been the paradox of traveling: time so preëmpted that, barring some extraordinary demand for a spurt, none could make levy upon it; consequently, time set free for a thousand personal delights in observation and reflection.

Since their landing in England, More had been much disturbed by the rumors crowding in on them. The Legatine Court to hear the King's suit of divorce, which had opened so splendidly in May, had moved through the evidence before it to no end but the Queen's grief and humiliation and the anger of the King. Cardinal Campeggio's proroguing the Court till October, men were saying knowingly, had been only a convenient pretext, for it would not meet again; but the King had been hearty enough at his hunting and feasting in the country as if indeed the evil business of the divorce had been left behind in Blackfriars. Some were even venturing the opinion that Queen Katharine's denial of the jurisdiction of the Court had ended this gesturing towards a divorce. Were reconciliation to be the issue of the whole sorry enterprise, More reflected, the graver error had it been to hold the empty show of the Legates' Court, for the weeks of these magnificent sessions had haled the divorce from its quasi-seclusion of diplomacy and courtiers' gossip and delivered it over to scandalous speculation in every quarter. And now men dared to talk with undisguised spite of Cardinal Wolsey. In the two months of their absence the spirit of England had altered in ways difficult to define; as More tried to find the right terms for the change, he thought most of a diminution of respect, the slackening of discipline that comes with thinking evil of those who should be beyond suspicion or with having corruption revealed in them. Respect is a tenuous relation and an absolute one. How many men could keep their integrity, he wondered, in the time that lay before them?

A shout on their left roused the whole train as suddenly as if, bewitched, they had been awaiting such release. When the concentrated noise of their riding broke into the fragmentary sounds of a company marking time, they could hear the approach of two or three riders on the spur-road they had just passed. Too small a band for any evil purpose, the veterans among the ambassadors must have agreed in thinking, for there was hardly a nervous gesture among them. The square, middle-aged man who rode first from the bosky lane, hallooing as he came, seemed vaguely familiar; yet More could not place him. Nor was the second, a yeoman too, identifiable; but the third rider to emerge from the bypath, lean, tall, and pale, he knew with swift delight in the encounter—the Bishop of Rochester.

Though he should not have been surprised at any simplicity Bishop Fisher might practice, More was momentarily amazed at the casualness of this episcopal train. Turning his horse quickly, he took it a dozen paces back on the road and sang out to the smiling, breathless old man the gay lines of Chaucer which were for him quintessentially the Kent Road:

> " 'Faste have I priked,' quod he, 'for your sake,
> By-cause that I wolde yow atake,
> To ryden in this mery companye.' "

"And remember," laughed Fisher between cough and gasp, "the newcomer said too, 'God save this joly companye!' "

"Such meetings are the joy of this road," More said slowly, as they came up at a quiet pace with the rest of the embassy.

The greetings over, Fisher played still with the Chaucerian coincidence: "I can even tell a tale if my yeomen prove shy of this august band. We saw you from the top of a hillock and guessed that you might be good company." With the candor that could not let even an ambiguity stand uncorrected, he added, "In fact, I was sure of you because we had your courier at Rochester yesterday. And you are stopping to visit me?"

It was as cordial an invitation in the eagerness of its tone and the smile about the keen eyes as any that the courtliest periphrasis could utter.

"Will you keep us the night?" asked Tunstall. "Perhaps we should try a longer stage, but we have been riding since early this morning."

"Gladly; but I am sorry, too, if that is all you will give me."

"We have been abroad, you know, my Lord of Rochester," Tunstall urged to mitigate their niggardliness. "And each of us is bound on some business. Marchaunt and some of the other young men, I imagine, go to Court to prove that we are not all churls; More goes to his family and the quiet of the country; and I go to my afflicted city. Every man has his harvest to tend to, you see."

Fisher nodded and was silent deliberatingly. Watching him, More marveled, as he had often before in the years of their friendship, at the wholeness of meaning which this man could convey in a few words, a simple motion. Here was the perfection of economy that made every bit of energy significant. Upon this pleasant thought the Bishop's next words, low-pitched in obvious caution, broke sharply but not irrelevantly.

"We have the plague here." He glanced back towards the road down which he had come. "But I asked my men to wait at a safe distance, and I took precautions myself." At More's quizzical glance, he insisted defensively, "I believe in not tempting nature. But you take it stoically enough. Has foreign travel made the homely things of England—even plague, alas!—so commonplace?"

"No, no," protested More. "The first terror is over, though, for we know already that the plague has spread from London. A man died last night in a little town we passed through this morning."

"And one will die here to-night, I think. He was unconscious when I left him. This plague is a fierce death, but a swift one. He was a gardener years ago for my Lady the Countess, and he has been living alone for a long time, rheumatic and feeble. The memory of old times, I suppose, made him always glad to see me when I came by occasionally; so the poor fellow asked for me in his delirium. The curate here is a good man; he let me know this morning instead of putting old Godfrey off as one deluded."

"So it was a good deed to bring you trouble and danger?"

"It was. You aren't callous, Thomas More, though sometimes you sound so. Why do you so often seem the idle mocker?"

But his friend's silence under the rebuke touched the older man to quick redress. "Perhaps, though, it is only that our humorlessness slides past your intention till we see the bow of your wit too late for recognition. I know how you meant your question. And it was a good deed for the curate to ease the old man's dying."

"And it was like you to go," More added. He would not risk again troubling Fisher's selfless clarity.

"The ways of this thing are queer," broke in Tunstall, absorbed in thought of what awaited him in London. "How did a lonely invalid contract it?"

"Three nights ago he took in a wanderer who had strayed from the road. That the fellow had lost the highway seemed odd to old Godfrey; but he thought him confused by drink. He must have been far-gone with the sickness. Yet some fogged remnant of courtesy evidently made him loath to be a curse and a burden, for he left at dawn the next morning. We must find where he crept off to die. I don't doubt he had the plague."

"We came on the end of the story first," said Tunstall. "He must be the man who died last night." Then he told of their own startling encounter with the evil which still clouded the thoughts of men London-bound.

Worry, however, and the strain of being honored company in the many hostels of their journey yielded to the genial, matter-of-fact hospitality of the Bishop of Rochester's manor house. He had been staying at Halling rather than in his city for the restful month since the Legatine Court had been adjourned. Here he gave his friends such an unpretentious welcome that they had the lively sense of being at home; were luggage unpacked, travel-tokens bestowed, and the tales of their experience all related, they could not have been more at ease than the Bishop's simple dinner and humble household made them.

By long habit a more active man than his associates, More had gone for a walk around the rambling, irregular manor house. The air was sweet with the mingled odors of harvest-time and quick with the brush and murmur of the evening. Above the moat the gnats danced in a little cloud that anticipated the gathering mist and smoke on the horizon. From an angle in the brick wall of the house, he looked west and north across wide fields still streaked with the movement of laborers. At such a time the undramatic, but infinitely varied, coloring of a landscape moved him more deeply than some brilliant scene could do. The western sky held the soft lilac tones which the eye can scarcely credit in their delicacy, cool enough to be the color of sunless air forever, not truly light, not dark, not even dull; it would linger a long time yet, deepening into night in a slowness irreconcilable with the measures that space day and twilight and dark. So the workers moved unhurryingly, and the oxen tugged the piled wains home to the threshing. It was a good harvest, men here had told him; and he had remembered that fear rode every wagon in the fields about Cambrai. Now, as he thought of that fear, he knew that it must be for men in England a remote, pitiful, unworrying plight: the kindest of them would eat their bread a little more thoughtfully because some spoke of starvation across the channel, but the shadow would scarcely touch most boards.

So it was with fear. Men hardly knew it for their neighbors; they could not, unless they were to jump at every twitch and stir, know it even for themselves until it had throttled them. And always the avoiding of the fear seems so simple to bystanders and those who hear the calamitous tale. To look before and after and to be unafraid—the words were common ones to mark a skill in living that few men More knew had attained. That thought, rather than the oncoming chill of the August evening, turned him towards the door: he must listen to John Fisher while they had time together.

He found the two bishops sitting in an island of light from which the shadows ebbed to gather in the great pool of darkness that was the hall of the manor house after twilight. Though Fisher would have no torches for decoration or display, he had had a light fire of brush kindled to mitigate the chill that spread at evening across the valley of the Medway. As More crossed the room, the crackle of twigs broke nervously through the quiet speech of the two men before the fire and out-voiced his own rustling progress over the rushes. He was, in fact, almost upon them before the talkers realized his approach. The conversation hung suspended for the moment in which he drew a stool up at his host's left and spread his knees to the grateful warmth of the fire; not till this instant had awareness of the cold reached him. At his involuntary shiver, the others chuckled.

"Time you came in," said Fisher. "Poor man, you may sit in my chimney corner till you are warm."

The banter in the Bishop's voice told More that he had come into a serious discussion, as indeed he had expected to come. For answer he bowed exaggeratedly, smiled in a little sidewise quirk of his lips, and waited. They would trust him to pick up the thread of their talk. From the pose of Tunstall's head, More judged that he had just spoken before the interruption: the firelight grooved his face deeply, from the vertical lines that study had puckered between his heavy, black brows to the arcs that still cut from mouth to edge of jaw as if the last-uttered words were lingering on the parted lips. The upward glow made a mask of this face—a mask of perplexity, More divined; so Fisher's words did not surprise him.

"You must grant that you're a seasoned diplomat; you and

More here have been going off to the continent for years. Still, I agree that it was strange to send you away in the midst of the Legatine Court. Of course, the Cardinal could hardly have gone. Yet I think the King wanted you out of the way."

"But why? I'm sorry, More, to be asking that question still. You probably think that you've heard it often enough in the last two months."

"I'm curious about all the possible answers," More answered quietly enough to leave the question open for Fisher's elucidation.

The older man spoke rapidly: "I think the King was afraid —perhaps not of you, but for you. Let me explain. Whatever happens, we of the Queen's counsel have all made enemies. His Grace wanted to dissociate you from the rest of us and from what lies ahead."

"Why?" More watched Tunstall's hands clench till the knuckles showed bone-white. "It isn't as if I were strong as you are, could write and speak with your courage—"

"Your courage is all right." Fisher was sitting so straight in his chair that his voice seemed to fall upon them from some judgment height. "And don't worry about your strength. You are tactful, as a man in his prime may well be; and you look to time and reason to make all the crooked things straight. And as an old man should be, I am tactless and blunt and impatient. Again and again, I remember the words of the Preacher: 'Ibit homo in domum aeternitatis suae.' And I feel that what must be done here must be done hastily, and what needs mortal witness must have it straightway, 'antequam rumpatur funiculus argenteus—' That imagery of the son of David is as terrible in its beauty as anything the Psalmist himself wrote." The old voice caught momentarily in a whisper between sigh and panting; but as More looked up unseeingly from the fiery lace of twigs on the hearth, it continued insistently, "If there is no other way, old men must make enemies recklessly."

"But you do not mean that the younger should not, too?" More's question was as quiet as if it were but Fisher's own afterthought.

"That is the counsel of perfection: granted. When the issue is clear, no man can hold back or reckon costs. But how often is it clear? Even if I don't always do it myself, I leave every man the right of weighing the values at clash. Though I can't reason about the little wrongs through which great rights may come, I will not condemn the man who settles with his own conscience the most imperative of conflicting duties."

"That is where we priests are freer than laymen," added Tunstall; "we haven't given hostages to fortune in the same way. Outside your counsels of perfection, Thomas More, a man who has wife and children and the added kin they bring him must think of his duties to them."

"And he may deserve to be called selfish if he acts still as though his life were his own only—or his death." Fisher's voice sank so low that More wondered whether he himself had heard or thought the last words. Then as if the old head were lifted in the most passionate movement of the Bishop in his most intense preaching, the voice rose: "But some men cannot see how we priests are free and weighted with responsibility for that very reason; they think we are presuming on a liberty that custom has given us. And that is the real point of the King's exempting you, Tunstall: Henry understands the nature of our freedom. You are a friend, and he is—fundamentally a kind man."

"What of you? He has more reason to consider you."

"I belong to the dead, or at least the old-fashioned, in his secret thoughts—if I trouble him there at all. His grandmother and his father listened to me. Why should he? So I must seem to him an inconvenient voice and a most inconvenient memory. You see, I believed him disturbed in conscience about his marriage, needlessly disturbed; and I believed that with assurance he would be at rest. So I justified him, but he didn't want justification. An inconvenient old dodderer."

"Have you known from the beginning that he didn't want to be justified?" Tunstall asked.

More, watching the eastern stars through the clouded, distorting glass of the high windows across the hall, found them helping him to a similitude for the spirit of the man beside him; his thought scrutinized the figure while he waited the answer of which he was already sure. In the pause of their waiting, he heard through the thick walls, as if it belonged to a far world, a horse's clatter cease, and he wondered with fragmentary attention who was riding thus late and upon what urgent business. The stir at his right, however, drove the desultory speculation away, for Fisher was ready to answer.

"I did not know. Scruples must be taken for honest coin. If we think them debased, the evil may be in our own thinking. Yes, I believed Henry; in fact, I still want to believe him. Foreign policy—infatuation—these may be the false counters. For myself, I trust him rather than my own mistrust. And I know now that one side of his nature hates me." He hurried through the remonstrance of his listeners. "He knows that himself, and he wants you safe from his hatred, Tunstall. Accept that kindness as long as conscience will allow. The sin of provoking that hatred is on my soul—though, God knows, I have seen no other way."

The agony of the last words drew him to his feet. As the younger men rose, too, he spoke warmly as if in sudden recollection of More's presence. "I thank God, Thomas More, that you stand outside this thing, this once that you are an amateur theologian. It is hard enough for us who are vowed to the battle to see it through."

The hand on his shoulder may have been seeking only support for the older man's steps after their long sitting, but it communicated strength in the pressure of its leaning.

"You have had a long day, and it is time for compline." Fisher's voice was even again as if they had been merely idling in chatter until they could call the day ended.

When they were but halfway up the dark room towards the door, it jerked open from without, and the square figure of a man blocked off the glow from the corridor. As soon as his eyes grew used to the dull light he had let into the room, he saw the three already approaching him and he cried out eagerly, "Did you hear the courier, then?"

More's "Yes" was swifter to catch Marchaunt's question than the "No" of the two bishops.

"From the King—from Woodstock. We must all report to him. It is not enough to report to the Cardinal."

Were there trumpets singing for him, Marchaunt could not have seemed more triumphant than now as he stood crying his news to a half-dark room. The hand on More's shoulder was not so much leaning as embracing.

CHAPTER III

PART of Thomas More's hope for the laying down of their ambassadorial pride, however, came to realization by mischance and part by the natural desire of some of the company to be about their own affairs. Since the Court was a mere nucleus abroad in the country, there was no need for some of the ambassadors' attendant gentlemen to ride after it and complicate problems of lodging and purveyance. And Tunstall, lamed by a fall from his horse, was kept in London. "I shall be a model bishop yet," he had said ruefully to More at their parting, "for here I must stay in my diocese. Or maybe my Lord of Rochester's prayer that I keep clear of the King's troubles is already being answered." Thus it was that Marchaunt and More, with a few young courtiers, rode westward to Woodstock; and that More alone reported on their embassy to a small, hurried meeting of the King's Council sandwiched between the morning's hunt and the afternoon's feasting and dancing.

Perfunctory enough that meeting was, for he could add little but the intimacy of personal report to the information the couriers had brought beforehand. When the King had left the Council, the others had lingered for further discussion. The Cardinal's expertness in secret diplomacy, More reflected in the midst of questioning, had accustomed these men to reservations, concealed instructions, and revelations to be made only in the private ear of the King and those whom he trusted; so they could scarcely believe that the ambassadors had brought home only the papers of which all the world might know. Norfolk and Suffolk, Rochford, and Gardiner, a new presence here, could not conceal their amazement at the duplicity of the French.

For the second time Viscount Rochford asked, "But the French? They seemed well-disposed?"

And for the second time, though he could not vouch for their disposition towards his questioner's secret interests, More answered with grave equanimity, "Perfectly. Madame, the King's mother, gave us special assurance of her son's gratitude to His Majesty and of his good will."

"But how will he show it? These words, words!" If the irascibility was Rochford's, the spirit of the outcry was common to these men whose nearly triumphant efforts for the advancement of his daughter had been recently and—More could guess their feeling—cruelly blocked. To Suffolk alone in this company could the fortunes of Anne Boleyn make no personal difference; and the fortunes of Anne Boleyn might be involved in the possibly sinister, at any rate concealed, agreements of the Emperor and King Francis. Understanding this and piecing out his reading of Thomas Boleyn's motives with what he had heard in the last few hours about his activities since the Legatine Court had been prorogued, More could be the more patient with the anxiety of the man.

"Yes, words, my lord. But after all, what else have men to use on such occasions?" He caught himself looking absently at Stephen Gardiner, who sat below Viscount Rochford. A flush on that strong, full face troubled him more than the petulance of Rochford: the King's new secretary had been too long at Rome, had studied too deeply the devious thinking of the politic of this earth; and the coppering of the heavy countenance spoke his unhappy seizing on an implication More had not realized until the words were uttered. Yes, sometimes there was money, too. But there had been none to spend among the French, even had there been any motive for it.

Norfolk's dry voice made a shrewd, rational comment: "Eh, Boleyn, you can't haggle with a princess as if she were a market wench. Madame might have said more, but if she didn't—" The shrug was perfect, More noted with swift appreciation of the fact that he had evidently been preparing to notice for a long time: Norfolk must have been shrugging at impertinent questions, contemptuously, trucklingly, mockingly, for most of his life. The shrug passed with a knowing tilt of the thin face that sharpened the beaklike angle of his nose. "This hasn't gone badly at all, I think. The money will ring sound when it's paid, and the openings for trade are good. For the rest, keep out of that mess on the Continent, I say. What would the Cardinal have brought us, eh? Treaties with everybody, canceling each other like a schoolboy's ciphering. Here we know what we've got."

"But to let the French trick us! Here His Grace of Bayonne has been assuring us that you ambassadors would see that treaty with the Emperor," protested Boleyn, loath, it seemed, to abandon this grievance that might be somehow redressed. In his voice anger struggled with such moral disgust as moved More to inward laughter. How priceless were honor and scruples and the observance of promises!

"And they got not a sniff of its ink," Norfolk added. "All right, we'll try some other way."

Suffolk turned a yawn into a rasping cough. "The French aren't really clever; and they can't keep a secret or a treaty. So it doesn't matter what's in the damned thing."

"Remember that the commissioners promised us that De Langes would bring a copy of it," More repeated from his first mention of the promise in his main report. "So you may yet have it."

"Yes, a copy of it." Boleyn's emphasis was so exaggerated that it seemed a flash of lightning across the quaggy marsh of this man's spirit. With a little sickened turn, More saw the copper flush mount again in Gardiner's face; this new secretary recognized the bitter smell of pitch, the grime of it in the whorls of one's fingers. He had dealt too much in secret instructions and half meanings and promises meant to be broken.

"Well, let's see when it comes—if ever," Suffolk offered them as a dismissing comment. He was impatient to end this business that interfered with the festivities of a golden day.

"We can't wait; we oughtn't to." Boleyn's protest had a desperate note in it. It could not stay them, however, for to his associates this was already an old story.

They straggled towards the door. Outside, More thought with sudden gratitude, the sunshine was clean and fresh; as he passed a narrow window, he was glad of its reassuring vista of tennis courts below, the lush green track of the Glyme through its meadows, and the gray roofs of the town beyond. This was a hint of a spacious, patient England. So hurried, Thomas Boleyn? Viscount Rochford, father of the Lady Anne, of two mistresses for a king, so hurried? And to what? Not to the love or the honor or even the common respect of these other men, who are using you with the sidelong mockery reserved for the upstart. More smiled at himself for thinking thus in his own middle-class complacency, as another might call it, of the ambitions of Boleyn's family, by marriage of the proud house of Norfolk, perchance by artifice about to win to the prouder, if less ancient, estate of the Tudors.

In his preoccupation More did not at once observe that one of the Council hung back, waiting for him, until the bulk of a man called him to attention. Stephen Gardiner. The uncertainty of his aspect, a diffidence painful in one who should be by now bold to make any encounter, troubled More and roused him to a whole-hearted greeting. He repented of his prejudgment during the Council session; it was not his to read the motives of his colleagues in what might be only the evil imaginings of his own mind. And he saw gladly that with his first words the cloud on Gardiner's brow was dispelled; this evil year's work on the divorce had made him fearful of fronting a former associate. The thought made More's solicitude the greater.

"Though you have been longer away, Stephen Gardiner, you were first home; so my welcome is a stale one by now. I saw you only at a distance before I went off to Cambrai."

"I'm glad you're back. You seem like a reminder of some permanence here." The full lower lip drew back as if to say more were to lose a perilous control over emotions that must not be released. In the silence that fell between them, through which More saw the sad, proud figure of the Cardinal moving, he realized that it had been bitter for Gardiner to pass from the side of Wolsey, who had first advanced him, to that of the King, whose favor would be a constant reminder of the tragedy of his disfavor.

When Gardiner looked squarely at him again, More moved onto safer ground than his thought had been treading. "How Italianate has Rome made you? We can tell something of the stiffness of a man's fiber by the speed with which he falls to imitating strange fashions."

"And do I seem Italianate?" The question had the right ease; the hard moment of their encounter was over.

"I have noticed an accent or two, but I think you'll pass for honest English still."

"That was honestly said, I hope. Seriously, though, I didn't enjoy the Curia. It was a great opportunity, I know, as the Cardinal urged when he sent me; but the everlasting equivocation and indirection of diplomacy are not for me. And His Holiness! He seemed a little less harassed than when I saw him last year at Orvieto—he was practically a refugee then. I'd not be on Pope Clement's throne for a dozen tiaras. Not that I need to worry about the possibility. There's only one man in the world I pity more." Gardiner's impulsive averting of his eyes to the gloom of the low-vaulted corridor reinvoked the tragic presence of the one who seemed, in his intimacy, more pitiable than the Pope beset by Emperor and King alike.

"Is Rome recovering from the Sack?" More felt that they must avoid people: the neutrality of things could better re-establish their intercourse.

"Yes, in most ways. It is a magnificent city. When I think of what scholars could do there, I grieve over all the ugliness and jealousy men take to Rome—to that beauty."

"But that is what law-courts are for; they try to turn the ugliness and the misery and the corruption into some kind of beauty. If that is so of temporal courts, how much more true must it be of a spiritual court! So it's all right for Rome to be a kind of hall of Æolus for the stormy winds of human contention."

"Was Æolus a strong ruler? I don't remember." And Gardiner would say no more on that score, for he changed the subject. "A minute ago I was feeling sorry that you had never been to Rome; now I think I'm glad that you haven't. Oh, but I can see you reveling in those libraries and the genius of this man, Buonarotti. I remember once Erasmus's telling me how excited he and Linacre could make you about Rome. But don't go for a while, Sir Thomas."

"Do you think I could go to Rome when two months in the Low Countries make me homesick to the point of wasting away? You remember how I was two years ago at Amiens."

Gardiner leaned away from him appraisingly and laughed. "One virtue of not getting fat is that you don't get thin either. I can't see any difference." Still what he had to tell More was not told; so he plunged ahead, "You should hear the Italians ask about you—or perhaps you shouldn't. At any rate, it was a pleasure. And not only the Italians, but scholars from everywhere. 'You are an Englishman? You know Morus? Ah!' I must tell you more about some of them—that is, if you are lodged here."

"Yes, they found a corner for me, since I am scarcely more than a messenger in passage."

"In passage? Riddles, riddles. Surely, this is a long way round to Chelsea, if that is what you mean."

Thus genially had the two found their path through the ambiguities of statecraft back to the unveiled simplicity of friendly intercourse. Men and ideas and books, the grave and the gay things of private life—More was asking himself whether they were enough. Gardiner and he had reached the door of the King's apartments, through which the secretary would, of course, go. He himself would go down into the sunlight.

A man waiting by the door, however, drew towards them. Thought had unfocused More's eyes; so it was Gardiner who first identified the waiter and caught him into the last teasing remark of his own, "Perhaps not so round-about, for here is Giles Heron to see you."

"Son Heron!" Not till the moment of laying his hand on the firm shoulder of this courtier son-in-law kneeling before him had More admitted to himself the full hunger he had felt to see some one from home. There had been no time to spare in London for even the brief journey up the river, and none of his young men had been there at hand in the city. Tactfully, with a friendly nod to the two, Gardiner went on into the royal chambers as the young man rose from his salutation. More's smile of appraisal held them silent for an instant.

"You are looking well, Giles. When were you home? And how are all the household?"

The bright, clear face clouded as if there were so much to say that choice of beginning was difficult or even as if the news were hard to speak. In the instant of that hesitation, More felt the chill that anticipates nameless evils, but it passed as swiftly as the shadow of a tree on a hot open road; for Giles looked up, his way chosen.

"We are all well, sir, thank God! But since His Majesty sent for you, may we speak as we go? He wishes to see you in the garden."

"Surely; we'll go down directly." As More answered, he twitched his gown straight on his shoulders; and the habitual movement, evoking thought of Dame Alice, who was ever urging this straightening, recalled the premonitory shiver. "All well? But you thanked God with more than usual passion; so all has not been well at home. What's the matter, Giles?"

"Not injury or illness, sir, for I guess what you are thinking. We had a fire—the barns with all the new-harvested grain."

"And that is the worst? You rightly said, 'Thank God!' I dreaded lest your news were of death or illness or the maiming of some one. Was anyone hurt?"

"There were burnt hands and singed brows, but no worse; and we saved the stables and pens."

"Good. The grain is a bad loss. When I left, it promised to be a plentiful harvest." And he thought of the fear with which men had reaped the lean harvest of Cambrai.

"It was a fine harvest. And the seed had not yet been put aside for next year; so it's a double loss."

"We'll find seed for next year somehow. And this that is lost was the increase of the earth, which God lent us; so I echo your thanks. What we lose by mismanagement or ill-fortune has been no less God's gift, and the loss is a gift, too—though a hard one unless we know how to use it."

"Sir, I'm glad it's no greater grief to you. Mother thought we should not trouble you with it till you were free of your business. She has been worried lest you be."

"That is like her—anxious to save me the material cares."

"She does manage well. And now I have gone against her wishes. Really, I had not meant to tell you, but my doleful face must have given me away."

"Let's say, rather, that I was too plainly inquisitive for any deception. And to prove my skill with the witness, one more question. You still haven't told me all the harm done?"

Giles laughed in mirthless embarrassment. "Sir, you make me resolve to keep clear of the law. Since you insist, the saddest part of the mischance is that the fire took the neighboring barns. The cottagers lost their stores, too. And it's bitterer for them—"

"Poor souls, yes! Their margin of gain and loss is so much narrower than ours. And the grain is something of themselves—their sweat and their calloused hands and the ache in their shoulders. Oh, Giles, this is a worry and a grief. We must plan for them."

They were halfway down the irregular stairs that made descent at best a halting progress; so a pause was natural enough. To More it was at that moment a necessity, for the pang of this heavy responsibility throttled his breathing. The cool, rough stone against which he leaned was reassuring to his hand, and sweet air filtering through an arrow-slit in the old masonry of the bastion lightened the dank, unsunned air of the stair-well. Through the loophole he could still see the fair, low-lying rich meadows of Woodstock Park and the woodland beyond rising to match the eminence on which the manor house itself stood; but through this cheerful scene, as through a painted cloth spread against the sunlight, he saw a confused inner picture of men gathering the thin harvest of Flanders from a grudging earth and men reaping the generous yield of his own Chelsea fields to feed the ravenous mouth of fire. Fear, the most elementary fear for life itself, upon them all. But whereas he had pitied the former fear, he could, and he must, act against this one; and in his heart he prayed for strength to act wisely. Breath came easily again. Fortunately, the pang and its assuagement had moved so swiftly upon him that he was ready to go on as Giles laid a solicitous hand on his arm.

"Father! Are you ill?"

"I'm all right, thank you. Since this has happened, I'm glad that we have time enough to plan for the winter. If I possibly can, I'll go home the sooner. Then we must put all our heads together. And now I know the worst?"

"Absolutely, sir." Giles's frank smile spoke such relief from a dreaded burden of news that More could even smile in return.

"Then tell me how it happened."

"We don't really know. The hay may have been damp, for it seems to have started in one of the cottagers' lofts. That's why you ought not to feel too bad about it. Some one may have been careless—we don't know. It was supper-time; so the fire got good headway before anyone discovered it. We had a terrifying evening of it—well, night really, for grain and straw and hay burn slowly. And the wind from the river didn't help. Still, I suppose the houses might have gone if it had been a north wind or a west one."

"That was a great mercy. If we have thin rations, at least we all shall have roofs over our heads. It doesn't much matter who was responsible, Giles, for we couldn't let anyone suffer, even for his own carelessness. And though it's meaningless to you, I thank God that we do not have the plague at Chelsea."

In the cryptlike gloom at the foot of the stair-well, More told of the fire he had helped to fight. Though he could scarcely see Giles's face, he could feel the mounting awe that made the young man's voice dry and strained.

"Did you not have, then, a kind of premonition?"

"No. I'm no prophet, Giles. Perhaps I'm too dull to read signs aright. At least, that incident had no personal meaning for me." More laid his hand on the heavy latch that would let him out into the garden of the second court. "Is His Highness alone?"

In Giles's hesitation, however, he read the answer before the young man said slowly, "The Lady Anne was with him."

All the anticipation of seeing Henry alone dried within More's heart: of one thing he had long been sure—Anne Boleyn always looked at him from behind the shutters of her dislike. Once he had thought that he must be too simple for her French taste, that she was merely indifferent to one so uncourtierlike; but he had recently noticed her refusing, as it were, to see those who were distasteful to her, yet nervously, preyingly, keeping them in view. If she were with Henry, the interview ahead would be a spiritless, awkward meeting.

Giles added abruptly, "I have messages to the kitchen, too. Shall I see you later, sir?"

"Good! And I should know then what I may do, how soon I may go home. Perhaps we shall travel together and talk of our wives as travelers do. Here I haven't asked you specially about our Cicely."

In the sunlight from the doorway, as More pulled the heavy oak inward, the young face glowed with a pride that touched his father-in-law deeply. "She is as sweet as ever—and dearer."

The words lingered happily in the second hearing that the mind made for itself while More watched Giles hurry away through the shadowy undercroft. Yes, love could be that—uplifted, generous, glorifying; this other that he was to meet was some counterfeit, changeling passion. In thought, he bade the young people of his household keep him a defending company through the next minutes.

In the park, somewhere beyond the hedges, the thin sweet voice of strings tuned the song from more ardent than melodious throats. More could not hear the words, carried by half a dozen singers, but the air was amorous and tantalizing in its repeated phrases. It broke off suddenly with a girl's shrill laughter and the flash of her rose-colored gown through the shrubbery; behind her hung the guffaws of her companions, and there was another woman's voice in the taunting chorus. So hard, so cruel! There was, however, no sound of talk as he came across the garden and perceived the flash of the King's jeweled doublet through the vines of, he remembered, a favorite arbor. In the simple motion of Henry's laying aside a book, More saw that he was alone; and anticipation welled again in its dried channel. The King had heard him and started up. As he stood waiting, smiling, apparently impatient of even a conventional obeisance, he seemed by some inner transformation the youthful King again. The thickness of his figure, the flabbiness of his face, the wrinkles about his eyes, the thinning of his hair were all unimportant; More saw them and did not see them, for the King was turning back the years to welcome him as a friend. Henry straightened his lute that, leaning perilously against the lattice, hinted that the book had not been long read this morning.

"Thomas More! It's good to have you home. We've missed you too much lately at Court."

"I do not mean to offend, Your Highness. Evidently, I just wasn't cut to the right pattern."

"Hah! You're no hermit. But some day we'll find one of these young popinjay classicists misspelling your name m-o-r-o-s-e. You'd better give him the lie beforehand and stay here a while."

"But if he makes good jests for you, Sire, had I not better go away and give him a chance? Consider, too, I beg, that I have need of my family, and my affairs of me."

"Suppose I have need of you?" Henry's smile was unchanging, but his tone had narrowed and edged as definitely as if the laughing eyes were frowning.

"If you command, Sire."

"But not if I merely ask in friendship and love of your company?" Henry's sigh was an elaborate bit of play-acting which both men enjoyed, for they shared the recognition of its half earnest. The King's arm rested heavily on More's left shoulder, and the great ruby on his forefinger blazed as with a little sun at its heart; the pressure and the brilliance together marked a King who could not turn time back, however hard he might be striving to do so at this moment.

"Why, I have had no one to talk books or stars with since you have been gone," Henry resumed plaintively, "and I wager you've not had either."

More laughed. "You do not send ambassadors abroad to talk either one, Your Highness, do you? The assemblage at Cambrai was a splendid one, but not notable, I should say, for scholars. So neither books nor stars played any part in the discussions. They would have mixed badly with crowns and ducats and pounds. Besides, even if we had had them, how could we admit to such pleasant conversations when we did not bring you home what you most wanted from the official sessions?"

"Ho! The secret treaty? Don't worry about that. We were ready to be glad to see it, if you could get a copy. That's all. Had I wanted it by hook or by crook, I'd have sent other ambassadors. I ask no pick-lock work of you and the Bishop of London. The rest were harsh about the matter after I left? Don't you worry till I am."

The pressing arm bore down reassuringly, but so uncomfortably that More smiled to himself and gauged the length of the path before them: Henry could be too affable.

"My Lord of London will be glad of that assurance, for we were sorry to fail in that part of our mission."

"Why, then, I'll send him a courier to-day. No, not you; you're not going yet—even on business that touches my love so closely. When Europe envies me such a councilor, do you think I'll let him escape so easily? Speaking of councilors, tell me something—" The arm lifted, and Henry stopped in his heavy progress; on the very threshold of his question, he seemed uncertain whether to ask it or not. When he continued, his countenance was a shade too veiled, his voice a note too non-committal to be frank. "Do you know a scholar named Thomas Cranmer? Cambridge man—quiet, but deep. He was at Waltham Cross last month. I hear there's good stuff in him."

"Cranmer?" More knew that he should have some association with the name, but he could not recall it. "I'm sorry; I believe I have heard of him, but I don't remember what."

"I thought you might know him. At any rate, watch out for him. I value your judgment of men."

Henry was so abstracted that More had the curious sensation that he would have made the same remark to whoever might have been walking there in the garden with him, for his mind was already made up about this Cranmer, and the interlocutor of the moment was unimportant. How had Cranmer caught the King's attention, More wondered as they walked on mechanically, and to what puzzle was he the key? Suddenly Henry turned to him as unexpectedly as with the last question:

"I knew there was something else I had been saving to ask you. Why didn't you tell me that Cochlaeus had dedicated his Cassiodorus to you?"

"I just didn't think of it, Your Highness. The book came out six months ago. Of course, I was pleased; but it's such a little book. And—anyway, you wouldn't expect anyone to go about boasting of a thing like that."

"Not you!" Henry laughed. "When the moralists get busy on my reign, they can say I had at least one modest man in my kingdom. But I might never have known of it, if I hadn't picked up Sichardus's *Chronicon* the other day. I like the roll of your titles in Cochlaeus's listing."

"Thank you, Sire." More felt himself flush. So he was not yet immune to such flattery. "Did you know, too, Your Highness, that Cochlaeus has dedicated his new book against Luther to my Lord of Rochester?"

"Hm!" The King frowned. "Very appropriate. Well, since you've been keeping unliterary company at Cambrai, I have a new book I'd like you to read." Again the King paused significantly. "I was looking at it when you came; I must have laid it down in the arbor."

"Yes, I noticed."

"Go back and get it if you like. It's a little volume, too, but very acute. I want to know what you really think of it."

That comment, which More recognized for a command, pricked his curiosity.

In the doorway ahead a knot of young courtiers had gathered to wait the King's entrance. More wondered how long they had been dallying there and from what vantage-points in the old pile of masonry or the gardens they had noted the King's approach and come scurrying to form his escort. Before the King acknowledged their readiness to bow, he added to More:

"Come to the banquet if you like; but I don't command you. It isn't going to be interesting. You'll have a better time reading."

Then he accepted the full ceremonial of the young men and swept away in their van. As the doorway muted their chatter and absorbed the gay colors and the coruscation of the jewels into its shadows, More thought of the beautiful unreality of garden scenes in a manuscript of the *Roman de la Rose* which he had handled in his boyhood. Not this pageantry, but a man named Cranmer and the unnamed book waiting in the arbor, constituted reality for Henry now. He had not mentioned the divorce; perhaps he would not mention it again, for the years of acquaintance which he had been so affably recalling should assure him that More had spoken once and for all on that score two years earlier. Secretly perhaps, More's relief told him, he had been expecting the King to raise the question again; for it had been on his return from Amiens in 1527 that Henry had first solicited his opinion.

It was in a good mood, then, that More walked back to the arbor to find the book the King would have him read. Still Cranmer's name went seeking its proper association hither and thither in his memory. Cambridge. But he had not been one of Erasmus's scholars there. In these latter years Cambridge had sometimes been meaning heresy and dealings with the continental heresiarchs. Then he remembered: when he was High Steward of the University, Bishop Fisher had asked his advice about some men suspect of error, but too circumspect to involve themselves in any open action. Could that be the proper connection for Thomas Cranmer? It was not fair to accept it without verification; yet that seemed the right circumstance of his hearing the name before. He was glad that it had not occurred to him in the King's presence, that he had not looked as if even a surmise had crossed his mind. Thought of the heretical connection confirmed itself, however, and drew forward an uneasy concern about how much the King knew of this man with good stuff in him, and to what service he would be recruited.

Because the little book on the seat in the arbor might hold a clue to the puzzle, More lifted it eagerly and turned to the title-page—*A Supplication for the Beggars* by Simon Fish. His pleasure in the King's affability died at the sight. He knew the worst about the book, for he had already been at work answering it in the precious half-hours he could clip from the other occupations of his busy life. It was one of the most hysterically disaffected books he had ever encountered; and the finding of it thus, with Henry's recommendation upon it, heightened his anxiety, his sense that the present reality turned about the King's interest in Cranmer and this poor little volume. For though, having leafed on to the opening page, he re-read its address, "To the King our Sovereign Lord," this was no royal book, proud of fine paper, expert presswork, and a rich binding. It was as fugitive a copy as the Bishop's men might search out of some London tradesman's stock. Assuredly, More would not banquet that afternoon.

CHAPTER IV

By the early part of October, the truth of Stephen Gardiner's jest about the long way round to Chelsea had become disappointingly clear, for, released from attendance on the King, More had to return to Westminster. There he had found accumulated papers waiting his action as Chancellor of the Duchy of Lancaster, and the promise of a busy winter grew with the shortening of the days and the thickening of the mists from the Thames that penetrated the Chancellery of the Duchy in the Precinct of the Savoy. Fortunately, however, for his peace of mind, news from Chelsea could reach him regularly, and his three sons-in-law and other young men of his household came and went often between Westminster and Chelsea. He had, therefore, assurance of his wife's skillful planning to redress the loss they and their neighbors had suffered so that the coming of winter should hold no terror they could avert of hunger or unemployment for any man; and he could almost feel as though he had been home to lay the plans with her.

Since the courts were to open on the next day, More sat busily among his papers on the afternoon of October the eighth. There were new pleas under the old, vexed headings in his docket: unjustified enclosures, trespass and theft in the digging of coal, the wardship of an heiress, the soundness of a disputed deed. The evidence, often homely and garrulous, resting sometimes on a confident assertion of what had always been within the memory of man, needing reinforcement by what he could learn or deduce about the relative trustworthiness and disinterestedness of the deponents, More usually enjoyed reading; it was reassuringly human and, in its own unmomentous way, vastly significant for the people to whose rights and wrongs it served to guide his judgment. To-day, however, it seemed remote, for closer problems drove this business back even while he turned and re-turned his documents. It was nearly time to set out for York Place and an interview to which Cardinal Wolsey had summoned him in a message by William Roper that morning: he was to come "secretly and urgently about four in the afternoon."

All through the morning the day had seemed to debate between rain and sunshine, as autumnal days often do; but by noon the haze had burned away and the air was golden with a curiously warmthless light. It was closer to the quality of the mid-winter than of the autumnal sun, which can often recapture the ardor of the summer. Walking in the garden of the Chancellor's house a little before this futile attempt at work, More had abstracted himself from dilemmas of state by the effort to define the impression of light and air; something in the atmosphere drew out the amazing, living yellow of the October landscape as he had seen greens and blues draw their own positive coloring into his daughters' gray eyes. Though the river winds were sharp to a man with a fixed pain in his chest and the drying leaves scuttled before him on the paths, he was glad to see that frost had not yet blasted the garden. Its summer beauty had spent itself unenjoyed, he reflected, for he had been abroad and his servants and clerks had been dispersed in his absence, but he found a late rose and proud clusters of Michaelmas daisies. Little though this garden was, he took deep pleasure in it to-day, not only because it could distract him, but also because he felt sure that the garden at home would be black by the time he reached Chelsea, and the approach of winter reminded him how few were the garden seasons a man of fifty-one could hope to enjoy. Here was one of them drawing to its close with the last of its blooms already open and the great moths brushing nervously among the shrubbery to find a refuge for the time when the sun should fail them. As he watched them gleam and darken with the varied fall of the sunlight on their wings, he thought that a moralist might draw some lesson from their anxiety; but he was not enough at ease to turn the reflection to profit. He could not see quite to the end of the analogy that was shaping in his mind. It still lingered with him now as he sat at his desk, and just when the door to the antechamber behind him shook to a knock, he felt that he was about to find the point of this idle speculation; with his summons to the visitor, however, he let it slip away. Were it a valuable thought, it would come again, matured for its waiting.

As the door turned angrily on its hinges—the idleness of the summer had not improved its temper—John Harris looked up from the desk by the window, where he was writing.

"Do you want to be alone, sir?"

"Not if it's William Roper, as I think. How does the brief go?"

"Well. It's nearly done; would have been finished had I not spoiled a page." As he spoke, the young man reached to set a fat volume of law on the shelf behind him—a careful, serviceable secretary, More noted approvingly. And as he caught himself in the thought, he added the observation that he had been in the last few weeks watching men more critically than had been his habit before his journey to the Continent. Not the journey, however, but the situation since his return had sharpened this perception.

Yes, it was William Roper who came through the antechamber into his study. His quick step and ruddy countenance told that he had been hurrying; his manner was eager in spite of the breathlessness which needed a moment of apologetic rest before he spoke. With a characteristic shake of his head and a shamefaced smile, he was finally ready to talk.

"Sorry; I hadn't realized I'd been walking that fast. Your stairs are deceptive, sir. We were working on some cases, and I let it grow later than I intended. I hope you haven't been anxious."

"Is it late, then?" More reassured him. "I haven't been watching the time. That's one advantage of having faithful young men around—you can leave the remembering to them. Ought we to set out?"

Roper looked at him uneasily. "That's why I hurried to get here a little early. Could you excuse me, sir? We have much to do before the courts open to-morrow."

"Of course. I suppose, too, that you would be just waiting and visiting with the Cardinal's gentlemen; that's not sensible for a busy man. One of the men downstairs can go along."

"Thank you, sir!" The fine face lighted appreciatively. This sensitivity was one of the things More found most satisfying in Roper. He was not spectacular, but he was swift to understand and to accept understanding without great ado. "After I had offered to go this morning, I thought it shabby to be begging out," the young man added.

"So you came yourself instead of sending a messenger?" More chided. "With such economy, I can guess whether or not you'll be working late to-night. But I'm glad of this sight of you. Will you walk with me to the river?"

"Shall I go ahead to the wherry?"

"No, no. We'll send John a Wood or whoever is downstairs. Don't be so niggardly with your company. I'm ready as soon as this other John passes on me."

In quick pleasure to be of service, Harris started up from his papers and ink-pots. Tall, though a little stooped from much writing and studying, he loomed between the window and

More, whom he scrutinized as he came forward. Having brushed back his own wayward forelock, he set More's cap at a more careful angle than its wearer's impatient gestures long let it maintain when he sat at work.

"Well, do you think the Cardinal's guards will let me in?"

"Where is your chain, sir?"

More looked at his mentor in mock-alarm; then he relaxed. "I doubt that the Cardinal wants to see me on Duchy business; so this is not an official occasion. Besides, young man, in my household you should be studying more serious responsibilities than gold chains. 'Vanitas vanitatum'!"

"But it is part of your office," Harris protested with a twinkle that belied the literalness of his words. "Otherwise, sir, you'll do."

"Now, there's enthusiasm for you. Eheu! the prosiness of youth in this day."

" 'O tempora! o mores'?" laughed Roper, holding the door.

"Exactly, though I think you all do very well as to 'mores.' " With an affectionate pat on Harris's elbow, he let the latter help him into his kersey gown. The extra warmth felt welcome, even indoors. The Cardinal was too much preoccupied, foreboding told him, to be disturbed at such uncourtierlike garb as this one visitor's.

As Roper and he emerged from the outer door of the Chancellor's House into the lane that led to the river, More paused.

"Have we time to stop in the chapel?"

"Surely."

Roper's answer had the right spontaneity; so they turned into the precinct of the Hospital. The uneven pavement, roughhewn blocks from the old, demolished Palace of the Savoy, made hazardous walking, best done in silence. Always, in the shadow of the new brick walls of Henry VII's charity, More thought of the mediæval pile which had stood on this site.

Cardinal Morton had often told the boys of his household tales of the dramatic history played out in this palace; and from that period of his boyhood More remembered the unsightly shell of the masonry, from which builders had long pilfered unmethodically. More than a hundred years the gutted ruin had stood, a memorial to the terrorism of rebellion; and still the name of the Savoy, which the Kentishmen had hated because of their hatred of John of Gaunt, lingered in his great-great-grandson's work. Yes, forever, out of the ruins and the ashes men tried to build anew: the thought beat upon his heart with such insistence that it seemed to have urgent meaning for the present, just as the fancy of the moths had had a little while before.

In thoroughly natural and easy fashion, More and Roper kept their silence; years before the grief of spiritual perplexity had established a strong bond between them, so that of all his well-beloved young friends and kinsmen, outside his own children, Roper was dearest to More. Long since, the merely legal relationship had disappeared from affection's reckoning. With a sharp turn, they were in the close, which seemed, beneath the ivied wall, a kind of antechamber to the gloom of the chapel. Needing no sign between them, the two men walked towards the altar, up the steps of which the western sunlight cast the mellow blue and amber and green of the windows.

Close enough for companionship, far enough apart for the privacy of prayer, they knelt near the chancel. Before he entered on the office of his private commemoration of Friday, More offered with special joy in the presence of this son his reiterated thanks for the grace that had won a fine soul to its proper peace. As Roper's dilemmas and enthusiastic errors had been a great pain, so the spiritual certainty that had issued from all the perturbation was an increasingly sweet assurance to More. Here was the peace of not one soul alone, important as it was, but of two; for her husband's happiness was Margaret's devotion. And their spiritual kinship made more propitious the future of their children, for already the bitterness of controversy beat upon the stanch and threatened to defeat all but the most steadfast in the hard time ahead. A home spiritually secure and undivided was the deepest blessing that childhood in this age could know.

Thus by the ante-chapel of blessings asked on his beloved, More came into the sanctuary of his private worship. Reverently phrase by phrase, thought uttered the *Pater Noster*, the *Ave Maria*, the *Credo*, and hearkened to the soundless echo of the words, golden as the bright music of bells across an English valley. *Et exspecto resurrectionem mortuorum, et vitam venturi seculi.* Remembering that, walking with it forever in his thought, a man could go unperturbed, however cruel the pressure; forgetting it, he must surrender to anxiety, to a thousand temporal urgencies, to mortal things when for him the immortal were reserved. Save the grace of God guide him, however, no man could find or keep the hard way of his salvation. *Miserere nostri, Domine, miserere nostri. Fiat misericordia tua, Domine, super nos quemadmodum speravimus in te.* Upon us —he drew into that intention the troubled souls with whom he shared the burden of perplexity in a darkening time, and he prayed that their fearful heaviness might be transformed from that of sin and unbelief to the fear and soberness of believing conscience. *Fiat misericordia tua, Domine, super nos*—with that petition his thought would dwell now as he went upon his way.

Though he did not see the movement, More knew that Roper had lifted his head and, absorbed in contemplation of the beauty of the altar which Italian craftsmen had fashioned, waited his own rising. With that action, More realized, too, the chilliness of the pavement, for they had knelt out of the sunlight. By contrast with the cool within, the air of the close and the lane seemed warmer than when they had entered the chapel; so they walked briskly to draw its warmth the sooner to them.

Not till John a Wood had handed them into the wherry and the boatmen had put off, did Roper turn as if to speak. Even then he hesitated. It was like him to prepare thus for the intrusion that a sudden remark can be when two are silent together.

"What is it?" More asked as if the motion had been true preamble to speech.

"I was thinking of what St. John's here always reminds me of," Roper's explanation began slowly. "Do you remember the time when we came away from it talking of heresy and dissension and I made you a false prophet by my own insistent prophesying?"

"I don't remember that last part. It sounds prodigious."

"You had spoken of our perhaps having some day to compromise with the heretics so that they might not deprive us of our churches, and I protested that you talked too desperately."

"Yes, I know that we have thought together on that sad problem—more than once. But what of our prophecies?"

"You know how I am—I grew so angry that you retracted and said, 'Well, well, it shall not be so, it shall not be so.' "

"And I was a false prophet then? In that case, Son Roper, we are two desperate-speaking men," More said so softly that there was no raillery in the words. Pity for the twenty years between them that would carry Roper further into the uncertain time than he could hope to look made it impossible to toss away the thought thus revived. "Yes, the time of division seems more imminent now than it could have seemed to any but a bleak-minded man like me three or four years ago. Truly, I am sorry that you see it now clearly, too, for I would with all my heart that I could still say, 'It shall not be so.' "

"I think the time is very close, sir." Roper's averted gaze

pleaded against inquiry. "But it's too confused—I can't say why."

"Well, Son, when the time comes, let us pray God that we be more generous in our judgments than the victors will be, for victory is a heady, cruel draught to most of us. That men hate in the names of rival kings is horrible enough, but that they hate in the name of Christ—" The broken thought hung between them, for neither would venture farther into what the other knew or foresaw.

On the landing-stage at York Place More stood a moment to watch the wherry pull off towards Westminster and the business by which William Roper's spirit was oppressed. What was pending in the Court of King's Bench, he wondered, for he knew that only an official secret would have sealed Roper's lips. 'I can't say why': the tone had been positive, had pleaded, 'I must not. I am not free.' *Free*—the word concentrated suddenly, amazingly, within itself the diffused emotions of the day's uneasiness; and the man most bound in all the kingdom was waiting for him in his enslaving splendor.

The great clock at Westminster began to strike the hour. Turning, More saw that John a Wood had disappeared, evidently to apprise the Cardinal's men of his arrival; for approaching the water stairs to greet him came the man of Wolsey's household whom he could least gently endure, Thomas Cromwell. More than ever, his confident, coarse, almost truculent bearing troubled More; he seemed so little worthy to be a great man's secretary, to mediate between the world and the grace and suavity which were always the Cardinal's, that the mere incongruity had in it an element of savage farce. At least, however, to give Cromwell full credit, no man would ever misread his intention: the long, hard lips, the narrow eyes, the hands clenched even now, when he was walking down a path, were all fair warning of the spirit within. He knew no other man who fronted the world with so clear a caveat as this Cromwell bowing now perfunctorily, unsmilingly.

"His Eminence asked that you come to him in the river gallery," Cromwell remarked dryly. "You know the way, Sir Thomas? I think he would prefer to have you come alone."

"Thank you. Yes, I know the way."

Yet Cromwell did not turn away at once, as he would naturally have done since they had entered a porch that formed the crossing between wings of the episcopal palace. With an expression as close to pity as More had ever seen that heavy, pallid countenance wear, Cromwell held him; in that look of compassion More read the truth of what he had thought incredible rumor—Wolsey had already ceased to hope, and his despair had infected those who depended on him.

"His Eminence is very nervous. I'm glad he sent for you, because he has been seeing too many people telling him this and that to feed his fears. And you are—gentle."

After a reluctant pause, the last word came with so unnatural an explosion as to be startling; but Cromwell had already turned abruptly away. "Gentle." The epithet was humbling, for, though More had heard it spoken sometimes scornfully by these same narrow lips, there had been no accent of mockery in its utterance now. It was as near a compliment as he had ever known Cromwell to speak. Was this grim, coarse man, adventurer and usurer, capable of gentler feelings than his harshness had led men to suspect?

By way of the cloister which skirted the privy garden of the palace—a cloister, More remembered though he had no heart for pure beauty now, of such grace and delicacy in gray stone as would ordinarily have slowed his steps to leisured contemplation—he came towards the gallery on the river. Outside the carved door, where, unwontedly, no guards stood, he hesitated debating whether or no he should knock; and as he considered, his eyes traced the iterated escutcheons of the paneling: Wolsey and the See of York and the tasseled hat of the Cardinalate. Responsive to the tracing, came the thought that whatever disfavor—even the disgrace of which men talked—could do, the Wolsey whose pride had spread his devices here stood secure: humbled though he might be, as Archbishop of York and Cardinal Prince of the Church, he was beyond the undoing of his political enemies, Boleyn and Norfolk and Suffolk. Perhaps, if the Cardinal could but recognize it, what awaited him was not tragedy but opportunity, release, manumission, even though as unwanted as ever faithful servitor's had been. Yet that which he had served best, pride—the King's and his own—was loath to set any man free. And humbled pride was one of the most grievous sights in all the world. So with the admitted hope that he should find the familiar pride not too suddenly abated, More opened the door.

At first the spacious, airy gallery seemed empty. The eye traveled up square by square of its matching windows looking to the river and the garden, light-warmed stone checkered with the natural somberness where only half light fell. In a moment, however, the unmistakable figure stepped from one of the far windows, where the Cardinal had been leaning agaze over the river. More advanced quickly towards him, anxious not to make too swift an appraisal lest he read beforehand more than he should see. Since the Cardinal had stepped forward a pace or two, he stood in the shadow of the wall between two windows so that only the firmness of his bearing and the simplicity of outline of his heavy figure showed clearly.

"I hoped you could come." The voice which could always give splendor to its plainest words was steady and easy, but the hand over which More had bowed quivered almost imperceptibly, as the leaf of a manuscript quivers to the breath of an eager reader before his hand has reached to turn it. Quietly those long, delicate, usually dramatic hands hid against the folds of his scarlet cassock, and Wolsey spoke as if he had not noticed their trembling. "You will wonder at my asking you to come when we have no affairs to discuss. Impulse. I wanted to talk to you. Last night I was thinking; and—strange—you are almost the only man I know, in the Court circle, I mean, who is not looking at me now in fear of his own fortune if mine change or in greedy anticipation."

"Your Eminence is overgloomy; you have many friends."

"And enemies. But this is not a question of friendship, but of interest and involvement. Besides, Thomas More, to deal honestly with you, I know we are not friends in the real sense of the word. We are too different—that's all. Standards, values. I wish that were not true, but it is. Still, we're not enemies either, I trust." More bowed a quick acquiescence, on which Wolsey seemed to reflect. "You see what I mean—you are not having to scuttle for a new warren because there's no room at Court for me; nor are you picking up my revenues, like—I might as well say it—Boleyn. Have you heard about his demanding those of Durham for years back?"

The question was too point-blank to avoid; so More answered as casually as he could, "I heard something of that when I first rejoined the Court, but I've grown used to not paying much attention to that sort of gossip."

"That's like you. Of course, there's talk. And it's true. That upstart, greedy fool!" The concentration of bitterness in these epithets that More had heard assigned to Rochford by many men in many tones of voice, but not before so venomously, testified to Wolsey's having pondered the roll of his enemies. And these same men had hated him for an upstart and were rejoicing now that, after years of sapping and mining, they saw the solidity of this upstart power tottering. But he was not going down easily; indeed, some of them might be like unwary pioneers trapped in the fall they had contrived, for always some one else stands by to observe how the work is done, to learn the evil lessons swiftly. Unhappily, More meditated watching the acid of the Cardinal's bitterness etch deeper lines about his deeply sculptured lips and temples, Wolsey had been too thorough a teacher of devious measures; these men who were repudiating him were not above employing his methods to more selfish ends than his had ever been.

As the passion of his scorn faded, Wolsey continued, "It's the satisfaction I grudge them. The work and the authority and the anxiety—God knows!—I've had enough of. And though you're not a churchman, I can say it to you who have been doing the work some of us have been too remiss in—to my shame I have served the King better than my spiritual duties. God make me a better bishop!"

The pain of this wrestling conscience was pitiful to contemplate in silence; yet it would be presumptuous of a layman to speak a confessor's comfort to the troubled soul. Less than comfort, however, would be an intrusion, would perhaps waken the oppressed spirit in turn to a silenced embarrassment. He had heard of the Cardinal's weeping in his distraught and humiliated state within the last few days, when the accumulating slights and insults of weeks could be no longer ignored; and he thought now that a nervous weeping might be easier dealt with than this inexorable examination of conscience that he had no right to hear. Nevertheless, he perceived, too, that Wolsey was a less tragic figure than compassion had presaged; for, though he stood here by the Thames bank gazing into the grayness of an October dusk while the Court was passing splendidly through London on the way to Greenwich, in thought he was not alone, rejected, cast into the outer darkness of futility. Not his the spiritual fire of Fisher or even the steady glow of Tunstall, but his office endowed him with a long-neglected, effectual power, secure from all the taint of the worldliness and the ambition and the policy that the King had used and thrust away. Since he had won through to recognition of that power, as pendant to the Cardinal's own obsecration More prayed that the saddest trial might be past and that Wolsey, Bishop and Cardinal, might be freed from the servitude he had devised for himself through nearly twenty years.

From his contemplation of the darkening river Wolsey seemed to draw comfort, for, though his upper lip pulled wryly downward, he spoke steadily: "But I did not ask you here to sit in the ashes with me, but to ask some things directly. Cardinal Campeggio sails to-day—a year from his landing—and by morning we shall know how I am to read the fact. To-night the book is dark, and there is no profit in trying to decipher it. Judging by all Gardiner has written me from Court, however, I can guess. I am no longer useful, and my presence would be a bitter reminder of failure to those who have waited already too long and cannot brook further failure. God knows! I understand the frailties of the flesh, but this infatuation passes any natural desire. The King has had years to think of the consequences, and he is evidently incapable of thought when he will throw away all that we have won in Europe. For what? If he were not King, she should be tried for sorcery; but then, were he not King, she would not matter. Bah! Less than a hundred years ago, a duchess did penance for sorcery through the streets of London. And this wench—keeping the King servile for four years—why, the thing's incredible unless there be sorcery in it."

"That is a new construction to put on fidelity, Your Eminence," More interposed in the hope of stemming the tirade which the Cardinal might regret and look back upon in fear of what he might have said. Even in the near darkness of the gallery, More sensed Wolsey's recovery from the hysteria towards which thought of Anne Boleyn was rushing him. A slow, long sigh, as of one waking from an uneasy dream, signalized the change in mood.

"And such talk is futile? Thank you." Wolsey spoke so thinly that the units of breath seemed to march single file past the pickets of his nervous strain. "Yes, I suppose it may be treason to talk so; but I have said all that only to you, and my walls have no ears. Still, it's an unfair burden to put even on you. The real point, though, is this: can you not somehow reason with the King? He respects you; he almost fears you. Without using it consciously, you have the power to make men think of what they are doing, and why?"

"His Highness has long had my opinion on this whole sad business of the annulment."

"If you could think of that as one premise, accept it tentatively, you might be able to do something on this other score."

"Since I cannot accept the premise, Your Eminence, there is no other score in my reckoning."

Again the Cardinal sighed, but with a sharper intake of breath than before. "You are probably right, and you are a braver man than I. If I had seen that years ago, if I hadn't separated young Percy and this Anne—" His voice trailed away in the melancholy contemplation of what might have been had he stood with those who wished to quiet Henry's scruple at its first rising. "Well, my light has been very dim in spite of my trying always to find the best policy. God send the King wiser counselors! If I have ever deserved your consideration, remember one thing when you have His Grace's ear at some time."

"I doubt his listening to me on anything much longer," More explained to qualify the Cardinal's thought, for he remembered Henry's enjoining him to read *A Supplication for the Beggars* and afterwards studiously avoiding any comment thereon. "But I did not mean to interrupt, Your Eminence. What should I remember?"

"My colleges. I began them late, but they are the most honest building I have tried to do. They mean more than this or Hampton Court, something that you and a few others care about. That's why I am asking you. Speak for them if there is need."

"Gladly, Your Eminence. But you are thinking too darkly. You will finish them yourself."

"With what? Debts? The gifts I have given the King? Remember Boleyn and the revenues of Durham; and that is but a beginning. I know; I have heard the wolves howling. Richard Fox died a year ago—I was saying a commemoration of him just before you came—but he finished his college. I shall not finish mine. I know you're not rich, but it's not just failure of money I fear: it's indifference and this lukewarmness that you've been fighting at the universities. It may take courage to speak up for things that matter, like learning. As I've said before, you have courage. If you have a chance—that's all I ask—I wanted you to know that I really care about the colleges, for themselves, apart from me and my pride."

"What I can do, I will with all my heart, Your Eminence."

"Thank you. I shall remember your coming to-day. It is late, I fear, but there will be guards outside the door to see you safely back. I want the darkness here a little longer; so I shall not go with you. God bless you!" The rich voice quavered in the benediction. "And pray for me."

So abruptly did the Cardinal turn that this seemed scarcely the ending of their interview. Yet ending it must be, for he stood abstracted, a dark figure against the far window that now made hardly any distinction between the dusk within and that without. In traversing the gallery, More remembered that Cato had spoken of old men's planting what they could never see come to fruition, building for posterity and the gods; that spirit had spoken here to-day. The Cardinal was not old in years, however, scarcely older than he himself. In the three or four years longer that he lived, though, Wolsey had come to stare over the edge of a great pit, despair, which he himself by God's mercy had never approached. Humbly he wondered how he could front such hopelessness as the Cardinal must be facing there in the darkness by the window. He had reached the door, beyond which there were lights and an escort waiting him; but in the shadows his hand fumbled for the latch across the carving of the panels—Wolsey and the See of York and a Cardinal's tasseled hat.

CHAPTER V

THE heavy fragrance of new bindings, suiting well, More thought, this meeting with Tunstall and Fisher, was for the time being the most pervasive force in the room. The others—the rustle of leaves as Tunstall read in his new *Supplication of Souls*, the occasionally violent breathing of Fisher as something in the little book he was perusing irritated him, the gentle cricking of the hinges of a book in his own hands, even the play of the sunlight checkering the floor of Tunstall's study—came and went; but the mingled harsh, beloved odors of ink and paper and leather hung unabating about them. While the two bishops read steadily, the one in More's answer to the troubling book that the other was seeing for the first time, More himself had been, he felt, more happily engaged than they, for he was browsing among a score of new Greek volumes that Tunstall had just bought. Beautiful books all of them, they stirred again, more sharply than before, the longing to be away from the cruelty and the emptiness of Court life, the longing, thrusting forward and beaten back since the bright morning at Cambrai, to be at the private strenuousness of his studies, his family affections, and his devotions. Not even such a serviceable book as this which Tunstall was reading keenly, with head inclined over the pages and lower lip drawn in as if he might speak at any moment a comment or a supplementary thought, satisfied this hardly defined longing: it needed doing, it seemed to be of some use in a vexed cause, he believed in that cause, and he was glad of the skill in him which it had drafted to its service; yet such work brought him little of the companionship of freer studies, little sense of the annihilation of time that is one of the chief certitudes and joys of devotion to letters. It bound him to the half-truths and half-errors of zealous, confused men in this England of 1529; whereas, these gracious, humane books—he found himself stroking the new Venetian Epictetus and Simplicius as if they were the hand of a dear child, and he smiled at the action—could set him free. Methodically, to gauge their power, he set the diverse volumes upright on the press where they had been lying and across the top of which his examination had strewn them. Brown and cream and gold-embossed, squat or tall or undistinguishedly middling in stature, too thin to bear a label on their backs or thick as a Bible—that was one way to measure books, but it could not discover the secret of their lure. Perhaps theirs was a Circean temptation, thought groaned, and the honest way of study must let them wait till all the present duties were served.

"Very good!" Tunstall looked up from the book and nodded with such emphasis of approval as seemed to More to decide his interior debate. "I like this at the end. He imagines the souls in Purgatory to be addressing us," he explained to Fisher, who had looked up from his own reading. " 'Remember our thirst while ye sit and drink: our hunger while ye be feasting: our restless watch while ye be sleeping: our sore and grievous pain while ye be playing: our hot burning fire while ye be in pleasure and sporting; so may God make your offspring after remember you; so God keep you hence, or not long here, but bring you shortly to that bliss to which for our Lord's love help you to bring us, and we shall set hand to help you thither to us.' You always get at the central mistake, Thomas, and let the minor ones ride. I suppose that's one advantage of being a lawyer."

"There ought to be some advantage," More said humbly

and miserably, too, for he realized that one party in his private debate a few minutes before had been the never completely exorcised regret that the law had won him from his chief youthful devotion to letters; and that regret always troubled him, for he knew that the law had been rightly his career and that his was no thwarted spirit. Settled rationally so long ago, the regret had no right to spring in thus intrusively. "Yet I am not sure that the lawyer's way is the best way to cope with these writings. Reason is often simply unequal to the appeal of prejudice and passion, good and bad."

"Yes," remarked Fisher slowly, "that's the trouble with some of these people—they're right and they're wrong at the same time, sometimes in the very same sentence. If they were all wrong, it would be easy to deal with them; and if they weren't so aggressive, it would be easy. Now take this man—Fish," he had fumbled back to the title-page for the name. "How confused he is!"

"Some things he says have real point, I remember, and I can believe that there's honest human feeling behind it," Tunstall pleaded. "But suppose we were to say even that much, straightway there'd be the cry that we agree with him in everything."

"You're too generous with this particular book," Fisher smiled and shook his head. "I'm afraid its chief motive is all too clear. I cannot imagine a more blunt attack on the property of the Church. It's a direct invitation to the King to confiscate wholesale and to discredit churchmen."

"Yes," More added, "when we look at it in the light of all this recent attack on the Cardinal, it becomes a very serious piece of work. And there seems to be method in its widespread appearance in London just now." He refrained from adding the further disturbing item of the King's recommendation of the book.

"Do you think this circulation of it planned—say with the

King's approval?" Tunstall was really asserting the idea rather than examining More. "It certainly has not had mine. If we must think that, we must think also that he has deserted us in this war against heresy. Then where do we stand?"

"Is it possible—you know better than I because I have been in disgrace longer than the Cardinal—that the King is framing new definitions of heresy?" Fisher's tone was whimsically, yet soberly, deliberative. "Henry has always prided himself on his standing as a theologian."

"Probably it amounts to the same thing." More's speculation was shaping in the act of analysis. "But my guess is that he would adhere to his definition of heresy, yet maintain that it doesn't apply in a case like this."

Fisher nodded. "I suppose that's partly what I meant—a drawing of invisible lines where they will be convenient, not letting one half his brain know what the other half is thinking. I know the Tudor mind of old, and I used to tell this Henry over his lessons that he was a casuist. That fact partly explains his keenness in debate; but it's a slippery gift."

"And many men have it, my lord. I am not vain enough to think that the King and I stand alone, and you know how I am belabored for inconsistency and vilified as a turncoat."

"Oh, but there's a difference, More," Tunstall protested. He reached across the table for Simon Fish's little book. "No one with any sense could fail to see that Utopia never was meant to be present-day England—I suppose it's what they say about you on that score you're referring to. Any man may keep his imaginative speculations separate from his actions; honestly, too. Keeping one's profession of immediate policy separate from action is another story."

"Perhaps you see the difference so clearly because you agree with me." More moved round the table to lean over Tunstall's shoulder. Though the latter had been fingering the book, he had not found the place he wanted. "It's much harder to convince Tyndale and Friar Barnes and, I suppose, this Simon Fish that I'm not a renegade from my youthful liberalism, as they would call it; and if they can call the names loudly enough, they think they are exempt from considering the ideas I offer them. Sometimes I think I could write their answers for them, maybe more adroit ones, too. For example, at the end of this *Supplication* Fish writes earnestly about the need of hospitals for the poor. I agree with him thoroughly on the need but not on the way of supplying it; but let me say so much and some one will cry out, 'Aha! In his *Utopia* he showed the miseries of the poor, but now—coward and time-server that he is—he has repudiated all his humanity.' I don't need to bother you with all this, though, and I ought to try not to care about the misunderstanding."

Fisher had been listening with a compassionate eagerness to interrupt; so he spoke in the instant of More's breaking off. "That kind of misunderstanding strikes something so vital, so essential to a man's integrity that he can't help protesting. I know. Surely, it's human to ask that people try to understand our motives, even if they can't accept our conclusions. I believe that the truth will ultimately prevail, but I don't see any sense in being supine about error, and there's no harm in trying to help the truth. I'm glad you cited the hospitals because they're the perfect illustration of our point. This man assumes that, if the property of the Church be confiscated, it will be applied to the relief of the poor."

"Oversimple that!" Tunstall exclaimed. "He evidently doesn't understand what little of that sort of thing we've been seeing."

"Simple? I repeat, you are too generous," Fisher asserted.

Tunstall sucked in his cheeks quizzically, then laughed.

"Your tone of voice came close to saying 'simple' for that last word, too. Come now, don't take me too seriously on that."

"Well," continued Fisher, "let's credit the man with sincerity and see what we can say even then. I for one can believe that we might see all the property of the Church secularized here in England and the poor not one hospital better off than they are now. In fact, I'd venture that were there to be secularization, some of the hospitals now in existence would be swept away along with other property. And these people seem to forget that the Church is trustee of the endowments that generous and pious men have been building up for centuries, a little and a little and a little, and diversion of those trusts would wrong the dead, break faith with them."

"Exactly!" said More. "If some of these men had a better knowledge of history—or perhaps a better perception of it—they'd be easier to deal with. Did you note what a hero this *Supplication* makes King John? May I take it a moment? Listen: 'such a righteous king' and 'so noble a king' and 'this good king.' It could be funny if it were not so serious. Shades of the barons who made Magna Charta!"

"And still some people will think it sincere?" With a humorous glance at Tunstall, Fisher returned to his original challenge. "It seems to me the most barefaced appeal to a king's cupidity; and it is craftily done. I agree with you, More, that the inconsistencies are sometimes almost comical; but sometimes, too, the casuistry is almost blasphemous."

"You're right in that," said Tunstall. "Let me find the passage I was looking for a while ago, please."

More returned the book to him and watched the quick eyes scanning the pages. Tunstall would remember the sense of the remark; yet he would be too scrupulous to cite it in the imperfection of memory. As they waited for him to locate the offending passage, Fisher smiled across the table as serenely as if he were, More fancied, a saint of some golden, untroubled age of faith: he could be quiet as whole-heartedly as he could be strenuous and passionate. And the watcher wondered which ought to be accounted the greater power of the old bishop's genius. Upon the contemplation of this question Tunstall's discovery broke sharply.

"Here it is. He says of Christ: 'He gave more to the temporal kingdom, He himself paid tribute to Caesar, He took nothing from him but taught that the high powers should be always obeyed: yea, He himself (although He were most free lord of all, and innocent) was obedient unto the high powers unto death.' Think of a man who calls himself a Christian using that analogy to prove that the Church should be subordinate to the monarch—any monarch. Can't he see that the literal truth of his statement will not excuse his failure to understand his implications? I half-expected his blasphemy to go on to point out that the high powers were right in their sentence of death; otherwise, he leaves his kings in an anomalous position. The analogy doesn't help them much. And he misses utterly the significance of Calvary. Perhaps you're right, More, that part of the difficulty is due to lack of perception. I seem to be proving your point and not my own. That's all right. What you say about historical perception interests me, because this 'new learning' seems very proud of its appeals to history."

"Yes, but how often the appeal rests in an idea—consciously admitted or not—of human history as static. It runs something like this: let us forget the centuries between and return to the practice of, let us say, the primitive Church. And the fact that this is not the world of the primitive Church, that more than fourteen hundred building, modifying, accruing years have passed since the last of the Apostles died—every year of them as full of human history, as vexing, as compounded of good and evil as last year or this—counts for very little. I can see the temptation to look to some achievement of the past as the ideal; it shows in a good many things besides our theology—our Latinity, for example. Ciceronianism is all right within bounds; but we need to talk of things unknown to Cicero. Perhaps we make ourselves ridiculous by forgetting the difference. Worse than ridiculous. How we shall impoverish ourselves if we throw away everything that the ancients or the early Christians did not have and stop doing everything they did not do!"

"I like your extension of the fallacy," Tunstall said with a chuckle, and Fisher nodded his appreciation. "I suppose, though, that some of these reformers would really agree to throw away all that the world has won. Temperamentally they are impatient; they're absolutists. Since evil has crept in, away with everything, they say."

"Temperament explains a lot," Fisher agreed. Holding speech suspended for a moment, he rose and strode to the windows across the room. There he stood against their narrow, blurred light, a tall black figure, head bowed, face half-averted. "I know, for I can be too much of an absolutist myself. It isn't the impatience I object to so much as it is the separatism in these men. They cannot see, apparently, that it is possible to stay within a society that has made mistakes, as all human organizations must, and work for the correction of the evils from within. In the name of the Church men in the past have worked against the corruption that has crept in, and their way is still good. But these subversive attacks deny any good, and they tend to silence loyal men who want to eradicate the evil and preserve the good; they imply that any criticism must be construed as attack and all loyalty as the condoning of abuses."

"And that is the predicament for Erasmus just now," Tunstall said heavily, "if I may bring him in as an illustration. Considering his writings proof that he agrees with them, some of the heretics cry out against him now for leaving Basle and for not helping Luther; they would draw him, willy-nilly, into their party. And the worst of it has been that he doesn't seem to realize that what you can say within the bosom of the family, as it were, there's no use, and even grave harm, in saying to outsiders and enemies. I've been worrying about him. He's not at his best in disputation, but how he loves it!"

Tunstall's sigh troubled More, who had been thinking of how entangling, yet preciously so, are the anxieties of friendship. None of them had seen Erasmus for years now, but the mention of his name brought his presence among them as he had come more than thirty years before—ambitious, prolific of enterprises, irrepressible, gifted with laughter; and now, with his great name made, much of his scholarly ambition achieved, his spirit a little dimmed by age and vicissitude, he was like them perplexed and beset, a man of whom his friends thought solicitously.

Fisher, looking down into the shadows gathering in Pater Noster Row, spoke first from the silence evoked by Erasmus's name: "If you are troubled about him, better tell him so. I know that he's quick to resent criticism; yet it penetrates and it goes on working in him with good effect. And he does respect your opinion, Tunstall. Would that England were a place kinder to scholarship than it is just now! I used to think that Erasmus should have stayed with us, but I'm almost glad he hasn't been back during these last years. The dead and the absent—'O terque quaterque beati!'" He had turned back to them; yet More could scarcely hear the delicately breathed apostrophe, which the passionate, glowing eyes confirmed. Then the warm voice rose again: "I used to be worried about him, but he seems to be staying within 'the bosom of the family,' as you say. That distinction is sound, Tunstall: what may be said while there is unity may be a yielding and a disloyalty in time of division. It will be ironic, I suppose, as well as inevitable, that division will beget division, each little group splitting off by itself."

"And the advocates of division can't logically object when those who disagree with them separate in their turn," More interposed.

"Exactly!" Fisher struck the table with his clenched left hand. "But do you think they'll yield the point? I pray, though, that the world never see that test made. Too much depends on unity in Christendom to risk the melancholy satisfaction of seeing division confound itself."

"Yet there seems no halting it," More answered. "I used to think that it was my own dark mood that made me see division as so portentous; but recently many men with whom I have talked speak as desperately as I have thought. Confidence and generous feeling and loyalty have been tottering like a building on rotted piles."

"At Court, you mean, and among courtiers?" Fisher challenged. "I know. History helps us to understand that, though, for all the struggles of the last century taught men that there's little that the world offers that has not its price, and that the man who wants to die in his bed trusts no one and gives nothing his real devotion. Sometimes I marvel that we have any standards of honor left; so I'm more desperate and more cheerful, too, than you. This distrust, this class hatred fomented by such writings as this are striking their roots deep in our English spirit; and it's going to be slow work plucking them out—educating them out, if I may mix my figures. All day—this is the sort of thing I can say 'within the family'—I have been thinking of the man who perhaps even more than Simon Fish is responsible for this *Supplication*—"

"The Cardinal?" Tunstall's question spoke More's thought, too. "Yes, I know his actions have much to answer for; he has seemed so completely the proud and worldly prelate that he has courted hatred—and not for himself alone. Yet he has served the King well, and I for one remember the malice and the self-interest of his detractors. I wonder how much longer he is to be kept in agony. These ten days have meant such humiliation as would move a heart of stone."

More, listening, saw the Cardinal again in the twilight dimming of his splendid state on that afternoon before he was cited in the King's Court; he saw the quiver of the jeweled hand, and he heard again the last plea of the man of whom he had seldom thought so well as when he left him in the darkness with his pride and his foreboding. Yes, in these ten days the Cardinal had drained the bitter draft of humiliation and breathed the dust and ash of his consumed magnificence; and to the incredible shame put upon him, he had added the abasement of an incredible surrender. Cardinal-Prince and Legate, he had pleaded in a secular court; he had abandoned his estate; perhaps in that very abnegation he had acknowledged himself to be at heart of the lay order, of the Court more than of the Church. And the agony was not ended.

Fisher, in the resumption of their discourse, might fully as well have been answering More's thought as the words of Tunstall after which thought had raced: "It is over now, I think. As I came from Lambeth this morning, I saw the boats gathering in the river off York Place, men hurrying like hounds at the kill, and I thought, 'This is the end.' I have had no great love for the Cardinal, but I have less love for the mean and the base and the vulgar who can flatter themselves only by gloating over the misery of their betters. All day I have been sinning in my anger over that scene. Evidently, the city expects the end to-day."

"The two Dukes demanded the Great Seal of him yesterday, we have heard," Tunstall offered as supplementary information, "and he would not give it to them without the King's warrant; so probably they returned this morning. He must have known it was only a matter of hours. But there would be no spectacle for the people in that surrender. Did they expect him to come downstream with the turn of the tide?"

"To the Tower? Yes, so my rowers said they had heard."

"The Cardinal? Impossible," Tunstall protested.

Slowly Fisher shook his head and tapped the mischievous book on the table before them: "When a book like this is apparently approved by authority, over your head, my Lord Bishop of London? Heaven forbid that the people prophesy truly! But it is not impossible. Still the tide has turned, and we have not heard, as I think we might have, of the Cardinal's coming down the river."

Tunstall started up nervously. "Let me see what my household know. Some of them may have talked with apprentices in the Cheap."

As the door clapped to behind him, Fisher asked as quietly as though this were some new, calm subject he was introducing, "Who do you think will have the Great Seal?"

"I don't know. Unconsciously, I must have expected the Cardinal to keep it in spite of everything. I have heard some talk of Warham."

"Life is sometimes kind. He is too old and weak. Besides, the Archbishop is involved in this whole failure of the annulment. He tried to help, but Henry judges results, not intentions."

"Some one yesterday mentioned Tunstall."

"No, no. He must not take it. The office is too much shadowed by danger of the King's anger, and Henry is changing almost beyond recognition. I have just been thinking that, if we are right about the seriousness of this book, the next Chancellor will be a layman. Do you remember what Fish has to say on that matter? We'll wait and see."

"Suffolk, perhaps?" More said musingly.

"Perhaps. Though I think the King may choose some one not too powerful, not too dangerous. After all, the two Dukes stand in somewhat the same danger as Buckingham did—too near the blood to be given much rein."

"I guess the last one I've heard mentioned is Dr. Stephen Gardiner."

"He's very young for the post; an able man, though," Fisher deliberated. "I'm afraid he's deep in the King's matter. Of course, that would count for him. I don't know; but I'll think it very significant if the new Chancellor is a layman."

From the silence beyond his thick walls and oak doors, Tunstall returned pale and more agitated than in his hasty going out. "They say," he began straightway as he entered the room, "that the Cardinal has been ordered to Esher. He went upstream hours ago. Thank God, it's no worse! But a monstrous report, too: it's rumored that the King is confiscating all his goods and taking York Place as well."

"But he can't!" More heard himself exclaiming fatuously before he weighed his words. "York Place isn't Wolsey's. It belongs to his see!"

"Exactly!" answered Fisher. The old bishop rose toweringly from his chair. "*A Supplication for the Beggars.* When he wanted to apply himself, Henry was always an apt pupil. But how many poor men will benefit by the Cardinal's goods or come to live now at York Place?"

CHAPTER VI

All the anticipations and anxieties of months drew safely to rest for More in his coming home to Chelsea later in the same week that had begun with the Cardinal's surrender. Always at his homing, More marveled at the swiftness with which the world's preoccupations receded before the full tide of his family affections and stranded on a remote shore of consciousness, as he had seen the river's drift beaten up on some inlet beach by the heave of the ocean thrusting the Thames back upon itself. This time, more than ever, household and home sprang so naturally into their rightful place for him that on his first morning in Chelsea he found himself wondering whether he had actually been four months away. To be sure, they had talked later than usual after supper the night before because he would not balk the curiosity of his children and his young retainers, whose questions had recreated the multiple experiences of his absence. Reliving those months in his account of their most significant events and observations—Cambrai, the journey to London, Woodstock, Westminster, and London again—he realized that in their very perplexities he had found rewarding challenge. He had seldom been so unhappy as in these last weeks, for he had not felt before the utter conviction of such change as marks the end of a world before its time, a conviction deepened in almost every strenuous waking moment since his return to England; still he had seldom been able to front circumstance with such equanimity and detachment as in this time. A year before, he remembered, he had in the agony of watching, contriving, and praying against death resolved to abandon worldly affairs if death prevailed; but Margaret had come back from the shadow like some more fortunate Eurydice, and he had had no warrant for the withdrawal he had meditated. Yet, though his gifts were worldly ones and the world had demanded his service in the last year and he had been happy in the strength that could spend itself in work, perhaps he had completed the renunciation in spirit, if not in fact. He was not sure of how he would accept an ending of offices and honors, but the thought of that ending had been long with him. Emotionally, this year with its augmented duties, achievements, and recognitions had been a kind of novitiate of withdrawal for him, so that retirement would be no true renunciation as the world reckoned, but an enlargement of experience; it would focus not on what he was giving up, but on what he was entering upon.

Now as he paced the terrace in the crisp wind of late October, he meditated on the chameleonlike creature man is: for weeks in the company of the perplexed, the equivocal, the failing, he had felt old, and in the last two weeks he had thought more than once that Wolsey could be only three or four years older than he; but this morning, though the stiff breeze from the river tightened his throat, he was young again. There was still warmth in the sun to rout the early chill; and though the fields close by, those of the luckless harvest, were brown from the new plowing, the distant landscape showed the unabating green of meadow and pasture; and the blue of the river repeated the blue of the serene morning sky. It was a fair world in which to be young. And it was still a good world, in which enthusiasm was as contagious as disheartening. With deep and humble pride, More gave thanks for the young lives that were his to guide through these few years—his and not his, for each bore the stamp of its own private pattern. He thought glowingly of the freshness of each personality which the questions and comments of last night had revealed anew—Meg's rejoicing in the will to peace that Europe had evinced at Cambrai, John's thoughtful interest in his meeting with Bonvisi, sweet little Anne Cresacre's delight in the splendor of the two princesses who had negotiated their sons' agreement, William Roper's compassionate report of the gratitude with which Wolsey had knelt in the dust to kiss the King's ring sent after him in his exile. Yes, one by one, the questions and the notings of significance had revealed the clear, responsive personalities of his young people. For each, there came back some shining instant from the evening's conversation.

Occupied with these pleasant thoughts, he had turned and re-turned in his pacing the terrace. On the last turn he paused to listen, for some one was opening the door just above him. As it drew inward, he saw Margaret bracing herself against it as if she would hold it open while she looked for him or called him. Seeing him thus close, however, she ran down the short flight of steps and the little path to the terrace. Even before she spoke breathlessly, her eagerness and the sparkle in her eyes told that she had news.

"Father, I'm glad you're close. When you didn't come in, I thought you must have gone walking far."

"Riddles, Meg. What has happened? Nothing bad, I know."

"Guess. Oh, but you never would; and I must tell you right away." She laughed with her secret so that the tip of her nose wrinkled back, and her hands twisted at her girdle. Wife and mother of twenty-four though she was, she could not hide the impulsive little girl in her who delighted to tease her father when he was in the mood for play. "I was afraid that you had seen them come and would be in before I could catch you."

"Them? You have me properly puzzled, Meg."

"Two men. One of them the Bishop of London's from Fulham; the other from abroad with letters for us."

"Us? Aha! I've guessed. Erasmus. I'd never have got it without your hints. Apparently I've been dreaming, for I saw no men arriving."

"My first thought was a groan: 'Business to take Father straight off again.' Instead, you have a thick letter, and I have a separate one."

"To prove you're grown up? What does your letter say?"

"I haven't read it yet. I came to find you at once. In fact, I don't believe I even greeted Erasmus's secretary properly. He is the pleasant young man who was here last year; he has a good accent."

"And you approve Quirinus Talesius for that? Well, so did I. Where did he leave Erasmus?"

"At Freiburg. Why, Father, what's the matter?"

"It's all right. I'm very glad, for I have been worried about him. Basle has had very precious associations."

"And you have been afraid he might go back? But that wouldn't be reasonable for him."

"Reason, Meg, has little to do with attachments and loyalties. Perhaps they are a little like this love that enslaves men. One man sees all the world in his beloved, though all the world think meanly of her. So an idea may draw all a man's thinking in one direction until he sees the test in something that others count trivial, and then he may consider something else accidental and secondary that almost everybody values as all-important. Had Erasmus gone back to Basle, I'd have been distressed, for I think that camp can never be his proper spiritual home. Even so, I believe I should have understood. He has much to work against, much to try a more patient spirit than his. His staying, none the less, to work within the Church is heartening. Basle was the deciding place. So, Meg," he paused a moment, holding the door open for her, "many circumstances prove me too faint a prophet. I needed to come home in order to say of all my foreboding what your Will forced me to say once in a similar darkening, 'It shall not be; it shall not be.' Now it seems as though all the crooked things will come straight ultimately if only we keep our courage to work patiently at them. Your world and your children's may yet be a whole and blessed one, fairer than this divided, sad one we elders have made."

Though More wanted to detain the young Dutch scholar who brought Erasmus nearer to them than even the conversation about him a few days before had done, he had to be content with a very brief interview for this first one. Talesius rode away on his further calls of state, however, with a promise to return to Chelsea for a true visit before his leaving for the Continent. His duties of delivering letters and copies of Erasmus's long-labored Augustine and of collecting his patron's English income once discharged, he would be freer to enjoy the hospitality which Erasmus's enthusiastic memory had pictured, More felt, over-generously. Nevertheless, they would do their best to make his stay a happy experience, for Erasmus's sake and—even in the brevity of their renewed acquaintance they could add in thought—for his own.

Having seen the two travelers on their way, More hurried back to the hall to read his letter and learn what their friend had written to Margaret, too. As he entered the hall, he heard the laughter of his girls, which Dame Alice's voice dominated in a curt, but good-natured, comment:

"The flatterer! And he always laughed at us English for kissing."

Amid a fresh peal of laughter, like the round of morning church bells in the varied pitch of the voices, More stepped into the group in the oriel.

"Is Erasmus trying to flatter his way into your good graces,

Alice? Poor fellow, you've kept him long on tenterhooks." Sitting down beside her, he laid a playful hand on hers.

"Well, listen to what he says. Will you read it again, Margaret, please?" She spoke so archly that More, in his amusement, squeezed her wrinkled hand as caressingly as if she were younger than she had ever been for him. At best puzzling to her, Erasmus had sometimes been even irritating; but he had found her susceptible to his ingratiating ways. He would enjoy this moment.

Margaret looked up from the sheet spread on her knee and smiled at her father. "You'll enjoy reading it all later. This is the sentence Mother thinks flattery: 'Effigiem illius, quando coram non licuit, libenter sum exosculatus.' It is amusing. What do you think Holbein would say at having his picture kissed?"

"Why," laughed More, "he should take it just as your mother does—for a compliment. Does Erasmus like the picture?"

"Oh, yes," the girls said in so enthusiastic a chorus that he knew Erasmus must have written charmingly about it. Margaret reached her letter towards him, then half-withheld it. "You want to read yours first, though. This is a sweet letter, but it doesn't have much that's serious to say. And yours must have, it's so long."

Evidently remembering household duties, Cicely, Elizabeth, and Anne asked leave to go. As he watched them cross the hall with a swishing of their skirts and a fluttering of sleeves, More waited with his finger under the seal, not yet applying force to break it. They were good to watch—strong and comely and alert, these daughters, wholesomely unlike the overjeweled, Frenchified maids-in-waiting of the Court in these last few years. Yet they liked pretty things and wore their gowns and coifs with becoming airs. Though he disliked flirtatious and seductive ways, More enjoyed in these daughters the natural, graceful desire to please that is a woman's right, especially if she be young and pretty; coquetry, he reflected, was this same sweet quality grown feverish and hard. At the muffled slam of the door on Cicely's skirt, her little squeal, the jingling of her girdle, and the laughter of her companions as the door swung open to release her, he lifted the seal.

To the accompaniment of the click of Dame Alice's needles and the soft leafing of Margaret's book, he read his letter. Graceful phrase upon phrase, matters important and familiar mingled in the inimitable manner of the born correspondent—this was Erasmus at his happiest, writing of European affairs, of work done, of new enterprises, and of his friend's family. This power of sustaining multiple interests at once and of moving simultaneously on several levels of thought was one of Erasmus's richest gifts, More said to himself as he looked up from his perusal to see if he might safely interrupt his wife and daughter.

"Yes, he likes the picture, I take it. How surprised he must have been in the changes in us all—especially in you young ladies, Meg! There are compliments here, but no kisses. Let me translate a bit that will interest you in a different way, Alice. He speaks of Cambrai: 'Now we rejoice at the fact that destructive discord has been done away.' And he says this, too: 'In truth, men are not unaware that they owe much of this joy to the most unconquered King of England, Henry the Eighth'—don't frown, Margaret; that's literally what he says, 'invictissimo'—'who has not rested till, by his superlative wisdom and equal perseverance, he has transformed apparently immedicable discord into the peace desired of all.' And he plans to write something in praise of the King's efforts for peace—'tam pium vereque Christianum animum.' "

"A second royal dedication!" said Margaret. "Does he tell you about his book for Queen Mary of Hungary?"

"Yes, is that in your letter, too? Maybe we had better not read each other's; for I know that when Erasmus is dictating a batch of letters he sometimes repeats at length. I'm not blaming him, for it's natural to say the same things to those who are interested in our affairs."

"So you'll have to read mine, Father, to test the resemblance. I doubt that they're much alike."

As Margaret handed him the letter, More noticed her start and look intently out the window. His eye had lighted on a few phrases: "Videre mihi videbar per pulcherrimum domicilium relucentem animum multo pulchriorem," before the contagion of Margaret's stirring assailed him. "Who is it, Meg?"

"More men. And these look like courtiers."

With a nervous pat at her coif, Dame Alice started up even before her husband; recognizing one of the men at a glance, she exclaimed, "Why, it's Master Marchaunt."

They could hear the servants at the door; so Dame Alice and Margaret, after hurried scrutiny to see whether the room did credit to their housekeeping, prepared to leave the hall. More thrust his daughter's letter, but half-read, into her book.

"You'd better keep it lest it be mislaid. I'll finish it soon. Marchaunt is probably just bringing some urgent business of the Duchy, something to be signed and sealed."

"Let's hope that's all," said Dame Alice. "We need your counsel here for a while."

But it was not all, for when the recent co-ambassadors had exchanged greetings, Hugh Marchaunt, with a little ceremonious bow and a click in his throat to clear his voice, said very formally, "The King's Majesty requests your immediate return to Court. If it is possible for you to be there, he bids you to an audience Monday morning."

Marchaunt's smile was calm and noncommittal as if he were pleased with the manner in which he had delivered his message,

More thought irrelevantly, and as if, too, he knew no more of its occasion than he had revealed. And at the moment of that observation, he wondered what could be of such moment as to warrant this gentleman-ambassador and to necessitate the secrecy which had not taken Marchaunt into confidence. In the typical stupidity of surprise, he heard himself asking:

"The King is at Greenwich?"

Marchaunt repeated his little bow. Then, having discharged his mission, he launched upon trivialities of Court gossip, which in his speculation about this summons More could not follow at first with even, he rebuked himself, common courtesy. He really did not care that the Lady Kitty had encouraged her dancing master. What Erasmus had written of the Turks in Hungary more concerned the future of civilization.

More paced back and forth in the great gallery at Greenwich. Strangely, here a few bends down the river from Chelsea, frost and the salt rasping of the sea wind made him feel far-transplanted. The impression of an alien climate had been strengthened by the strident, nearly night-long merrymaking of the Court, after which the palace seemed sullenly empty this morning. The guards in the King's antechamber, amused that any courtier should come with the rising sun, had offered him the warmth of their fireplace; but to the thick atmosphere of that inner room he had preferred the chill air of the gallery. The mustiness of stone and oak and long-hung tapestries was less distasteful than the exhausted air which an ill-drawing chimney still further choked and sooted. In fact, despite the uncertain north light through the mullioned windows, he was enjoying again the tapestries that he remembered as the chief delight of this palace. So familiar were they that the gloom made little difference, for being in their presence served as a swift recall of designs but half-revealed and colors obscured. These could not vie with the splendid modern hangings of Hampton Court and York Place; so they were now somewhat neglected, sagging and dusty, even a little frayed. In their sturdy workmanship and spirited artistry, they had been telling for more than a century their story of Christ's ministry from the wedding feast at Cana to the Last Supper. Spoils from France they had been to ornament this Placentia when it was the proud new manor house of Duke Humphrey. More smiled to himself, for the "Good Duke's" name recalled a frequent thought of his own student days at Oxford: black as were some of his deeds, Humphrey had had rare taste in books and tapestries and architecture, in some of the things that make the grace and charm of life. In their way, these weavings of green and blue and scarlet yarns, deep-toned as the windows in Amiens Cathedral, held as pervasive a magic as the beautiful volumes of Petrarch and Saint Augustine which he had admired among the Duke's books at Oxford. Here, the eye of memory saw, though the eye of the body was half-defeated, was the centurion at the very moment of saying, "Domine, ne te fatiges: non enim sum dignus, ut meum sub tectum intres"; and here was our Lord with Martha and Mary against such a glory of sunset as that of last evening when he came up from the river to the palace and looked westward to where Chelsea should be in the blackness of earth beneath the frosty flame of the afterglow. "Martha, Martha, sollicita es, et turbaris per multa. In una autem re est operae pretium: Maria sane bonam partem elegit, quae non auferetur ab ea." Thus his own heart echoed the good counsel.

The door to the King's apartments creaked, and Henry Norreys, blinking, perhaps from late gaming, perhaps from the smoke within, summoned him gravely: "The King's Highness wishes to see you, Sir Thomas."

Through a blur of now-gathered courtiers More followed the King's gentleman into the privy chamber, on the threshold of which he passed the one man in the whole assemblage whom he saw clearly in his own character—the Duke of Norfolk. Was that really a smile on the Duke's usually narrowed lips, a good-natured bit of encouragement? Or did his own needless, even foolish, perturbation read the signs confusedly? Norfolk had passed, and More stood with Norreys inside the closing door.

Across the chamber, Henry blocked the firelight, legs set far apart and furred gown gathered back by his hands hidden in its folds. Another figure, withdrawn slightly into an embrasure at the left, More made out to be Christopher Hales, the King's new Attorney-General. This was, then, some formal matter needing witnesses, for Norreys joined Hales. As the King bade More rise from his salute, his voice had the same friendly, anxious note in it that had touched More in their interview at Woodstock.

"You came last night, they tell me, prompt to the asking."

"We should not have caught the tide this morning, Your Grace." Even to More's own ears the words sounded very much like an inept apology.

Henry smiled. "The tide. It makes so much difference." He was staring from under his puckered thin brows as if he were aware, not of the man before him, but of some distant, repugnant scene. More wondered in the flash of his observation whether the King were seeing the thousand boats thronging the Thames off York Place just a week before. With a nervous lifting of his eyes, Henry seemed visibly to adjust their focus before he spoke:

"Thomas More, you have been a good councilor, one of the most faithful a king ever had. That is why we are the more confident that you will accept and bear well the charge we wish to lay upon you. We would have you be Lord Chancellor, to administer mercy as well as justice in our name."

"Sire!" Hearing his own voice in the dry syllable of protest,

More wondered that it had found so much issue. The careless phrase of some one in Cardinal Morton's household, forty years before, a compliment on some long-forgotten witticism—"Make a canonist of him, and he'll be Lord Chancellor in his day!"—raced in his thought now. After Morton and Warham and Wolsey, all chancellors in his lifetime, he could not fill the post. But the King was looking at him quizzically as if he could read the discomfiture of his surprise. "Your Grace, I am not able, not worthy, to hold such an office. After the great prelates who have had it—I am merely a lawyer, a pleader of cases, no judge."

"For one thing, we want you because you are a lawyer. For another, you have been an excellent arbiter in the not inconsiderable affairs of our Duchy; and there is good warrant for making him steward of greater things who has proved himself faithful in lesser ones. Those are reasons that the Council has urged in their agreement on you. Beyond them, however, is my own special love for you and my faith in your integrity, which I would have redeem my Court o Chancery. It has fallen into low repute."

"But there are some worthier the task than I." What had the Bishop of Rochester said about the next chancellor's being a layman?

"We do not know them. Come now, it cannot be two months since we talked about commanding and asking. Frankly, I ask you to take this heavy work—Herculean, it may be: I do not just command. If it were merely an honor we offered you, I should have little hope of persuading you to take it; instead, it is an opportunity for hard, necessary work. We need you."

Listening to the earnest words of this plea, More thought, as he had often before, of Henry's skill in finding out a man's vulnerable spot and striking at it unerringly; for he had heard him use many appeals with many sorts of adversaries in debate or pleading. By their years of intercourse Henry had made himself at home in the mansions of his councilors' thinking; yet he had contrived to let few—"at least not me," More corrected himself—know the way into the secret chambers of his own motives and purposes. For lack of understanding of the King's intention, he must take these words at their face value. Somewhere within, however, a warning that had been shaping through the last two or three years—a warning of change in the King's character—stirred as if it would force itself out into open recognition; but straightway all the old habits of loyalty and friendship and hope nurtured on the promise of Henry's youth thrust themselves into the breach to beat back the doubt. "Only defect in you," they counseled, "can you allege, even to yourself, as claim to exemption from this charge." Henry's simplest plea, "We need you," could hold no guile.

"Consider, Your Grace, that I am advancing in age, that I am past the flower of health and strength. This post needs abounding energy—"

"You a valetudinarian!" The King squared his shoulders in a hearty laugh. "A poor excuse for a man whose father still sits on the bench. Furthermore, I'll not admit the plea that you're old, for that would make me old, too."

"There are many years between us, Your Grace."

"Perhaps. Still, I knew you when you were a very young man; so you may not call yourself old in my hearing. A lame excuse! If you wanted an excuse—" Henry's voice sank to its sweetest, most ingratiating tones—"you could do better than that."

"Then, will you not believe it genuine, Sire, and no excuse?"

An amused frown tossed the direct question aside, and Henry went on from his own thought: "Suppose we say that you prefer Chelsea and your charming family and your scholarly conversations and study to the service of the realm and especially of an old friend who has rejoiced at all these blessings for you and favored them? What is that phrase of Horace—I should ask my

Lord of Rochester to reteach me my humanities—'caecus amor sui'?"

The imputation of self-love and the King's ascribing to selfishness his longing for retirement, which he had himself been imagining as a wholesome, earned release, outraged More beyond power of protest. If that were the appearance his desires wore, how could they claim any validity?

"If all a man's thought of his own will and desires be selfish, Your Grace, who can escape the sin? Must he not think of the better and the worse use of his gifts and powers and the grace God has given him?"

"Is there any question of better and worse here?" Henry's voice remained level, but the tone had edged. More noticed the two men at the left, just barely within his line of vision, look round momentarily and return to their little play of respectful inattention. They had been prime enemies of the Cardinal, he remembered, with recurring thought of there being something ominous in the King's choice of him to succeed archbishops, some of whom had been cardinals as well.

"May I speak freely, Your Majesty, without giving offense?"

"Surely!" Henry spoke with reassuring wholeness of emphasis. "You ought to know by now that your independence is one of the things I most prize in you. I need some unsubservient, free men."

"It is your speaking of need that troubles me, Sire." More lowered his voice to a husky whisper. "I cannot further your cause. You have known my inmost conviction—"

"Be assured, I will never infringe your liberty of conscience. I know your opinion, spoken frankly and courageously; and, knowing it, I ask you to take office. There are other matters for which I need you. Believe me when I say they will not cause you any uneasiness so long as you hold before you honor and justice, as you have always held them." Suddenly Henry seemed to be studying the pattern of the rushes at his feet as intently as if there were nothing else to consider. The steady crepitation in them, which always troubled a quiet room, the effort of the two witnesses to accommodate themselves to the main silence, and the King's heavy breathing filled what seemed long minutes. More would think only of this open, unmistakable promise which Henry was phrasing with conscious scrupulosity; he would hear the King out. Finally the latter looked up from his contemplation with the same generous smile that had turned the years back during their interview at Woodstock. "Thomas, do you remember the charge I gave you years ago when first you came reluctantly enough into my service? Perhaps I have sometimes seemed to forget it, but I have always been grateful to you for recalling it to me. Yes, I know your reminders have been subtle ones—not expostulations—and the more effective therefor. Now I ask you to be my Chancellor, not for any advantage to me save the restoring of justice and impartial mercy in this land. That affects my name and my honor as King."

"Since you ask so, Sire, even in my unworthiness to follow the great men who have held the post, I must accept. I will try to be not too unworthy."

The physical fact of his kneeling, for he perceived that the King's hitherto concealed right hand held the crimson pouch of the Great Seal towards him, was but an imperfect symbol of the confused humbling of his spirit. He had distrusted and misread Henry's motives, and as retribution for the secret evil that he had done he must accept this service on the King's frank terms; yet still the ugly doubt only half-groveled in the presence of his repentance. Like a stubborn ranter in the stocks, it whispered, "Not service—servitude." Desperately, to silence it, he held out his hand. The leaden seal throttling the drawstrings of the pouch, which should have been cold, was hot from the King's holding it. A little more and it could leave a brand. With the crimson purse in his own right hand, he leaned forward to kiss the King's—unseeingly, for he saw instead the delicate, quivering hand that had surrendered a week before this same token of pride and power and servitude.

II

“O SIMPLE FAME!”

CHAPTER I

As the escorting company paused within the doors of Westminster Hall to realign in true processional, More felt himself shudder as a swimmer shivers from the first cold shock of the water. He had not thought that so many men as thronged the far-extending hall would come on a gray morning to see him, unused to ceremony and impatient of pomp, enter upon his office; in the last twenty-four hours he had thought much on the responsibilities to which the King was calling him, but not till now had he realized fully that one of them must be henceforth the distasteful thing that is state. He could almost have smiled at his simplicity, for of course he had been in youth accustomed to the dignity of Archbishop Morton as Chancellor, and he had often enough seen Warham and Wolsey in processional with the Great Seal borne before them; but their magnificence had been compounded of their multiple honors, and what belonged to the chancellorship had not been cut away from the splendor of archbishopric and cardinalate. Now, suddenly, he understood that this office which he had accepted had its elements of spectacle regardless of the man on whose shoulders the velvet and the fur and the great chain rested smotheringly: the office testified to the magnificence of the King, whose judgment and voice and hand its incumbent became. "Lasciate ogni speranza voi ch' entrate" might sound a strange inscription to cut above the arches of Westminster Hall, but could the proper word for individuality replace "speranza," More reflected, Dante would be identifying accurately these precincts of the King's Courts. In a few minutes he himself would be for all that he did here no longer Thomas More but the interpreter of the mind and the conscience of the King.

That thought frightened him with a concern very different from that which had prompted his hesitancy of yesterday morning: he had, the last years had been proving to him, little comprehension of all that stirred in that mind and conscience. Otherwise had it been in the days when Henry had laid an affectionate arm across these sagging shoulders, when they had talked of books and gardens and stars, when the King had asked a friendship untinctured with servility. Yet it was in the memory of those days and in the hope that they might be partially recalendared that he was going now to take his oath of office at the far end of Westminster Hall.

Though he lacked the crosses and pillars of Wolsey's superb processions and the Great Seal, the scepter, and the book held their state unaccompanied by the Cardinal's hat, More knew that his was a more pretentious escort, with its dukes, marquises, and earls, than he would ever have thought needful for the assumption of his office. They moved slowly forward, the Chancellor—in his own view of the matter—mercifully lost between the two chief peers of the realm. Norfolk and Suffolk, keeping uneven step, thrust towards each other in the irregularity of their rhythm. Rank upon rank, the faces of the assemblage retreated before the impersonal vision of one seeing only with the eyes of the body; they were faces with the arrested animation, the fixity, of faces in a tapestry, real and unreal in the same moment. Only an occasional one forced itself from the background with an undeniable plea for recognition: here was Antonio Bonvisi, who brought swift recollection of his kinsman seen in the pageantry of scarcely three months before; here, Erasmus's messenger looking so confident a delight in the spectacle as should have routed any faintness of heart; and here, John Harris severe enough in attention to suggest an inward struggle against the temptation to reach forward and right some detail of the Chancellor's appearance.

With the retreat of these and a few other insistent faces, the marble seat, towards which they were moving, drew upon them; and, as if concerned for possible nervousness, Norfolk glanced sidelong at him. In the moment in which More noted the look, the Duke with an unadmitting smile had turned away. Norfolk was with him: the thought should have brought him pride and elation, but it brought only the shadow of remembering that he was with Boleyn, too. The misgivings that had assailed him when he had sat as but one councilor among these lords paced his mounting of the dais until, with all the splendor gone blank before him, he prayed for strength to trust them and to walk the way of his duty unfalteringly. It must be strength, he knew, not only to take up but to lay down as well should the time demand the action, and the hardness of withdrawal clamored at his heart. From this abstraction he returned to awareness of the instant when the Duke of Norfolk, fronting the concourse in the hall, was waiting a silence in which he could speak. Before them heads bobbed and thrust as the crowd surged in the wake of the last cleaving marchers; then the rustling stilled, and there were only nervous peripheral motions like the wash on the shore when the central agitation of a pond has passed. More's gaze searched the throng from the far edges, ragged and still urging forward to see and hear the better, inward to the neat ranging of the lords temporal and spiritual close to the marble seat.

Here truly were friends, gratitude assured him as the quick interest of Tunstall at one point and Gardiner at another spoke for his eye. Their regard shone as clearly as though they had never been mentioned for the post they had come to see him assume. Less evident was the appraisal of Bishop Fisher, alert but cryptic in the intentness of his gaze, a steady, unyielding, unjudging fixity of countenance. Was it unjudging? The thought had disturbing force, because with it came recollection of Rochester's remark when last they talked: "I'll think it very significant if the new Chancellor is a layman." The question that had tormented him in wakeful hours during the night lifted its head again. Was he himself abetting some malign scheme in succumbing to the King's persuasion?

His silence won, however, Norfolk began to speak in the great voice, ill-consorting with his spare figure, which he could command on occasion: "Devoted subjects of our dread sovereign, we have come here on a solemn errand which I pray God may prove auspicious to the whole realm, for the King's Majesty has raised to the high dignity of the Chancellorship Sir Thomas More, a man whom you all have known to be of extraordinary worth and competence. His excellent qualities has the King tested amply in many and weighty affairs entrusted to him both at home and abroad, in the offices which he has filled, in embassies on which he has served, and in his daily advice and counsel on occasions of every degree. No man in his realm has the King found more wise in deliberation, more sincere and open in utterance of his opinion, or more persuasive in the carrying of his conviction."

More could hardly follow the words longer, for they wandered back and forth like fen-trapped travelers beguiled by the *ignis fatuus* of harborage ahead. In marveling at Norfolk's rhetorical prolixity, strange evidence of formality in a man whose ordinary speech, even in Council, could be pithy and full-flavored, he missed more than once the trail of expostulation and compliment by which the King's spokesman would lead the assembly to approve the King's choice of Chancellor. He forgot his own diffidence in amused reverie on the incongruity of his appointment since all men must see the fall the office had sustained in the passing of the Seal from the proud hands of Wolsey to his own undistinguished ones. As often, amusement was at the moment a gallant bearer of the assault on sensitivity, for More could feel that the Duke's continuing protestations of favor had a shade too much solicitude in them, moved perilously close to the edge of patronage; yet he could smile in the secret resolve that, whatever unread motives had prompted his appointment and this pageant of his installation, men should see him capable of doing all that in which the true dignity and distinction of the office inhered. Suppose they were in this moment thinking him a man of straw? By God's grace, he would win for the King's justice something more than the desperate fear and awe with which men had come to regard appeal to the magnificent court of Chancery. Only the most superficial, negligible prejudice could think simplicity and dispatch inconsistent with justice.

A little shamed at his wandering attention, he came back hastily to listen to the sentiments with which Norfolk was obviously framing his peroration. It would soon be over. Looking sharply at the assembly, as a man who has caught himself falling asleep beneath a preacher's eye gathers energy to seem alert, he surprised so amused and quizzical a frown on the Bishop of Rochester's face as warned him that the unguarded lines of his own face might have been betraying him; but the assembly showed no other intelligent eye to chide his inattention. Rightly, the company was listening to the Duke, not watching the idling Chancellor.

"Wherefore, receive this your Chancellor, at whose hands you may expect all speed and fairness in rendering the King's judgment."

The Duke's last words, like the charm in some old wives' tale, set the listeners free for the stirring, the rustle, the little coughs, and the whispers that had been deferentially restrained. Quickly, however, the company returned to a but-breathing silence, for the Duke turned to summon the Chancellor to his oath. As he rose to step to the marble table, where Norfolk laid open the Bible, More felt himself unsteady with the curious sensation of distance between the exaltation of head and the heaviness of feet that he had known years before at his student disputations. Unafraid though he was, in the moment when, with hand on the unseen page, he fronted Norfolk's still formal presence, he felt a pervasive, delicate tremor against which control straightway stiffened itself. It was not fear; yet it contracted his voice to a thin, small one, strange as the voice of an awed child. In his secret prayers at his Communion a few hours earlier he had taken this oath of office; so the repeating of it now before men had no right to send panic through his veins. Clause by clause, he repeated after the Duke the six-fold oath that laid upon him the most momentous duties he had ever undertaken. "—And I will secure and advance the profit of the King in so far as I am able reasonably to do; so help me God and His holy Gospel." These last words, which he could speak in a now-emboldened voice, hung between them for a moment before the private, intimate personality slipped back into Norfolk's face.

The Duke smiled, the breaking of the formal assembly began, and More lifted his hand from the vellum page, which lifted reluctantly with it. The twentieth chapter of Saint John: it was a proper, moving passage on which to have registered his oath. "Be not faithless, but believing," our Lord had chided another Thomas. "Believing"—he wondered whether the King had dictated the choice of that chapter or whether Norfolk's humorous acumen had found it out.

Released from the coveted discomfort of waiting for and then beholding the spectacle in this late October chill, the company broke into the confusion of men pressing in opposite directions. Shivering, half from the cold that penetrated even the unfamiliar weight of his robe, half from the relaxation after strain, with his eye More followed curiously a strenuous figure elbowing, shouldering his way down the eastern wall. If that man did everything with such sturdy inconsideration of those who blocked his path— An unusually narrow opening turned the hurrying thrust of the man to an edgewise insinuation, and More could see his face as he heaved himself together and eased through the crevice between taller, less mobile men. Thomas Cromwell. Was he not with Wolsey, then, at Esher?

That wonder had, however, no time to grow, for the cleavage between the men pressing outward, their curiosity satisfied or their business inexorable, and those thronging towards the dais had been achieved; and the press of those anxious to speak the hurried, fragmentary congratulations of a great occasion shut out More's view of the hall. He was touched by this generous, personal expression of feeling by men of many tempers; in the warmth of his own appreciation he could even take with amused equanimity the obvious sycophancy of some few eager to be seen in the line. How few they were! The little troubling that they caused him in thought vanished with the glimpse to his right that a sudden parting in the crowd afforded: there at the other southern corner of the hall a second, rival court was holding, a thronged island curving out into the main stream of exodus, in the place where his father would be sitting in the Court of King's Bench. Only in that moment did he sense the pride that his office would be to his family. Lord Chancellor! Yes, there would be reverberations of this new state invading even the quiet precincts of Chelsea.

When the pressure of those at whom he could only smile with a murmur of formal thanks began to relax, the friends who had been holding back approached him. Foremost among them came Bishop Tunstall with Erasmus's messenger, Quirinus Talesius, whom with his characteristic thoughtfulness the Bishop must have rescued from the neglected state of the stranger. The young face, alight with pleasure, and the young manner, not too thoroughly schooled in formality, delighted and moved More.

"We did not count on my having this to report to Erasmus," Talesius said with a glowing smile. "It has been magnificent."

"You must leave such adjectives to Erasmus's own delight in elaboration," More answered laughingly, for he had already gauged Talesius's ability to accept the light coins of his jest at their face value.

"What an interesting, colorful colloquy he could make of such a scene! I will remember all the details so that he need not lack the sense of being almost an eye-witness himself." The eager young gaze, seeming to pick out the very warp and woof of the Chancellor's robe beneath the deep pile of the fabric and to finger the scarlet pouch in which the Great Seal lay, reinforced the promise of exact report to Erasmus.

More laughed. "A colloquy? That would be one way to make oneself beloved by all schoolboys."

"Not of one realm alone," interposed Tunstall. "Are you not terrified at the prospect?"

"It is the most appalling aspect of the office I have met yet," answered More. "So, young man, before you go back, I shall have to issue a writ in restraint of your activities as literary adviser to Erasmus. Remember, I'm counting on having you again at Chelsea, and long enough this time to fill your head with other matters than inspirations for colloquies. Are your errands to the rest of Erasmus's friends all done?"

"By no means. But my Lord of London sent after us so that I should not miss to-day. I am glad beyond measure that he did."

"We don't induct a Chancellor every day," Tunstall explained half-apologetically; "so I thought that even His Grace of Canterbury could wait a day or two for his greetings. I don't remember whether Erasmus would have seen the Cardinal installed here or not; but at any rate, I'm sure there's no one he would be happier to hear of in the office than you. It would have been a shame, then, to let him miss the vicarious pleasure; so we depend on you, Talesius, to report the morning's work faithfully."

"Indeed, you may depend on me. Though I could not follow the great nobleman's address, your John Harris, my lord, who had worked towards me, interpreted it for me briefly; and eyes are good, whether one knows the vernacular or not."

"They have their own understanding, haven't they?" More contented himself with the simple comment, sorely tempted though he was to congratulate Talesius on his getting Norfolk's turgid address in the probably swifter periods of John Harris.

A fresh assault of well-wishers threatened to sweep them on; so Tunstall caught momentarily at More's arm as he said, "When you are alone and weary after this, think of all the things you would wish me to say, and believe them said with all my heart."

And they were gone, the sure friend and the young man of the earnest eyes through which another friend would see this as the morning of a brilliant, auspicious day. God make the heavy prophecies that had beleaguered his own heart false as such enthusiasm branded them! In the consciousness of that prayer, he acknowledged the new felicitations the more fervently; perhaps the wishes of a man's friends could gird him with armor proof against the arrows of self-distrust and despair. In the background of his thought, hope was struggling to find the Hephæstian forge on which to shape such impalpable mail, when a hand laid lightly on his elbow made him look up into the clear gray eyes of Bishop Fisher.

"Have you thought at all of what I said about a lay Chancellor?" The voice was gentle as the arresting pressure on More's arm. "Do not remember it against me. I am no longer worried."

The tone of his voice, the relaxed touch, and the quick, considerate moving past to make room for those still coming on were all witnesses to the Bishop's trust, a precious possession.

Finally, the company had dwindled to those who handled the business of the Chancery and those who formed the policies of the King. They looked suddenly very small and unimportant in the almost emptied reaches of Westminster Hall, for the arches of the roof seemed to spring farther and the beauty of gray stone to shadow the spirit more deeply when the men beneath were few. From his contemplation, through which the troubled doubts whispered again like the remnants of a stubborn dream waked from and resuccumbed to, Norfolk recalled More sharply:

"God's body! What's to be sad about? Things look good from the top of the ladder; and there's nobody plucking at your heels."

"It's just the moment between different moods, my lord. The routine of work will cure my melancholy humor."

"Work? Well, if that's your nostrum, no need to worry: you'll be merry enough in no time to dance a jig. They tell me there's plenty of work accumulated, for the Cardinal, much as he thought he knew, never learned his proverbs; nor watched a juggler at a fair, either, I take it, or he'd have learned how many swords and balls he could handle at once."

"Could the juggler teach him to avoid the sword of Damocles, my lord? With all that were his own to manage the Cardinal was, I think, most deft."

"I don't know much about your Damo-fellow—some clerk's tale, I suppose; but York over-reached himself and left some of his duties undone."

"Ah, my lord, is temperate ambition—or, better, the unambitious doing of duty—an everyday virtue? We price it high, I think, in very appreciation of its rarity. The Cardinal has done many things remarkably well. Where he failed, who might not fail?"

Norfolk's ruddy color deepened, less in anger, however, his next words showed, than in recognition of a reproof he would not disclaim. "Six months from now tell me what you think of his doings as Chancellor. This is, after all, where you can't help judging him. There's plenty to do right here."

"Naturally, my lord, for the sessions are more than two weeks old, and the Chancery has been idle."

"Stubborn! There are enough men, however, ready to call him the haughtiest subject that ever lived; so you need not raise your voice unless you want to. Anyhow, you can change things for the better here without fear that the reforms will offend anyone except the scoundrels." The approach of some one behind them interrupted Norfolk till he was sure of the newcomer's identity. "Eh, business already, Master Secretary?"

Gardiner's answer consisted in a simple inclination of his head and the extending of some papers to More. Since his office indicated their source as clearly as if they had borne the most magnificent royal superscription, Gardiner made no explanation, nor did More need to offer any apology for perusing them straightway. After the first startled realization of their contents, he read swiftly, oblivious to the desultory conversation of Gardiner and the Duke. This was monstrous—memorandum upon memorandum for the denunciation of Wolsey which the Lord Chancellor must formulate against the opening of Parliament eight days off. Had all the humiliation of the Cardinal-Legate's submission to the lay court achieved no more than this fresh assault upon his fallen pride? More had heard it whispered that Wolsey had pleaded in the King's Court, instead of claiming the exemptions of his estate, for fear of the jackal temper of the Parliament to come; the miscellaneous items in the King's papers suggested ground enough for that fear. Where could the

Cardinal, who had had scarcely the foresight of the unjust steward, turn in hope of leniency? Vainglory, usurpation, oppression were the burden of these melancholy notations. From the last paper in the group, a hasty jotting about undischarged, long-due debts, More looked up to discover that the Duke had already disappeared and the King's Secretary was watching the turning of the sheets in his hands with gloomy intensity. The unasked question evoked a half-reluctant answer.

"Yes, His Highness wishes all this alluded to—not, of course, specifically as yet—in his opening of Parliament; and knowing your habits of speech, he feared you would be too gentle unless you knew the whole truth. Not all of these are items in the indictment; rather, they're materials gathered secretly for His Grace. So, though they cannot all be communicated in detail, they will give you an idea of what the King has learned."

"But surely, Dr. Stephen, the King has been deceived by the Cardinal's enemies. This is a pitiful medley."

Gardiner flushed—a slow dark mounting of the blood that spoke his personal confusion, perhaps even remorse; for More had heard men muttering that the envoy and secretary whom Wolsey had schooled had been the agent of his fall. In his own knowledge of Gardiner he had not credited this rumor, but it was now an uncomfortable recollection. Little as men respected the Cardinal, they were quick to brand as turncoats and traitors those whom he had fostered, now in the camps of his enemies. And it helps timeservers little in the judgment of the world that they plead an honest change of heart: the men who are keepers of their neighbors' consciences are quick with the scourge. Though he himself exonerated Gardiner from the basest charges growing out of his fortunate transfer to the King's service in the autumn of Wolsey's prosperity, More was troubled by his present demeanor. The close line of the Secretary's lips and the leveling down of his eyelids, until the pupils of his eyes were nearly veiled, might be evidences of grief, but they had a stubborn, uncommunicative quality that baffled scrutiny. When he spoke, voice as well as gaze seemed to come back from a great distance.

"His Eminence has been his own worst enemy." Then, as at Woodstock, Gardiner emerged from the alienating disguise of an uncertain, almost sullen manner; he looked squarely at More for a moment before his eyes focused down the far reaches of the hall. "I can guess what you are thinking, and I honor you for it, Sir Thomas. You don't believe all these things. But the King does. And last Friday the Cardinal signed his acknowledgment. What can we say in the face of that? To-morrow, probably, he will be condemned. When he himself has surrendered like this, how can anyone defend him?"

The repeated question demonstrated Gardiner's own misery more clearly than an elaborate protest could have done, but More could not console him. "Whom the King delighteth to honor," he thought without warmth or pride or expectation of gladness.

CHAPTER II

Two days later More came home to Chelsea, for the first time in the dignity of the Chancellor's state, to the establishment of which Norfolk had lent him this barge of his swift traveling from Greenwich. Responsive to the trained power of his rowers, his appreciation of the grace and the sweep of their motion along the curving Thames mingled with anticipation of home. The thought was a cloak against the frosty air of late October. He would be landing at dusk, for the sky beyond Westminster was already flaming beneath clouds that threatened to bank down in storm; let it be seasonable rain to nourish their fields or an early snow, there would be warmth in his hall and on the hearths of the cottagers. Through the wise management of Dame Alice, they seemed all secure against the malice of winter, for no man would be hungry or vagrant because of their mischance. Indeed, by God's grace, More could in his new office give employment to some men who might otherwise suffer through the winter; and it promised to be a hard one. He would have a barge of his own and extra servants in the household. To be sure, though, he would never rival the household the Cardinal had had—poor fellows! many of them might wear their livery thin before they were snug in service again.

At his landing he left his men to the mooring of the barge and came swiftly through the garden. An east wind, raw enough to send a man gladly indoors, the crunching of leaves and twigs on the garden path, the massing of the westward clouds, and the glow of his house ahead heightened the sense of blessing which he had missed in the troubled days just passed, but which had escorted him home, redoubled in atonement for its absence. There was work to do and he could do it; there was power given him in trust and—with the grace of God—he could fulfill the trust honorably. For the first time, therefore, he found himself truly reconciled to the King's insistent demands on his service; no longer vexing himself with doubts, he would go straight forward so far as the road stretched clear.

Yes, there was a good fire on his hearth, if the cheerful windows spoke truly, and he hoped to find Erasmus's messenger the well-settled guest awaiting him. As he came up the terrace, the dogs at any rate had heard him coming, for they set up so enthusiastic a barking that the door swung open before him. With his thanks to John a Wood, who helped him out of his cloak with an almost disabling anxiety to be respectful, he passed into the hall. A quick scrambling on the hearth half-compensated for his disappointment in not finding Talesius there: the four boys of his household, sprung to their feet at his coming and roughly lined up in salutation, round-eyed and awkward, cast a ragged shadow across the room. He returned their solemn greeting with such gravity as made even the shyest among them—a pale, overnervous, bookish little boy, new in the household—smile delightedly. They moved, then, as if to leave the room.

"Wait a minute, boys. I'm not going to dispossess you if there's another fire in the house. What are you doing? Telling stories?" They must have been, he was sure, unless boys prone on the hearth had changed greatly since he had served in Archbishop Morton's household.

"Yes, sir."

"Havelok the Dane or Guy of Warwick?"

"No, sir. The Field of the Cloth of Gold."

"And burning Tyndale's Testament, sir."

"Realistic young moderns, aren't you? Well, see that you tell them fairly."

"Yes, sir."

Perturbed at the latter topic, though he would not have the boys guess the fact, he passed up the hall towards the more private precincts of the house. Why should these youngsters be telling the story of Tyndale's Testament? A light in the small parlor drew him thither. Here he found, with greater good fortune than he had hoped for, Dame Alice, Margaret, Will Roper, and the young Dutch messenger silhouetted companionably before the fireplace. For a moment before stepping over the threshold, he stood in enjoyment of the picture—the three young people seated on the hearth-bench, evidently busy together over a book, and his wife reading her devotions in the chimney corner beyond them. Dame Alice—so easily distractable was she?—started up with a little cry and the thud of the book at her feet.

"Husband! We feared you were not coming. And we wanted to see you arrive."

"Another time, then, I must come by full daylight, but I warn you I'm no grand spectacle, no Cæsar on the Nile."

"But, sir," said Roper, for the trio had risen, too, in eager welcome, "may not Chelsea count you its Cæsar till it boasts a loftier claimant?"

"If it's any joy to my family and I can keep my head through the boasting. But I'll abdicate at once as soon as a new Cæsar appears. I hope we are not talking riddles for you, Talesius; we have a family habit—no doubt a bad one for visitors—of talking in jests."

"Do not worry about me, sir. I enjoy the spirit of the jests even when I cannot follow, but you are all so thoughtful to speak in Latin for me that I may never develop the curiosity about English that I should have. Every once in a while it sounds enough like Dutch to make me think it not a hard language."

"Latin is so convenient a tongue that no foreigner should apologize for not knowing English unless we English should also for not speaking Dutch and the other vernaculars of our European friends. So Latin it is as much as possible while you are here unless we must name some English thing for which the rest of the world has no name. But do sit down again, for we have plenty of time before supper, have we not, Alice?"

"Unless the journey made you ravenous. The lights have only just been brought in."

"Not hungry; but I am thirsty."

Instantly Roper crossed to the doorway to summon one of the story-tellers to service. As they were ready to settle into place again, More stooped to pick up his wife's Book of Hours where it had fallen unnoticed by the others.

"Must you start all over again? Did I interrupt you in the midst of a prayer?"

She laughed at him with the quick, dismissing laugh of common sense that could be both her most engaging and her most irritating trait. Sometimes More envied the completeness of rejection that she could achieve, and then at other times he wondered whether good sense could ever accomplish the final exorcism of perplexing thoughts. The interrupted prayer was, however, a matter of the right size to be laughed at; so he presented the book with a grand flourish and had for his pains a pat with it on the crown of his head. Rubbing the spot in mock ruefulness, he came to his chair on the opposite side of the fireplace. Talesius sat within arm's reach, with Margaret next him on the hearth-bench. Before they returned to their interrupted business, however, a boy came bringing More's tankard of water —the pale little story-teller.

When the child had left the room, More leaned towards Margaret: "It is shocking not to know one's own household, but I must confess I have forgotten that youngster's name."

"Richard Purser. His father brought him last June, I think."

"Thank you. Yes, I remember. Fortunately for my memory, I can plead that I have been away most of the time since then." A new boy, of not too-well-established antecedents—More wondered whether he or one of the others had been telling of the burning of Tyndale's Testament; then he rebuked himself for falling into the vulgar error of blaming the stranger.

"How has your visit gone this time, Talesius, when England must seem a little more familiar than it was last year?"

"Splendidly, sir. Everyone is so kind, so eager for news of Erasmus, that I am glad the wishes are imponderable or I should be staggering under the weight of them. That is the marvel of the spirit, sir, is it not? Its freight of thought seems limitless."

"Yes. I like your figure. And I am glad his English friends have had the intelligence to stand by Erasmus. There has been so much yelping at his heels that I have half-trembled lest some of us waver in our affection."

"But do you not think his moving to Freiburg, with all the inconvenience and discomfort and even danger to health that it meant, has convinced people of his allegiance?"

"I could wish so with all my heart, but I find so many men, not invincible, but unconvincible, that I grow discouraged. There, I was not going to think about discouragement during this visit with you. I have felt so assured of good to come, to-day, that disheartenment seems half a lie—as if, like the brethren who hate me and vex Erasmus, I should take one example for condemnation of the whole and try to make an autumn of cheerlessness out of one crow if I cannot make a cheerful spring out of one swallow."

"You should not disguise your feelings for me. You see, I have known Erasmus to be melancholy in the bleakest sense; so it seems to me a natural state."

"For thoughtful men? Yes, I fear it is the growing sin of our age. Reason and the larger, more generous gift that is understanding ought to be able to find ways through the sloth and the materialism and the unbelief of our world; and not seeing the way, thoughtful men find despair easy. Erasmus, who is a little my senior, and the Bishop of London, and I, and others of course, have lived to see what happens to fine enthusiasms in such a time as ours. We looked to see the humanities make life gracious, and we have lived to see Cambridge, for example, raked by heresy and Oxford slumped into indifference. The terrible human passion for generalization has ruled that all academics are either enlightened scholars and Lutherans or orthodox believers and obscurantists. You would think the equation written in Scripture, so religiously do some men try to apply it. We have seen a scholar like the Archbishop, for example, enervated by the cruel pressure of the time; and we cannot charge the weakening to old age, alas! for his mind is as critical as ever. That is the unmercifulness of life. If Erasmus talks of coming to England, do not encourage him; he would find other men besides His Grace of Canterbury changed beyond bearing."

"I doubt that he will think seriously of it, for traveling is a real hardship to him," Talesius said deliberatively.

"Though there is no one in all the world I should rather have visit us, I am sadly reconciled to his not coming back. As I tell Margaret and Will here, you young people are going—God willing—more than a generation farther in human history than we melancholy elders. But before we yield place, we must try to make it a better world for you than we have found it, or it will soon be a far, far worse one. I do not mean in material ways, like comforts and possessions, but in spiritual ways, the true wealth and centrality and unity of life. We must not say another dark word, however, for I have just been feeling that we can send Erasmus heartening report of things here."

"There is your being Chancellor, for example, sir. I shall not soon forget Tuesday."

"Yes, it is all right to tell Erasmus about that; he will know that I am not likely to be vainglorious over the office. But to-day's happenings are the real news. For one thing, the King has accepted the treaty that His Lordship of London and I labored on last summer."

"Excellent!" cried Margaret with the obbligato of the young men's voices. "That means a great satisfaction for you."

"Yes, and I am as susceptible as a schoolboy still, it seems, to the flattery of achievement, for this sent my spirits soaring the very first thing this morning. One of the happiest aspects of the whole business, now that it is over, is the King's marvelously good temper. He has been positively glowing all day long."

"To your private satisfaction, sir," said Talesius solemnly, "add thought of how much this treaty means to us on the Continent. England has her natural bulwark that could make her—Heaven forbid!—the last stronghold of the West if the worst befell; but we in Europe have trembled, literally so, at these continuing wars of Christian princes when the Turk is on our threshold. Hungary seems doomed."

"Erasmus's comment is dark indeed. He writes that a good part of the country is laid waste." More could feel the shadow of this tragic picture descend upon them. How pitiful it was that modern Christendom, in its dissension and division, should abandon the ancient kingdom to pillage and slaughter and the invading faith of Islam!

"And that must mean a far crueler destruction than war causes nowadays among civilized peoples," Roper added half-aloud.

"Civilized warfare! How long is it since the sack of Rome, Son Roper?"

"Then you agree with the Utopians?" asked Talesius in the

effort, it seemed, to bring the conversation back from immediate tragedy to the neutrality of generalizations.

"On the score of peace I do with all my heart. How we can claim to be Christian people and go on, age upon age, calling Cain our father passes my weak understanding. I suppose this treaty has been so dear to me, not just because I had a finger in it—I believe I can say that honestly—but because it brings our world a little, very little, nearer the peace of God's order. The morning of the proclamation in Cambrai, Meg and Will, I thought that if such a peace could last through just your children's lifetime, there would be some genuine hope for the world. As it has been, men fight and fight; then those who are left come together to talk terms and to sing *Te Deum*, and go home resolved to break their oaths at the first expedient moment. There! I am sorry to have turned bleak again. My family know this for an old story of mine."

"Still, we need to think of it often enough to fix the necessity of peace in the minds of those who have any voice in the making of war," Talesius insisted. "Modern warfare, with its development of cannon, is losing whatever glamour of heroism it once had; so I, for one, should like to hear all that you can say on the subject."

"That is a rash invitation, young man, for the easiest thing in the world for me is to be lengthy in discourse. The Duke of Norfolk is not the only prolix man in this kingdom. And if you do not believe me, ask the first heretic you meet. The brethren complain of my wordiness, for evidently they are too lazy or too busy for any doctrine that cannot be put in a nutshell; and if we left even that measure to their choosing, they would find us the most stunted shell, that of a nut no honest squirrel would trouble to store. At least, that seems to be the way they feel about my own efforts, and I am not conceited enough to think that they single me out from my fellows."

"You make them sound ungrateful. Frankly, I envy them."

"Envy them? Are you a riddler, Talesius?"

"By no means. You do not know what I was doing this afternoon. Raiding your book-presses. And since I could not read this *Dialogue for Tyndale,* I inveigled Mistress Roper into translating for me. I have been enjoying it hugely. We stopped at a particularly interesting point."

"Meg, Meg," chided More, "are you translating truly?"

"Yes, indeed. To save your vanity, Father, we were just in the midst of your miracle, which I myself think one of the pleasantest parts of the whole book. Let me finish the chapter now, and I shall show you how true a translator I can be. This is how it goes on, Talesius: She—the young bride, you remember—'was within the year delivered of a fair boy, and in truth he was not then—for I saw him myself—more than a foot long. And I am sure he is grown now an inch longer than I.'

" 'How long ago is that?' said he.

" 'By my faith,' said I, 'about twenty-one years.'

" 'Tush,' said he, 'this is a worthy miracle!'

" 'In good faith,' said I, 'I never knew that any man could tell that he had any other beginning. And this is as great a miracle, I think, as the raising of a dead man.'

" 'If it seems so to you,' said he, 'then you have a marvelous seeming, for I believe it seems so to no other man.'

" 'No?' said I. 'Can you tell what is the cause? None other surely but that acquaintance and daily seeing take away the wonder—just as we do not at all wonder at the ebbing and flowing of the sea or the Thames because we daily see it. But he that had never seen it or heard of it would at the first sight wonder much to see that great water come wallowing up against the wind, keeping a common course to and fro, no cause perceived that drives it. If a man born blind had suddenly his sight, how greatly would he wonder to see the sun, the moon, and the stars; whereas one that has seen them sixteen years together marvels not so much at them all as he would wonder at the first sight of a peacock's tail. And no true cause can I see why we should, in reason, marvel more at the reviving of a dead man than at the breeding, bringing forth, and growing of a child to the state of a man. No more marvelous is a cuckoo than a cock, though the one be seen only in the summer and the other all the year. And I am sure, if you saw dead men as commonly called to life again by miracle as you see men brought forth by nature, you would reckon it less marvelous to bring the soul again into the body, its shape yet retained and the organs not much perished, than from a little seed to make all that structure new, and add a soul thereto. Now, if you never had seen a gun in your days nor heard of any before, if two men should tell you, the one that he had known a man in a paternoster while conveyed and carried a mile off from one place to another by miracle, and the other that he had seen a stone more than a man's weight carried more than a mile in as little time by craft, which of these would you, by your faith, take for the more incredible?'

" 'Surely,' said he, 'both were very strong. Yet I could not choose but think it were rather true that God did the one than that any craft of man could do the other.' "

"Enough, Meg," laughed More. "That may not be the end of the chapter, but it's the end of that particular business. I acquit you on the translation; so do as much for me on the sentiments."

Talesius looked up from his listening with an enthusiastic light in his eyes. "I like it, sir. There is one pity about it, though: no one who does not know English can have any idea of what you are writing now. You should do a book like this in Latin for the rest of the world as well as your Englishmen. How Erasmus would enjoy it!"

"But this is just a temporary, locally serviceable book. It is written first of all for the people who do not understand Latin and who can be cozened by any plausible preacher into doctrine of the most perilous sort. Then, too, it is written for even the learned like Tyndale himself who would bring Scripture into our homely tongue. And since I see no harm in honest translations of the Bible, I am glad enough to humor my readers by talking as homely language as ever they fancy. Such writing is not for scholars, unless they be some of these newfangled Cambridge men, nor does it, I pray, need any warrant of long life. Besides, since confuting heresies is not the writing I should choose most to do—you see, like a boy cornered, I have saved the real reason to the last—I think maybe I am entitled to a little enjoyment in the doing; and I do like English."

"Then, Mistress Roper should be your interpreter, for we know how busy you must be; and it is a shame to let only the fortunate continental who can visit you here enjoy such a book."

"I must beg to be excused," laughed Margaret. "I cannot neglect my family; and you heard Father boast—I declare, that is what it really is—about his prolixity."

"*Mea culpa*, Meg. Some day, though, I shall be as brief as any Spartan could ask."

"Let us know ahead of time," exclaimed Dame Alice, with a click of her book that might have done service, her husband laughed to himself, for a click of her lips. "I can't imagine when it would be unless at your dying."

"Not then, I fancy; for I shall probably be too hurried to speak with beautiful brevity. I have earned your teasing, I admit, for with all I have said just now I have hardly begun on the things I want Erasmus to know."

"He will be curious about the King's cause," Talesius suggested tentatively.

"I suppose so." More hoped that his shake of the head was positive enough without any definite rebuke. "But I could not, if I would, give half so complete a report on that head as many others you will talk with before you leave England. A while back, though, you mentioned telling him about the Chancellorship; and that reminds me of another reason for my sense of perfect felicity. Tell Erasmus that I have high hopes of our accomplishing some of the things—I should say 'reforms' if the word had not been recently monopolized—that Colet and he used to talk about."

"And you, too, according to what Erasmus has said."

"Well, they let me listen, anyway. For years now our best bishops have been making sound reforms, and the standards of our episcopacy—the Cardinal in some respects an unhappy exception—have been high. There is new impetus just now, I think, and I hope we can keep it right in spirit. I know this is vague-sounding, but it is confident; and that is the important thing to tell Erasmus. I shall even recant enough of my doleful sayings to venture that he may some day come back to an England rid of many of her old abuses, political and economic, as well as ecclesiastical, but still enough of a mortal realm to need criticism."

"He will be all agog, as I shall be, to hear what is happening from now on in England."

"Do not let him expect too much, then, all at once. We shall see, we shall see. Parliament meets next week; so you may hear more about 'reforms' before you leave England. Now, unless I am reading that frown amiss, Alice, we should be getting ready for supper. I shall write Erasmus a little note directly afterwards, Talesius, for I cannot tell how my time may be restricted in the next few days; and we must go on talking the main report later."

CHAPTER III

In the chancel of the Blackfriars' Church the incense lingered among the now-extinguished tapers, and the chants of the choir seemed to hover, too, as a benediction on the unstirring congregation. Finally, however, his private devotions finished, the King rose from his knees in a great upheaving of crimson and ermine. As he passed up the nave of the church, the rising behind him of the Lords Spiritual and Temporal and the Commons made a swift surging sound and sent a wave of scarlet asweep through the shadows of the aisles. Though this was a less magnificent congregation than had gathered here scarcely six months before for the Legatine Court, it wanted little, More reflected, of the splendor that the human love of color, rich fabrics, furs, and jewels could provide.

Judging by such lavishness of garb and ornament, no man could have known that the realm dreaded to hear what aids the King might ask in this Parliament. These prelates, nobles, and burgesses looked prosperous enough to warrant a high appraisal of the wealth of the kingdom; yet for generations the exactions had been heavy. No fortune among the old nobility had escaped the confiscation that followed political attainder—yes, and, paradoxically, sometimes motivated it—or been much rehabilitated by the grudging restoration of part of the spoils to henceforth fearful heirs; and no pretense to station and wealth among the upstart nobility rested on a secure foundation. The churchmen had been for years restive under the Cardinal's expectation of gifts, his exactions, and his recently exercised power to suppress foundations and divert endowments; and the burgesses had been vexed by the trade-disrupting, depressing warfare of Europe. Money would mean shrewd dealing among these men, keepers of their own and their neighbors' purses, moving showily now to the opening of the Parliament.

Absorbed in thought of the temper with which they would greet the business ahead, More passed in the close company of the Council through the gallery that, bridging the Fleet and piercing the old wall of the city, linked the convent with the King's palace. Outside, a gray November mist hung over the rivers; but it could not discourage the exuberant cheering of citizens astrain for the least glimpse of the pageantry shaping in the great hall of Bridewell. In the imminence of his speech opening the Parliament, More found heartening in this enthusiasm of the people—heartening and recollection, too, of the populace of Cambrai exulting over their peace. The optimism of common men struck him more than ever as an amazing quality; rulers, then, must indeed fear when they find the people sullen, passive of hand and tongue, indifferent to splendor. These, rather than violence, presage the fall of governments.

As he waited in an antechamber, More heard with sharpened perception the conglomerate noises of the assemblage he must address: there would be among them decorous claiming of precedence, remnants of private business, gossiping observations, and cautious, exploratory whisperings about the agenda of this session. Much as a speaker's training may fortify him against fear of an audience, it may not utterly exorcise the demons of that fear—the strictures of the throat, the groping about the heart, the unwilling weakness of the knees, which crowd the icy moments before the emancipation of the speech itself. Even long-used though he was to being the voice of a body or of a delegated will, More was grateful for the island of silence among his colleagues on which he stood now; for his neighbor, Viscount Rochford, had nothing to say to him. Better so, since all Rochford's present interest centered in one cause, his daughter Anne's.

Like a panicky student before his first disputation More rehearsed the headings of his discourse—no, His Majesty's: the King's concern for the welfare of his people, especially for the protection and fostering of the trade upon which depended the prosperity of the realm, Cardinal Wolsey's abuses of power and trust as detailed in the King's papers, the grief of His Majesty at this betrayal of his confidence, the pitiable issue—but in the face of the Cardinal's surrender who should deny its justice?—of the trial just ended, the urging of such administrative reform in the Church as Parliament could properly undertake. He could foresee how avidly men would listen to what the King wished to tell through him of the fall of his greatest minister, whose power had seemed as secure as monarchy itself, for many in this Parliament would scarcely remember a time when Wolsey had not spoken and acted for the King. It was little wonder if the Cardinal had sometimes said, as his enemies were charging, "I wish" or "I and the King." Wrong as had been this arrogation of importance, surely the temptations to it had been manifold. In the moment of this melancholy thought, More knew that, if what must be done to-day were fair sample of his speaking the royal will, there was little likelihood of his falling into the Cardinal's danger for saying, "I wish" or "I and the King wish."

As he had been before, More was assailed, too, by the thought that Henry had the amazing capacity of being right in motive and wrong in method, or the reverse; for, though the people should understand the provocations to the King's action against Wolsey, some of the charges read like indictments of His Majesty for supineness or even—the secret mind could scarcely admit the thought—treachery. The Cardinal had not been more anxious than Henry himself for the legatine authority, for example, and the papal bulls supposed to have justified the *Praemunire*. On the plane of private morality it seemed incredible that the King should have chosen that particular instrument of chastisement or vengeance; but were More not to sit in public judgment on the King, he could not reveal his own blind observation that folly, if not knavery, stood confessed by the measures of his sovereign. Better to think that in this action, as in so many others, Henry had been swayed by men more patient, more calculating, less impulsive than he. More caught himself looking speculatively at his neighbor. Of the Cardinal's particular enemies at Court, this Thomas Boleyn, impatient as he was when the goal seemed almost won, had been the most cautious and silent worker. Norfolk had been blunt of speech, and Suffolk callous in action; yet neither of them was capable of the insinuating malice at work upon the King. It seemed certain now that Henry would rule for a long time in such a jealous interpretation of his kingship that any who craved power must be content to exercise it deviously, to accept influence as a substitute for delegated authority.

From these thoughts More woke to the realization that the heralds were crying the approach of His Majesty to his Parliament. In a few minutes now, he would stand at the King's right hand within the very precinct of state, and speak what the King would reveal of his thought. He would bid the Commons select their Speaker; and in recollection of his own service, half a dozen years back, in that difficult post between Crown and Commons, he pitied the man they might choose. Yet he knew that this man would never have to mediate between an offended House and a Chancellor invading its liberty with the more than royal processional of maces and pillars and poll-axes, of crosses and the Cardinal's hat and the Great Seal itself. The

Chancellorship had changed. In what he had before thought a pitiable fall incurred by the office, he now saw a positive value; for, a commoner himself, he could narrow the gap between the will of the King and the comprehension of the people. An unspectacular service, but an honorable one. Were this what Henry had meant by his need of More's service, very well; at least, he knew how to stand by the throne usefully, ungloryingly.

So occupied with Chancery business had More been that it was natural for him to be still thinking of it, as, responsive to the King's summons, he left Westminster early one afternoon for York Place. These first days in office had tried his resolution not to add his voice to the disparagement of the Cardinal, which time seemed to be augmenting rather than lessening. Whereas for lesser men shame can be swift and half-merciful, even in the disgrace of Wolsey, it seemed, there must be excess, the splendor of ignominy prolonged, a pageantry of abasement. At that instant he reflected with a little chill that he who had supplanted the Cardinal in one of his places was going thence to see the King, who had supplanted him in another; and shadowing that thought came the still more grievous one that this interview recalled his own twilight visit to Wolsey on the last day of his pride. More than a month past, that was, but such a month as renewed the double ambiguity of time that makes the same happenings both incredibly remote and incredibly fresh in recollection. Dreading to find the King in the very gallery where he and Wolsey had parted, More approached the now magnificently reanimated palace.

That fear of a most pitiful irony died, however, as he followed Henry Norreys, who had detached himself from a noisy, laughing group in a music room to come as far as the door of the King's study with him. Almost on the threshold they met Dr. Nicholas Wilson, one of the royal chaplains, evidently just emerged from conference with the King. He stopped More a moment in passing.

"Erasmus's edition of Augustine is beautifully done, isn't it?" he commented enthusiastically. "His Grace and I have just been examining some of the volumes."

With this pleasant introduction to his own conference in mind, More entered the richly Italianate little chamber, which, though its furnishings bore the stamp of Wolsey's taste, did not recall for him the intimate presence of the Cardinal. In very relief from the depression of spirit in which he had anticipated this visit to York Place under its new master, he warmed to their interview. Across an ornate table of some exotic, dark wood that suited well his jewels and velvet, Henry looked up in the transient blankness of one distracted from what he has found all-absorbing; then he smiled, released the book which he had been reading from the flattening hold of his elbows, and pushed back his chair.

"You've come in good season, Thomas More. Prompt, as well as wise and eloquent; and still, I suppose, you will try to tell me you aren't serviceable enough. Ho! You will have to learn other ways if you want people to take you at your own mean estimate."

"Your Grace is generous as ever. From another man I should call that flattery, but—"

As if to minimize the ceremony between them, the King held out his hand carelessly for More's salute. "But what?" If not itself flattery, his smile was an invitation thereto.

"But you have no need of such an instrument to your desires. It serves the weak alone."

"Now you offer me a conundrum," Henry laughed, "for you are not exactly a weakling."

"Nor a flatterer either, Sire." The little inclination with which More spoke caught for his eye the flash of the firelight on the King's jeweled hand: he was still wearing the great ruby the Cardinal had given him. That recognition here in York House made a rebellious inner voice cry out that the King was offering him conundrums. How did Henry really feel towards the man he had humiliated, despoiled, turned out in the winter of his displeasure?

Almost as if the King had read this turn of thought in his sobered countenance, he drew his hand into the shadow. "At any rate, prompt you were, even if we give some of the credit to the convenience of this house to Westminster. In fact, I'm not sorry that we moved Parliament thither. The city has no house available so commodious, so comfortable as this; in avoiding the plague, then, we achieve this luxuriant beauty. The Cardinal is a connoisseur; such things"—his hand suggested the sweep of the richly appointed room—"are his real genius. Hampton Court; then all his remodeling here; the buildings at Oxford. Had I not seen it all with my own eyes, I should not have believed one man capable of such magnificent designing. And his taste! There wasn't a thing at Hampton Court that I would not myself keep; and the same thing here—none of the indiscriminate buying of just anything lavish that some of my subjects are guilty of. But you have no great love for such things."

"Not for myself, but I enjoy them in the right places. This has always seemed to me a beautiful house."

"You once told the Cardinal you preferred it to Hampton, I seem to remember hearing."

"Perhaps not in every sense. The two cannot be compared. We were talking, I believe, of certain parts—the river gallery especially, which is one of the most beautiful I've ever seen, spacious and restful."

"But somewhat severe. I like this style better—more color, more life. Stephen Gardiner has been telling me much about the new art in Rome; it appeals to me. Maybe I should have been an Italian. Were I, I suppose, I should know how to match craft with craft, duplicity with duplicity."

Henry's voice had scarcely shifted its emphasis from the lightness of his art criticism, but his upper lip hardened across his teeth till the vertical lines in his cheeks went white; and More knew that they were to talk of neither Wolsey's æsthetic sense nor the splendor of Michelangelo's Rome. Some compliment might have tempered the bitterness of the King's staring into the fire; yet it would be only the deferring of something which he had been on the point of divulging in recent conversations, something which More had already more than once watched him considering and postponing. So this time he waited, silent, offering neither encouragement nor resistance to what the King wanted to say. If mere receptivity could help, this thing were best said clearly and finally; for More could not but divine the subject on the edge of which they now stood. With his dread mingled pity for Henry, who was trying to ask again what had already been thrice refused him. Between their silences the idling crinkle of the open book, not yet accustomed to lie flat, sounded irrelevantly. The King laid his hand on the rising leaf, and with the apparently absent-minded gesture, his thought found release.

"The best minds of my realm, and yours is one of the very best. You must help me to find a new way, the right one. All the others have been wrong."

"Sire!" If Henry would hear it, More hoped the plea of the one word would be arresting enough.

Without stir or glance at him, the King said more gently, "This time hear me through. Say if you want that you are listening to me thinking aloud; but withhold that hard judgment of yours a little while."

So new was the tone, so honestly patient and perplexed was

the King's manner, that More bowed his acquiescence. Not to listen this last time, for they seemed to agree tacitly in that thought, would be churlish; therefore, he would listen till the inevitable demand should put a period to the King's reflection. Though Henry was not looking at him to note the movement of resignation, he timed his resumption of speech truly.

"After so many promises broken, I cannot have my cause pleaded at Rome and myself made the laughingstock of Europe. Myself? No, England. They have all presumed too much on my patience—the Emperor, Katharine, this legate Campeggio, Pope Clement himself. I wonder what kind of man he thinks I am. Recalled the case to Rome. A just tribunal, I suppose, with the Emperor's German guards standing watch. So in his fear he says I must go on living in sin, outraging man's ordinance and the law of God; in pure fear the Pope does not care what becomes of my soul—or Katharine's. We must end it straightway, not with years more of appeal to Rome."

When he turned to More with the direct challenge of voice and gaze, his eyes were red as if with tears barely restrained.

"But the power of determining such a question belongs to the Pope alone," More said as deliberatively as possible. This discussion must not strike the pace of argument.

"So it has seemed," Henry's rejoinder kept the right evenness of tone. "But he is afraid of something—the responsibility? the consequences? Who can read his motives? There must be some way of giving him confidence to see the right. I think we have found the way. Do you remember my asking you about Thomas Cranmer? A good man, I think, for he has hit on what needs doing to convince the Pope—appeal to all the universities, here and abroad. Some one suggested something of the sort before, but I hesitated to betray so intimate a matter to the world. Now, however, pride and delicacy are useless. We must deal with the problem as we must. Gather the opinion of

Christendom; the very weight of it should end the hesitation. We have searched the Fathers and the Doctors; and some of them help us, and some of them are ambiguous and unavailing—"

He did not add that some of them definitely worked against his cause, More noted in pity for the ambiguity into which his affairs had driven Henry. The disputant in him found this listening hard, for there was challenge in these observations; but he had long since determined never to dispute the divorce even with Henry himself. The admission through his silence that some of the Fathers and the Doctors argued the soundness of the marriage he would repudiate halted, momentarily, Henry's analysis of the new plan. From this impeding thought he seemed to recall himself with a fresh effort at such confidence as could not concede that the opinion of Christendom, gathered laboriously, perhaps even deviously, might militate against him. It was hard, very hard, for More not to inject that possibility.

"But our age has learned men. Besides, this is a modern problem. With all respect to Holy Writ and the Saints, is it not reasonable to suppose that the wisdom of our time may supplement and interpret them? If we could put the specific question to Saint Augustine here"—Henry laid his hand on the new book before him—"he might answer in different terms from those of generalization and commentary. So, if we can send the Pope the opinions of all the universities, he need not fear any longer: he will but bow to a judgment rendered. There may, of course, be some intimidation to dictate an adverse opinion; but even then all the world will be able to see where prejudice and sycophancy have ruled. It is the plan. All Christendom shall decide, and put an end to this caviling, this interminable playing for time. 'The Pope may die.' 'The Emperor may die.' Well, so may Henry Tudor. Then what of England?"

Henry contemplated the melancholy thought in a luxuriance of gloom from which he wanted no rousing. Gradually, the mournful lines that seemed to draw his face forward relaxed and his countenance returned to a strainless ease. A half smile about his eyes pleaded for similar relaxation in his listener.

"You do not disapprove the plan? You should hear Cranmer explain it."

"No, I see nothing in it to disapprove," More answered warily, for as a lawyer he was trying to forecast the direction of the discussion for which the King was now ready. Cranmer's program seemed to him likely only to fill time harmlessly and futilely while the proper tribunals at Rome were at work.

"Then you approve!" Had Henry clapped his hands and danced like a child, he could not have shown a clearer elation than the three words revealed. It was cruel to cut short such a triumph, but perilously necessary.

"Sire, there is a difference between the two. I do not disapprove; I cannot approve. But there is no need of my doing one or the other. I am no canonist, no theologian; the question is for them."

Henry pushed his chair back with so deliberate a harshness that he himself winced at the scraping on the tessellated floor. Making no effort to carry his weight lightly, he padded to the fireplace. A quick turn suggested that he would stride back the half width of the room that he had set between himself and the man he had forced again into unhappy recusancy; but he halted sharply. With his right hand on his dagger, his head lowered, he spoke in the studied slowness and steadiness of speech that, because of its very rarity, could convey a sinister determination.

"There is need of your deciding—my need. Granted you are neither canonist nor theologian, you are a wise and honest man. With you among my counselors in this matter, I should feel the greater sureness that I am right. You are not stupid. Is it stubbornness?"

"Not that, Your Grace. Believe me when I say that I will serve you with all my strength so far as lies in my power."

"But in this you still say what you said two years ago?"

"That in so far as my poor understanding can judge of matters outside my study, Your Grace need have no scruple about your marriage? Yes, I think your grief and pain unnecessary. But I leave all the disputation to the doctors. Only with you, Sire, have I assumed even the small authority of one man's private conscience discussing the question with another's."

"That is it." The King's hand dropped from the dagger-hilt, and he came back to his place at the table. His voice was as gentle as that of a father remonstrating with a confused child. "You are thinking of this as a matter of private conscience. I honor you for that straightness of thinking; but you must take a larger view. Will you not try to help me in the matter?"

Torn between the impossibility of refusing an honest plea for help and scruple at seeming to promise more than the issue might let him fulfill, More dropped to his knees. His forehead pressed against the cold ruby as he spoke anxiously.

"But, Your Grace, if conscience give me no other light in the matter? Must I not always remember your own most generous lesson to me at my first coming into your service: that I should look first to God, and afterwards to you?"

"That is all I ask—ever." Henry's voice was warm and kind. "You must follow your conscience, and it is a good one. Yet I truly believe that study may help conscience. There are other men who have been convinced. My cousin Pole, who went to Paris last month, has promised to consult the faculties of the University. And his has been a delicate conscience. Believe me, I do not ask you to force conscience in this matter. Yet, when you ponder all that the doctors have found, if you are persuaded, remember that there is no man I am more eager to have among my advisers in the matter. Consider that this is more than a private question, for we imperil the realm because of the judgment that has been visited upon us. Must not a king's conscience act by different principles from those which govern simpler men?"

In the pause made by the King's unanswerable question, More wondered what ointment of reproof a brave confessor might apply to that sore conscience. Though he must be silent, for the question demanded a different reply from any he could give, he longed to suggest that a king's soul could no more take his crown and his privilege before the bar of judgment than could Dives his moneybags, and that a king's dust came to as common earth as that of Lazarus. But when he was refusing part of the duty of the spiritual doctors, he could not assume part of their liberty; he could only be troubled at this fresh evidence of a tendency growing in Henry's thinking of late, the tendency to regard his kingship not as a charge from God, weighted by obligation, but as a peculiar favor, free from all responsibility. This shaping philosophy of monarchy, adumbrated in Henry's words and actions, made his course utterly unpredictable: reason enough for worry to one who thought beyond the morrow's values. Reason enough, too, to give what aid he could, if no more than the tempering of extravagant action.

"View the matter from that angle," Henry pleaded after the silence which he must read as willingness at least to accept instruction.

"I shall study, Your Grace, to understand what your doctors have found. My own search would be little likely to guide me beyond what I have already thought to be the right. So, if it please Your Highness, will you assign me as tutors those of your counselors who have labored most profitably on the matter?

You have suggested that I listen to Thomas Cranmer. And to whom besides?"

The King's smile could have heartened the most timorous spirit. "Generously said. That is all I ask. You have talked already with Stokesley, haven't you? Strange: I should have thought him likely to convince you. But there are others, too. Cranmer first of all, and Doctor Foxe and Friar Nicholas. They have searched deeply and subtly. If these and many more were not the brilliant men they are, I might doubt the justice of my cause; but hardly a man goes far into the question without coming to my support. I am sustained by the thought that the right will prevail."

"And I stand in the same faith, Sire."

The King looked at him in some perplexity. He seemed about to reply, but he evidently thought better than to challenge again the mind he could not understand.

"Well, let me have good report from your tutors. There was something else. Yes; what do you think of the new Speaker of the Commons? Thomas Audley's not too strong a man?"

"He seems anxious to do what is expected of him, a dependable man."

"That is something. His Eminence found him so, I believe, in his household. We must watch him and see how well he keeps the House to business. It is odd that anyone should have mentioned His Grace of Canterbury for Speaker."

"Archbishop Warham is revered, Sire. The people have every reason to respect him."

"Yes, but Parliament must talk about some churchmen less revered than he and about some ecclesiastical practices."

"And may not Parliament find Convocation acting with it, Your Highness, perhaps even before it, so that there need be no antagonism between churchmen and laity?"

Henry smiled as if he were thinking many entertaining

ideas; but he said only, "Convocation is sitting to-day, isn't it? I should like to be listening down there in St. Paul's. They must be less afraid of the plague in London than of us here when they shut themselves up in the city for their deliberations."

"They flatter us, then, Your Grace, if they think us such monsters that the plague itself is less terrifying; but maybe they have simply chosen it as the greater test of their fortitude. There are brave men among the clergy. Seriously, though, is not St. Paul's the customary place for the holding of Convocation? It is, after all, a separate body from the Parliament."

"True. And no doubt they need secrecy for their doleful meditations. Why do you look so bewildered?" Henry chuckled at the amazement he had provoked. "If the Cardinal is guilty of a *Praemunire*, as he has acknowledged, so are all who acted under authorization from him. Christopher Hales has reasoned it out neatly: there is hardly a cleric in the realm who in strict justice can escape outlawry and the confiscation of his goods. A pretty situation, isn't it?"

Henry seemed to enjoy the consternation of More so completely that he spoke with incongruous gayety. Unjust as had been the pleading of the *Praemunire* against Wolsey, who had obtained his bulls with the express license of the King, it had made some show of legality; but this extension of the danger to the clergy of the realm was the most flagrant casuistry. More could not smile in answer to the King's cunning grin.

"Christopher Hales is a keen lawyer, Your Highness; yet as a lawyer, too, I think he has missed one point."

"Hah! We must not miss a point in so nearly perfect a case. I never dreamed of so complete a sweep as we can make now. But what is your point?"

"Is it not possible, Your Grace, that every layman who has

profited by these unlawful bulls—supposing them to be that—is plunged into complicity, too, in this monstrous illegality?"

"Magnificent!" Henry struck the table resoundingly. His palm must have been still stinging, however, when the import of the question came home to him. The bubble of his enthusiasm burst in a thin "But—"

"Exactly, Your Grace. How can any of us lawyers draw up an indictment against a whole people? Remember, Sire, how I have sometimes played the poor fool for your counsel, and let me say one thing more. Have you considered whose name would head the list of accomplices, guilty before or after the fact?"

The King swore softly but forcibly; then he laughed, a little hollow, rasping sound. "Like a lawyer, you are using the *reductio ad absurdum.*"

"Like a lawyer? More like a logician, I think. Yet, consider, Your Grace, that the law, once strictly applied, is a singularly impartial dealer." So rash a warning was he venturing that More spoke with very careful humility: here was a point of prime importance for Henry to see undistorted by anger or wounded pride.

"You are bold with the jester's privilege, Thomas More." Henry's frown, however, was a half-appreciative one. "And the worst of it is that I have to think the jest whole earnest. All I can say is that I'm glad I have you safely in my service, so that you're not suggesting your sharp ideas elsewhere. Go now and gloat over the thrust that struck home, as a Chancellor's should when there is need."

Did he really see the need now? So calmly did Henry return to his reading, though the spine of the book before him cracked under his elbows, that More wondered as he left the room whether the thrust had reached the mark or not. He recognized, however, that the King had dealt him some sharp blows. Pacing the corridor that would bring him into the companionship of courtiers and his own escort, he counted them to the rhythm of his step. Henry had committed him to more and more consultation and, inevitably then, to further solicitation on the divorce so that what he would have ended he had succeeded only in postponing; Henry had shown that his learning was applying itself to hunt down texts in his favor in Scripture and the Fathers—amusement and anger contended as More thought of Erasmus's labors on his Saint Augustine being thus pored over; Henry had revealed a disturbing confidence in a new conception of royal conscience, immune to the scruples of ordinary men, dangerous beyond all imagining were it methodically fostered; and—sharpest blow of all, because reason could not parry it, nor courage admit its force—Henry had boasted in a half-dozen words of winning a most strategic ally. If Reginald Pole, returned to the Continent a little while before, were enlisted in the King's cause, how few remained unsuborned! Queen Katharine had been always fond of this son of her dearest friend; she had even dreamed of redressing by the marriage of the Princess Mary to him the wrong done Margaret Pole's family through the judicial murder of young Warwick—the crime that, innocent of it though she was, had darkened her marriage. And now young Pole was serving as an agent in the process that would bastardize the Princess. Emerging into the light and the chatter of the King's antechambers, More felt incredibly lonely; there was no one in the world to whom he could reveal the burden of his perplexed thought.

CHAPTER IV

"T. CARDINALIS EBORAC." The signature on the paper before him, one of a sheaf of documents concerning Wolsey's colleges, on which Gardiner and he had just been conferring, invoked for More the question of whether or no the last act in the drama of humiliation had been played out. It seemed to bring the ghost of the sick man at Richmond back here to Westminster Hall, the scene of his long magnificence in the Chancellorship. Since the afternoon's pleas were over and few men moved still through the vast reaches of the hall, More, bowed over his desk, had time and the disposition to meditate on this strange tragedy of genius and pride and vengeance. The day before yesterday—no, the day before that, the seventh of February—had concluded the King's seizure of York Place; and to-day from that palace had issued the King's general pardon for the Cardinal. So it seemed ended. With the refinement of cruelty that judgment deferred can be, the Cardinal's enemies had driven him to the edge of a great pit, whence the King's tardy relentings had thrice rescued him; he had been sick—even to danger of death, those who had seen him had reported; he was an old man, though not yet sixty, a poor man beyond the imagining of men who do not value luxury, a spirit crushed. Yet, if the reports of these dreary months could be believed, his was, too, a spirit finding itself, turning even in the dark eleventh hour to the work of the neglected vineyard. Was he discovering, now in the winter of his defeat, at the Charterhouse at Richmond some of the peace and the strength that

More himself had found in another Charterhouse in the undecided spring of his youth? Was he knowing, beyond the malice of men, the abiding, patient spiritual consolations that he could have and that he could give as Thomas, Cardinal of York? He must go northward to his see, his enemies were insisting. And no doubt they thought that they were completing his deprivations by what they considered exile. Remembering his own parting from the Cardinal four months before, More hoped now that his going could be so illuminated by what opportunity and duty he saw before him that the regrets would fall away like night mists outridden.

Pitiful though the events of these months had been for the Cardinal, More could not help feeling now that the whole balefulness of them was not for him; inscrutably it was withheld so that no man could know on whom it would finally fall. Only that it was withheld, that it was not ended with the merciful ending of suspense for Wolsey, seemed certain. Men do not stop with one successful wrong, he reflected, as thought read the roll of the most implacable foes of the Cardinal: Norfolk developing in his power a belated suavity; Rochford, recently made Earl of Wiltshire and Ormond, grown overbearing through pride in his daughter's power; Anne Boleyn herself so confident that she had been prevailed upon, rumor said, to send the Cardinal what little comfort a bit of her golden girdle could be to him. Yes, they were learning swiftly enough the ways of—what was Chaucer's characterization?—"the smyler with the knyf under the cloke." And with typical blindness they might realize too late that others could learn, too, for in some lessons there is a terrifying democracy of instruction. He wondered, for example, if he alone had noted the assiduity of Thomas Cromwell, narrow of lip and eye and spirit, timely ridden away from Wolsey at Esher to Henry at Westminster. Had this serviceable man—the King had called him that a day or two past—found York Place a haunted house? Or had he in his nature none of that faculty that imagines and conjures up associations?

And he wondered, too, if they who saw a portent in the King's seizing of York Place were overtimorous men. That deed was just completed, but it had seemed inevitable more than three months before when Wolsey had set his treasure in order for the King's occupation. More remembered his own too-simple protest at Tunstall's report of the intended confiscation. What had he said? "The King can't take it. York Place is not Wolsey's; it belongs to his see." That elementary fact remained true, for Wolsey had dwelt at York Place only by virtue of his archbishopric; it was not—and Henry must have seen the distinction as clearly as the Cardinal himself—his to give away as he had given Hampton Court. Yet in full cognizance of what he was doing, the King had seized the palace; and Wolsey had no dwelling left him in this southern region, where necessity compelled the prelates of the realm to live for long periods, except the manor house of Esher that belonged to his doubtfully held see of Winchester. It was ironic that Wolsey had anticipated his holding of that see *in commendam* by begging Esher from Bishop Fox, when the latter, old and blind, had grown indifferent to the treasure of this world.

Sitting in the February grayness of the great hall, More let his melancholy thought drift to the case in which he stood in his own conscience. He was one under orders; in his drawing up of documents and his speaking the King's will he was the agent of another's responsibility. None of the routine actions of his office had snared him in personal obliquity; but as he had read through and around the motives presented him as legal justifications of what had to be done, he had grieved that this present chancellor was Thomas More. It was not in a merely misanthropic temper that Seneca had written, "Whenever I have been among men, I have come home a lesser man." Nor was it, conscience checked itself, mere Pharisaic superiority that set itself now in judgment of the men he served unsympathetically and the service he rendered them. God knew that he had sins enough of his own. He should never have added to them this constant sin that the want of whole-hearted endeavor must be.

Upon such penitential thought broke the sudden awareness that there were people approaching him from the hall. It was late for any petitioners; yet he was still here among his documents; so he could stay a little longer. As he listened to the footsteps on the pavement, he realized that some one had undisturbingly brought in lights during his dreary meditations, and had perhaps crept away solicitously thinking him engrossed in work, whereas thought had been all too unprofitable. Solutions to these vexed problems were incalculably difficult to reach. Or was he but incalculably dull to be so beset by them?

"Antonio Bonvisi!" he started up in eagerness that utterly routed the dilemma, for here was the friend who had been often the skillful physician to low spirits. "It is a long time since I have seen you."

"And whose fault is that, Lord Chancellor?" The rich voice was playful enough to temper the rebuke. "Do you scorn the city now? Or have you forgotten the way to Crosby Hall?"

"Neither, as you shall well see when I descend upon you in my old fashion and weary you with much talking."

"That you cannot do; yet the talking I do not deny. But if you love to talk and I to listen, who has any right to complain? All I have to fear is that you have found a better listener."

"Where in truth? It has been years since Dame Alice jested away your advice to her. Perhaps a man can demand that his wife listen to him; but who is there besides on whom he can absolutely rely?"

"Well, for you, there is the King. Who has not heard of the delight that His Majesty takes in your company?"

More glanced beyond the softly furred shoulders of Bonvisi to the unknown man who accompanied him and who hung back, a thin figure, with more than the diffidence of the unintroduced. Then he said quietly, "You must not fall into the vulgar error, Antonio, that makes time stand still by thinking that what has been will always be."

The merry light in Bonvisi's eyes dimmed in perplexity. With the passing of their greeting, however, he seemed to recall his companion. "I have brought a friend who is anxious to talk with you," he began. The need of waiting his friend's approach at that hint seemed to belie the latter's anxiety, but finally the shy head bowed in readiness to acknowledge the introduction. "Sir Thomas, may I present my friend William Thorne? He is a merchant of Winchester."

The hand that More held momentarily in his was cold, stiff, unforceful, the hand of one afraid, he perceived in a swift rush of pity for the stranger. Had he a case pending at law? Or what misery had beaten him down to the cramped, trapped creature who seemed to look out sidewise from the dull pupils of his eyes?

"He is a kind friend and a thoughtful, conscientious man; so it seemed a pity that he had never met you." Bonvisi was speaking casually, yet a shade too explicitly for a matter-of-fact situation. "The Bishop and I have been resolved that when he was next in London, he must meet you. Had I known beforehand that he was to be here now, I should have made sure of a time to avoid any awkwardness that—"

"Awkwardness!" More interrupted. "You know it could not be that with such friends as you and Tunstall."

Bonvisi smiled, and, as if encouraged by his example, so did Thorne—a shadowed flicker of the muscles about his eyes that spoke of even a possible beauty in this so strained face.

"Still, Thomas, we are both busy men; so we can be realists enough to admit that, in spite of all the good will in the world, we find some times too crowded for one detail more. You might be bound out to a banquet this afternoon, for example, or there might be a dozen suitors waiting for your ear."

"Neither is the fact just now; so you cannot escape. I must have my visit. Shall we sit down?"

"I must go over to the Abbey on some business," Bonvisi pleaded in excuse of his not accepting the suggestion. "If you have the time for a visit with him, I'll leave Thorne with you now. That will be more interesting for him than the price of brocades that the Abbot has ordered. And I'll be back for you, Will, as soon as the business is done."

As if, after all, he would go too, Thorne half-rose from the chair in which he had seated himself in answer to More's invitation; but the alacrity of Bonvisi's parting forestalled him. More turned straightway to this unhappy visitor in the hope of setting him at the ease that he desperately needed; for, even if he came with some request ungrantable before the law, he should not be made to suffer in the cold, still agony that had paralyzed him.

"Have you known the Bishop of London and Master Bonvisi long?" The trite, inevitable first question had the proper neutrality, More hoped. "I wonder if they have not spoken of you in some connection, though carelessly I have let it slip."

In the instant of that speculation, he understood who this man was: his friends had indeed mentioned him in the anonymity men cast round the confidences that are both private problems and abiding human dilemmas. He was "the good man overwhelmed by despair" who had given center to their thought and discussion one midsummer afternoon before—remote time—the embassy to Cambrai. Irrelevantly, More saw their little group in Bonvisi's garden and heard again the compassionate, perplexed comments run from thought to thought; and he recalled, too, the morning in Flanders when, as they rode, Hugh Marchaunt had disputed uncomprehendingly with Tunstall about the mere folly of the overscrupulous conscience, and the latter had adduced examples of the self-torture of good men. All this reshaped itself in memory as he watched Thorne gathering the words of his answer.

"My father knew Master Bonvisi for many years, and I fell heir, as it were, to his good friendship." True, the man could be much younger than he had first seemed. "I have not known my Lord of London long. He has been kind to me and helpful."

The last word had trailed so softly after the more confident utterance of the first part that More waited a moment to be sure the thought was ended.

"That Bishop Tunstall always is."

The shadow in the blue eyes seemed half to lift as Thorne leaned forward, "You cannot know how helpful . . . for you cannot ever have needed help . . . as I have." Now More did not let his voice reach after the trailing one, for the alternate explosiveness and fading of the short phrases suggested that something long concealed was fighting its way, like a swimmer tangled in seaweed, to the surface. "He does not just laugh at you and call you foolish to think about such things. Almost everybody says, 'You ought not to trouble your young head with such worries. Forget them, and enjoy life.' His Grace doesn't say that. And you don't either, do you?"

"I try not to laugh at any one unless he will laugh with me. That is no great kindness to achieve."

"But it helps. Yes, I can see that. And you don't dismiss

young men just because they're young and unimportant? They must come to you often; you seem so strong."

The last word smote bitterly upon a spirit just risen from humbling reflection on his half service, the reluctance of his office. How strange a tenant is the mind, long able to keep grief and worry sitting concealed within doors, while the world goes unperceiving by!

"It isn't exactly strength that helps us sometimes, is it?" More said in slow comment. "Is it not often the sense that the other person could say, 'I think I can understand; I know'? He doesn't say it exactly, but always it seems as if he could."

"Oh, no! That cannot be." Thorne drew back with a little shudder. "I can see what you mean about strength, though. I suppose it is their strength that makes some people laugh as if the troubles did not exist. Or are they just afraid to admit them? That thought helps sometimes."

In a surer situation More might have spoken about the danger of trying to judge others' motives when we are not even certain of our own; but this man's spirit did not need the chastisement due to pride. He said only, "Perhaps there is no rule about this strength or weakness. May not each situation have its own needs?"

"Yes." The sibilant prolonged itself in a weary, yet relaxing, sigh. With it, More heard again Will Roper, worn apathetic in his struggling with the fierce unhappy heterodoxy of youth, sighing, "I suppose so." That was years ago, before he had won through to certitude. Was this man's sorrow heresy, too? He sat very straight and clenched in his chair, staring out across the darkness of the hall. When he turned back to More, his gaze had cleared a little, and his voice had a note of patient pathos in it that More found very touching.

"May I tell you about it? You may be shocked, for it seems monstrous even to me . . . sometimes."

More let a remonstrative nod speak for him.

"Sometimes it doesn't seem to be much . . . I ought to be able to fight against it . . . and then it seems to beat me utterly. I'm not an irreligious man. It could be easy if I were. I would not care, then, I suppose. I'd just jump and be damned." Inwardly More started at the violence of the last sentence. Was it but a figure of speech, or did it reveal the heart of this misery? But if the startling showed, Thorne did not notice it. "The trouble is, I care. Faith does something for men: I can see that, and it is a good thing that I want to achieve, too. I have tried and tried. What can I do?"

"Try, and pray. All our minds are stubborn things."

"No, it isn't that. At least, I don't think it is doubt; my mind is trying to help me, not to hinder. As far as believing rationally goes, it is all right. I can say 'Credo' honestly, but I can't seem to feel it. My heart is dry and cold, a waste land waiting for the sunlight of God, and it never comes there. Have you ever noticed in a cathedral how the sun falls through the high windows in a long shaft till it seems to sink a well of warmth and color through the pavement? All day long that bright place moves and changes its shape, but if you're kneeling back out of its reach, you have only surmised its warmth; you have not felt it at all. And—I can guess what you are thinking—suppose, though, that you try to move into that sure, bright place, to edge just a little nearer it, and you cannot. Something holds you there in the cold and the dark until evening draws the shaft away and even your longing cannot climb it any more. And some day you are able to kneel at the bottom of the shaft, and your heart is singing until you perceive that the light and the warmth are falling to right and to left and before and behind, but that you have brought such a cold darkness with you that there in the very midst of the glory you are cut off from it. That's what I always feel. Sometimes I go up close to the choir in Winchester or here in St. Paul's, as close as I can go to the high altar; and I think, 'Now I shall feel God. I shall pray and go away blessed.' Then, somehow, though I am still there, I feel myself dragged back the whole length of the nave and cast out on the steps. And I seem to grovel there, whence I can scarcely see the great east window for its distance. I cry out, 'Lord, let me in just once, this once.' "

His clenched hand groped across the marble table as it might grope for the step above him where in imagination he lay blinded with anguish and despair on the steps of the cathedral. He had told so much, however, More divined, that now he must tell it all.

"And then?"

"Then nothing happens. The words that are fire in my heart are only spent breath when I have uttered them."

"Yet you believe that they could be more?" More kept the question gentle enough so that it seemed no more than a statement.

"For other men? Yes. But I don't see how they can be for me since they haven't been. I have tried and tried to make them more."

"The trying is much, for some day you may feel the words rise like a flame, not to be stayed short of heaven. Do not your spiritual counselors urge you still to pray and to be faithful in watching?"

"Yes." There was a strange apathy in the voice that had been passionate a moment before. "The waiting grows long, however; and the time in which I can be . . . accepted grows desperately short. Suppose I stay out my time, and I have not won my way into God's mercy?" He checked the rising terror in the question which cried for whatever comfort a human voice could give.

"Of the workings of God's mercy, no man can be sure. You

cringing there on the steps may be nearer attaining it, with a little more effort, than some confident fellow skipping gayly out of church, smiling to right and to left, and flattering himself that he is God's good companion. The devil may be whispering such foolish conceits in his ear as shall keep him from ever thinking soberly of his own unworthiness. We should come from our prayers in a kind of cheerful sadness if the praying has made us see things past and instant and to come more clearly through the eyes of the spirit than through the dull eyes of the body alone. I, for one, find myself puzzled by the man who can dust off his knees and turn back to his lying or theft or slander or lust as if he had but suffered an inconvenient interruption. Of course we cannot know that, but for what has had the semblance of prayer, he would not be still a worse man than he is or that there is no room in God's mercy for him. We cannot know; but we do know that true striving cannot fail."

"If it fail, then, it cannot be honest striving, you think?" The thin voice fled into the shell of terror from which the energy of Thorne's picture of his misery had seemed about to release him.

"No, not that at all. Say rather that we cannot know, and—strange as it may seem—that least of all can one know for oneself. We must leave the judgment in so hard a question to God, for He can read more clearly than we the blurred palimpsest of our intentions. You are a conscientious man, not fallen into this distress for lack of thought, but perhaps for excess of thinking. Have you some wise, comforting priest for your confessor?"

"Yes, he is a good man. And my Lord of London has let me come to him when the terror seemed about to master me. Perhaps that is why it has just beset me so fiercely because I fear to lose his counsel now that he is translated to Durham. I am glad of his advancement, of course."

"So are we all!" The warmth of his own exclamation surprised More, for this was the first time that he had admitted, even secretly, his rejoicing that the hoped-for separation of Tunstall from the jeopardy of which they had talked with Bishop Fisher months before was being effected. Durham was a large and splendid and powerful see, and above all an isolated one; in the King's nomination of Tunstall, then, it was possible to see not only his advancement of a logical candidate but also his exemption of a friend from a danger closing upon the men who stood too near him. "He will be often in London, however," he added in consolation of Thorne, "for he will have to be here for Parliaments and other duties."

"But he will not be right there at St. Paul's—perhaps not even at Durham House, for the Boleyns have it. That isn't right."

"He will be somewhere close, we may be sure," More interjected quietly, for he would have no discussion that mention of the Boleyns invited.

"Not close enough, I am afraid. You see, I have not told you all of this curse upon me. The despair is monstrous enough, but —this is how I met the Bishop: he followed me up into the spire of St. Paul's one day when I thought I could struggle no longer. That is the temptation I have to fear beyond even the dryness of my heart. Twice I have gone up there."

So he had meant "jump" literally in that earlier vehement moment in their conversation. "And His Grace persuaded you to come down—both times?"

"No, the first time."

"And what brought you down the second time?"

"Cowardice, I suppose. Just fear to end the fear I was in." It was a bitter confession to make, the weary hanging of his head declared.

"And may it not have been the mercy of God?"

"The mercy of God?" Thorne looked up dazed, like a man snatched from peril by a hand he has not seen.

"Yes. Consider that the love of God held you from that last temptation and brought you down from the dizzy height. Perhaps the mercy of God fought off the fiend of your destruction that day. Do you remember what the prophet says in the ninetieth psalm: 'The truth of God shall compass thee about with a shield; thou shalt not be afraid of the night's fear, nor of the arrow flying in the day, nor of the business walking about in the darkness, nor of the incursion or invasion of the devil in the midday'? That shield is no little round buckler that scarcely can cover the head, but a long, large shield that covers the whole body, made—as I think Saint Bernard says—broad above with the Godhead, and narrow beneath with the manhood of our Savior Christ himself. It is like no shield of this world which, though it defend a man on one side, lets him be wounded upon another. But this shield is such a one as encloses a man, as the prophet says, and encompasses him so that his enemy shall hurt his soul on no side. Surely that day, though the devil was able to tempt you to the height, he was not suffered to assail you beyond your power to resist."

"Do you think so?" Thorne's voice was still thin, but warm now with hope.

"I do. So you can thank God for having strengthened you in the resistance, even if you were not strong enough to avoid the first temptation."

"Do you think I dare thank God, when I know how weak I am?"

"It might help you to know how strong you are, too. You must do as some of the wisest men, the physicians, do. Though one be never so cunning in the working of cures on other men, if he fall sick himself, he does not trust to his own knowledge and skill, but he sends for such of his fellow doctors as he respects and puts himself in their hands. And I have heard doctors confess that they did this partly from fear lest they make themselves worse by imagining every symptom to be more suspicious than it truly is. If men who give reason a high place, as do the physicians, recognize such a fear, how much more may the rest of us need to avoid the perils of our dreadful imaginings! At the least symptom of them, we must put ourselves in charge of learned and virtuous guides who will not laugh, to be sure, at a scrupulous conscience but will try to temper it with the good counsel that we should think less of the fear of God's justice and be more cheerfully mindful of His mercy."

"But if a man have no touchstone to God's mercy?" This time the question begged for refutation with heartening eagerness.

"Suppose rather that he does not know all the virtue of the touchstones he has. Thanksgiving is one. If you can thank God that He kept you from the fierce temptation of self-murder, that is much. It is not just that He has kept you alive, for you might chance to die by His will almost as soon as by the devil's soliciting; but that He has kept you alive to the hope of His mercy."

"But always that hope just makes the heart more sick and desperate than before."

"Not always. Believe that. Remember what Saint Paul says of hope as abiding with faith and charity. Thank God for that hope, deferred though it may be; offer Him the aspiration that keeps you clinging to the steps of the cathedral, lifting yourself up to see the great window beyond the altar. Suppose you did not long to enter in and to kneel in the light of God's glory; then you would need to fear lest you be lost."

"And do you really think that I should not fear now?"

"Yes. Cease to consider your fears at all. Suspend judgment, as it were, of your undeserving until hope has redressed the balance of conscience for you."

"I . . . I don't dare."

"Just by yourself—no. What man could dare to approach God, if he came by no way than that of his own unworthiness?"

"But other men do not feel as I do; they cannot be so hateful in God's sight."

"How can we judge? The gay of this earth may stand in far sadder case than the man who dares not rise from the dust. Then, too, you would be surprised at the men who have at some time felt as you do; they make a great company, a fellowship of grief and dread, reaching back surely to the making of man and forward—it may be to the end of the time of man. All by himself, what is man? The psalmist was crying an old, old woe when he lifted up that song of the bewildered spirit. No man finds God by his human faculties alone, but by the downreaching grace and mercy of the Father and the Son and the Holy Spirit."

Thorne sighed. "The other day I heard a man arguing that such a faith is weakness. He said humanity would never grow up—that was his phrase—till men thought in terms of their strength, not of their weakness."

"Yes, I have heard of such reasoning, which always seems to me proof of the snares of pride. Sometimes it is a very great weakness not to acknowledge one's limitations, isn't it? By facing them, one may win back to strength through them, even if in no better fashion than shorn Samson; but if a man ignores them and boasts them out of his thought, he may be dragged in the dust with Achilles for no more than a prick of a wound. Man seems to be a nobler and more honest creature when he sees that he is but man than when he lays claim to omniscience and denies in his pride the existence of what his senses cannot know."

"I agree with you. There—that seems presumptuous to say. But what can one answer the man who is so confident?"

More knew that his casual smile could not betray the joy that Thorne's words were to him; that his diffidence should have retreated sufficiently to permit even that half-retracted 'I agree with you,' was a triumph for the fearful man.

"There is no knowing what will reach any one spirit. I use, however, one homely little tale to set some of the proud men thinking sometimes. When I was a student at Oxford, I used to visit occasionally a cottager out on the Woodstock Road, an old, old man, who was both tenant and pensioner of my college. Half-blind as he was, he would bewail the fact that the stars of heaven had all been put out since his youth. He used to sit by his door and point out to us the places in the sky of the constellations which he insisted had disappeared because he could not see them. It was no use our telling him that we could see them. He then pitied us doubly: we were not only cheated of a beauty that had been snatched away, but we were also self-deceived. Is it not often true that the men who deny what their reason does not find are in the same sad case as he? So if a man comes to tell me of a vision he has had or a miracle that has been vouchsafed him, I cannot laugh at him for being an overbelieving child or dismiss him as a madman. How silly it would be of me to assume that I know all that can happen to man! I can say only that it never happened so to me; and if the men who testify to the wonder are better men than I, saints and prophets, shall I be weak enough to laugh at them?"

"If they are saints, are they not safe from all doubts and fears and the lack of confidence that any man's laughter could induce?" Thorne's words spoke a frequent conception of sainthood among those who found their saints in the *Legenda Aurea*, the niches of a reredos, or the glass of cathedral windows.

"They are men as well as saints. I say that in praise of them, not, as some men are saying it at present, in any lessening of the honor due them. We can thank God for giving mankind such grace as lets some men triumph over their weakness until they reach the strength that is saintliness."

"But it seems wrong to think of weakness in connection with the saints," Thorne looked up in now thoroughly interested expostulation.

"Yes, if we stop there: if we say with some misguided men that, since the saints had their sorry human weakness, they cannot be deserving of any respect from us; if we say that they were as bad as we are or that we are as good as they—it doesn't much matter which. But when we read Scripture and their lives and their own writings, we see how they struggled and suffered and did not yield to the despair that their sins engendered."

"It must have been easier for them than for most men."

"Easier? Consider that some of them must have been very positive, headstrong people; otherwise, they would hardly have had the energy to persevere as they did. And that same positive, bold spirit must have tempted them to many a foul fall. Isn't Saint Peter the best example of that? Yet because he did not despair of God's mercy, but wept and called upon it, how highly God took him into His favor again!"

"That is true. I hadn't thought of it that way before. You make it sound very interesting."

"Not nearly so interesting, though, as the facts are to meditate upon. You must read the writings of the good men who have fought against despair and all its companion devils."

Thorne smiled, a normal little shamefaced grimace. "My Latin is very rusty. I had a few years at Winchester, and then everybody decided I was no clerk. I doubt that I could spell my way very far through the saints."

"There are good books in English, even if their authors do not stand to the stature of the high saints. We must make you a list, if you like."

"I should be most grateful."

"And I know some other Wykehamists who ought to be glad to help us out, for no man who wants to read for his soul's good need go unprovided."

The thud of a distant door punctuated their conversation with a reminder. For an instant they seemed both to be listening until the steps in the hall confirmed the conjecture which they shared.

"It must be Bonvisi," said Thorne, rising. "I have taken a long time." As he stepped nearer More, he was looking so fixedly at the papers spread on the table that More wished he could sweep them out of sight to keep them from laying a new penitential weight on the conscience of his visitor. "I can't ever hope to tell you how much you have given me to think about . . . and to hope for."

Half-choking on the last words, Thorne bent, clutched the fingers of More's left hand in a convulsive grip, and pressed his dry, hot lips against the upper hand. So swift was the action that More had to throttle his gasp of dismay lest he wound the sensitive spirit and make of this terrifying episode a new cause of self-consciousness.

"Not mine, Almighty God, but Thine these thanks!" he prayed secretly. "Let this poor man's heart come to Thee in Thy mercy and loving-kindness."

Having released his hand, Thorne drew back into the shadows, where for the few moments that Bonvisi might stay to talk he would stand as silent, More knew, as in the moments when he had hung back unintroduced. But this might be a good silence to leave uninterrupted. As he strained to see how close Bonvisi was to them, More realized that the middle finger of his left hand was aching from the pressure of his ring upon it; with the other hand he steadied himself against a sudden weakness compounded of humility and fear before his grave responsibility for the peace of mind of those who sought his counsel.

CHAPTER V

When he had waked to hear before dawn the stir and twitter of the birds in his trees, More had lain listening, absorbed in happy fancies about the return of spring. Nervous as the musicians for a court ball, the blackbirds and the linnets had been tuning up long before they were ready for the full choir of sunrise; and farther off, a nightingale's throbbing song blended with the indefatigable, agile trill of a wood wren. Spring . . . and more than that, for this Sunday that promised to be a golden one was Mayday. Bud and leaf and blade and the staggering young creatures in the pastures had in the last few days warned More of the excitement of spring. As if he had needed warning, he laughed to himself, when he was as avid as any man of the delight of the season. Long ago—in one of the springs when he had been living in the Charterhouse—he had reflected that a man can know the exhilaration of May, the fragile, amazing freshness before the lush days of June come, scarcely seventy times; for a few years he loses to the innocent unremembering of childhood and perhaps a few to the insensibility that falls on some old men. And here he was now past his fifty-second birthday; so the unnotched tally grew short enough. Yet the apathy of aging had spared him, he reflected, for he had been as eager in these last days as the youngsters of the household emancipated from their winter clothing and their outworn winter games. Eight months before—yes, that carried him back to September at Woodstock—this Mayday had seemed fabulously distant, for between had loomed the prospect of a lean winter for his neighbors even more than for his own house; but, by the grace of God, they had managed and had scarcely felt the pinch. What kind of winter, he wondered, had it been in Flanders and Hainaut where men had dreaded famine? Could they lie idly in their beds and bless the bounty and the loveliness of their earth? Even in his sympathy, though, thought was a rebel, for to somber meditation on the misery of others it preferred delight in the immediate joys of birdsong and the blended scent of orchard and hedgerow. Spring—he must savor it as if it were to be his last. Yet that thought brought with it no morbidity; anything that could be called fear seemed preposterous on such a morning.

The gladness of the season had companioned More to Mass later in the morning. And now as he waited in front of the Church of All Saints, gazing across the rain-brimmed Thames to the incredible green of the Surrey shore, he found himself singing. The tune was some long-remembered one that he could not identify straightway; and while he was feeling back through recollection to locate it, William Daunce, who had asked to walk home with him from church, came up to claim his company. So the idling tune was turned out of doors nameless. Somewhat perplexed over his son-in-law's request for this walk and his apparent diffidence in explanation, More looked sidewise at the young man. Evidently, he must aid the reluctant thought.

"Is anything the matter?" he asked tentatively.

Daunce raised his eyes with a smile that looked uncertain of how it would be taken. "You will laugh at me, no doubt, sir. But I have been in an odd predicament lately."

His pause invited encouragement; so More, gauging that the matter was not too serious, said lightly, "How so?"

"Well, I have friends."

"Is that a strange predicament? Suppose we tell your friends what you think of them; that might remedy the evil."

Daunce laughed appreciatively. "I can't blame you for making fun of me when I come so haltingly to the point of my tale. This is it: Some of them have suits pending before you, and they think that maybe I can help them; so sometimes, knowing that I am your son-in-law, they offer me presents—tokens, as it were. Oh, things like gloves and a ring once and a dog that Elizabeth would have loved. That was just yesterday. I hated not to take it, it was such an amusing puppy. But I had to tell him—"

"The puppy?" Though the situation was serious enough to dim the gold of the morning for him, More wanted to keep their tone light to make the telling easy for Daunce.

"No. At least, he'd not appreciate your calling him that. Well, I had to tell the man—you'd rather not know his name—that he could do as much for himself as I could possibly do, because you are always ready to hear every man, poor or rich. So there wasn't any use in his offering me a present."

"You were right, Son. Indeed, I like your being so scrupulous in conscience. But why did you put on such a hangdog air to tell me this, for it is much to your credit?"

"For one thing, people will hardly believe me; they think that I am being stand-offish, now that you are Chancellor, as if being related to you had gone to my head."

"They won't think that long if you are firm and impartial in your refusal. In time they will come to see that you are right."

"I don't know, sir. You see, the people who have come to me have had these suits pending a long time, or they have had experience with Chancery before; so they know how they reached the Cardinal. It's sort of a habit with them. They can't understand the change."

"We'll have to educate them, then. I have great faith in the human power to learn. Keep on refusing the presents, for there are many other ways that I may oblige both your friend and you. If he is a deserving man whom you can vouch for, I may be able at some time to speak a good word for him or write a letter to some one who could advance him. Or if he has a plea before me, I may be able to persuade him and his opponent to some reasonable agreement. But this one thing I assure you on my faith, Son, that if the parties will carry the case through to judgment at my hands, although my father stood on the one side and the devil on the other, his cause being good, the devil should win his case."

Daunce looked at him with a glance of rueful approval. "I admit you're right, sir. But it is a new fashion for the court. And it does leave us out."

"Still, Son, of what use to you are these trifling gifts, however large, beside a clear conscience? You and Elizabeth may have your gloves and rings and dogs without relying on suitors for them."

They had come to the path leading to the house, but More intended to walk on through his gardens; so their pace slackened to accommodate their parting. Daunce smiled a little self-consciously.

"You are not angry, sir, that I brought this up? I thought you ought to know."

"Bless you! why should I be angry? No, I am glad that you told me. When there's no harm done, there's no need for reproaches."

"Thank you, sir. And thank you, too, for letting me walk with you."

"I can echo that, but what about your wife? I doubt she will thank me."

Daunce looked back. "She is coming with Margaret and Will and the children. They'll catch up with me in a moment."

So More turned into the garden. Though he would not let William Daunce know how seriously he was perturbed, he had to admit the worry to himself. It was hard on these young people to be so closely linked to him, to have their way to make in the world, and yet to have that way blocked, as it were, by the fact that they were kin to the Chancellor. Happy as he was to have his four young families beneath his roof, he saw sharply now what he had previously but thought upon as an academic matter. By degrees he must assure his children their separate establishments and separate lives so that they should not stand by his prosperity alone, nor fall were he to encounter misfortune. A near-by thrush tried so ardently to down the last melancholy thought that More laughed in spite of himself. Why, were this his last spring, he would give thanks for it and enjoy it, and yet do some planning, too, against the uncertain future. Will Roper, older than Giles Heron and William Daunce and his own son John, had his way already partly made; so for him and Margaret there was less need to worry than for the others.

The shout of a boy on the other side of a hedge startled him. He listened for a moment to locate it accurately. Yes, a little way ahead some youngsters were playing; and it was early after church-time to have a game at such pitch as the excited cry betokened. Reluctantly, he passed through the next opening in the hedge to the grassy alley where two boys were tossing a ball with all the energy of their slim bodies. Their doublets cast on the hedge, the nervous shortness of their breathing and shouting, the ruddiness of their winter-paled skin, and the glow of sweat upon them, all told that this game had been some time aplay. In the instant of catching the ball, little Edward Corning, who was facing him down the alley, fumbled in such dismay as would have been comical at a more innocent time.

"Butter-fingers!" gibed the other player, who, because his back was turned, had been spared the terrifying apparition of their master. Straightway, however, he saw that his playfellow's error was no ordinary miscatch. He whirled in such haste that had More's arms been outstretched, they might have encircled him. As the two youngsters were collecting their wits after the surprise of his interruption, he reached back in memory for this second boy's name. It had a curious way of eluding him—the name of the nervous, half-bold child who had been one of those talking about the burning of Tyndale's Testament one night on the hearth of the hall—Dick Purser.

"What's this?" he asked without severity. "Did you get home from Mass so early? You must have run all the way." Mentally he was checking on his own movements to be sure that he was committing no injustice in the questioning. Since he had not served the Mass this morning, nor sung in the choir, he had been among the first from the church; and the decorum of his household usually kept the boys in their place till their elders had left. William Daunce and he had walked deliberately, but not dallyingly, home. Such conscientious checking, though, was made unnecessary by the boys' opposite reactions to the question: young Corning, ordinarily a quiet and obedient boy, went so pale beneath the sweat that he looked like a child exhausted with fever; but Dick Purser took on a not unlikable squareness of shoulder and jaw that had little fear in it.

"No, sir," he said in a taut, small voice that confirmed the strain of his posture. "We didn't go to Mass."

The color stole back into Edward's face, for the admission was made and the earth had not opened to swallow them. He edged closer to his companion in guilt, and together they stared at More. Defiantly? He could not read their expressions surely enough to decide. He shook his head gravely.

"What happened?"

Dick gave so little sign of continuing their confession that finally Edward volunteered a word:

"Nothing."

"We just didn't go," Dick said as if in correction so that there might be no misunderstanding.

"Oh! Whose idea was that?"

"Mine," Dick exclaimed with a little sheltering gesture in front of Edward that won More's admiration. He would not be too hard a boy to deal with. "I persuaded him to stay home, too."

More looked at Edward. "Is it fair to let him claim the idea?" At a slow nod from him, he added, "Then you may go along. And come to me in the library after dinner."

With a gasped "Yes, sir" Edward ducked through the hedge. He had even forgotten his doublet. Fortunately, More thought, the day was warm enough for him to be running no great risk in his scanty clothing. But he reached one of the doublets to Dick Purser, who struggled obediently into it.

"Why did you suggest your staying home?"

"I—I don't believe in going to Mass." This defiance on the edge of tears touched More deeply.

"I see. Let's find a place to sit down."

He laid a hand gently on the boy's thin shoulder; Dick twitched convulsively but made no effort to pull back. Poor youngster! He was beginning early. Perhaps the times were encouraging a precocity that made thought of these children's future dark indeed. More wondered, as they seated themselves on a bench around a turn in the alley, what his grandchildren would be like when they reached the age of this little fellow.

"You spoke up well, Dick, to keep me from blaming Edward. I liked that. So I think we can reason this out." He watched the nervous tension ease a little with the commendation. "How old are you?"

"Ten, sir."

"Ten. And you came into my house last summer?"

"Yes, sir."

"And when did you reach this decision about Mass?" He had wanted to say, "You are very young to be making such momentous statements of belief." But this child needed to be treated with some maturity; above all, he could not be laughed at without danger of hysteria.

"Before that. That's what I was taught."

"By older people? Never mind whom now. And you thought you should believe them? Well, a child accepts what his elders teach him until he is able to think for himself. But there are older people, too, who believe in going to Mass. Suppose they are right and the others wrong?"

"They can't be right; that is superstition." The child spoke insistently with a little sidelong glance as if he half-expected to be buffeted for his boldness.

"Dick, that is a very hard word to use for people's faith. You will see as you grow up that many thoughtless people call any practice they do not themselves like or understand superstitious. Sometimes they are just confessing their own ignorance. Do you remember the parable of the Pharisee and the Publican?"

"Yes, sir."

"Well, think about the possibility that those who pride themselves on not being superstitious and who call other people that may be very like the Pharisee and as wrong as he was. You may keep the whole question open in thought for a long time. Meanwhile, think, too, about the fact that Christians have for centuries and centuries, farther back than our imaginations can reach, believed in the Mass—not just the fanatics and the ignorant, but the wise and the brilliant and the holy ones. Maybe, they were right, and the few in our own day who set themselves against this heritage are wrong. That, too, is something you may hold in mind and think about. Here is something, though, to consider right away. You are studying Latin, aren't you?"

"Yes, sir."

"Then you can follow the Mass. You don't have to feel, as some unhappily do, that you can't understand what it means, every word of it. Put your thought on it, and you will find it real and beautiful."

"But I don't want to."

"That's different, then. Now think hard about some other questions. Did I make you come to my house to live?"

"No, sir."

"Your father wanted you to come here, didn't he? For some reason he wanted you to be educated in my household. And he knew, and you could have known—if such a question ought to trouble a boy of ten—that my household is a Catholic one. Now, you don't have to stay here; you may ask your father to take you away. But I should be sorry to have you go, for you have a good quick mind. If you stay, though, you must do two things: you must honestly try to understand what all the boys in the household are being taught, and you must keep any ideas that you have met before that are different from this teaching completely to yourself. Let's put it this way: if you want to talk about these ideas, come to me or Master Roper or Master Harris or Father Larke. You must not talk about them to the other boys, whose fathers have sent them to live here in the expectation of their being reared in their faith. Do you understand?"

"Yes, sir."

"And now if you disobey in this, we shall have to treat you as a disobedient boy. You can't change your ideas all of a sudden. I don't expect that. You have to have time to understand it all—perhaps years before you can say quite positively, 'I believe.' But right away you can stop talking to the other boys about these matters and trying to influence them in any fashion. If you disobey now—and I hope sincerely you won't—we shall have to punish you, not for your ideas, but for your deliberate disobedience. Is that clear, Dick?"

"Yes, sir." The boy spoke in a thin voice that wrung More's heart for him.

"But if you are going to be unhappy on those terms, we must let your father take you away. Do you want to leave my house?"

"No, sir." The two syllables were more whole-hearted than their antiphonal companions had been a moment before, and there were tears in the boy's eyes. More must not seem to notice them.

"Then we understand each other. And I'll try to help you get things straight. They will be needing you at the house now. Always speak up clearly and honestly, Dick, as you have done this morning. I like that."

"Thank you, sir." The boy made as if to hurry away, but at ten feet or so he stopped. For a few seconds he stood rubbing the side of his head solicitously. Had he expected to be cuffed? The gesture and his nervousness and the thinness, now somewhat remedied, in which he had come to Chelsea, all suggested that the child had once been harshly treated; so perhaps he did not really understand the methods of More's discipline. On this misgiving broke the startling question: "Am I a heretic?"

It was not only startling, but a little comical in its awed tone; it must be dealt with delicately lest the pride of error take hold on the sensitive spirit of the child and he come to feel himself distinguished. "Some of the ideas you have heard from your elders are heretical, but you had no way of knowing that and you did not ask to be taught them. So there's no need of labeling you with a name."

"Oh!" With the noncommittal exclamation, Dick was off towards the house. An interesting boy, who was going to need a good deal of patient help. As that commentary registered in More's thought, he wondered what youngsters of this age were going to live to see. If Dick Purser lived to be seventy, his three score years and ten would carry him down to 1590, almost to the end of the century. What would England and the world be like then? Would all the vexed problems be settled in a united

Christendom? Sometimes such questions had occurred to More as doleful ones, but this morning his wonder had a tinge of half-regretful exhilaration. It would be good to see as far into the future as these little lives would stretch. The unreasonableness of man! Cicero was right when he made Cato say that men would be as loath to relinquish life after eight hundred years as after eighty, for there would always be the children just starting out, whom love or solicitude would wish to follow to the end of their days.

CHAPTER VI

His interview with the youngest heretic he had chanced to meet —ironically enough a boy in his own household—came back to More a few weeks later in the midst of an assembly called by the King for the discussion of heretical books. He had heard tales of Lollard children, he remembered, little ones indoctrinated not only with the tenets of their elders but also with the passion to bear witness to them; but those whom he had thus far had to deal with on the suspicion of heresy had been mature men—tradesmen, merchants, clerks, university graduates. "Am I a heretic?" He heard again little Dick Purser asking the question in the moment when the King declaimed sonorously:

"In Holy Scripture, in Saint Matthew, we find the express command: 'Colligite zizania, et alligate ea in fasciculos ad comburendum.' You have been gathering these bundles of cockle, reverend and learned doctors, in order that we may warn all our subjects that here is no wheat for their sustenance, nor even tares for the fodder of their beasts, but most rank and poisonous weeds destructive of the health of the soul as some noxious plants are of the body. Nay, how weak is that trope! For no poisoning of the body, however violent its paroxysms, even to their issuing in death, can compare to the destruction wrought by pernicious doctrines that plunge souls to the pit of hell, to writhe in endless torments. By comparison, how sweet a draft were the deadliest sorcerer's brew, how palatable a pottage were mandrake roots! Therefore, were we to neglect our manifest duty to pluck up and cast into the fire these deadly, destructive weeds of doctrine, and to warn all men against them, we should all be derelict in our duty as councilors and ghostly guides and sovereign."

In a pause for breath such as often interrupted the rhetorical effects of which Henry was very fond, he swept the company with a magnificently imperious gaze. One by one, as he looked down on them through narrowed eyelids, he seemed to be reading a roll and summoning the silent inner man to testify to the doing of his duty. The glance tarried long enough upon each man, More fancied, for the question, "My Lord of Canterbury, are you guilty of neglect? My Lord of Durham, are you? Master Secretary, are you? Dr. Wilson, are you? Master Latimer, are you?" When that penetrating gaze had passed More himself, he ceased to follow it, for a fascinating, disturbing new thought had presented itself: Could the King, turning the searching look inward, meet the scrutiny unabashed? Practically all the men assembled here in Saint Edward's Chamber had been, according to their opportunities, vigilant to prevent the spread of dangerous doctrine. Warham and Tunstall, neither a rich man, had in characteristic charity spent their own money to prevent suspected books from coming to sale; they had preferred cornering the supply to confiscating the stock of possibly innocent merchants or to prosecuting for heresy those who might buy the books and be corrupted by them. Fantastic enough their humane efforts might seem to more practical men, but genuine efforts they had been. Had they stored the volumes on their shelves instead of having them trundled to the fire, what libraries of Tyndale's New Testament the two bishops would have! As he contemplated the strange fancy of volume upon volume locked away at Canterbury or Lambeth or Fulham, he saw regretfully the unbought volumes, especially those of Greek letters, on which Warham and Tunstall would more gladly have spent their pounds. New College, Oxford, and the University Library at Cambridge would be the poorer by reason of the bishops' anxiety to save men loss and suffering. Surely these two could plead their honest endeavor.

Some of the younger men present—Hugh Latimer for example—had been looked at with suspicion by the most irreconcilable of the old theologians; but they, at least, More thought, remembering the attacks on his friends Colet and Erasmus by theologians of the same order, were entitled to the benefit of the doubt until humanism and heresy—by no means essential comrades—were properly dissociated. In the heat of controversy every man may find himself bludgeoned with the all-damning epithet of the moment; and "heretic" it was now. Light-mindedly, perhaps, he was trying to recall the eloquent phrase with which (according to a tale that had come some years past from Cambridge—these gossiping university towns!) Bishop West had grudgingly dismissed Latimer—"Master Latimer, you somewhat smell of the pan"? Something of the sort. Well, there was nothing like disagreement in ideas to make nostrils delicate.

His scrutiny ended, the King resumed his charge to the company: "In order that we may all know how numerous and how detestable are the errors before us and that we may not perchance condemn the innocent with the iniquitous, we must listen to a summation of the abominable doctrines set forth in these books." He stared severely at an oddly assorted lot of volumes on the table before which the notaries sat writing, little books and ponderous ones, some evidently perverse enough to need no discrimination of error, since from them protruded no markers such as feathered the tops of others. "Master Secretary, will you read us the lamentable passages? And may the Holy Trinity preserve us from the corruption that has crept in here!"

Thus enjoined, Gardiner advanced to the table. As he sorted his way among the books and the papers which gave key to the objectionable passages, the rest of the company stirred in the readjustments of men who know that they will be a long time yet. Tunstall smiled compassionately at More. Yes, there was to be no novelty here for him, who had been reading these sadly repetitious books and their fellows for more than two years now; yet he would listen seriously enough, for every man in power who came to see their danger would be an ally won in the war against spiritual and social chaos, against the very gates of hell. For the sake of Dick Purser and thousands of other corruptible innocents, this work needed doing. So More returned the smile, as if to say that there could be no boredom here.

"This is the catalogue of the number of the worst errors," began Gardiner, after he had drawn out one sheet from the collected papers. "In *The Parable of the Wicked Mammon* there are thirty-one chief ones; in *The Obedience of a Christian Man*, thirty; in *The Revelation of Antichrist*, forty-eight; in *The Sum of Scripture*, ninety-two—" Yes, More's thought commented in secret, the lists could grow to overpowering length; yet for some of the books the number could not be drawn out and the list said but "the whole thesis and sum of the book with points too numerous to set forth in detail." Such, he noted with some interest, was the case with *A Supplication for the Beggars*. How did Henry really feel about that book? In it and in *The Obedience of a Christian Man* there were many passages, which others might call cockle, that the King, in view of his waxing appetite for power, might well think wholesome sustenance.

With that speculation came the rebuke which Tyndale would administer to just such thinking: somewhere in *The Obedience* there was a section with the thesis: "He that judgeth the king judgeth God." Was that passage listed among the errors? Pat to the question came the answer, for Gardiner had proceeded to read the excerpts and the particularizing summaries, but it was an uncertain answer in that it selected a slightly later point in Tyndale's exposition: "He says that a Christian man may not resist a prince, being an infidel and an ethnic. This takes away free will." Adroitly selected, but disappointingly; for the issue remained obscure save to the few who held the double key—knowledge of the book and of the King's recent thinking about the nature of sovereignty. But Gardiner had read on as far as the ninth error in the book when More recalled his attention to the listening: "Every man is a priest, and we need no other priest to be a mean for us unto God." So they had passed from the treacherous ground of ambiguities concerning temporal and spiritual sovereignty to the surer ground of Tyndale's attack on the sacraments.

On and on the reading went while Gardiner's voice grew strained and the learned doctors turned as blank of countenance as undergraduates succumbing near the end of their first winter-morning class to the combined pressure of their early rising, their lack of breakfast, the dead, chilly air of the school, and the monotony of a voice, itself grown weary. It should have been different with this company on a May day in Saint Edward's Chamber; yet the comparison was very tempting. Soon, however, some of the errors of *The Revelation of Antichrist* waked the delegates of the universities from their apathy, because they could hardly listen with indifference to such tender compliments as this book paid them. Amid a startled rustling in the company, Gardiner read: "The universities are the very confused cloud and opened gate of hell, and this cloak of all other is most noisome and doth most hurt and damage." For the first time in many minutes, he looked up from the reading, and his voice freshened in a renewal of energy, for he was sensitive to an audience grown suddenly alert. With a little dramatic gesture he turned the leaf and sought on for the next amazing sentence marked for notice: "Whosoever first ordained universities, be he Alexander de Halys, Saint Thomas, or any other, he was a star that fell from heaven to earth; there are brought in moral virtues for faith and opinions for truth." These matters of opinion, rather than doctrine, injected themselves into the business of the session with an engaging novelty.

Though this book had its allotment of doctrinal error such as its extreme assertion of justification by faith: "Christ took away all laws, and maketh us free, and at liberty, and most of all he suppresseth all ceremony" and "Faith only doth justify," it had also its ingenuous revelations. It may have been mere ineptitude that dictated the emphasis of one pronouncement—"No labor is nowadays more tedious than saying of mass, matins, and such, which before God are nothing but grievous sins"; but the stir of amusement in the assembly indicated that they were willing to take it literally. The King frowned; but the Archbishop's weary eyes lighted in a twinkle and the deep lines of his cheeks twitched as if he were about to speak. Noticing the movement, Gardiner halted in his reading and bowed his head.

"You were about to say something, my lord?"

"Nothing in particular," Warham remarked diffidently, but apparently he considered it a shame to keep the interrupting idea to himself. "I was only thinking that there's some hope for that man, for I never heard a more honest confession of the lazy Adam in all of us. Tedious labor, indeed! That is a serious argument."

While the enumeration of the offending passages continued, More fell to thinking of the whole effect of them. Through many of them shone certain cardinal doctrines that set themselves against the judgment of the centuries, doctrines that would turn debate back to the time of Saint Augustine and of even earlier Fathers, yet that had some right to be called historical ones. Besides these, however, which could still tempt the dialectician and the theologian, there were others of no clear lineage, chaotic, hysterical utterances that forecast a confusion of spiritual tongues as the only conceivable result of the tangled private idioms of prophecy. The Pentecost of error . . . a thought to keep by one; yet perhaps a thought best kept to oneself, for its allusion might seem to some men blasphemous. These books quarreled among themselves—"stellae errantes, quibus caligo tenebrarum in aeternum servata est"; yes, perhaps such were the wandering stars of Saint Jude's thought. This *Sum of Scripture,* for example, from which Gardiner was reading now, agreed with some of the others in its doctrine of justification but stood against some of them in its assertion of universal election: "We need not labor by our good works to get everlasting life, for we have it already; we be all justified; we be all the children of God." And later it set itself against its own denunciation of good works by a humanitarian outcry: "A man shall be reproved for no other thing at the day of judgment but for forgetting the poor." A few pages later it shouted defiance to the exaltation of temporal governments by Simon Fish and William Tyndale in a thesis that claimed for all Christians an exemption more complete than that for clerks Saint Thomas of Canterbury had defended: "No man is under the secular power but they that be out of Christian estate, and out of God's kingdom." Yet the book had, too, its moments of quietistic thinking that suggested for its author at least some perception of the temper of the mystic and the saint; many who had never stood in danger of judgment for heresy could say *Amen* to such a sentence as "A true Christian man never plaineth to the judge of the injury that is done unto him." Though that doctrine, if all men were to take it straight to heart, More reflected, could close the law courts and send him back to the leisure he had coveted, this book appealed to him as more truly spiritual in motivation than most of those held up before them to-day. But the distinction he was trying to make was a hard one, for the danger of any one of the writings could be gauged best by its intensity of conviction. None of them could be dismissed as insincere or merely pusillanimous. The pity of honest, gifted, disinterested men's differing among themselves—even to the sword—struck at his heart.

Eventually the tale of error was told through, and Gardiner, with a bow to the throne, seated himself among the notaries. Bracing his elbows against the arms of his chair, Henry pulled himself to a more erect position than his long listening had induced and waited for the inevitable readjustments among the men before him. When the stirring had subsided, he began to speak again:

"Since you, reverend and learned doctors, have marked these lamentable errors for condemnation, it is unlikely that you should thus tardily disagree among yourselves; yet, if we be in any danger of destroying good grain with the cockle, we should be warned. Does any man doubt the perversity of any of these books? My Lord Chancellor, you looked about to speak."

"To little profit, Your Grace, for I was wondering whether we should retrieve an innocent sentence or two; but there is no book I am ready to defend in its entirety."

"And charity may be deceived by isolated sentences," Henry resumed with unction; "so we had best determine our judgment by the tenor of the whole work. Would anyone else speak?"

The embarrassed silence of men who think a question unnecessary fell among them. What was there to say? Interesting to contemplate in the group were the nervous movements detached from personality, the interlocking fingers, the almost soundless tapping of a foot, the straightening of a cramped back. But no one seemed to be meditating speech unless it were Hugh Latimer, who sat very straight and tense as if the mind were at spring. In the moment of the observation, More half-hoped that the King would not notice that look, for he would be sorry to see Latimer plunge himself into the danger that defense of any of these books in the whole would entail. Five years before, as High Steward of Cambridge, he had more than once heard

Latimer preach both in the University and in the church of the Austin Friars—yes, that was the time of the young scholar's difficulties with the Bishop of Ely; and he had recognized then a notable gift of reaching people that it would be a pity to have silenced by any generous, ill-considered impulse. Those years before, the Cardinal had vindicated Latimer and undone the prohibitions of his diocesan. Who now could do as much for him, were he suspected afresh? As Chancellor and Legate *a latere*, Wolsey had had a power in matters of heresy that resided now in no one man, nor even in any coöperation among several men. To his relief, he watched Latimer relax as one more listener awaiting the King's word.

"We have, then, your approval of the condemnation of these opinions?" The King seemed to deliberate with himself.

"Silence, Your Grace, is ever counted assent," Archbishop Warham said gravely. His gaze searched the faces of the delegates from the universities.

"It is proper for us, then, to proceed to the second matter of this conference," the King declared. "So vexatious have become the cries for translation of the Scriptures into English that we must consider whether or no such a work be necessary to the spiritual health of our kingdom; for it is the part of a good prince to grant his people's prayers for such things as are necessary to their well-being, but it is equally his duty to withhold from them whatever things, ardently desired though they be, he clearly perceives to be inexpedient or dangerous. Therefore, reverend doctors and counselors, I wish you to speak your opinions in this matter fully and candidly as you have given thought to it."

That there could be only one mind among so many men seemed impossible; yet the silence hung among them as if it were a pall let down from the vaulted roof of the Old Chapel, as this chamber was sometimes called. Though More had one thing he wanted especially to say in the discussion that might ensue, it was not a comment with which to open debate. From man to man his gaze, like the King's, traveled appraisingly until Henry caught the first movements of speech in Warham's heavy brows, dark against the gray-brown of an old man's skin.

"My Lord of Canterbury?"

"As Your Grace well knows," Warham began with a little inclination of his head, "the Church has never had a single fixed policy on translations of the Scripture into the vulgar tongues of Christendom. Such rendering has seemed right and convenient to the Fathers of the Church at some times and not at others; there have ever been, as we all know, sound and approved translations of Scripture into English. So that which is suggested has no novelty in it. These older translations, however, are in so rude an English that they must seem to modern men more difficult to read than the Latin. Our only question is whether or no this is the right and convenient time to put the whole body of Scripture into English. I am the oldest man here, and I have observed the temper of England over a long time; and I remember no time when it could have been so dangerous to distribute the Bible in the vulgar tongue broadcast in the land. We must deal first with this idea of private interpretation, which would set up any man, however simple his understanding, as adequate interpreter of thought no less difficult, dark, and profound when turned into English than it is in Latin or Greek or Hebrew. We should hardly accept any barely learned man as a correct interpreter of—let us say—the laws of the realm, wherein it is far less easy to go astray than in the Bible. Its secret meanings are as deep as the mysteries of God, not to be laid bare by one man's thought, but only by the continuity and the coöperation of the thought of many men, whereof the Church is the trustee. When we turn the Scripture into the common tongue, we must make sure that the men who read it are ready to submit their interpretations to the guidance of the Church. It is the disposition to do away with guidance that seems to me the most pernicious modern tendency. It is monstrous to set the Bible against the Church, without which there would have been no Bible preserved to men."

In a pause that seemed rather a rest than the ending of the Archbishop's speech, Bishop Tunstall leaned forward in a supplementary comment: "Though we are all orthodox here, it may not be amiss to add what needs saying more and more often: that it is monstrous, too, to seem to set the Church against the Bible."

Warham nodded gravely. "Yes, each stands by the other. I would make just one more comment. Through a long life, I have seen much of good and of evil, but I have never seen the evil which could have been righted merely by any man's having the Scriptures in English; so I for one cannot see the urgency of the matter. Were sound and reverent scholars to do it at some time, I believe that the translation of the Bible would be for the edification of common men; but I see no need for haste in the enterprise."

"You suggest a group of scholars to work on this translation?" the King inquired. "How should they be chosen? Should we not commit the matter to our universities?" He beamed upon the delegates of Oxford and Cambridge, whose power as allies he was just beginning to sense.

Warham frowned. "Without casting any reflection on the doctors of the universities who are here to-day, I question the likelihood of a satisfactory translation if we take the matter to the universities. I am thinking, you see, of a university's right to be contentious and speculative, a right which is hardly congruous with the need for final, authoritative interpretation such as the translation of Scripture demands. Moreover, though I do not hold with the narrow detractors from the merits of scholarship, I fear that orthodoxy is far from a fixed virtue in the universities; and we could not be absolutely sure of the temper of all the men we might appoint. The bishops, or a group of them, I believe, would make the surest body to undertake such an enterprise. Even then, I doubt that the time is expedient. Simple men of little education—or, indeed, none at all—get ample instruction in Scripture from the clergy through the translating or the paraphrasing of the lessons and the gospels and through sermons drawing upon Biblical texts and personalities and stories. Men who apply their minds to understand and follow the lessons of their preachers will never be starved spiritually for lack of a Bible. So I believe, Your Grace, that the matter is of no great urgency, especially when we consider the labor and the difficulties."

The King nodded gravely before his look searched the rest of the company, many of them now alert as if to speak. Having passed by some of the delegates of the universities, his gaze came to rest on Tunstall: "My Lord of Durham, what is your advice in this matter?"

Never too confident a speaker, even when he could be most persuasive and eloquent, Tunstall stared straight before him for a moment while the pucker between his brows deepened. His long hands closed on the edges of his gown, and his elbows squared almost imperceptibly: the old habits of timidity, More thought, the little traits that experience softens without ever wholly obliterating them.

"In the last analysis," Tunstall finally began, "I agree with His Grace of Canterbury. But I may see some phases of the question in a little different light—really a difference of emphasis. I am not at all worried lest our English scholarship be inadequate to the task of translation, for all of us here know how rapidly our universities have advanced in the study of the languages of Scripture and how richly our libraries have been stocked with the necessary books. And we remember what valuable aid to his labors on the New Testament Erasmus found in England. So this recent fashion of mocking at our universities as obscurantist seems to me only a cloak for what is itself a kind of obscurantism. Such things are hard to define. It seems to me thoroughly desirable to set our scholars—there are enough of them of assured faith for us not to worry on that score—about the work of translation. Even if it be not essential to have the Scriptures in English, we probably all agree that it will foster true religion and do good in the realm."

"Enough good to justify the labor?" the Archbishop debated more with himself, it seemed, than with Tunstall.

"I believe so, Your Grace; but I agree with you that it is a large labor. For myself, I should urge against haste in the matter because there is still critical work to be done on the text. The labors of Erasmus, for example, provide a model for other Christian scholars, but we do not yet have our Hebrew and Greek texts so harmonized that the translator may work confidently without delay over divergent readings and interpretations. But—Master Latimer?"

The latter had leaned forward so eagerly that his anxiety to speak could not escape notice. At Tunstall's direct invitation, however, he flushed and half-stammered in his apology: "I did not mean to interrupt, my Lord of Durham."

"But I have really finished the one point that I wanted to make. I should like to see the translation made, but it can be, I believe, a more lasting and satisfactory one if we are not too precipitate about it."

At a permissive look from the King, who had, More remembered, recently heard Latimer preach at Court, the Cambridge man launched the question that had caught Tunstall's eye: "Can we wait, Your Grace? Perhaps better, ought we to wait? I sympathize with the scholarly hesitation of which you speak. But is that the most important determinant in the question? All of us here can read our Bible at least in Latin; many of us, in Hebrew and Greek as well. It is a commonplace to us. And I venture to say that we find great joy and consolation in the reading and that we resort often to the lectern or the press where we keep the Scriptures. Suppose we were not so learned; ought our lives to be the poorer by the deprivation that any man who has read his Bible would feel were it taken away from him? Yes, I can anticipate the objection that the deprivation is less real for one who has never known the thing he lacks. Yet, if the thing be good, is not that a specious objection? Perhaps it is even a selfish one—"

There was courage here, More thought; misapplied, however, for no one had raised an objection that warranted the harsh epithet. The charge of selfishness, he knew from experience, is a peculiarly cruel and unanswerable one. "I for one think it better," Latimer was continuing, "to let men have the Scriptures in English even with some imperfections in rendering than to wait till we have all the critical labor finished. We are not afraid now to say that Saint Jerome did not always have the best text before him nor make always the best interpretation of a dark passage; but nobody thinks that Christians for more than a thousand years have put their souls in jeopardy by following the Vulgate. That would be fanaticism. The sooner we extend men's opportunities to know the great guide-book of their faith, the better."

Now that one of the delegates of the universities had spoken, the others found their tongues loosed, so that like buttresses about a cathedral many opinions grouped about those already uttered. There was no true addition to the contentions already raised, however, but rather repetition of the salient ones. Several men insisted on the unpropitious times; some day, they urged, let the translation be made, but not now when men were already being stimulated to the pride of individual judgment and prophecy and were being urged into a superstitious reliance on Scripture as the only guide to faith. Finally, one of the Cambridge men, Dr. Edward Crome, More remembered, apparently in animadversion on Warham's advancing the instruction of the pulpit as fair substitute for the Bible in English, warmed to attack on negligent and ignorant clerics.

"We should have the more reason to urge men to listen to their preachers," he declared vehemently, "if we could be sure that they were worth listening to. But can the blind lead the blind? We remember the similitude and the second question: 'Nonne ambo in foveam cadent?' If we are not to let the laity have the Scriptures, we must see that their priests truly preach to them, and we must remedy the education of many and many a preacher."

The King's frown stopped the speaker abruptly. "That is a matter beyond the scope of the present discussion. We must leave the regulation of the clergy to the proper authority." Henry bowed to the Archbishop, then turned to More, who had seen in the last remark his opening. "And you were about to speak, my Lord Chancellor."

Forcing his energy against the inertia of long sitting and long listening, More answered quickly, "There is but one thought that I would add. First of all, though, I agree heartily with those who see in either the practice or the policy of the Church no bar to the translation of the Scriptures into English; and I agree that it would be a meritorious work. I see only one objection, and it may be as much beside the point as Doctor Crome's, for it, too, is a question of education. When we have our Bible in English, will a vastly greater number be able to read it than can now read the Latin? Or will it help men more to have an English book on their knees which they cannot understand than to have a Latin one? We may, as Your Majesty has said, leave the education of the clergy to the Church; but who is to provide for the education of the laity? The Church does much there, and the charity of good men has done much in the erection of grammar schools, and some few towns, through the harmonious agreement of all the citizens, maintain schools for the teaching of the rudiments. But as a nation have we ever thought that all men should be taught to read, and have we ever devised any plan to achieve that end? In truth, could the Bible in English teach any unlettered man to read it to his edification, we should have to proclaim a new miracle to confound the skeptics by their own device."

Amid a little laugh from the company, he lapsed into silence. Since, as he had himself admitted, the question of how to educate the laity to the enjoyment of the Bible even in English was not clearly relevant to the discussion, no one seemed moved to contend with him. The King smiled with a strangely impervious expression which More had noted of late; sometimes he seemed to be refusing to admit that he had felt a palpable thrust.

"Never did I think that you meant Utopia to be England, my lord," he said as if to remind More of his geography.

"Yet never should I think a precept false, Your Grace, merely because it had occurred to the Utopians sooner than to us." More spoke with a conscious humility, for he wanted to make his point clear without giving offense; and the idea was far more important than any personal recognition of his seriousness. "But surely there is no virtue in the multiplication of books from the printing press if we give no thought to the multiplication of readers."

"Yes, there is something there to be thought about," Henry conceded with a magnanimous, but wholly dismissing, nod. "One other question before we discharge this meeting: is there any hope of amending this New Testament which William

Tyndale has made? I have heard him praised as a good scholar whom there may be some likelihood of recalling to the obedience which he seems to have rejected."

More could not help wondering if this were not for the King the most important question of the whole session. Certainly *The Obedience of a Christian Man* contained so much to please a king that Henry may well have meditated winning Tyndale from the doctrines which had carried him into exile, in order to make of him an ally in the divorce. That Henry could not have asked a more provocative question, the stirring among the company well testified.

"Your Grace," began Crome eagerly, "though I agree that Tyndale has made serious errors in the translation, they seem to me easily amended; for they are the same few repeated, and many of them do not gravely affect doctrine. When I examined the book, I thought them more frequently accidents of individual interpretation than serious aberrations."

"I must differ from you," Tunstall interrupted with unwonted fire. "You judge, I fear, Dr. Crome, with either too little discrimination or too great charity. Believe me, the book is so permeated with error—sometimes indeed with this sort: a word that twenty years ago was innocent enough but that of late has been twisted to a special heretical application—that it were easier to undertake a fresh translation than to change this one. Let me recall the figure that the Chancellor used in his *Dialogue Concerning Tyndale,* when he likened the correction of this book to the attempt to sew up the holes in a net and said that it would be as quick work to weave a new web of cloth. I am remembering fairly, am I not?"

More nodded, not only in corroboration but also in relief at the fact that Tunstall's citation made further comment from him unnecessary. Reference to his *Dialogue* put him adequately on record. Tunstall's vehemence had apparently silenced any latent desire in the delegates to defend Tyndale's Testament and answered the King's question. After a marked pause, the latter spoke in obvious peroration to the discussions of the session.

"From both your arraignment of error in these pestilent books and your open discussion, worthy doctors, I conclude that this is no meet time for the granting to my people of any translation of the Scriptures, lest it tend rather to their further confusion and destruction than to the edification of their souls. Yet since this unhappy state may be mercifully amended and my people may show that they deserve so great a privilege as the having of the Scriptures in the vulgar tongue, I will, as you advise, cause the New Testament to be faithfully and purely translated into English by learned men to the end that it may be ready when my people's behavior shall warrant their receiving it. And that the sense of to-day's deliberations may reach all the clergy of the realm, will you, my Lord of Canterbury, draw up the necessary proclamation? Henceforth, then, let no man approve what we have condemned or venture to reopen a discussion that has been fair and unimpeded. Do you as faithful subjects so report to your universities, learned doctors. And for yourselves, believe your sovereign grateful for your loyal and obedient service. Such do I command you always to render—to your own advancement and the profit of the whole realm."

While the company stood respectfully, the King swept magnificently from the Old Chapel into the Parliament Chamber on the west. Straightway, the Archbishop was engaged by Gardiner, who had been busied with the notaries during the last discussions. Yes, there was to be a proclamation. As More was pondering that fact with no great confidence in the success of the gesture, yet with a certain gratitude that some ambiguities had been removed and that the King had committed himself further than before to the defense of orthodoxy, Tunstall laid a heavy hand on his shoulder.

"So! What is this new heresy?" he demanded with exaggerated severity. "Have you been taking unfair advantage of my license to read these dangerous books? Come now. Are you really so bewildered as you look?"

"Indeed, I am, if you are holding up a true mirror for me. What are you talking about, my lord? I thought everything I said to-day impeccably orthodox. So, unenlightened, I can't even say, 'mea culpa.' "

"Your question about innocent sentences in some of the books there roused my curiosity. Till Stokesley comes home, I am still acting as your ordinary; so this is a regular inquisition. To what sentences were you alluding? In what books? What makes you so confident that your private judgment of them is sound?"

"Please Your Worship," laughed More, "I am not so speedy a man as you. I meant no harm, Your Reverence. I was but thinking that one of the books, *The Sum of Scripture*, was a strangely mixed one. Some of its pronouncements put the ordinary Christian to shame. The only one I remember now—is it not a good sign that I do not carry heretical doctrines around in memory with me?—is the sentence about a true Christian's never complaining to the judge about an injury done him. And you can see why I should remember that. So I need not abjure and carry a faggot, need I, Your Grace?"

"You have made a plausible defense. And indeed, the sentiment all by itself seems to me to do less prejudice to faith than, let us say, to your own profession. Suppose all men were to act on that precept, what would become of my Lord Chancellor?"

"That was the engaging thought that prompted my question. Perhaps it is just as well, however, that the King did not find it an interesting one."

"Yes, his sense of humor is none too certain a quantity. But seriously, Thomas, if you are not an Anabaptist like Friar Barnes, are you turning quietist? Sometimes lately I have found you thinking in gravely impractical counsels of perfection."

"Is it my fault that I have been mistaken for a practical man? But with equal seriousness, Cuthbert, let me ask one more question. Are there not times when the impractical counsels of perfection are the only alternatives to culpably pliant counsels of imperfection?"

Tunstall turned to look him full in the face. When his gaze relaxed in a smile, it was the smile of a man who understood and could say nothing in rejoinder.

CHAPTER VII

So there had been no sun for ten days? Though More himself had not noticed this gloom of early December as a harassing phenomenon, he remembered it now. In mid-morning the fog still welled in from the river and hovered thickly between the house and his new building, whither he had come to work alone a few hours earlier. He had observed then that "day" was in such a season only a title of courtesy, for not even the luminous cold spot that a fog-bound sun sometimes is had been visible in the southeast; but he had not thought of the long sunlessness until William Thorne had mentioned it as one of the many enemies, the legions of despair, that had encompassed him again. Poor man! Perhaps he had so often thought of the analogy between the sun and the light of the spirit that he was more open than most men to the assaults of this northern gloom. Thorne's thought dwelt as passionately on the beautiful, inspiriting glow and warmth of the sun as if his ancestors had been Magians, whose worship stirred again in him. For ten days, according to his account, he had watched the short daytime of late autumn play its few variations in dreariness and merge its brief gray in the heavier gloom of starless nights, and then, this morning, the terror of returning days that were only deprivations of light and warmth and grace of spirit had brought him on a lonely ride to Chelsea. After their wrestling to exorcise the demons of this fresh despondency, he had insisted on riding off alone again. At parting he had actually smiled in a smile as wraithlike as the winter-dimmed sun. Would he pass even one wayfarer on the road to Westminster or, for that matter, on the usually more-traveled road thence to his inn in the city?

Now, before he returned to the morning's work, More prayed that the troubled spirit might go home less burdened and less lonely than it had come: "Merciful Father, let Thy light break upon this poor man's heart more gloriously than ever the sun of heaven broke through the mists and the fogs of earth; strengthen him with the inward peace that fears no evil even though a man walk through the valley of the shadow of death. Let him not faint as one seeking and not finding, knocking and not entering in; but let him come to Thee through the merits of Thy Son Jesus Christ." To the silent aspiration of his prayer, he added a few much pondered, favorite verses from the Psalter: "Scapulis suis obumbrabit tibi: et sub pennis eius sperabis: Scuto circumdabit te veritas eius: non timebis a timore nocturno, a sagitta volante in die, a negotio perambulante in tenebris: ab incursu, et daemonio meridiano." But to the next thought of the falling thousands and tens of thousands there was no going on; for he could pray only for the sustaining and encompassing mercy of God on all the sick of heart, the bereaved, the broken. The fellowship of the living and the dead had never seemed to him more real than now when there met in his meditation the man who was riding through the fog to London and the souls recently sped on their longest journey—his father's and the Cardinal's. "Requiescant in pace!"

As the ancient words moved on his lips, he realized that some one had already knocked softly on the door; at the repeated sound he crossed swiftly to answer it.

"Son Roper! Come in. It took me a while to hear your first knock."

"You are busy, I know." Roper's gaze rested on the strewn

papers and books. "So I shall not keep you long. I was not sure that your visitor had gone."

"Yes, long enough for me to be deep in meditation—not work. Didn't Thorne return to the house? I urged him to warm himself before he set out on his cold ride."

"No, he must have gone straight off. Who is he—if the question does not violate confidence? I saw him when he arrived this morning, before he came over to you. And then I thought I had seldom seen a man so haunted; he looked as one dead might look if the homesick spirit could come back to him. I'm sorry, Father; it was stupid of me to use a figure like that now."

"Don't be troubled. I understand your thought, and it does in a sense describe Thorne. He is a friend of Antonio Bonvisi, and he has been coming to me off and on since late last winter. Sometimes, he thinks that just talking to me helps when he is troubled."

"I remember how it has helped me; so I can understand his coming to you when he feels as he must have felt this morning." The glow in Roper's face was a very humbling tribute.

"Help? Perhaps listening is the greatest help one can give. That and prayer afterwards, for the poor unaided voice of human counsel is a weak instrument; but when we draw into the company of those who have suffered and grieved and praised, century upon century, we are strengthened with a strength that is mightier than anything we have or are. Then the pain and the grief contract to their proper stature, and we can live with them."

Roper nodded silently as one who understands the spirit of an experience though he has hardly known the fact of it. Then he spoke in the gentle tone which accommodates itself to grief: "It does not hurt you too much, then, to think about your father? I have been wondering if—I do not mean to be presumptuous, Father—if I could help you at all. You have seemed so silent these last weeks, so much withdrawn. Of course, we all know how busy you are, but this silence—"

"Has seemed a kind of brooding? Perhaps it has been. Sit down, Will, if you have time."

"Surely, Father, if you have."

More was touched by the young man's insisting more than usually on the title of affection as if his own bereavement had recalled the death of John Roper six years before.

"Have I been brooding?" he asked. "Yet my grief has not been rebellious, I think, for my father's life was full of achievements and honors. Nearly eighty—that is a long life. But death is always a wrench, for we expect to find our loved ones still in the familiar places. For a long time, surely, we think of them as but absent, and then the waking to remember that they will not return is a grief. Some day, I suppose, we come to think of them utterly as gone before us. Meanwhile, though, the things we did and said, or failed in, that changed their happiness come to haunt us. Like the ghosts of the unappeased in the lore of the ancients, they camp on the thresholds of our hearts."

Roper was staring at him, he realized suddenly, with terrified intensity. His voice was scarcely a whisper when he said, "But, Father, you can't feel like that. Your father was so proud of you, and you were always a dutiful son. If my father could have felt half that joy in me!"

"He was proud of you, Will, in his way. Do not let that old grief worry you still. He has been dead six years, and the wrong that he did you in his will is righted now; so leave the rankling and the self-reproaches to the peace of eternity."

"But if you have anything with which to reproach yourself?"

"Will, you never thought of being anything but a lawyer, did you? And you never found yourself thinking in an utterly different idiom, a different intellectual and spiritual language, from your father's, so that you had to feel that you puzzled him? I have never doubted that my father chose wisely for me, and I have never rebelled; yet neither have I put wholly away the interests and the ways of thinking that he could not understand. Probably I have been a better lawyer than I should have been a scholar or a clerk. There is never any proving a notion like that beyond the last shadow of a doubt; and it is less than manly to say seriously, 'If I had had a chance, this might have been.' What a stubborn tenant, however, is the mind with its too active wonders, stubborn sometimes beyond the discipline of the will! It may be, though, that the dead, remembering the perplexities of our dust, have gone to a more complete understanding of our failures and our efforts than the earthly understanding can ever achieve. In some things, I suppose, we fear the eyes of the dead, but in many others we dare hope that they read our hearts truly."

"I have thought something like that when I have looked upon the strange face of one dead. It seems as if life so abstracted, so distilled in the alembic of death, must be perfected in the drawing away from mere mortality. Often, on this side, however, it seems a cruel alchemy that has been at work."

"Even in the going of the old, Will? Death is the last phase of the miracle of life, beautiful and strange as birth, and as much a part of the whole inexplicable human experience. It is cruel in its personal ravages; perhaps not even that, however, except when a very young life is cut off. That is why the miracle of Jairus's daughter seems to me the most beautiful of all—even more so than that of the widow's son with its more powerful incentives to pity. 'Non est mortua puella, sed dormit.' "

Tears in Will Roper's eyes halted the words that More himself, as an older man long used to solemn, but unmorbid, thought about life and death, could say without weeping. The words were for him, and probably for Will, freighted with recollection of their watching in the valley of the shadow two years before. For days then, he had known that they might see the doctor turn away from Margaret's bed and hear him say, 'Mortua est.' But she had come back to them, and with her coming, he had felt that death would never again seem terrible—only awesome and strange and sadly beautiful.

After the silence of their shared recollection, Will reached out to press his hand; and with the movement he appeared to recall his errand. "I did not come, though, Father, just to revive your grief, but to ask you whether you could see Hugh Marchaunt some time to-day. He wants to talk with you. Did he seem to you strange last night when he came?"

"Yes, a little. But of course, he was tired, and there was no chance to talk with him alone. You look troubled about him."

"I am. Don't think me foolishly sensitive this morning, if I say that he, like the man who was here, seems to me haunted by worry or grief. He isn't himself; so when he asked if you would see him, I came out as his ambassador."

"Surely, I will. Send him out whenever he is ready."

"Thank you, Father. I left him at breakfast. After he goes, do you want my help with all these papers?"

"I'll be glad to have it, Will. Really, though, like the good lawyer he was, my father left his affairs in clear shape; so there is little to tax us. Thank you for being willing to give the time, however, for two pairs of hands move faster than one—not to mention two heads."

It was always a joy to deal with Will Roper, More reflected, as this eldest son-in-law went quietly out into the fog again. He had the rare faculty of observing needs and stepping unobtrusively in to aid—an unspectacular gift, yet a sensitive and endearing one. The pity of the alienation of John Roper and his eldest son, which he as an outsider had never been able to comprehend fully, came back to More with renewed intensity. From his student days at Lincoln's Inn, he had esteemed the older man, and he had come to love the younger as his son; so it had seemed incredible that the shadow of bitterness had intervened between them. Good men, in the special sense of the words that fitted the Ropers, were so rare that the world needed their undistracted energy, and the wasting of it in misunderstanding seemed a lamentable dissipation.

When the new knock sounded on the door, More knew that Will had come so far with their guest and would go away considerately as soon as he answered the knock. In the instant of opening the door, he understood why Roper had described Marchaunt as a man haunted, for, though just awaked, he looked like one kept torturingly from sleep. As he stood in the doorway, his eyes were dark holes in a taut, sick face. Having always thought of Hugh Marchaunt as a youthful courtier, More had never before considered his age; now, however, as he greeted him, he was struck by his aging in the few months since they had met. Here was a man for whom the values of life had changed utterly. So complete was the transformation that More felt puzzled as to how to break the embarrassed silence of his visitor, who had moved from the door like a man in a trance.

"Let me take your cloak," More said solicitously. "You will be too warm in here and too cold when you go out later."

"Thank you." The words sounded like the automatic response of the sleep-walker. A delicate shiver passed through Marchaunt's frame as he helped him with the cloak, but it was not the shiver of cold. When it had passed, Marchaunt spoke in a more natural tone, "Yes; but it doesn't seem so cold here as in the North."

He sat down in a curious rigid weariness of body as if he had been for a long time disciplining himself to resist the strain that had all but overpowered him. The niggardly light from the east windows, however, corrected More's first impression of his guest amazingly: his darkly circled eyes were steady, peaceful, aglow with some purpose that had triumphed over the strong enemies not yet routed from the other fortifications of the body. Already he had fought through tragedy to the quiet of griefs accepted and a resolution made. What they were, More hoped that Marchaunt might be able to tell, for therein must lie the explanation of his coming, unannounced and accompanied by only one groom, last night to Chelsea. It was the first time he had ever come to More on any errand but a message from Court to be delivered somewhat cavalierly that he might speed away again. This time, however, instead of communicating his business, he had sat the evening through in silence by the hearth, like—fantastic thought—a man without home or abiding place come to know them hungrily, vicariously, in another's possession. But last night More had not seen his eyes clearly enough to read their expression. Now he must await what Marchaunt would tell him.

"You have been north?" he asked in a friendly, neutral manner.

The question startled Marchaunt beyond all provocation in the words. "You didn't know? I went with Sir William Kingston to Sheffield. You knew that the Cardinal was dead?"

"Yes, we heard the next day, I think, when the word came by post. You yourself have been back but a day or two?"

"Since Friday. To-day we go to Hampton Court to attend upon the King's Highness. That is, we are supposed to. I am not sure I shall go." Marchaunt looked at him with an undecipherable fixity of gaze. "You do not laugh at me for that; I must have half-expected you would."

"Why?"

"Probably because once I should have laughed at anyone who

talked like that. You may have forgotten what a fool I used to make of myself; but I have remembered in the last few days—the way I acted when we were coming back from Cambrai, for example. I used to think that the Court was everything, and I'm afraid I was scornful of people who did not agree with me."

Indeed, these words revealed so great a change in Marchaunt that More could not speak lest he show a restraining surprise, but he could look the sympathetic encouragement that was the courtier's chief need.

"And if you had any reason to remember the things I have said sometimes in your hearing, you know how I have disparaged the Cardinal. For a year now, I have been changing that judgment—it wasn't really thoughtful enough to call a judgment, just the glib, popular thing to say that was passing round the Court. But since a year ago I have been rather fighting a conviction that has won. There was more to Wolsey and his office than we thoughtless fools could understand. You look skeptical."

"Then the look is false. I was only wondering—sympathetically, you may be sure—what had brought you to this conviction."

Marchaunt, staring through the little-revealing window which he faced, waited so long before answering that More wondered further whether he had been too urgent in his curiosity, and had but blocked instead of aiding the explanation that a strange new reticence in the man retarded. From the square of light across which dull, fogged branches reached and retreated in a newly risen wind, Marchaunt's gaze came slowly back to his host's face. The look made a more direct plea than the words it prefaced.

"May I tell you from the beginning? It may seem long,

but it will be clearer that way. But you must be busy. Do you have to go out to Hampton to-day?"

"Not till to-morrow. The report to the Council will hardly be made before then. Besides, the King understands that I am detained by my father's affairs—the proving of his will and other business."

"He is dead? I—I had not known. I'm sorry. I ought not to trouble you now with so melancholy a story."

"Better that than a gay, discordant one. If both our hearts be oppressed, we shall not offend each other's seriousness by levity and misunderstanding. I appreciate your thoughtfulness. But it is no lack of love or respect for my father which makes me feel that it is wrong to let bereavement dry up all our human sympathy and turn us inward to the arid pastures of a selfish grief."

"That is a generous feeling. I never knew your father, but of course, I have seen him in the Court of King's Bench. Everyone respected him."

"And that is, I suppose, the praise that would have been dearest to him."

Marchaunt studied his countenance again with an almost disconcertingly luminous gaze. "There are so few of whom we can honestly say that, sir, in these days. If it will not weary you, then, I should like to tell you what happened to me that began with the Cardinal. The first thing was about a year ago. I went out to Esher with Sir William Shelley at the time when he had to demand York Place. You remember?"

More nodded, for the arbitrariness of that seizure had gravely disquieted him. He was not likely ever to forget the episode.

"Of course, the Cardinal made some protest," Marchaunt went on. "Anyone would have expected that, for conscience was on his side. I think that even then I admired him because, desperate though his case was, he did not grovel as much as, from my earlier estimate of him, I should have expected. But the thing that set me thinking was what he said at the very end when he had really surrendered. I remember one sentence: 'I most humbly wish His Majesty to recall to his most gracious remembrance that there is both a heaven and a hell.' At the time, I know, some who heard that repeated scoffed as if it were an old wives' tale of a goblin to scare babes. They said the King was no Henry the Second or John to be intimidated by such words and that Wolsey was no Saint Thomas of Canterbury. I couldn't help feeling, however, perhaps because of our having talked of the Cardinal's courage once, you remember, that it took more courage than all the Court put together could muster to say even that much. And I have thought, too, more than once since then of how little our ordinary actions—oh, everybody's, but it's especially true of the people at Court—suggest any real faith in the heaven or the hell that the Cardinal knew something about. I never before had thought so well of him as that night; he had something—resources I suppose we should say—that I had never perceived before. Well, that's the beginning of the thing for me. You've heard of the episode before, I imagine; so it can't seem like much to you."

"Yes, I have heard echoes of what the Cardinal said, but not from anyone so close to the situation as you were."

"The next thing doesn't concern him at all, but it helped to change me. When my wife died in the summer and the baby—"

"Oh! I am sorry, Master Marchaunt. I had not known of the child."

"Yes, a boy. I might have had a son. But he was stillborn, and Elizabeth died of the fever. You probably knew that we weren't deeply attached to each other, but we were trying to make our lives over, and the child was to be a bond to save us from what we had seen happening in the empty lives at Court. Elizabeth was more sensitive to that than I was at first. She was so happy in thought of the child—I suppose that's natural for a woman. Or perhaps it was because she was more reckless, and more depressed afterwards, in all the flirtation, the rottenness, of Court; and she wanted to leave it. That's why her dying seemed so cruel, just when we were trying to make something out of life together. If we had been passionately in love, I couldn't have been more rebellious. What had been the use of our trying to be decent and honorable? We might as well have gone on bound for the devil. Perhaps you can imagine, sir, all the sort of thing that tormented me."

More remembered the time when he had spoken his condolence to Marchaunt on the death of his wife and been almost flippantly repulsed, so little had the true sentiment showed through the Court-hardened exterior; he was glad now to be redressing the severe judgment of that moment. "But the rebellion did not last, you see," he said gently. "Did you come to feel that certainly her soul is in better case than it might have been had you not both changed?"

"Yes, little by little that consolation crept into my thought, and I understood more, I believe, of what Wolsey had meant by his message to the King. I have even dared to think that Bess might have died as soon if we had not tried to right things between us; at least that is a mystery I can leave to God. And I have wondered whether it is not the beginning of—the word sounds strange to me on my own lips—of salvation for us when we are able to say that."

"And more than the beginning, perhaps. Certainly that, however, for Christ in His agony prayed, you remember, 'Non mea voluntas, sed tua fiat.' And it remains the prayer by which we lay aside rebellious griefs so that we may go ahead making the crooked things straight and the dark places light so far as lies in the power that the grace of God has given us."

"That's what the Cardinal was able to do. I know how the Court felt about his being ordered to York: it was meant as a punishment. Even I thought some of the rejoicing mean and vengeful. And I suppose that when his enemies found how he took it, they moved for his arrest—to see whether the Tower would do what 'exile' hadn't done with him. You should hear how well people in the North speak of him since his going thither in the spring. I wasn't up as far as York, but even those who arrested him at Cawood tell how charitable he was, and humble in demeanor and conscientious about his duties all through the summer and autumn. It is a pity that he never reached York; he was to have been installed on the Monday after Northumberland took him into custody. Hearing that sort of thing about him made me wonder how many of us who called him proud and worldly and self-seeking would have salvaged anything from such disaster. Most of us, I'm afraid, wouldn't have had any aids to start with; and they are what his office gave him. That is something to think about."

"Yes."

"The most moving fact about him, to me, didn't come to light till after his death. He was a very sick man when we came to Leicester Abbey; it didn't seem possible that he could live so long as he did. But all the time, though he would not listen to those who tried to tell him that he would be able to go on, for he matched his knowledge of medicine with theirs, he bore up with wonderful spirit. He had dignity, and he wasn't afraid to speak out at the end. He said much more to Sir William Kingston than I can remember, but I can't forget some of it. For example: 'If I had served God as diligently as I have the King, He would not have abandoned me in my gray hairs.' He spoke, too, of having knelt before the King for hours to dissuade him from something on which he had set his heart; and I have wondered since whether sometimes the Cardinal was blamed for things that he really tried to prevent. It is odd, isn't it, how little by little a harsh judgment will veer round like a weather-vane to a gentler one?"

Remembering how the same wonder about Wolsey's responsibility and influence had annotated his own thought on Henry's policies, More nodded. He could make no comment, however, to interrupt Marchaunt's explanations.

"I suppose that, if I hadn't happened to go with Kingston, I should never have thought of these things. I might even have scoffed at what I was going to mention a moment ago. When they were preparing his corpse, they found a hairshirt under the delicate linen that always seemed such a matter of pride to him. And I suppose there are people who won't believe that. It doesn't seem credible. Now if it were somebody else—the Bishop of Rochester or even the Archbishop—but the Cardinal!"

"And you think some people will scoff at him for his ascetic practice? Surely, they will rather reflect on its significance as you have done."

A deprecatory smile flickered on Marchaunt's lips. "This sounds very conceited, I know, Sir Thomas, but I can't help thinking you are too generous in your judgment. I am afraid many men will laugh and call the Cardinal either a hypocrite or a superstitious fanatic. They won't understand that a man can change. And that's what I've learned most of all because I have seen it happen to me."

The certainty in Marchaunt's face was eloquent against the pessimists who doubt the possibility of true change in mankind, for he was speaking from conviction. The man who can affirm his knowledge in such a matter stands irrefutable before the skeptic who can say only, 'Personally, I do not know.' The two men studied each other for a moment, content to let their conversation wait. Finally, Marchaunt resumed his tale.

"And that's what I really came to you about. You have been very patient, and you are a busy man, I know. I wondered, though, whether you could not help me. As we rode back to London last week, I kept thinking that the life I had been living was ended, that I hadn't any more real ties to it, and that maybe I could start something like a new one in a new environment. Do you think I could go into a monastery?"

The question came with such abruptness that More could not answer instantly; nor could he wholly gauge the temper of the impulse behind it.

"Yes, there would be no difficulty if you are sure that the good new life for you lies there. You must consider very earnestly—I know this sounds more doubtful than I mean it to be—whether you are just renouncing and escaping from something evil or truly seeking something positive in the cloister."

Marchaunt smiled the slow, tolerant smile of one who has already settled with himself the difficulty raised by another. "A year ago I should not have understood what you were talking about, I think, had you said that to me; but I know now that one isn't thinking about renunciations when he feels as I do, but about opportunities. That seems to me a slightly hopeful sign—as if I were not absolutely on the wrong road. Now I wonder how I can go about making sure whether I could live that life worthily. I know that you will suggest my talking to a priest, but—I suppose I'm diffident or shamefaced about doing that. Maybe I have an old prejudice and a sort of fear that I'll be rushed into something against my judgment and perhaps beyond my capacity. I have to do something right away; yet it mustn't be irrevocable in case I am not strong enough."

"Have you thought of living in some community for a time

without vows, not even as a lay brother, just as a lodger? That would give you quiet in which to know your own heart better and familiarity with the religious life. You could take as much time as you needed to make wholly sure of your decision, so that the question might never rise again."

"That's what I want to do. How should I go about it? If it's not too personal a question—how did you do it? I've heard that you lived at the Charterhouse once."

"Yes. I'm amazed that you have heard about that. A friend and I in the uncertainty of youth tried to live regularly and severely to test our powers and see whither we should direct our lives. They were very profitable years, still precious even though my vocation seemed to be for the world. You have thought of the Charterhouse? It is a noble rule."

"I'm afraid it's too austere for me; I'm not even a beginner in meditation and asceticism. Should you suggest any other order, sir? I really have never given them much thought. I've just fallen in with the idle generalizations that everybody, or almost everybody, makes about monks and friars. Now I really wish I knew more about them."

"I was drawn to the Franciscans as well as the Carthusians; and I have had friends in several orders. I know more about the Benedictines recently, I suppose, because we—my wife and I—are of the confraternity of Christchurch, Canterbury."

"That would take me away from London." Marchaunt's thought had laid hold of this suggestion. "I mean that as a good point, sir. Though I've admired Sebastian Newdigate recently for his determination in going into the Charterhouse right in view of the city, I doubt I have that much perseverance."

"The world keeps very far away from the cloister. For that matter, if you feel drawn to the Carthusians, there is their house at Sheen. But I thought of your introduction to monastic life as perhaps best gained in a less austere environment. Then when you have the thing all worked out with yourself, you may, if you will, choose the Carthusians after all."

"I like that idea. I know I haven't the right gifts of temperament for the most ascetic orders. We at Court used to joke often about Newdigate's being a monk, but I can understand how he could be. Still, sir, the troublesome question for me—How?"

"Should you like me to write to the Prior of Christchurch? I'll be glad to."

"If you will. Believe me, sir, I don't think I've ever known what 'purpose' means till these last days. Maybe I've only half a life left, but I'll use it."

More could believe him. Amazed still by the implications of the change in his guest, he rose to go back to the house with him, for the morning's work-time was over.

CHAPTER VIII

The luxury of staying a little while with his family after dinner on a day when the courts were ordinarily in session, instead of taking his barge for Westminster straightway, was just stirring a train of pleasant fancies in More's thought when Giles Heron crossed the hall.

"Busy, Father?" It was a more casual and unselfconscious greeting than he had expected, for little actions in the last day or two had suggested that Giles was avoiding private conversation with him.

"Only in thought about all of you. It seems as if I have so little time nowadays to enjoy my household in action that I gloat over a real opportunity like this."

Giles laughed and drew a chair close. "Well, what I have to say isn't very serious, sir. Just that you've cured me of going to law, if that's any satisfaction to you. I suppose the lesson will save me from wasting my patrimony in litigation."

"Ambiguously said, at best. I can understand your being vexed, Giles; still you have no need to be bitter. You had no case; and the law, if we serve her fairly, is an impartial dealer. No court could have given you the decision. Instead of making rash resolutions, just remember that the decree can be favorable only if the case is good. We are not trying any heroic methods in Chancery, nor putting forth any effort to make the law a kind of plague."

" 'Cured' wasn't a very good word there, was it? No, I really don't feel bitter; in fact, I can even see that the case couldn't look as sure to any one else as I thought it—beforehand. So I say honestly that I've learned my lesson. I . . . I am sorry that I didn't see the matter clearly at first, because I'm afraid I may have embarrassed you."

This was as definite an admission of error as the proud young spirit could make; so More listened to read the full apology behind the half plea that the matter be ended between them. "Don't trouble yourself with possible embarrassment for me. But think of how serious it could be for you if men could whisper it about that you had won an unjust case on account of favor and influence. That last is often an ugly word on the lips of mean men."

"I know it." There was so unrepentant a twinkle in Heron's eye as he answered that More wondered what was to follow. "In one way, sir, I don't regret this suit, because it gave me a chance to see you in a new rôle. No, honestly, I'm not flattering."

The jingle of her keys announced Dame Alice's approach, and the lines in her forehead, More noted as she came towards them, showed that she was worried. Almost as if she would shut Giles Heron out of hearing of her question, she drew very close to her husband and spoke in a restrained, low voice.

"What has happened, Thomas?" The question hung mystifyingly between them for a moment while More sought clue to its portentousness.

"Why? What is the matter?"

"Aren't you going to Westminster to-day? You've not been so late as this before."

"Oh! You had me scared, Alice, that something had happened. It's nothing worse than the clearing of the calendar at the Chancery. Yesterday we were able to write in the registers that no suit remained undetermined; so for maybe a day we have a breathing spell. But if I know Englishmen, it won't last, Alice; there'll be new pleas straightway. In fact, I am not even assuming that there will be nothing to do for to-day, but I am going to sit in the Court later in the afternoon for my usual open time. Maybe we'll start a new case to last thirty years or so. Were you worried that I had lost my office?"

The frown on Dame Alice's brow relaxed, and she smiled shamefacedly. "Well, anyway, I wondered. But no cases to be heard in the Star Chamber or in Chancery? I never heard the like."

"Nor did any one else, Mother More," chimed in Giles Heron. "But I can understand how he does it, if he treats everyone with the same dispatch as he treated me. Really, though, that is a proof of hard work, because some of those cases were hanging fire for years and years."

"As a matter of fact, not to boast by any means," More said in his most magisterial tones, "we think that the King should issue a proclamation this eleventh day of February, memorializing one of the most remarkable events in English history—the blankness of the calendar in his esteemed Court of Chancery. Don't worry, though: he won't. And don't worry about my office, Wife. When I am thrust out or resign it, you shall know. And now, to set your mind quite at ease that I am not turned idler, I must go downstream to Westminster. Will you tell the boatmen, please, Giles?"

The alacrity of the young man's leaving seemed to prove that in his thought all was well again between him and his father-in-law, for the doubt which had kept him dodging half-guiltily in recent days was completely dissipated. As Giles hurried past them, the young women of the household, gathered about the hearth, looked up to see the cause of the commotion; and straightway the room was filled with voices and the stir of many people.

"Who will see me off?" More called above the mild hubbub

of women's and children's voices. "Where are your cloaks? The afternoon is warm, the sun is out, and I need hands to wave to me."

By late afternoon it seemed as if his coming to Westminster Hall had been a needless formality, for no one had presented any plea; perhaps, some of the notaries were jesting, the registers had been bewitched by the preternatural inscription entered in them the preceding day. Just after More had answered, "Perhaps, instead, this first unseasonable hint of spring has tempted all litigious men to gentler sports," the thud of one of the great outer doors warned of some one's coming. Swiftly recalled from his idle mood with its sense of well-being, More pulled his gown straight on his shoulders and glanced down to see if the rose were properly centered on his breast. It would hardly do to have the Chancellor looking all awry like some buffooning potentate in the Corpus Christi plays. When he could discern his visitor's identity, however, More laughed to himself for his pains; there was no need to be solicitous about the dignity of his office with the Bishop of Durham.

As Tunstall came close, More was shocked at the weariness implicit in his step; he walked with the lag of a man who had been long abed. Yet they had been meeting often enough since Parliament had assembled for any serious illness to be out of the question. To be sure, for a month past, all the prelates had seemed men oppressed with worry, for the monstrous charges preferred against the clergy of the whole realm under the Statutes of Provisors and Praemunire had preluded incalculable penalties. Because of his just-ended long membership in the Southern Convocation and his presence at Westminster for the Parliament, Tunstall had been, by courtesy, listening in on its sessions; perhaps that fact explained this dejection, far different from his usually meditative, but cheerful, temper. So obvious was his depression of spirit that its contagion routed the ease of mind that had been More's to-day.

While clerks and notaries were withdrawing, the silence of the two friends was natural enough. With the merest glimmer of a smile, Tunstall acknowledged More's solicitous greeting and sat dully down to the right of the Chancellor's chair.

"Are you ill, Cuthbert?" The question seemed scarcely to strike the dread armor of apathy, behind which sheltered More could not guess what grief. "Is anything wrong?"

"Wrong?" Tunstall seemed to meditate on the white knuckles of his hands, clenched before him on the table. Without parting his hands, he struck the table forcibly enough, certainly, to hurt. "Wrong? God forgive us! I say *us*, because what has just happened here will happen all over again in the Northern Convocation; so I am not condemning my brothers and flattering myself that I'll escape the same fault. Money was not enough, though how the Church will raise it is far from a simple problem. They had to agree to the new title—without being able to see what it really intends to imply. Don't you understand? You look bewildered."

"I am; but I'll try to pick up the thread as you go on."

"I'm sorry. I suppose I was forgetting that you are not in Convocation. If you were, though, I should not have to tell you the miserable tale. And I ought not to bring you my anger. It's a mean business imposing on one's friends, thrasonically, the fine sort of courage that storms out of earshot of those who have provoked the outburst. And within earshot the best display it can muster is silence. Well, there is the end of the matter first. Even if you are not in Convocation, this is no secret resolution for the guidance of the clergy alone. We shall all hear of it again and again to our shame; so I am not betraying confidences to the enemy. Thomas, I'm sorry. Really, I had thought to have myself under better control. It's a ghastly thing—this human power of agitation. You could never seem the enemy. But this business almost seems the end of England as a Christian state, if we are to mean what the words say; and that precipitates hostility between clergy and laity in a new sense. Just where it will all end, I cannot see. It's so vague that I haven't any right to burden you with what the optimistic probably think mere horrible imaginings. And I haven't any right to talk riddles to you either; so let me make what has happened clear. We have all had nightmares since this session began—prophetic ones straight out of the Old Testament, not cheerful, go-by-contrary ones such as Pliny held by. Convocation acknowledged the clergy's guilt, fantastic as everybody must know the charge to be. How I should like to know what really passes in the King's mind! Not a very helpful digression, I suppose. I am as bad as a garrulous witness."

"Often I feel that a garrulous one puts us on the right road; whereas a close-lipped one may hold back a great deal just because no one asked him the evocative questions. I for one have never held with the barristers who thunder, 'Answer me yes or no.' " While he played with the idea that Tunstall's allusion had created, More thought that the bitter jests of the last few moments suggested that his friend could at least give outlet now to his agitation.

"I'll get back to the point, all right. Acknowledgment was not enough, of course. Ours was a disease that only gold and silver could cure. So they compounded the precious elixir. Money, money, money. We'll have to make it up like the poor slave in the comedy, 'suum defrudans genium.' Tell me, Thomas, why do some think that the Church has inexhaustible treasure? Oh, I know—generalizations like those in *A Supplication for the Beggars* about the clergy as locusts devouring the substance of the kingdom. But do people really believe that sort of thing? Apparently, they do. They can't see—rather they won't try to—that the Cardinal's wealth was notorious because it was exceptional; that there isn't an English bishop who is a rich man in the popular sense—one who has wealth for himself; that, instead, the Church handles a great deal of money, but that she handles it. It comes in—that's all they can see; they refuse to recognize that it goes out, too. Education, charity, the caring for the old and the sick and the lunatic—these will all have to suffer. And for what? The money for the clergy's pardon will support a new war or new orgies at Court or new favorites and their fathers and their uncles and their brothers and their cousins. The trouble is that most lay fortunes in the country were dissipated in the civil wars of the last century; whereas the Church has conserved and held in trust century after century. It goes on using its treasure lifetime upon lifetime. That's what some of these moderns without any sense of history forget, if they ever knew it. They see a jeweled cross or a miter, and they think what they could buy with its value; and they don't think of how long that particular value has been serviceable in that particular way and how long it can continue to be. But you don't need to be argued with on that score."

"Still, I like to listen to you speaking passionately, Cuthbert. It's a rare occurrence, you see."

"I am ashamed that you should ever see me so; yet—I know I contradict myself—I came to you because you're one person I can safely rant to. That's a grateful way to use one's friends. And I know, too, that it's selfish of me to burden you now because you have your own worries."

"As for here," More suggested a clean sweep of the table before him, "we are feeling to-day very free from worries." He knew, however, that Tunstall could see nearly as well as he himself the occasions for worry in the drift of policies and influences in the kingdom.

"If you have one such heartening day amid your duties,

the more unkind I am to bring you our distress. But you have heard so much, you'll have to bear with me to the end of the present business."

"And are you sure that it is to remain just your distress? Many times when the heretics talk of the Church as all Christian men, laity as well as clerics, they're talking of course the language of historical and current truth; where they go astray is in matters of interpretation of the fact. Evil that befalls the clergy will be evil for the laity too—ultimately, if not immediately."

"But I wonder how many people see that—not merely heretics, but some who pride themselves on their loyalty to the Church and their orthodoxy. At any rate, the money was not the end of the demands. They had to vote the new title. Thomas," Tunstall leaned forward in amazement, "you don't know about it? The King's demand for the title *Supremum Caput Ecclesiae?*"

Supremum Caput! The words so staggered belief that More could not speak for a moment. Had the King's appetite for grandeur brought him to this appalling presumption? He could trust himself to say only, "I had not known."

Tunstall looked at him as if he had questions he wished to ask, but he seemed to lay them one side. "A heart of stone would have pitied the Archbishop," he said in a voice more quiet now since the worst of his revelation was made. "I am not blaming him, for I don't know what I should have done in his place, what anyone could have done. Yet often it seemed that, were there some firm, illuminating guidance, Convocation might have refused. If the Archbishop could have been as he was twenty years ago! Not just in health and energy—he has aged pitifully, though, in the last few years—but in the intangibles. Having to defer to York with all his slights and invasions of prerogative has been, I suppose, sapping Warham's spirit for years. We didn't think about that till something crucial showed how the old quiet confidence and positiveness had died in him. He is no longer the strong leader who defended Dean Colet back in 1512. That's the right year, isn't it?"

"Yes, as I remember. But the King, too, approved of Colet's work. I don't say that in any disrespect to my Lord of Canterbury, whom I love deeply, you know; in fact, the Archbishop acted for Colet long before the King's approval put the final quietus on his enemies. There's a difference, though, between acting independently of Henry and acting against him. We can both see that."

Again Tunstall seemed startled into possible question as if an undercurrent of unspoken conversation ran beneath their words; but he returned to his narrative. "If it were not for this sword of Damocles that the *Praemunire* has been, I suppose the Archbishop could have asserted his authority as legate *in perpetuum* and spoken as with the voice of the Church; but the Cardinal made the legateship a prerogative too scantily respected to be of much power now."

"Yet the See of Canterbury's legacy is an ancient, permanent one—of a wholly different sort from the Cardinal's special authority."

"You are too good a lawyer, Thomas, I fear, ever to understand that very few people can make the logical distinctions that are commonplaces to you. We see the difference. How many others do? The King, for example?"

"Of course." Henry's power of discernment, even when there was discrepancy between it and action, More felt that he could always attest.

"Ah!" It was less a word than a sigh that drew slowly through Tunstall's lips. "Not as legate, then, but just as the Archbishop of an isolated province could Warham speak at all. Perhaps—but there will never be any knowing now, for the action, even if time nullifies it, can never be expunged from history—if he had led Convocation to resistance, the King would have withdrawn his demand. Would to God that they could have put the thing to the test! Rochester was the only one who spoke out uncompromisingly. He saw where the thing was taking us and denounced it fiercely: 'It will shame us in the eyes of the whole Church.' But unhappily, much as men respect his strength, they are afraid of his counsel; and I suppose—Heaven forgive me for the harsh judgment!—calculating men think of how little the King approves of his frankness and unglozing honesty. Had he been Archbishop, though, I wonder whether he could not have given Convocation some sturdiness of resolution to withstand the King's demand. He was able to hearten them at least to the reservation, 'So far as the law of Christ allows,' which leaves conscience some safeguard. It may be sheer nervousness on my part, but I can't help feeling that this vote by default to-day—that's what it amounted to: 'silence gives consent'—is one of the most fateful actions in our national history. The sanguine are already saying that the words are an idle form, that they won't really alter anything, and that the reservation vitiates the presumption in the form. I heard several salving their consciences with such syrups as Convocation broke up. That was harshly said. I'm sorry, Thomas, for I haven't any right to judge my brothers like that. We're all tarred with the one brush, for we in the Northern Convocation will be forced to the same vote. That's all I can see to do, to vote and record our protest. You don't approve that course?"

"It is not mine to approve or disapprove. I was wondering—suppose you were to refuse?" As More offered the suggestion, however, he regretted it, for it brought a pained look of confusion to his friend's face. The years should have taught him, he chided himself, that no man can be conscience to even his nearest and best beloved without arrogating dangerous privileges.

"To what end?" Tunstall's voice had not even the vigor of resentment that More would have welcomed at the moment. "I believe in resistance if it can achieve anything. If it just sacrifices everything, however, may it not in the long run be worse than yielding somewhat and saving something from destruction?"

The question needed no answering. More felt certain that all that he could say to urge a stiffening of spirit Tunstall's own heart had already told itself, for this debate between wrong from which right may come and the right which may draw incalculable wrongs in its train was an old one. To a man urging the first position sophistically, he had been on occasion severe in rejoinder; but Tunstall's was a good mind allied to a sensitive conscience. When he spoke, it was not in answer but in a kind of reflective corollary to Tunstall's question.

"The two essential tempers of mankind are on such matters so opposed that they can find no middle ground. More and more, I am coming to think I must be, like Bishop Fisher, an absolutist. But Cuthbert, I will never say that Convocation should have done differently, whatever it may do; I may wish, however, or wonder with my 'suppose.' God knows, I could never say confidently, 'Had I been there, thus had I done.' "

"Thank God, your spirit doesn't have to be vexed with such dilemmas as we are plunged in. We bring them to you to think about, but the ultimate weight of them is ours. Thomas, that strange look of yours again! What is the matter?"

"Perhaps nothing of any account. I was just rethinking what I've already said: that the distress of the clergy is likely to reach beyond them to all who can say that they are of the Church in as wide a sense as any man ever used the term. Modern society is closely knit. Even if ever in history it were possible to harm one class in the state without ultimately hurting all the rest, it cannot be done now. Exactions made now of one group will reach out eventually to the others. Perhaps the laity will not fully understand the change in the profession of the Church here in England; so lest they hold outmoded ideas, they may be put on oath to this new title. Will it not then concern them?"

"Yes." The sigh in that one syllable confirmed the white misery in Tunstall's face. "But it may not ever come to that. What you say, though, about the unity of society—that is something that Parliament needs to learn. Yes, how simple a view it is that can let men think that, in a modern state, one group can be made the social scapegoats! That's what the measures of this Parliament really mean. Last year I thought my Lord of Rochester overhasty when he denounced the Commons for seeming, through their actions, to cry 'Down with the Church!' He had reason to be alarmed, these more recent measures show pretty clearly. Teach the people that particular attitude, and they may take it suddenly with a new prey. 'Down with the Church!' Well, why not 'Down with the King!' 'Down with the Nobles!' and even 'Down with the burgesses, the landowners, the merchants!' until only those who have nothing to lose remain, as poor as ever because they have destroyed everything in the frenzy of taking it away from those who have it?"

"And perhaps all because they had nothing to lose, not entirely through their own fault. There's the thing we have to change, Cuthbert. I believe in Parliament. But I have no sympathy with the cry 'Down!' whether it be from heresy or rebellion or the pride of the powerful and the rich. The latter may not say, 'Down with the poor!' but the selfish among them often seem to be acting on the thought. 'Up!' is a better cry with which to start the mending of our world. That's why I believe heartily in education. With education, we can come to trust our Parliaments and even the groups that are not now admitted to Parliament. Are you laughing at me, my Lord of Durham, for a dreamer of mere Utopias?"

"By no means. I was only thinking that the gates of hell may prevail before the gates of Utopia. Can we achieve the necessary understanding soon enough to ward off disaster from our society?"

"It's strange, Cuthbert: I must be a chameleon in temperament. A desperate-thinking man can send me over to the optimists, but nowadays I cannot bear to talk with anyone who thinks that all is well with the world and that the next centuries will preserve all our institutions and customs just as they are. Perhaps it's the same with you. Well, though I have no illusions about the evils of our society, I have faith enough in the patient constructiveness of time and life and human nature and the purposes of God to feel that we may trust some things to the future. We may die disheartened and go down to the dust in defeat. That doesn't matter. If the ideas are good, they will ultimately triumph. And I'm not thinking just in terms of the personal vindications of history, hope of which has sometimes cheered the vanquished; I'm thinking of the prevailing of ideas, even though the men who hold them are utterly forgotten. The men have their immortality elsewhere; so they do not need to be remembered in this world—Tacitus and other wise men notwithstanding."

Tunstall blinked back the dimming of tears. "Unlike him as you are, Thomas, you are a great deal like Bishop Fisher. You both have a power to see things simply and directly that I wish heartily I had. It seems as if you could front a hostile universe with your resolution."

The generous words evoked a misery of spirit that More could not have defined; without looking at Tunstall, he said slowly, "God keep us all from such a test! If it be bad for us to know our strength, how much more fearful must it be ever to learn utterly our weakness and live!"

"Thomas, what is this shadow? I brought you our trouble—selfishly, but again and again as we have been talking, I have felt that you had a weight of your own that it is wrong for me to increase. What is the matter?"

"'Matter' is too definite a word. Frankly, I don't know. Vague feelings, the things that make a man on a dark road look behind him or a wife beg her husband to put off his journey for a day. I should laugh at myself for a womanish soul. But let me ask you one question in turn. Why were you surprised that I did not already know what Convocation was to do?"

That they were thinking together was evident from Tunstall's reluctance to explain his former amazement, but More felt the explanation was essential—he needed some confirmation of the confused inward promptings. That or whole-hearted exposure of their falsity.

"It's as hard for me to be definite about that as for you about your forebodings. Yes, they seem to me as clear as that, Thomas. I was, I suppose, too easily surprised. I thought that of course you knew as one of the King's Council."

"And you have discovered that it is possible to be that and yet not of his counsel."

"It's a kind of compliment to you that he doesn't want you to know some things beforehand. Do you know who was the King's messenger to Convocation—running back and forth with demands and offers of compromise? Young Boleyn. And what about the new councilor?"

"Thomas Cromwell? I don't know a great deal about him. I thought better of him in his relations to the Cardinal than I should have expected to think. That is something."

"Almost too much," Tunstall's slow shake of the head seemed

to say before he remarked: "I distrust his influence—vaguely, perhaps unjustly. But I remember Reginald Pole's telling me how Cromwell recommended Niccolo Macchiavelli's writings to him once. That's worth bearing in mind."

"Worth bearing in mind," More reflected. There was nothing else that Tunstall and he needed to say about their perplexities, for unhappily they were thinking together.

CHAPTER IX

A WEEK later, as More waited the King's emergence from the chapel at York Place, he remembered with no little amazement at its not recurring sooner, his jesting with his wife on the eleventh of February about a proclamation the King should issue. Which of them had had that particular inspiration? It sounded like his own too often untimely joking. And he had added something about a memorial to one of the most remarkable events in English history; in that he had spoken with the unwitting truthfulness the fool sometimes achieves. Their old jester, Henry Pattison—how was he faring in the Lord Mayor's household?—could have done no better, or perhaps no worse, than the poor fool who in years past had occasionally made sport for the King's delectation. Was that, by any chance, the explanation of Henry's attitude towards him—a refusal to take at face value the seriously intended expostulations, advice, and pleas which he had addressed to him since he had accepted the Great Seal? November, December, January, February—nearly a year and four months. It had been the longest year in his life. Such a thought belonged to the impatience of youth, for it is the posting of time that, conventionally, age should notice and deplore. Perhaps from to-day, he would have time on his hands because of the proclamation of the King's new title on the eleventh of February.

Upon More's debate with himself broke suddenly the creaking of the doors, borne outward before the King by his gentlemen. Inasmuch as he had been awaiting that signal, it should not have startled him; he had been wandering in thought, however, far from this gallery at York Place. By the time that Henry's resplendent bulk with the delicate figure of the Lady Anne doll-like beside him filled the graceful arch of light in the doorway, More had come back to the realization of what he must do quickly. He had debated the question so thoroughly that he must not be again overruled, persuaded against the counsel of his own judgment. In this resolution he stepped forward to bow at the King's side; he must secure his audience before the most assiduous of the courtiers, blurring the light within the chapel, debouched around them.

"Thomas More!" Henry's voice rang with a delight More dreaded to hear. "It's a long time since you have been on hand to pay your morning devoirs." Gently he lifted the little hand resting on his jeweled sleeve and kissed it: "I'll come to you, sweet, in a few minutes."

Though she curtsied to Henry with a coy, alluring smile, the Lady Anne had only a frown for his Chancellor, who remembered at that moment how she had been prevailed upon to send the Cardinal in his disgrace a snippet from her golden girdle. Would she send some token after him to Chelsea? Before that engaging thought had slipped away, her own little court had closed round her and drawn her from their sight. Henry grasped his arm so companionably that, though More knew he was to have his private audience, he could not feel the confidence of even a few minutes before in the outcome of the interview.

"I was wishing just this morning that you were here to talk to, and you have divined my thought," Henry asserted with invading enthusiasm.

"Then it is fortunate that my impulse brought me, Sire," More said, faint-heartedly enough, for he was sorry to lose the advantage of presenting straightway to the King the matter on which he had waked to meditate and pray in the night watches of this past week. What the King had to say to him might utterly thwart his own intention; yet he could not thrust in his petition without waiting Henry's revelation of his thought.

"Let us walk in the river gallery," said the latter with a backward, dismissing glance to a few courtiers who lingered in the doorway of the chapel.

On the way thither he chatted so amiably and so steadily of trivial things that More wondered whether he had foreseen the business which he would thus avoid. Though ready to interject a polite syllable when it seemed needed, More was deep in more somber reflections than suited Henry's exposition of the remodeling he planned to have done at York Place during the coming summer. More had not been in the river gallery since his last visit to Wolsey; that fact alone might have brought back thought of the Cardinal, but a more potent agent was the temper of the master whom they had both tried to serve. As his eye noted again the not yet obliterated insignia of the Cardinal on the carved doors, he recalled one picture created by Hugh Marchaunt's report of Wolsey—he had knelt before the King for hours to dissuade him from some resolution. Perhaps, then, this arbitrary will in one who could be all grace and affability and disarming solicitude had been shaping through the years when common assumption had blamed the Cardinal for evil policies. Had the latter ever wanted to surrender his office? No, that thought seemed patently absurd.

"If we cut a canal from the river to the pond in the garden, perhaps we can decoy the swans thither," Henry was saying. Agaze upon the brimming river, where a brace of swans floated almost as immobile as the water that mirrored them, he leaned against the window by which they had stopped. "How delightful a picture they will make gliding in upon us in the garden!"

Was Henry dreaming some beautiful illustration in an old

romance, More wondered, remembering garden scenes of magical enticement on which the manuscript artists of the last century had lavished their genius. One of the oddest elements in the King's many-sided temperament was his fondness for playing at things archaic; so it would be not inconsistent for him to try to create such an atmosphere for his private garden. And there, no doubt, he would think, not of the subjugation of the Church in England, but of the witchery of Anne Boleyn, strolling beside him. A strange, strange picture—so real and so incredible an attachment in the gay, pastel world of romance!

"Delightful!" Echoing the word himself, Henry beamed upon his fancy. "But, Thomas, what has happened to your imagination? You don't warm to the idea at all. Never mind; I know you are a busy man. And it's very inconsiderate of a monarch to complain because his ministers are busy. So let me tell you what I've had in mind to say; then I'll send you packing off to Westminster. I grow more and more pleased with thought of my foundation at Oxford. It will take time yet, I know, to perfect the plans; but it is just the thing we need there. So I am convinced I shall not regret the outlay for it."

The words seemed to flow from such sincerity as touched again More's amazement. Could Henry speak thus without even the cloud of admitting to himself that the endowment was his only because he had tried to sweep all Wolsey's property into his own wide purse? And could he fail to notice the disparity between the small endowment exempted from confiscation and the great college Wolsey had planned? Henry seemed incapable of duplicity, he reflected, because he was incapable of the necessary moral distinctions. That was another odd fact of his nature. At the same time, More realized, the King in acknowledging his pleasure in the plans was thanking Gardiner and him as definitely as he ever would; and it was good to know that their advice had not utterly failed. The Cardinal had died uncertain about the fortunes of his college at Oxford—that at Ipswich had been lost irretrievably; but now, three months after his death, Henry was relenting towards a remnant of Wolsey's dream.

"Yes, and I am pleased with the universities." Henry had turned in the moment before he resumed his discourse; so his face was in shadow instead of in the full light from the river windows. "I have heard Oxford and Cambridge condemned as hotbeds of heresy; but the doctors impress me as being very sound men. And by the way, Thomas, we have such a body of opinions from the universities of Christendom as should stagger even the most obdurate disapproval."

He could feel the sharpness of the King's scrutiny, before which he hoped for an unrevealing countenance. In recent years, he thought miserably, Henry's amiability had almost always preluded a return to the question of the divorce; in the same instant, nevertheless, he saw, too, that the King was unwittingly aiding him to make his own plea.

"You have talked with some of my counsel, I know," Henry continued, "and they have reported how attentively you have listened to their arguments. Dr. Cranmer is especially quick to praise your willingness to be reasoned with. But still you are unconvinced, I take it, for you have not told me otherwise."

Though the King's tone was casual and patient, he paused as if the last words had been a question.

"Still, Your Grace."

"And for the old reasons?"

"Yes, Your Grace. All the new reasoning assumes the doubtful premise as proved."

The King frowned. "Well, no matter. I had hoped you were won over."

"Since I am not, Sire," More was surprised at the nervous speed of his words now that he had his opening, "is it not best that I withdraw from office? Will you not take back the Seal as graciously as you delivered it to me?"

The frown deepened into a very midnight of offense or perplexity. "Why? Have I not been well-pleased with your conduct of the Chancery? I see no reason for your withdrawing. No. I marvel at your thinking of it."

"But, Sire, if I cannot be serviceable to you as you wish me to be?"

"Have I sued for my divorce in Chancery? Until I do, your views naturally distress me, but they do not affect your office. Here you have made my Court of Chancery a power for justice in the realm; you've proved me right in thinking the Chancellor should be a lawyer. And you want to give up now. I don't understand you at all, Thomas, lately."

"Is not that fact sad reason enough, Sire, for my request? I must be an irritation to you; so it were better for you to give the Seal to some one more helpful. It is too great an honor and a trust to leave to a man you cannot look upon with full favor."

"No, I will not hear of it. I command you to keep the Seal; and hold what counsel you please with your own conscience."

"Thank you, Sire. But I had hoped to persuade you to release me."

"Lazy, are you?" There was a hint of laughter in Henry's voice. "At any rate, Thomas, you are not the only one who can be stubborn. And now"—the laughter was unmistakable—"tell me one thing. Does what happened in Convocation the other day trouble you?"

"Since you ask, Your Grace, yes."

"Don't be overdelicate and squeamish. That doesn't concern you, but I suspected you would be alarmed. That's something for the Bishops to think about; it doesn't affect anyone else."

"But the Church is one body, Sire, clergy and laymen. How can it fail to affect everyone in the realm in some sort?"

"Oh, they have the money hidden away all right. And for the rest"—Henry shrugged magnificently—"a few words. What do they change? 'So far as the law of Christ allows.' That is perfectly clear."

Within the next weeks so many, even among the clergy, seemed to agree that the terms of the King's new title were perfectly clear and changed nothing that More wondered whether his doubts were, as Henry had charged, overscrupulous. Yet the flutter of some incidents disquieted him. The refusal of Reginald Pole—not, after all, won to abetment of the divorce—to be Bishop of Winchester or Archbishop of York in succession to Wolsey, rich bribes though these dioceses were, had seemed to ruffle the King little. In spite of the spread of tales about the violence of temper with which he had received his cousin's excuses, Henry had recently borne himself with the assurance of a victor. He had been well-pleased with the year-long labor and searching of his agents, whose spoils of quotation from the Fathers and the Doctors and lists of scholars who had answered the King's questions to his satisfaction now lay in impressive bulk before More. In a few hours he must go into Parliament to report the present state of His Majesty's appeal to the universities; and though all men knew that he would be speaking for the King, this necessity of his office revived all his old distress about the ambiguity in which he stood.

For four years the question of the divorce had been moot; and time after time through these years Henry had solicited his opinion. Such a pitiable matter had no justification, then, for returning thus—especially on a fair, bright day in March. Easter was ten days away; so Parliament must be adjourned for the holy season. Before men left for home, however, the King had determined that they should know the opinions of the universities and carry back report thereof to their constituencies. It was not easy to convince the ordinary Englishman that the King's motives were truly scruples of conscience, for, perhaps unimaginatively, such a man remembered a few facts that to him were stronger arguments than the subtleties of the canon lawyers. Chief among these facts was the nobility of the Queen's character, for she was to the people a personification of the virtues they thought most queenly. And now, she who had come to England nearly thirty years before, young, gravely charming, if not beautiful, eager to win and to give devotion, was about to be cast off when repeated childbearing, grief, and neglect had robbed her of health and grace, and aged her prematurely. In spite of all the serious questions attendant on the two marriage contracts which the elder Henry Tudor had made for the Spanish princess, whose dowry and whose value in international relations he had been loath to lose, the people remembered simply that the second marriage had been sanctioned by papal dispensation and that Katharine had been married to the young King as a virgin widow, clad all in white with her hair hanging loose. At that time surely, with a bull to cover every contingency, ordinary men reasoned, there was no motive save that of telling the truth in thus proclaiming the Queen a virgin widow.

Recently, however, that assumption of twenty-two years before had been questioned, not by the direct assertion to which the Queen had publicly challenged the King, but by the repetition of hearsay, by hypothetical questions, and by the legalists' discussions of probability. As a lawyer, More knew, he himself might agree with the scholars who had subscribed to these opinions piled before him on the table in reasoning that, in the absence of conclusive evidence, there was strong probability of the consummation of the marriage between Prince Arthur and Katharine. But as a judge, he could not help feeling that one small detail of the events a quarter of a century before had been significant: Henry the Seventh had proposed that he marry his son's widow. Disparity in age and even the formal relationship between them made the suggestion monstrous enough if the young people's marriage had been but a form; had it been a reality or had those with closest knowledge of the facts believed it a reality, the old King's proposal passed belief. Finally, though he knew that the Queen's oath in her own cause would not stand in law, as a man More felt that the oath deserved respect; and though the King's refusal to answer her direct appeal might be attributed to an honorable reticence, there was little enough of that quality in his character. It might have been far more considerate of the Queen and more honorable to say, "She is mistaken," than to adopt the dubious course of hypothetical questions: "Is it lawful for a man to marry the widow of his brother who has died without children?" and "Can a papal dispensation validate such a marriage?"

"Doctor utriusque juris, Alexander de Bonzamninis; Doctor legum, Joannes de Smiconibus; Doctor utriusque juris, Bartholomaeus Jovaria; Doctor legum, Ludovicus Columbatis; Doctor legum. . . ." Yes, what had been true among the English bishops and scholars seemed to be true abroad: in general, the canon lawyers held the dispensation invalid on the assumed premises, but the theologians spoke with far less positive and unanimous voice and in smaller numbers, and the chief defenders of the marriage were theologians. These opinions in front of him, More reflected, impressed by their very bulk. But how did answers to hypothetical questions or quotations culled from rare books advance the real case? With that wonder came a pleasanter one to consider. Had Richard Croke in his year in the libraries and universities of Italy had time for any books besides those he had searched for material to support the King's cause? Saint Chrysostom's *Margaritae*, the Canons and Acts of the Councils with annotations in Greek, and similar books sounded like interesting reading; yet it seemed a pity that a scholar should scan the treasures of Italy with an eye to but one subject. To how strange an end had Croke been using the Greek he had learned under the patronage of Erasmus and Fisher and Warham! And still the real questions remained unanswered because the answers were not to be found in the subtleties of masters and doctors or in the world's most splendid libraries.

When first Henry had revealed his scruples, three years and a half before, More had disclaimed the right of the theologian and the canonist to pronounce an opinion. Like Fisher and Pole and others, however, he had pleaded with the King to set his conscience at ease, for the highest earthly authority of Christendom had sanctioned the marriage, on which both Henry and Katharine had entered after deliberation and in good faith. The sure wrong of an annulment or a divorce had seemed then far more serious than the conjectured wrong of the marriage in 1509. And ever since, as a friend and a counselor, he had been able to say to Henry only this: "I hold still to my old judgment." Except for repeated private solicitation, the King had, indeed, kept his promise not to infringe on More's conscience; he had not frowned too severely even on his Chancellor's refusal to sign the letter to Pope Clement in the previous summer —the petition of the Council, with many nobles and prelates besides, for a speedy determination of the King's cause. Yet the King's patience was running short; and what this announcement he must make to Parliament portended troubled More.

To be sure, he had heard the first question of scruple and sin pass into questions of state, the most often urged of which concerned the succession, a matter properly Parliament's to decide. He could understand men's worry for the realm were a woman to rule, for English history offered but one tragic precedent; but he maintained that the state of the realm had improved immeasurably since the distant feudal days of Matilda and Stephen. Because of that fact alone, the precedent was no true one.

Furthermore, the education of the Princess Mary, like that of his own daughters, was following the noblest pattern of liberal scholarship in this new age. At least, he corrected, it had been until Henry began to stint and humiliate his daughter under the influence of her mother's rival. That unnatural attitude, however, could not endure: the Princess would be restored to her due position and opportunities. So he for one could contemplate without terror the prospect of an England ruled by a woman.

The returning warmth of the midday sun fell welcomely across his desk in his private study adjoining the Star Chamber and seemed to dazzle the documents before him into unreality. In two days April would be upon them, and Easter not far beyond; then it would be pleasant to ride off through the spring-quickened country. "So priketh hem nature in hir corages," he mused, seeing in his mind's eye a laughing company of a century and a half before mounting their beasts at the Tabard in Southwark. It would be simple to join them—an easy ride hence into the city, then over the crowded, noisy, ever-fascinating bridge, and there he would be. Or it might be quicker to cross to Lambeth by the horse-ferry and, after traversing quiet, greening countryside, come up with the pilgrims on the open road.

On such vagabonding thoughts a knock so tentative that he was scarcely sure he had heard it sprang arrestingly; with equal tentativeness he said, "Yes? Come in."

As the door turned inward, it disclosed no more startling face than that of John a Wood, who had offered to keep watch outside so that the work necessary before More went into Parliament might be done without interruption. His ruddy, wide-eyed countenance looked more amazed than ordinarily, if such extension of his habitual surprise were possible.

"Yes? What is it, John? Come all the way in."

"Sorry, sir, but he won't go away till I ask you can't you see him. I told him you couldn't, not till after the session. He thinks he's important."

"Who is he?" More could picture an entertaining encounter between his most faithful, dogged retainer and the debarred visitor.

"He won't say, sir, but by the look of him, he's a Spaniard, and I've seen him somewhere before."

"That sounds as if he might be one of the Imperial Ambassador's household. There's really no need of shutting him out now, for the actual work is all done. If he seems likely to stay, I'll explain that I have to go to Parliament. Were you much troubled?"

"No, sir. There were just a couple of men, but they took 'No' for their answer. Nobody very important."

"Who? You know I have tremendous curiosity."

"Well, the first one was that merchant from Winchester, the one who's been to see you often; only he seemed more cheerful to-day."

"Oh, Thorne. And he seemed in good spirits? Excellent."

"And the other was Master Cromwell. But he said it wasn't anything urgent, and he wanted to know if the Imperial Ambassador was here. But I said, 'No, he just has to finish some work that oughtn't to be interrupted.' So he said, 'All right,' and smiled and went away."

"You're a good warder, John. I'll have to have you keep the keys always when I'm busy. But we mustn't make our visitor wait too long."

"No, sir." Obedient to the suggestion, John turned so hurriedly that he stumbled against the door.

In a moment of waiting, More found his joy in Thorne's apparent good spirits marred by wonder over Cromwell's errand and his asking—perhaps with elaborate carelessness—whether de Chapuys were within. Was there any connection between his coming and the arrival of this foreign visitor? There might be no more than coincidence in the facts, which picked up no clue to significance in his present knowledge; but the sort of coincidence that wakes a perturbed curiosity. The reopening of the door broke off his debate.

"Sextus Rosilius! I had not heard that you were in England again."

"Just back, my Lord Chancellor," said the young man to the accompaniment of a bow freshly practiced in a more ceremonious court than that of England. The dark eyes smiled vivaciously. "I have come from the Emperor, by way of Germany and the Low Countries, and I bring you greetings from half of Europe. Naturally, His Majesty wished to be commended to you; and all sorts of men along the way—scholars and friends of your friends—said, 'Shall you see More? Our salutations to him.' "

"Thank you." More set a chair for his visitor, himself a friend of old friends in Flanders and, for his age, a much-traveled Imperial envoy. "We must talk of them all some day. Who are some of them?"

"To judge by the volume of his messages, Juan Luis de Vives at Bruges would be easily first. He misses England."

"Vives! I'm glad to hear of him. I have been enjoying his new treatises and thinking that we must send him a book by a friend here, Thomas Elyot, as soon as it is out. It is partly in the same field as Vives's essays—education. Have you ever met Elyot? He used to be clerk of Council, and he's a rising diplomat."

Rosilius's nod called attention to the new fashion of collar he was wearing, a fine, narrow pleating that set off his handsome dark head admirably. "I have barely met him—a brilliant man, isn't he? But your Cerberus, if the name would not offend him, told me that you are very busy; so let me do to-day's business with exemplary dispatch."

More chuckled at the new title for John a Wood, who would scratch his head at it and ask, "Is that meant to be insulting?" Then he explained, "Right now I am limited for time, because I must be in Parliament soon. But that fact need not preclude your coming to Chelsea when you can for a leisurely visit."

"I shall be happy to. This errand is a simple one. Naturally, I brought back a good many letters, including some from the Emperor for you; so His Excellency thought I should ask you whether he may bring them to you, formally and officially, you see."

Rosilius obviously knew that the question would require a moment's deliberation; else there would not have been this preliminary inquiry before the presentation of the letters. While thought raced for him, More noticed irrelevantly, as if the observation were another's, that the Fleming sat gracefully at ease: his dwelling at courts was giving him confidence and suavity. If they gave only such ornaments of life! But they produced also questions like this suddenly torturing one. Why had Cromwell come exploratorily, thinking to find the Ambassador and barely missing his deputy? And what should the Emperor be addressing to him that required formal delivery? Here seemed a meeting of coördinates that it would be mad to count merely fortuitous. And were there reason for caution on the part of the Imperial Ambassador and for espionage on that of the King's agent, then he could not receive these letters and keep them secret. Furthermore, he must tell Rosilius only enough to give his refusal some grace so that it should not seem rude or panicky.

"I cannot tell you how sorry this situation makes me." More was grateful for Rosilius's undismayed smile at this melancholy opening. "You must not take offense nor alarm M. de Chapuys.

Believe me, my personal feeling towards you and His Excellency and His Majesty the Emperor is unchanging; but this is not a matter of personal feeling. You will try to make them understand that, will you not? Since things are as they are here, were I to receive these letters, however innocuous, I should feel that I must communicate them to the King, and perhaps to the Council. And had I even one harmless letter to show thus, I can foresee the drawing of the conclusion that I have had others. Let them be saved, please, to a more propitious time."

"But, my lord, you are above that kind of suspicion." Rosilius emphasized the amazement of his words with a hearteningly bewildered look.

"You are thinking me just overtimorous? May the development of affairs bear you out and make liars of my fears! I know; it seems as though I have so completely proved my loyalty to the King that I should not incur suspicion, no matter who comes to see me. Yet this is no normal time; so it is wrong to encourage suspicion. Besides, so small an act as receiving these letters might end the liberty I have always had to speak to His Grace freely without the imputation of any ulterior motive to me. And the King knows me to be devoted to the Queen's cause as well as to his own welfare and honor. But should anything happen to make him doubt that twofold regard—unjust though the doubt would be—I could no longer be his servant or the Queen's."

Rosilius pursed his lips appraisingly, "Yes, I can see that conclusion from your premises; but I cannot see that the courtesy of an ambassadorial visit need embarrass you like that. Of course, I do not know what the letters contain; yet His Majesty would remember his aunt's unhappy position here and not do anything to aggravate it. The letters must be harmless enough to read to a dozen Councils."

"That may be. Indeed, I trust they are; for otherwise their

mere existence is dangerous—and not to me alone, as you recognize."

The young man nodded shrewdly: "The searching of Cardinal Campeggio's baggage?"

So quick an application of his own vague premonitions disconcerted More; for, though the analogy of that search eighteen months before was not wholly sound, it carried a certain appropriate warning for the present emergency. He let a little deprecating gesture speak for a direct answer; but he could neither waive the implications of the question nor offer it any confident denial.

"I am sorry you feel so," Rosilius said earnestly, "but I shall do my best to convince His Excellency." The slowness of his speech and the compassionate steadiness of his gaze troubled More anew: it was probably not going to be easy for his visitor to report on this interview with just the proper emphasis. And he knew that Rosilius would be a conscientious messenger.

"Assure him, please, that this nervousness is no reflection on him, and that it is not, I believe I can say honestly, a matter of selfish, personal concern—"

"We know that well," Rosilius interrupted. "In fact, His Excellency has heard that you have wanted to resign the Seal."

"If de Chapuys has heard even that," More reflected, "it is right to insist that we have no private communication after this; for the newsmonger never expects to go home empty-eared." Who could be the Imperial Ambassador's informant that knew so secret a matter? But he made no comment on his visitor's remark beyond whatever eloquence a lift of the brows may command.

"Not personal concern, but official," he resumed. "So long as I hold my post, I must consider its duties. Ask His Excellency, then, to forbear for the present, please."

"I will do what I can, my lord. And perhaps I should not try to come either for a time."

"Thank you. I believe that will be best for a time if you promise, too, not to misunderstand." More studied the troubled young face: this friend of old friends with news from them recalled the gracious, free intercourse of his years in private life. "Store up for a while all the reports of our friends abroad, for I still shall want to hear of them when I see you next. After a little while things will be better."

"May that be soon, sir!" As Rosilius rose and took his hand, his dark eyes were still shadowed.

Even when the door had thudded shut behind him, More stood in touched concern over the perplexity he was inflicting on others. It was a miserable necessity which thus intruded on decent, unstrained human relations. And now he must report to the Houses of Parliament what the King's agents and scholars had found to be the opinion of Christendom on the divorce. Sadly enough, his own words echoed in thought: "After a little while!"

CHAPTER X

"VENI, Creator Spiritus"—the glorious words of their hymn were still ringing in More's thought as he stood momentarily just within the door of All Saints' Church to accustom his eyes to the full brilliance of the sun on the river. In the acceptance of the light, he saw the Duke of Norfolk waiting a little apart from the small Chelsea congregation outside, yet looking so much a member of the after-service grouping that he must have been a worshiper, too.

Gathering his surplice securely on his arm, More hurried down the steps to salute the Duke.

"Good afternoon, my lord. Have you been to vespers with us?"

The Duke started as if he were really taken by surprise. "Eh! Yes, but for just part of the service. I got here early, and they told me where you were. It wouldn't hurt me to come over on such a fine day, I thought, and have the walk home with you."

"We are honored, Your Grace. And shall we not set out?"

The admiring parishioners made way bustlingly for their own friend and his noble guest. Once clear of the group, Norfolk thrust his arm through More's and adjusted his pace; he frowned on the surplice, on which his hand thus rested. Though the frown puzzled More, he held his peace. The Duke gave the linen an irritated tweak.

"God's body!" he exclaimed. "My Lord Chancellor a parish clerk—a parish clerk! You dishonor the King and his office."

So that was the trouble! More smiled, partly at the profanity to which the Lord Admiral reverted in excitement, and lifted his arm a trifle so that the surplice might ride the more openly. "Nay, Your Grace must not think that the King, our master, will be offended with me for serving God, his master, or count his office dishonored."

"Do you think he'll see it in that light?"

"I do, my lord, for the King has sometimes most humbly served Mass himself. For such service as you have caught me in to-day, Your Grace, he will not be vexed at me; indeed, I could wish that there were always so good a chance of his being well-pleased with me."

"That he may easily be, if only you will be more temperate."

"More temperate? Your Grace, I did not know that you enjoyed riddles."

"By our Lady, that's no riddle. You have spoken out rashly in the Council a couple of times recently. Have a little sense, man."

"But, my lord, what else are councils for? I have believed that we should speak out there, and nowhere else, so that the King might have the not ungoodly fare of all our opinions, mixed and sauced and spiced for his delectation."

"Maybe, maybe. But you forget that your fellow-councilors have feelings—pride and interests and influence, too. That's the trouble."

"But, my lord, surely we all understand that those private . . . feelings must be laid aside when we are considering what is best for His Majesty and the realm. Otherwise, we are no true Council."

Norfolk patted his arm and turned a full, ingenuous look upon him. "Sometimes, though, the things that serve some man's private interest are really the best things for the realm, and then he isn't really thinking selfishly at all. We all ought to be big enough to see that."

"Big enough? You rule honest, even if misguided, opposition out very summarily, Your Grace."

With his free hand Norfolk was plucking budlets from the hedge; impulsively, he tossed a couple against More's cheek. "Come now; we haven't any quarrel. And for all I care, we could all talk as freely in Council as you and I here in your garden. But they don't all feel that way. Just face the fact. Thomas, Thomas, I used to think that I could make a diplomat—in this domestic sense—out of you. You have had the training, God knows."

"I must not be an apt pupil, Your Grace." Though he spoke humbly enough, sure that the Duke would not be deceived by his tone, More wanted to laugh with some one who could enjoy the joke of anyone's having thought him likely material for domestic diplomacy—political opportunism and intrigue, as it must seem to non-practitioners. He wanted, too, to remark that Norfolk could be more tolerant than some of the Council, for, so far as England admitted of security, he belonged to a little group immune to the worries that beset the climbers and the adventurers; but he remembered that the chief of these was the Duke's own brother-in-law, Thomas Boleyn, formerly Viscount Rochford, now Earl of Wiltshire and Ormond—it all had a magnificent roll; yet, of course, even so much was not enough. Was Norfolk really pleading his case?

"You're not so simple as you pretend to be, not so simple," Norfolk exclaimed in mock-despair. "But you're like a youngster in your ability to disarm reproof. You ought to see, though, that not many men can comprehend your temper. It's a dangerous one, for it may run you into disaster. You've been lucky that the King understands you."

"And you, Your Grace." In fact, More felt better assured of the abrupt, but not unfriendly, penetration of the Duke than he did of Henry's understanding.

With an even kindly pat on the surplice, Norfolk returned to his expostulation: "It's not as though you didn't know how to be tactful. Now that day in the Lords, nobody could have been more discreet. I was proud of you then."

"When, my lord?"

"When you were announcing the opinions of the universities and Wiltshire asked you what you thought. Yes, I know it was unfair of him; but after all, he gave you a chance to show how skillful you can be."

"Do you think that was his intention, my lord, when he put the question? I must have misunderstood."

"By our Lady, that's a pretty one! We're not deceived about his intention. But you handled him well: 'That I have many times already declared to the King, my lord.' You probably couldn't hear some of the chuckles. And what could he say to you after that?"

"He will ask me the question again, I fancy; but he shall have the same answer for his pains."

"And what are you laughing at, I'd like to know?"

"Not at the Earl of Wiltshire," More protested in mock-alarm. "No, if Your Grace will not be offended, I will tell you: I was enjoying your definition of 'discretion'—your definition and the illustration that I unwittingly gave."

"Now take that seriously, Thomas. You were silent then gracefully. If you can be once, you can be again."

"In the same situation? Yes. But not on other questions in the general deliberations of the Council. The Councilor who is silent fails in his duty. He is useless and even—I shall borrow a word you used a few minutes ago, Your Grace—dangerous. For myself, I shall gladly be silent on all the vexing questions on one condition."

"Wisely said. What is it?"

"Will you still say, 'Wisely said,' I wonder, when I tell you?

Try to, please. If I may resign the Seal, be out of the Council, be just a plain subject who ought not to meddle in affairs of State anyway, I'll be silent as the grave."

"God's body! No."

"It is a sure way of silencing me, my lord."

"But we need you. That's absurd."

"Need me for what? His Majesty knows my opinion now on several matters that I do not mention to others—enough, I know, to show him how useless I am. You have just been telling me—kindly and generously, to be sure—that I make enemies on the Council. Why should any of you want me to stay on, unless as a penitential exercise, a kind of *memento mori* at the feast? And that's no very honorable or satisfying rôle, Your Grace. You have always been my good friend, but never before can I have been so grateful to you as I shall be now if you help me out of office. There are not many men who trouble you with such a request, I dare swear; so believe it sincere."

"Eh! It is singular enough, I grant you; but it's impossible."

"Still, my lord, consider that, if you help me in this, you will crown all the kindnesses you have ever done me with the only one for which I have ever pleaded. If the occasion arises for my resigning, help me. That is not much to ask."

"It may be too much." Norfolk's gruffness, however, could not disguise the fact that the plea had moved him.

"It's strange, isn't it?" More caught himself kicking at the tender new grass as they mounted the terrace. "Flatterers have told me that I am a good lawyer; yet I am notably unsuccessful in pleading for myself."

"Well, they say that physicians can't cure themselves. Don't you worry about resigning, though; there's no need." With that, the matter was evidently ended for the Duke, who sniffed audibly and delightedly the aroma of the supper awaiting them.

Ordinarily, the shouting of the children at their play in the alleys of the garden made an accompaniment to his studies, remote enough to be pleasurable and undistracting; but this morning, as More sat reading the new work of Tyndale which had come only the day before from London, the merry noises outside were an almost painful spur to him. Far rather would he be holding a kite string for a grandson in this bright April wind or hunting wildflowers in the meadows. Yet for the sake of these youngsters he must deal with this book while he had time; so even yesterday afternoon he had begun to mark the passages that roused the disputant in him. Now he leafed back through the volume to recapture the sequence of his impressions. In some ways the thing that he found most amazing in Tyndale was his depreciation of the ordinary intelligence.

"And of prayer we think," he reread, "that no man can pray but at church; and that it is nothing else but to say *Paternoster* unto a post." Where had Tyndale met so debased an interpretation of prayer? And how could he presume to suggest that the Church had ever taught, or any individual Christian ever believed, that men could pray only at church? The attack on images here was of a piece with the rest of the sentence in its easy, false assumption that men prayed to the representation which was but a reminder, a visible concentration of their own thought. He had never seen a beast deceived by a scarecrow in the fields—and sometimes not even the crows took it for a man; no marauding dog, that might slink from the terror of a human form, turned tail at the simulacrum, nor did any cat, purring and arching, rub against it in expectation of a stroking. What men, then, in Christendom thought that they prayed to a statue or a crucifix, however closely they might cling to its base? In fact, he had sometimes wondered when he had read of the beautiful idols of the ancients whether they had not thought of their images as representations, not as very gods.

A few pages farther on lay the passage that in its taunts had wounded him yesterday more deeply than he would have thought this little book capable of doing. Now, forearmed against sensitivity, he read it again to test its effect: "M. More hath so long used his figures of poetry, that (I suppose) when he erreth most, he now, by the reason of a long custom, believeth himself that he saith most true . . . Let, therefore, M. More and his company awake by times, ere ever their sin be ripe, lest the voice of their wickedness ascend up, and wake God out of his sleep, to look upon them, and to bow his ears unto their cursed blasphemies against the open truth, and to send his harvestmen and mowers of vengeance to reap it.

"But how happeth it that M. More hath not contended in like wise against his darling Erasmus all this long while? . . . Peradventure he oweth him favor, because he made *Moria* in his house: which book, if it were in English, then should every man see how that then he was far otherwise minded than he now writeth. But, verily, I think that as Judas betrayed not Christ for any love that he had unto the high priests, scribes and Pharisees, but only to come by that wherefore he thirsted; even so M. More (as there are tokens evident) wrote not these books for any affection that he bare unto the spirituality, or unto the opinions which he so barely defendeth, but to obtain only that which he was hungered for. I pray God that he eat not too hastily, lest he be choked at the latter end; but that he repent, and resist not the Spirit of God, which openeth light unto the world."

It was appalling to find oneself prayed for and to feel no gratitude, but rather a kind of resentment, stirring in one's heart. That More beat resolutely back, for still he would believe Tyndale to be writing not in malice but in misguided—yes, benighted—zeal. What a power of invective dwelt in the man! What a shrewd skill in making evil the motives of other men! More had expected to be attacked in the book. Why else should it have been called *An Answere unto sir Thomas More's Dialoge* instead of having some doctrinal title like that of *A Disputacyon of purgatorye made by Johan Frith,* bound up with it? But while a man may smile to find himself mocked at for a poet or a self-deceiver, the comparison of him to Judas puts a grievous burden on charity. The wrenching of all his motives awry by the innuendo of the last paragraph left such an aching in spirit as brought back memory of the torture to nerve and sinew the physical wrenching of a throw from his horse years before had been. If even this one man thought, or would have others think, that he had written his defenses of the faith—painfully wrought books, as they were—from mercenary motives, what could he do? A denial, even a retraction, rarely catches up with a libel once loosed upon the credulity of men. So here, staring out of the heavy black letters, lay the accusation that some men would read believingly as long as Tyndale's book should live. It was a fabulous warrant of longevity that this little device of type conferred on whatever anyone delivered to it. And a terrifying one, for, after all, the book which he was meditating in answer to Tyndale ought to have small meaning in a few years. In a few years, too—no, that was excessive grace to give the selfish pity—his own helplessness before the slander of these pages would have small meaning. Pride was a mean enough property at any time, and a useless one now when he could not let fear of being hurt drive him from the battle to which values far dearer than office or fame had vowed him. Vindication from the charges of time-serving and venality he must leave to the ultimate justice of God, for they had nothing to do with the soundness of Tyndale's doctrines. And it was woefully easy for Tyndale and him and all men meddling with disputation to be betrayed into evasions and confusions of the issue; they were all like hounds on a bright day so giddy after a new scent that they let their first fox elude them. Meanwhile, Reynard, resting in covert, meditates his escape, a safe crossing of the country the hunt has just traversed. So it could be with some of these pernicious doctrines. While the disputants bayed their vindictive personalities, the unrefuted ideas might be corrupting the innocents.

Sharp as were the thrusts against him alone in this passage, they wounded less grievously than the unkind cut at Erasmus. "He made *Moria* in his house." That far-off, happy visit lay beyond such barriers of experience as made it seem to belong to another life. Around him now, almost nothing but the words on the page could recall the incongruously gay week of Erasmus's illness, during which Folly held her madcap harangues. How they had all enjoyed her wit from its ingratiating first play to its all-disarming, all-excusing reminder that she who spoke was *Moria!* Erasmus, looking down into the marketplace from the windows of the old house in Bucklersbury, had laughed that anyone who took Folly seriously ought to replace her on the rostrum. And one friend after another had caught the contagion of the laughter. "Valete, plaudite, vivite, bibite!" Those gay words, rising up in thought now, had strayed into an alien world. Then all the mockery had been "within the bosom of the family"—Tunstall's or Fisher's phrase—and no man could have dreamed that the book would ever seem to the heretics encouragement of their separatism and reviling. Twenty-one years! Still even that fact of distance could not explain the misconstruction. Was Tyndale a humorless man? The possibility was interesting to consider, for it might explain much. Yet he could hardly have failed to read Erasmus's prefatory letter, one of the most charming letters ever addressed to him, wherein just the right temper of interpretation was suggested too clearly for the dullest wit to miss. "Relaxation for study"—in seeing only the seriousness that was evident enough in the book, a reader must miss all its joy. Perhaps that was the real difficulty for Tyndale and some of the other brethren: they belonged to a world that had lost all its capacity for joy. Not that they could be any more serious, Heaven knew, than on occasion men like Erasmus, who had, however, more range, more plasticity, more sense of the mixedness of life. Some rigidity, more apparent to the senses than to the reason, and therefore not easy to define, was creeping into the human spirit.

At this rate, though, More chided himself, he would make scant progress in his reading; so passing over some of his markers at intervening places in the book, he resumed at the point where he had broken off the night before—the corruption of ceremonies. Old attack as this was by now, he could not leave it unread, lest he overlook some new direction or some new subtlety of abuse. And suddenly with Tyndale, he was in the midst of a plea for true knowledge of Greek and Latin and Hebrew, to which he could most heartily say, *Amen.* With a quickening of recollection, he read: "Remember ye not how within this thirty years and far less and yet dureth unto this day, the old barking curs, Dun's disciples, and like draff called Scotists, the children of darkness, raged in every pulpit against Greek, Latin, and Hebrew; and what sorrow the schoolmasters, that taught the true Latin tongue, had with them! . . . Yea, and I dare say that there be twenty thousand priests, curates, this day in England, and not so few, that cannot give you the right English unto this text in the Paternoster, *Fiat voluntas tua, sicut in coelo et in terra,* and answer thereto."

Thought could go no farther for a time. How strangely Tyndale wrote! In a little passage More could find himself reading sympathetically, and then, without warning, the thought had outrun itself into some new distortion like this of the last sentence. Surely there were some—and however few, too many—priests in the realm who had scant learning and small capacity or eagerness to learn. But 'twenty thousand . . . and not so few'? He wondered whether he had not had fully as wide experience of clerical learning as Tyndale, for he had worshiped not merely in city churches and in the chapels of the Court and of great houses and in well-served country churches, but also in remote, poor, ill-priested ones, where he had stopped in his travelings for Mass or vespers. And though sometimes he had grieved at the barbarous accent and the garbling of the magnificent, never-to-be-hurried words of the liturgy, he had chided himself out of any direct uncharity by reflection that the Holy Spirit listened with no earthly pedant's ear and that it was not his to know what gifts of ministration the boorish curate might bring to the human necessities of his parish—gifts perchance more availing for the comforting and the saving of souls than a nice scholarship alone might be. Yet men could have both. That was a problem, again, to be worked out within the family; for though the Church had sometimes made shift with lamentably imperfect vessels, she desired more nearly perfect ones. On that score, at least, there could be no attack on the principles or the purposes of the Church.

For the conditions in England which through two hundred years had fostered ignorance, she had little direct responsibility: she could not save her priests from the repeatedly decimating plagues of these centuries nor counsel them to save themselves by fleeing the danger often synonymous with their pastoral duties. No wonder was it, then, that her workers had sometimes gone half-trained into the vineyard, many of them to make up in devotion for what they lacked in instruction. Almost as little as for the plagues was she responsible for the other circumstances which had thwarted learning in England: when there is war in the realm, the way of the scholar is hard. Prices rise, food is scarce, endowments and charity contract, and men's spirits grow faint. If to-morrow may destroy all one's world—and self is but a tiny item in such a desperate reckoning—in the bloody holocaust of war, one must be a rare philosopher to keep himself at peaceful study as if he were to serve out the Psalmist's term. Can young people growing up in an uncertain age ever outdistance the temptation to brood upon the futility of their own efforts? And worse still, even in their old age, can men avoid infecting the next generations with their own dilemmas? Those who have lived no more than on the edge of wars must have heroic faith in mankind if they are not to say, "How can we keep ourselves quietly at this work which cannot serve the world to-day, whereas to-morrow there may be no civilization left to serve?" Was it any wonder that the arts and sound learning and the basic scholarship of the clerks had decayed, for, far from being indifferent to the peace of the world, civilization thrives with it, and with it dies? By little and little, the reparation of the defects is wrought, provided men have the patience to see themselves accomplish little and the faith to believe that the work will continue past their own small lives. But unless it be done within the family, it is no reparation; and the starting anew in revolution—as if mankind could ever disown its past!—means destruction, waste, a long retrogression before progress emerges again from the ruin.

Yes, the working from within was the surer way, and in many ways the more honorable, for the man who flouts his own training must seem an ingrate. Here was Tyndale educated now in the learned tongues, which he would have had no opportunity to explore had not learned churchmen fostered such studies. Why did he set himself in unmitigated attack on the authority which had made possible his own education? For surely, were there little learning in the realm now, there had been far, far less without the protection and the encouragement of the Church. Within the Church, to be sure, there were many minds now as always; and scholars disputed fierily about the meanings of the Fathers and the Doctors, who knew now companionably in Heaven the truth which they had sought on earth to comprehend and to reveal, and in the interpretation of which they had sometimes differed vehemently because they desired it vehemently. Even the darkeners of the last generation, the Scotists, who had vexed John Colet and Erasmus and tried the patience of those anxious for a liberal scholarship, were not undeserving of honor for their loyalty to a teacher of brilliant mind and beautiful spirit. They erred, indeed, in reading him too narrowly and too exclusively, but most of their errors were in their own weak spirits and not in the teaching of Duns Scotus. Nearly forty years back, Oxford had had room for both the lectures of Colet, sounding the return to the "old theology" of the Fathers, and the lectures of the persuasive Scotist—More could not conjure his name across the years—who had delighted the University with the first lectures under the Lady Margaret's endowment. Of course, the latter had had the larger audiences; that fact had once troubled More, but now he could understand Colet's steady smile, which was a lighting of the eyes rather than any noticeable change in the muscles of his face, when he had protested that numbers did not matter, that a little group—even one man alone—could start an idea on its conquest of the world.

A few years after the hearsay experience of that meeting at Oxford of the old and the new that was older still, he had himself come to feel the power of a little group. Grocyn had let him lecture in St. Lawrence's Church on Saint Augustine's *City of God*—London had had room then in one of her churches for the young lay Platonist as well as for the timorous theologians who in other churches denounced the dangers of scholarship. For some days the church had been thronged; then on a rainy day only a few score had gathered to make a steaming, dejected audience. "Do you want to postpone it this time?" Grocyn had asked in a carefully noncommittal tone while they waited in the vestry. And though More did not remember the words of his refusal, he remembered the glow of Grocyn's look as he said, "I was afraid you might be discouraged by so few; but since you are not, this will be the best lecture yet." So it had proved, for every man in the little group had chosen against odds to come; and when they were through, in the exhilaration of sharing his thought with a few alert, quick-springing minds, More knew that never again should he worry over few or many in any matter not to be instantly and finally concluded by the pressure of numbers. Were the cause good, even the momentary overbearing of numbers counted not a great deal in the rectifications of time.

Still, one could not leave all to time; while he could, he must try to speed the vindication of the right and the confounding of error. On that premise, he must return to the tantalizing book before him. He felt half-grateful to it on one score that Tyndale would scarcely recognize; statements meant as gibe and reproach had evoked happy memories, had brought back friends who were safe in the peace of eternity, and had summoned up ancient, potent thoughts to exorcise the weariness of his spirit.

CHAPTER XI

By midafternoon, the frostiness of New Year's morning had moderated a little under the influence of a pale, almost warmthless, indifferent sun. Though it had been delightful walking, whether they kept to the well-rutted roads, where false ice offered the constant fun of cracking beneath their feet, or ventured across frozen stubble and fern—crisp, yet resilient, to the stride—the walkers seemed all glad to be within doors again. At a wise distance from the fire they stood a few minutes, still laughing from the exertion of the last spurt, when John had challenged them to see who could reach the house first. For the elders it had been the exertion of holding back the while they appeared to be competing mightily, but for little Thomas Roper it had been a magnificent outlay of energy that let him now crow over even his grandfather.

"I did win, didn't I?" he asked between puffs, as his mother undid the scarf about his neck.

"Right enough, you did, young man," More laughed. "And for that you shall ride into the hall in triumph."

Lightly he pinched the rosy cheek of the youngster, whose anticipatory squeal was as much one of delight as of alarm. When Margaret had her son free of his wrappings, More stooped to let him clamber to his shoulders for the ceremonial ride. So the returned walkers burst in on the stay-at-homes in the hall—John and Anne at the head of the procession, Margaret Roper and William Daunce in the middle, and the young champion beaming from his lofty mount. With a loud hallooing, fierce enough to make Dame Alice and Elizabeth Daunce cover their ears in mock consternation, More rode his grandson twice around the hall. When they drew up before the fire, both somewhat breathless with excitement, he let little Thomas down gently on the hearth; but hardly had he straightened himself than John Daunce was begging for a ride, too.

"Are the others safely out of the way?" he asked his daughters. "If they aren't, I'll be as weary as the poor ass in Aesop."

"Horrible!" Margaret exclaimed, as the new young squire clasped his plump arms about his grandfather's neck. "But don't expect to be carried around yourself, as the ass finally was."

When John, too, had had his ride, the children scampered off at a nod from their mothers, and their spirited steed, resuming his human dignity, leaned against the pillar of the fireplace. His breath came with a painful shortness which he hoped the others would not notice; as much to disguise it as to repair the disarray of their sport, he smoothed his rumpled hair. Just when breathing was becoming almost natural again, his wife looked at him so sharply that he thought, "Ah, I am discovered!" but the instant softening of her gaze quieted his alarm. The prolonging of that quizzical, insistent look whetted his curiosity beyond bearing.

"What is it, Alice? You look like a mischievous youngster with a secret to be teased out of her."

"As for the rest, tilly vally! But I do know a secret. It's there behind you, leaning against the chimney."

The delight in her voice seemed incongruous to More in the moment when he saw the new object round the edge of the fireplace at his left—a staff glinting with gold, a magnificent walking stick, sturdy enough to shame no practical use. What a comfortable speeder of his steps it would have been in the hour's walk they had just taken, More thought, while a more sobering question thrust itself forward.

"Where did it come from? Is it a New Year's gift?"

Dame Alice nodded in thorough enjoyment of her mystery. "It came just after you went out. But you'll have to guess who sent it."

"Guess and send it back?" Was the sigh his own or his vexed wife's? She had labored with him before on that very issue. "But I'm as grateful to the unknown donor as if I could keep it."

"This you must keep." There was undisguised triumph in Dame Alice's voice. "Foolish as you have been about the other presents, you cannot help yourself now. Examine it closely."

At this injunction, More realized that he had but looked at the staff in its corner, as if to touch it were somehow compromising. In the moment of laying hold on it, he understood his wife's exultation, for the gold head bore the Tudor rose.

"The King! But this besides the goblet he sent yesterday? I do not understand. At any rate, you are right, Alice: I cannot send this back. It is beautiful."

"So was that other cup this morning." The little edging of her voice troubled More, for he had thought the explanations of the morning's refusal all ended.

"Yes, we agreed on that," he said. "But there is a world of difference in the circumstances of the two gifts. The King has no suit pending before me as Master Vaughan has had. To take the one gift would put my honesty and the King's justice in jeopardy, but to refuse this would be a churl's insult."

"Honesty? What harm is there in generously intentioned gifts? You make yourself too delicate of conscience. Who ever heard of the Cardinal's holding such nice scruples?"

"And, Alice, who ever heard of his being rated high in honesty till he found his soul in the last year of his life? After all, though, if I strive to follow the Cardinal in his virtues, and—God rest his soul—he had great ones, there is no need for me to emulate his vices. I have enough to do with my own."

A decorously repressed chuckle from Margaret escaped despite her effort. So quiet had been the circle of young people at the hearth that the two elders might have been alone in the room. More turned a mockingly severe eye on the disturber, who was waiting such an invitation to speak now that she had betrayed her amusement.

"So you emulate your own vices, Father? That is a new prescription for the good life."

"You would notice a slip like that, Mistress Pedant. But you all see the point, I think."

"Still, I'm glad there's one present you cannot send back," Dame More insisted as determinedly as a schoolmaster might with a docile, but stupid, pupil. "You've been foolish enough, saying, 'No, I thank you. Pray believe me grateful for your kind thought,' and the rest. Where does all that get you, Thomas—running counter to a custom that no man has ever thought evil?"

"You do make me seem sadly fantastic, if not worse, Alice." More studied her hands plucking vexedly at the rich stuff of her new gown. "Perhaps even a little Pharisaic—'I am not as other men.' But on this score, at least, I think I'm right: in our bartering world there must be some things that have no price. Justice is one of them, and loyalty another. There have always, I thank God, been enough other men who have felt the same way to save common honesty and self-respect from the stigma of oddity. But even leave all such values out of the picture, what should we want with a gold cup or two more? Worry for you in the safe-keeping, my dear."

"Well, that's the kind of worry I could do very well with,"

she retorted with so coquettish a toss of her head as robbed the words of their asperity. This was a mood in which More especially enjoyed her—when the seemingly humorless words were a conscious invitation to his own playful spirit.

"Vanity of vanities! And what a glutton you are to run up the devil's score, Alice!"

"What do you mean?" In the moment of her question, she sat up more stiffly than before to the accompaniment of a crackling and rustling in the bodice of her gown. The beautifully unconscious motion of her hands smoothing the tight, silken surface was a perfect commentary on her husband's teasing. Too late, she saw its application and laughed with the rest of the company.

"Mean? Why, madame, if God does not give you hell, he will wrong you greatly." The shocked frown on her face, however, invited some tempering. "You take very great pains to earn it. Tell me truly—does not that new gown nip you sharply?"

"That's like you," she protested, "never to notice a gown except for some trivial detail."

"Like its comfort, my dear? Women are brave souls to rate that so low. Why, you cannot even laugh without a penitential wince racing straight after the last chuckle."

"This gown was not meant to be laughed in," Dame More explained with a discreet smile. "It is for state occasions, like the coming of the King's gentleman while you were out traipsing through the fields in that ragpicker's cloak of yours. Somebody in the family must make a decent appearance to keep up your state."

"So it isn't vanity at all, but unselfish devotion to your husband, my dear? I must remember that when I'm tempted to tease you again."

"And mend your moralizing, Father," Margaret interjected.

"Here in one moment you were threatening Mother with hell-fire and in the next speaking of immediate retribution and penance done. Sounds inconsistent to me. But now, honestly, is not Mother's gown a pretty fashion?"

"To tell the truth, Margaret," said the older woman, "I think it would look better on you than on anyone my size; but it's hard to think of matters like that when one's hankering for a new fashion."

"Aha! If I'm likely to see this gown in versions to fit the different girths of Anne and Cicely and Elizabeth and Margaret, I'd better get a good look at it now and hale all my criticism out once and for all. Walk away a little, Alice, and let me see you full length in the light. Yes, it is a stately gown," he remarked appreciatively; then he added slowly, "And it looks warm and serviceable." That was evidently so startling a quality to attribute to such a gown that More repented of his sober comment in the instant in which his wife frowned. Quickly, he seized the King's walking staff, strode across to her, and thrust it into her hand as if she were a character in a pageant and he the stage-director. Responsive to his posing, she held the attitude to perfection while he stepped away to appraise the picture.

"The Chancellor's Lady!" he declaimed in the accents of a Court chamberlain. "My dear, you look the rôle for both of us. And as for the gown, I shall not mind at all seeing it multiplied in my family."

Amid the clapping of their little audience, he kissed Dame Alice's hand ceremoniously and escorted her back to her chair by the fireplace. As he bowed before her, he was grateful for the noise and stir their tiny play had evoked, for the breath strangled in his chest, to be freed only in a spasmodic cough when he had turned away. It had not, however, escaped notice by Margaret, whom he caught gazing at him with the anxious, silent question which had remarked his coughing at a stile in the midst of their walk.

Many times in the next few weeks, when the chill, sunless weather aggravated the pain in his chest, More surprised that solicitous look on his daughter's face. He had lived with the irritation long enough to be undismayed by it; yet he had recently been admitting to himself that it had grown far worse since the previous winter. He had even just after the opening of the new session of Parliament combined a family visit to John and Margaret Clement with a plea for the former's most impersonal professional advice. It had been very sobering advice, which he had since found thrusting itself in on his busy thoughts.

So occupied with its questions was he one morning in the last week of January that he did not hear Margaret come into his study, nor had he time to conceal his perplexity in a neutral studiousness. Beyond doubt she had caught him in a dark mood which only the truth could excuse. After a glance at the not-too-pressing work spread out on his desk, Margaret drew a footstool close to his side. Though it was the young matron, decorously coifed, who slid to this favorite seat, she became in the simple action the earnest little five-year-old, who used to sit thus after her mother's death and win him from his most doleful moods with her serious, "What's the matter, Father?" So natural was the question now that he wanted to stroke the rebellious curl of more than twenty years before out of her dark hazel eyes as he repeated the familiar answer to that query:

"Nothing, dear, that life will not mend in God's good time."

"Yes, but meanwhile we ought to know." This was 1532, with Margaret a woman grown; so the remembered drama of her childhood ended with this mature solicitude. "Margaret

Clement told us how worried John is about your health, and —it doesn't seem quite fair that we shouldn't have known first from you. Yes, of course, we realize that you want to spare Mother worry, but sometimes sparing seems a not quite trusting; don't you think so?"

"Perhaps, though you know that I should never think of it that way—at least in connection with telling you something. But this is nothing new, Meg. That pain in my chest. It goes back years and years, as if I were an old soldier nursing his wounds half a lifetime."

"But it's worse recently, Father," she insisted without interrogation in her voice. "What does Doctor John say?"

"That I may miss my father's age by a year or two, but that's no desperate outlook, for he exceeded the Psalmist's allotment by nine years, you remember."

Margaret's smile was scant tribute to the success of his jocularity, for she returned to the central question with a persistence that she must have learned from Dame Alice, More reflected appreciatively, rather than have inherited from her own mother. "On what conditions does John prophesy so patriarchal a term for you?"

"The conditions are always hard, aren't they, Meg? He agreed with all the other doctors I've ever talked to—rest, diet, and medicine. If they'd only say just the last two, I think I could be a good patient, but all three! According to the proverb, I must be very wicked, for rest is the scarcest commodity in all my goods."

"If you must have it, though, Father, you can find time for it. Think of all the time you make for everybody else's needs, for all sorts of business."

"It's so much easier to do that, Meg, than to say, 'No,' to the demands or to take time out just to be sick. You know how lazy I am in some things; that's probably why I never have time free to rest."

"Suppose it's time to get well in," Margaret urged, harking back to the first heading of his protest, "not really time 'just to be sick.' How long did John think you should take?"

"That's the real difficulty, Meg: he would not set any term. As it has been a slow trouble coming, so it may be slow departing. It might be months before there would be any improvement, and then the change might be just by little and little. Why, Meg, I might be a well man again only on the eve of my dying, and much good my health would do me then."

"But, then, you might live on and have some good from it, you paradoxical Father."

"Just length of years, however—what is that worth? That is the question I have been debating with myself. I keep on with my office and the other things and I die a little sooner; I abandon everything and I live a little longer—just barely live. And who can tell that the sword wears out with use or rusts away in idleness the sooner? There never is the same sword to experiment with twice. And Dives in the Gospel is not the only man, well or ill, who has heard, 'Thou fool, this night shall thy soul be required of thee.' So, Meg, I think I shall just work on as wisely as I can with the strength I have in these latter days. No, my dear"—for she had hidden her face against the desk in a sobbing gesture that recalled the anxious child—"I say that in good hope of years to come. Even great doctors like Linacre in his day and our own Clement have been mistaken; you see, being scientists, they must judge on the showing of the body and they cannot count too much on the spirit, the will to live, or on the unaccountable mercy of God. You yourself have proved that to us, Meg." In the remembering, he heard his voice retreat to a husky whisper.

Margaret turned in the quick impulse to comfort him;

her hand, unnaturally cold, seemed to cling to his even in the motion of sympathy. "Yes, I know you have something that the doctors cannot count on in all their patients. But, Father, John Clement knows that, too. It is his being alarmed that frightens me."

"Probably you should read his alarm quite differently. Let us say that, knowing me—and loving me—he cannot be, despite his best efforts, strictly impersonal and professional; so he is needlessly perturbed. I remember Linacre's telling of how quick young doctors are to imagine themselves sick with every new ailment they study. It takes time for them to become indifferent to their own little symptoms; and I suspect that lively concern about their friends and family is for doctors another stage of the same imaginativeness."

"But other doctors have given you the same advice, Father, you said. You cannot count them partial to you in the same way—not all of them, can you?"

"True, lawyer Meg," he said with a little laugh, "but, then, you see, they don't know my tough spirit. So they are under a disadvantage, too, for the giving of advice. Either way we look at it, I must not take the doctors too seriously. Isn't that a fair conclusion?"

"A sophistical one, it seems to me. But I should know by this time that you can be very stubborn on matters that concern your own good." She rose with a little scraping of the stool on the bare oak floor. "Still, I think the good advice may seep in by little and little, and you will alter affairs to gain some rest. Perhaps you can cut down your writing a little—especially against the heretics; that would help."

"Maybe. I can think about that."

"You sound very doubtful and unconvincing."

"That writing seems to me one of the important things that I must keep on doing, Meg." As he rose, his hand rested on a stout, unopened package of suspected books that a messenger from Bishop Stokesley had brought him that morning. Yes, this writing of his was still necessary, in spite of all he had done for four years now.

"Oh, but I know you, Father. Everything you are doing will seem too important to give up; and you will keep on being just as busy as you are now," Margaret groaned. "You must stop letting just anyone that comes take up so much of your time—including me."

She opened the door in the very definite movement of flight, but what she saw outside made her turn back abruptly. "My Lord of Rochester is just dismounting at the house."

"Bishop Fisher? And do you think I should begin by shutting him out?" He laughed at Meg's grimace, very like a delicate echo of the small boy's indelicate sticking out of his tongue. "Think of his age, Meg, and his frailty; yet he has never spared himself."

"You are hopeless in a few things, Father," Margaret exclaimed in a tone between laughter and sighing. "Shall I have them show His Lordship here?"

"I'll come with you. I'm not valetudinarian enough to wait for an older man to come to me," he answered, as he twisted into the cloak that hung on the back of his chair.

A few minutes later, he and Bishop Fisher sat alone before the fire in the hall, for, having paid their respects to him, the rest of the family had returned to their morning occupations. Impulse as he was riding past, Fisher had offered as explanation of this unusual visit that in its casualness carried thought back twenty years, as had some of the details of the just-ended talk with Margaret. Was it but impulse, More asked himself, that had prompted his old friend's stopping? As he studied his silent guest, rubbing his numbed hands above the fire, he noticed many subtle changes that recent months had wrought;

never before had Holbein's sketch of the Bishop seemed so true as now, when the dim eyes of a friend had caught up with the prophetic eyes of the artist. The wind-whipped ruddiness of his face was strange in skin through which the structure of the skull showed as if here were no separate bone and flesh but rather infinitely delicate sculpturing in rose-tinted marble. Seen in sleep, More admitted to himself with a certain sense of shock, this would look to be the face of death; yet he had seldom seen a countenance more passionately and tenaciously alive than this. Of all the men he knew, John Fisher had most surely that incalculable quality of which he and Margaret had just been thinking—the will to live, which could set at naught the most thorough doctor's predictions.

Suddenly the Bishop looked up from his intent gazing into the fire. "No, don't think my coming utterly unconsidered. When I decided to attend the Parliament, I knew I must see you, by hook or by crook. I guess it is crook, though it might have been better had I contrived to be night-halted at your very door. Fortunate to find shelter, you know."

Though More could guess the significance of this irony, he must have looked genuinely puzzled, for Fisher laughed merrily.

"Tell me," he said, almost mischievously, "did you know that I was not summoned to Parliament?"

"No." The simplicity of such an omission would have been funny were it not ominous.

"Neither Tunstall nor I. Somebody must have had an inspiration about the easy way to achieve unanimity in Convocation and the House of Lords. But it was too easy. He should have found ways of isolating Rochester from all news; I dare say Durham may not hear about this Parliament till it's all over—that is, if anything keeps my courier from getting there." He smiled at More's appreciative chuckle. "I suppose that's meddlesome of me, but the crassness of the omission called for meddling."

"Could it have been accident?" More asked as much in curiosity about the Bishop's answer as in attempted exculpation of the fact.

"Accident? It would be arrant superstition to think so pretty a coincidence due to chance. No, much as I believe in the Christian charity of suspending judgments, there seems to me no possibility of glozing this situation with gentle interpretations. We were not summoned. Now I'm curious to know why, and I'm more alert than ever to protest if protest be needed."

"Naturally, for not summoning you serves as both a kind of confession—if you rule out accident—and a warning. That was foolishly done as well as high-handedly. But that is not the end of the experience for you, my lord, if I read the twinkle in your eye aright."

"By no means. When the King heard that I had come—I wonder what he really said—he sent for me. So I waited for him yesterday morning close by the chapel to greet him on the way to Mass. And when he saw me there, just for a second his look wavered between amazement and the most complete malevolence I've ever seen on human face; but when he spoke, his words were gracious as sunshine and smooth as honey, 'My Lord of Rochester, I did not mean to put you to this inconvenience. They had told me that you were ill; so I rejoice not only at your coming, but also at your recovery. Now I shall look to have the benefits of your advice as of old.' And all the Court smiled at their cue; they had not seen that first involuntary expression."

"But sometimes, Your Reverence, the King, like all the rest of us, wears an expression not too easily or clearly decipherable. We have to take a man's profession of concern as sincerely meant."

"God mend my evil, suspicious nature, then! But I heard to-day that Henry was very angry afterwards at not finding me still waiting his pleasure. Yes, I slipped away, for I had said my Mass at six o'clock; so it seemed to me no irreverence not to join the Court for theirs at ten. So much for one bulletin. You may hear other versions of it at Court, and much as it sounds now like old wives' gossip, it may grow worse before it dies from exaggeration. More seriously, how are you feeling? You needn't look so surprised, and don't think I have taken Thomas Cromwell into my service. No, I know that you have been ill simply because one of your rowers told one of mine, over a can of ale, I suppose, that you have had a bad cough lately."

"The cough is true, but I can hardly call that illness. The spring will ease it—sunlight and fresh air again."

"Spring? I pray you may be better before then, for there are three weary, busy months ahead of us. Be careful. These two years and more in the Chancery have been hard on you, but you have been a valiant champion against the Philistines."

"Champion? What have I done? What could I hope to do?" More asked miserably.

"Just holding on, I know, doesn't seem spectacular achievement, but it has been sometimes the noblest work in human history—partly because there is no personal satisfaction, no sense of dreams achieved, in it. More than once recently I have waked up at night and wondered what might have happened in the last years if you were not Chancellor, if the Council were all of a piece. You think you haven't done much; think, too, of what has not been done because you stood for values and principles against a standardless lot. Yes," he added in lighter tone for he could not help perceiving More's discomfort, "Rochester gets all the news, and that by fair means. When even a man's enemies speak well of him, his friends can be sure of their ground; and there's the case you stand in. That's true of another young man, too, Reginald Pole."

The "too" struck More as very amusing, for he was by many more years older than Pole than was Fisher older than he; but the inappropriate word passed with a smile of deprecation between them.

"Pole," the Bishop resumed, "is going abroad again. Had you heard? He has defied the King utterly."

"I had heard only that he preferred Colet's house at Sheen to the grandeur of York, and that he had no mind to be a prelate."

"That's true enough. By the way, your friend Lee at York has heavy work ahead of him."

"Yes, but Tunstall and he will work well together in the North."

"I could wish he were a stronger man, for soon there will be but one archbishop again. Warham is failing fast. But to return to Pole—he has let the King know that he cannot support the divorce and that he will not remain silent; so he has won leave to go into exile."

"Exile!" A swift feeling of pity for the King's young scholar-cousin moved behind the word. To be sure, Pole must have spent already about a third of his life in study abroad; yet that fact could not diminish the tragic difference between the travel from which a man may come freely home and that which it is hazardous to end. And on the present, unequivocal terms, Pole had gained permission to go into exile.

"That means, you see, that he will be a power for the right now," Fisher said exultantly. "A strong man, and he has chosen." Then his voice dropped to a playful tone. "Has not this been just about the proper length for a casual, wayside call? Oh, Thomas, I cannot tell you how glad I am to find you not really ill." The warmth of his handclasp confirmed the simple earnestness of those words.

Before the Bishop released his hand, he added carelessly, "By the way, it may not interest you, but I have suggested to the Imperial Ambassador that he write me only in cipher if he see any need of writing at all. I trust M. de Chapuys implicitly in his devotion to the Queen's cause; still one never knows what may happen to ordinary letters."

This veiled warning, then, confirmatory of More's own half-shaped fear, was the central purpose of Rochester's visit? Not a cheering thought, they seemed to agree in the gravity of their parting.

CHAPTER XII

HITHERTO More had not greatly admired Dr. Richard Curwen's preaching, to which he had listened on other Sunday afternoons when he had been at Court. It was ordinarily too unctuous to be stimulating. So, like many of the courtiers around him, he did not doubt, he slipped comfortably away in thought as soon as he had heard enough to assure him that this was to be a commonplace sermon well-larded with flattery for the royal palate.

As often before in these early months of 1532, when Parliament was girding at the property and the privileges of the Church, he recalled gratefully the visit Bishop Fisher had paid him, as if inconsequentially, "in passing." Such genuine personal concern in these distressing days touched him deeply. The actions of this Parliament had been drawing the perplexities so swiftly towards a climax that More had felt increasingly both his impotence in the government and the disfavor in which he stood with his associates in the Council.

To be sure, near the end of February Archbishop Warham had uttered his protest against all the measures enacted in the present Parliament derogatory to the Pope's authority or to the privileges of his own See. If only Warham in the preceding year could have led Convocation to unified resistance in the sad three days of their ignominy! This protest would go down in history, no doubt, but it could not undo the great surrender. His Grace, weary and ill and old, could not live to see very much of what might ensue; and the judgment of history might be kind to him, for he had had no precedents to guide him nor any light by which to read the future. With Saint Paul all who bore responsibility in this England could say, "Videmus nunc per speculum in aenigmate." Were the words of the King's new title but a form, or were they as fateful as the "Mane, Thecel, Phares" that Daniel interpreted, at least the terms of the Archbishop's protest would accompany them into the judgment of posterity. "The privileges, the prerogatives, the preëminence, or the liberty of the metropolitan church of Christ of Canterbury"—so much lingering in memory prompted the thought that the mighty words in the whole protest were substantially the same in Latin and in English, as if by that fact the genius of language would confirm the blending of cultures upon which he liked to insist when some of his scholarly friends grew disdainful of the vulgar tongues. Perhaps this problem for the Church in England was a matter of more than a monarch's ambition: it might be a phase of a great cultural problem. Could not England, however, be proudly insular and national and yet be the true heir, and no stepchild, of ancient culture? And could she not, without defrauding her genius, keep her full allegiance to a united Christendom?

With thought of the Archbishop's utterance came the recollection of Tunstall's also after the Northern Convocation, as he had prophesied it must, had followed the Southern in surrender. Analyst as he was, he had ventured to point out that ambiguity usually intends its words to have one sense in the dictating of them and another in the accepting, so that men are led to believe them a mere form until it becomes expedient to interpret them to the letter. And peacemaker as he was, he had offered the phrase "in temporalibus, post Christum" to clarify the title, the apparent presumption of which he thought repugnant to the will of Christendom. With but the softening of a subjunctive, he had dared to assert, "But if these words be understood to apply to things spiritual, the King may not be supreme head of the Church, since this is not permissible by the law of Christ." Though More had speculated as to whether his own handling of the dilemma, were he a bishop, would not have differed from Tunstall's, he had found this expostulation a heartening one. It must have troubled Henry at least a little, for Tunstall, like Fisher, More remembered with a chill of concern for his friends, had not been summoned to this session of Parliament.

Though such thoughts consorted ill with the serene, uncourtly beauty of the Observants' Church at Greenwich, to which their company had swaggered or minced or strolled from the palace, bringing their preacher with them, the sermon still made no great demand on attention. Dr. Curwen had already been speaking for twenty minutes or so in a vague tirade against Friar William Peto's sermon here before the King on Easter Sunday. Paying enough heed to note the headings under which the royal chaplain arraigned the Provincial of the Observants, More half-wished that he had kept Easter here instead of at Chelsea, for that discourse of Friar William's must have been as courageous in its way as Dean Colet's famous sermon on Good Friday on the eve of war with France. Perhaps even more courageous, for Henry's temper had changed much in the intervening nineteen years, and though a Christian King could view the denunciation of war somewhat academically, he could not miss the personal challenge—if Dr. Curwen's shrill reiterations were faithful to the Franciscan's plea—in Friar William's warning that he should put away covetous, worldly-minded, flattering counselors, lest they make him another King Ahab.

After a dramatic pause, the preacher flung his arms wide so that his lacy surplice fluttered as if a great wind were blowing round him in the pulpit. "This man, then," he cried, "who by his profession has renounced worldly affairs, has presumed to meddle with them and needlessly to exhort our gracious Lord the King. Listening to him here, I was scandalized at his arrogating to himself blasphemously the grace of knowing the mind of God. Did he not with base insinuations declare that we know not what monarchs who have ruled wilfully and oppressively—his words, my friends, not mine—lie now in the pit of hell, like Dives in the Gospel crying to the poor in heaven whom they had abused? It is a moving picture, but a fantastic, even—God forgive the man and count his false doctrine ignorance, not malice—a blasphemous one. . . .

"I agree, indeed, with my misguided brother in this much: that God has set the Prince to be complete sovereign within his realm; but to say that and in the same breath, as did this proud friar, to talk of accountability, as though a King were some sniveling bailiff, misses being impiety only through the charity of the listeners. You, O gracious King, chose to spare the man—to his amendment, we may all pray. Believe, Sire, that he has some notable parts; else he were not Provincial of his Order."

Prompt to that invitation, lips curled among the courtiers, and a hissing titter skipped from bay to bay of the somber nave, in which this rustling, perfumed congregation seemed as much out of place as would the brown-robed friars in the feverish gayety of the neighboring palace. More could not see the King's face, darkened by the cloth of state above him, but he could imagine how bland a salve this discourse was laying on the wounded pride of Easter Day. Quick on that thought followed his noticing one among the Observants, whom he realized now he had been watching for some time. Out of the uniformity of the brown figures in the shadows of the rood loft this one arresting face, now averted towards the high altar, looked with the incalculable blend of peace and embattled passion which is the enthusiast's. "Wholeness, indivisibility,"—with such concepts pointing the way through meditation, More found himself feeling for some remembered, but not immediately apprehensible, quotation from the philosophers; and in the search he had missed some of Dr. Curwen's oratory.

"How dare any man," he was demanding, "say that the King has not chosen his counselors wisely? To say that is to dishonor His Majesty's judgment. No doubt"—his voice grew rich with the unction of a premeditated rhetorical flourish—"in the day of our Blessed Savior there were self-appointed critics, Pharisees, who thought that our Lord chose His servants unwisely; had they been consulted, they would have named quite other men than the holy apostles and disciples.

"All minds, all hearts, all souls within his realm—these must be His Majesty's; else do we diminish his sovereignty and impugn the wisdom of God, Who has set the King above and beyond the judgment of all men. We must put away half-loyalties and cavilings about the dictates of misguided consciences and rest with undivided fidelity in the will of the King. . . ."

Yes, More reflected with head bowed and eyes veiled from the scrutiny of young Viscount Rochford on one side and the Marquis of Exeter on the other, this was unabashed exposition of the royal supremacy, a doctrine that outdid in abjectness the time-honored flattery of sovereigns. "A few words. What do they change?" Henry had asked about a year before. Such a eulogy as they were listening to, with its irreverent analogies, was part of the answer. Evidently the saving clause had been meant to be no more effectual than Bishop Tunstall had feared. Even the apologetic intensity of the preacher was finding its natural ending, however, and he came dramatically to the thrasonical wish that Friar William were present to hear himself thus confuted and to answer if he could.

The smug voice hesitated; the congregation stirred excitedly and stiffened into attention. When More lifted his head, the friar whose intensity he had observed—Warden Henry Elstowe, he could see now by the light through the clerestory windows—was standing close to the foot of the rood, a lean brown figure with hands outstretched above the upturned faces.

"Your Majesty," he cried in a resonant voice that silenced the last of the incipient murmur, "before any man leaves this church, I shall, with your august permission, answer for my absent superior, whom we have all heard challenged by this eloquent doctor. I am the warden of this house, where one guest has mocked and insulted another, and I can speak only the blunt, uncourtly speech of the truth, as I see it. Our Provincial is absent on business of the Order, as Your Grace knows, not out of cowardice, as your chaplain has suggested. I shall be brief, Your Majesty." Henry had not even nodded his permission, but, taken by surprise, he held himself braced forward on his elbows. More could imagine what thunder was gathering on his brow while, unperturbed, the warden hurried on in his protest.

"In the house of God, Sire, we stand each man in his degree, unprotected by the lying flattery that makes hard—not easy and pleasant, as some men think—the way of the rich and the powerful and the lordly of the earth. Kingship is the inestimable gift of God, as Friar William declared to you on Easter, but like every gift of God it is weighted with responsibility. If the earthly peace and security of thousands of subjects are in the hands of a Prince, how reverend, serious, and devoted to the honor of the Prince and of his people must be the counselors who uphold those hands. From him to whom much has been given much shall be exacted. For twenty-three years, Sire, we have thanked God for your wise and beneficent rule. Do not mar that thanksgiving by any lessening of your vigilance. Be warned that there are sycophants and timeservers

—yes, and false prophets such as lured King Ahab to the worship of Baal—always seeking to worm their way into your confidence. They serve the lying gods of this world, vanity and folly, covetousness and lust, and hatred of the good way that is hard; like the priests of Baal, they will call upon their god in the day of reckoning, and the true prophet will say with Elias: 'Cry with a louder voice, for he is a god, and perhaps he is talking, or in an inn, or on a journey, or perhaps he is asleep and must be waked.' O Sire, trust the men who give you hard warnings, but distrust those who, vowed to the service of God, which should make men unafraid, dishonor Him by fair, flattering words that do you no honor. That, I believe, is what Friar William would reiterate in answer to the challenge of Dr. Curwen, who has spoken like one of those false priests who led Ahab to destruction. Judge, Sire, in your wisdom, which of the two has spoken the more truly to you. May the Holy Trinity keep you long in that wisdom, Your Grace!"

When Henry with an impatient glance at the warden, whose resolute grip on the parapet of the rood screen contradicted the humble inclination of his head, had nodded curtly to Dr. Curwen, More remembered that the chaplain still stood in the pulpit. Flushed and shaken-looking, the latter hurried through a lame peroration. Was Henry listening to him or was he meditating on the exhortation of Warden Elstowe, one more evidence that discerning and fearless men were rousing to oppugn the headstrong royal will?

Within the range of More's downcast vision, amazement still held most of the courtiers paralyzed. The King's rising, however, effected some release for them, especially in the awed murmur, "Who is he?" Immediately after the King's departure, in an angry striding up the nave, had made their own movement decorous, Viscount Rochford thrust past More so violently that the latter was curious to watch his subsequent action. In a dozen steps he stood close enough to Warden Elstowe, who had just emerged from the loft stairway, to strike him, as his threatening posture indeed suggested he might do.

"You proud, beggarly coward," young Boleyn shouted in a voice that needed no eavesdropping. "If you were a man, you'd have my glove in your face. Being what you are, though, you ought to be drowned like any other mongrel."

Friar Elstowe lifted his head as imperturbably as if all the energy of his remonstrance had burned itself out, and, though the light was but uncertain where they stood before the screen, he seemed to smile at the irate nobleman.

"Sir," he said, in tones as quiet as those with which he might have thanked Rochford for a compliment, "these threats are for courtiers."

Much as mere human curiosity longed to observe the sequel of that rebuke, More moved beyond hearing with the current of exodus from the church. Just by the door Norfolk lolled with one elbow resting on the holy water stoup; as he sighted More, he reached eagerly for his arm.

"Tell me, Scholar Thomas," he said, drawing him to one side in the porch, "did Ahab have anything to do with Jezebel —her father?"

"Her husband; she drew him to the worship of Baal."

The Duke laughed as at some overpowering jest. "Better yet! I thought I had them right, though I'm no Bible-reader. You know, those friars have a wit. Jezebel! Wait till I tell Wiltshire."

"My lord!" More had not realized that application before. In a moment of genuine anxiety for the Observants, he wondered if they had meant all that their allusion implied.

"God's body! Wait till I tell Wiltshire," the Duke, untroubled by any scruples, repeated. "He doesn't know Scripture any better than I do, I wager."

When Parliament reconvened in a few days, More still had not heard how the King's wrath was to move against the bold warden of the Greenwich Franciscans, but that some chastisement would be visited on his temerity, no one at Court doubted. In his youth, Henry might have matched wit with wit and shown a brave man's respect for courage in another; he had changed in nothing, however, more markedly than in the dulling and the coarsening of his wit, which he could no longer trust to be as a fine Damascus blade at his service. Unaccountably enough, as More waited to speak the King's pleasure to the Commons in the Chapter House of Westminster Abbey, his thought dallied with speculation as to the King's probable treatment of Friar Elstowe and his superior, who would undoubtedly suffer, too, for his original attack on the false counselors of His Majesty.

Speaker Audley was explaining that the Chancellor and the lords who accompanied him—how impressive they looked in their furred robes and their gold, More reflected, as if they were truly noble men who were only shrewd calculators of their own profit!—had urgent business to present. Done with his exhortation that the Commons hearken to the voice of the King thus deigning to speak among them, the Speaker smiled with the diluted, obsequious blandness which had been More's chief impression of him from the time he had first encountered Audley in the Cardinal's household.

As More uttered the conventional salutations of the King, he noted compassionately the restlessness of the House, a far less peaceful group than usually sat in this octagonal room. Three weeks before they had begged that the Parliament be dissolved, but instead it had been merely adjourned for Easter;

and they who had already complained of the weariness and the cost of their attendance had been forced to spend Easter away from their homes or to incur fresh labor and expense in traveling thither and back. They were men sick of a business for which they had no great heart; and that business had been the legislation in despite of the Pope and the petition against the Ordinaries! Anyone who believed these apathetic or harassed burgesses to be passionately disaffected should see them this morning, looking with one accord a single disgruntled query: "What more?"

Having completed the brief introduction which his state and the dignity of the Commons prescribed, he launched his message proper: the King's request for a subsidy to fortify the northern marches. "It is long," he concluded, "through the grace of God, since we have been troubled with the costs of war; so a moderate expenditure to avoid the grievous one, in money and goods and human life, of actual warfare should commend itself to all loyal men. His Majesty asks, therefore, your deliberation on what aid and grant you will make so that, when you go home, you may have the assurance of peace in the land. As he has ever been a good and solicitous lord to you, and as you hope for the continuance of his favor, he charges you to weigh the matter most earnestly."

Amid an ambiguous murmur from the men before him, he bowed to the Speaker and returned to his seat. Though there was precedent for the silence of the Commons in the presence of the Chancellor, to whom the Speaker alone replied—he remembered with a chuckle for the occasion when Wolsey had found the House loftily muted—there was warrant also for the Chancellor's staying long enough to make sure that the King's will was clear. When, therefore, Audley had thanked him perfunctorily and turned to the burgesses to bid them ask any questions they wished, there was nothing startling in the jerky rising of a small, hawk-faced man on the left fringe of the assembly. That he should stand thus promptly surprised More only because he had felt that this man had ceased to listen as soon as he had revealed the tenor of the King's request; to the latter half, at least, of his speech he had thought him morosely inattentive. With the quick look which wins a little circle of quiet in a restless audience, the small man waited for a moment as if uncertain of the impulse that had thrust him up.

"Mr. Speaker," he began in a voice that shook slightly, "we do not doubt the royal anxiety for the peace of the realm nor the wisdom of these lords who have come to us this morning, but we too have eyes and ears to perceive the state of the kingdom. Who says that the Scots will invade England? Didn't they have enough of us at Flodden? Surely, if there were real ground for this fear, the northern men here would know about it; they would already have been petitioning the King to see to their defenses. I'm not a fighting man myself—" The laughter which interrupted this declaration trailed away in an uncertain murmur. Did the rest of the House sympathize with the scared temerity that was speaking here? Or were they only restraining the desire to hoot it down? In the necessary pause, however, the man took heart so that he spoke on more confidently than before. "What I mean by that is that I cannot judge how great the danger looks from the military point of view. But I want to ask a question—for information. Does anyone think that the Scots can attack us without foreign aid? And who's going to help them?"

So definitely a question for information did this seem that the Speaker looked to More: "My Lord Chancellor, can you answer as to these matters?"

"Only that the King's Grace has had reason to think the French not averse to helping the Duke of Albany. No doubt, he is anxious to avenge the very defeat at Flodden to which the honorable member refers." It seemed fair enough to disclose the one item of information offered the Council to give color to the King's request for this subsidy.

The little man smiled apologetically, perhaps in admission that he had not really expected an answer to his challenge; he went on lamely: "But we have been led to think that the French are hand in glove with us, and now we don't trust them. As I see it, the foreign power we ought to spend any time conciliating is the Emperor. He can do us more harm than any other ruler, and he has reason to be angry, the way his aunt has been treated. It's a disgrace to the nation. There's the real danger to peace, because if the Queen is not the King's true wife and the Princess is not legitimate heir to the throne—well, where are we?"

This plain speaking had so disturbed the wonted blandness of Audley's face that he sat impotent, glowering at the blunt inquirer and glancing fearfully at Norfolk and the other lords. Mere unregenerate curiosity made More wish that he could turn enough to read their faces; but the least such motion would admit cause for embarrassment in a straightforward question which, after all, did greatly concern the Commons and the welfare of the realm. Probably having surprised even himself by his audacity and having grown sensitive to the hostility of the Chancellor's noble escort, the protester hurried to the purpose of his argument.

"We all know how the people at large feel about this business—we've just come back from our districts, and we've heard people talking more this time than ever before. Therefore, Mr. Speaker, I move that we humbly petition the King's Grace to take back his lady, the Queen, and put an end to the murmuring of the people and the danger of foreign harm to the kingdom."

There could be no doubt of the general approval of this motion, for several voices hurtled together in an indistinguishable seconding of it. Fatuous, then, as was Speaker Audley's demand:

"Do you mean that as a motion?" it gave More time to rise and address him.

"Mr. Speaker," he said while the lords of his escort, divining his purpose, rose too, "this is a new matter which it is the privilege of the House to discuss thoroughly, without prejudice to any man for the uttering of his opinion, before it is communicated to His Majesty. We shall withdraw now, and it is as if we had not heard the proposal of this question."

As the import of this comment struck the man who had spoken, his dark face blanched noticeably; here was, More thought, no heroic defiance, but a sturdy, impolitic honesty which he himself liked thoroughly.

"Who is he?" Norfolk asked harshly in the moment of their passing into the cloister of the abbey.

"Is it not better that we should not know, Your Grace?" More countered as quietly as possible.

"A west-country man, perhaps, to judge by his speech," remarked Suffolk. "Cromwell will identify him for us."

"For that matter, the Chancellor could ask his sons-in-law," Norfolk insisted truculently.

The shadow of broken faith chilled More till he shivered in the slight involuntary spasm that the mind can evoke from the body. "My lords," he urged in a calmness belying his inward distress, "it is the ancient privilege of the Commons to speak their minds with impunity. I am sorry we could not have foreseen this incident and left in time."

"I'm not sorry," Wiltshire interrupted angrily. "There's too much nonsense about privilege. Those friars at Greenwich, and now this gallows bird! Bah! And those who defend them are as bad as they themselves—I don't care who they are. Privilege for these upstart, seditious traders and beggarly Observants! Sir Thomas, I'm surprised at your patience with these riffraff commoners."

More could have laughed at the exaggerated emphasis the Earl placed on his modest title, as if thereby to divorce him from his order; instead, however, he remarked, still with a forced calm: "His Grace found me, my lord, in the Commons, where honest speaking, though wrong, has never been counted sedition. And I have ever heard that blood is thicker than water."

It was Norfolk, recovered from his choler, who laughed for them all: "And there's some saw about the pot and the kettle, Wiltshire."

The dark flush that seemed to change even the contours of Thomas Boleyn's long face was not due wholly to the resounding slap that his brother-in-law laid on his heavy shoulders.

As they emerged from the precincts of the abbey, More wondered whether such a muttering of storm as they had just heard —and there had been a few other signs of resistance in both houses during this session—preluded the gathering of effective opposition, or whether it came too late to do more than foil the supineness of Parliament.

CHAPTER XIII

How loud sounded the scraping of chairs into place around the Council table after the silence that the King's coming had brought like a sword among his councilors. Like a sword. As they waited the King's words, More could feel the anger of Wiltshire with Bishop Gardiner restrained only as if the pacifier had thrust a blade into their disputation; in the moment of phrasing that impression in thought, he groaned to himself over the vexing habit that worries have of running together in recollection. Here he was thinking in terms of the strange book which he had been reading late the night before—the unsigned *Treatise Concerning the Division between the Spiritualty and the Temporalty*. Who, calling himself a good Christian and expressing the most plausible, mild-mannered regret at the recent lamentable "great unquietness and great breach of charity through all the realm," could have written this little book that emptied its casks of oil on the fires of division? And was it but ineptitude, tragically culpable as that could be, or was it malice that had thus confused oil and water or fire and flood? That book would need much careful appraisal, he told himself as he strove to put it out of mind in order to concentrate on whatever might be the afternoon's business. And by this time, the whole Council was ready for the King's explanation of their meeting.

"My lords," he spoke abruptly with a sudden massing of energy in his flabby face, "if what I hear be true, this Convocation is still contentious and stubborn, little inclined to the obedience they profess." Though Henry looked studiously down the long table before him, More could see the curious glances that Gardiner's chief baiters cast at him, glances of which the Bishop himself was aware, for in his fever-sallowed face the old dark hue of health mantled unnaturally. He sat very still, however, his eyes unadmittingly attentive to his own outspread fingers rising and falling soundlessly on the edge of the table. "They had our simple, unmistakable request for their acceptance last Friday; but forsooth, they could not decide on it straightway. Even though they adjourned then till yesterday for the express purpose of debating the matter, each man with himself, they seem to have been of little better mind when they met yesterday. I have heard that there was unseemly talk of compromise and limitation rising from a narrow, untrusting spirit. My Lord of Winchester, what can you tell us of the session yesterday? Is the matter settled? And are these ugly rumors false?" The inquisitorial hurtling of the questions must have pleased the men who had been heckling Gardiner before the King's arrival; they gave no sign, however, beyond the fixing of their hitherto covert gaze on the Bishop's face.

After a little start of acknowledgment of the King's direct address, Gardiner seemed to have retreated into deep consideration of how he could answer. "Your Grace," he finally began slowly, "your information should have included also the fact that Convocation meets again to-morrow. That means that the matter is not ended and that any report of our action"—after stressing *any* markedly, he had relapsed into a forced neutrality of tone, which broke off in definite hesitation—"is premature. Is not thorough understanding of the matter more important, Your Grace, than haste?"

"In so clear a business both are possible—unless the clergy pride themselves on a refractory spirit," the King retorted. "But what happened? What was proposed?"

"Sire"—this time Gardiner's answer strode directly into the

field—"I am not the Archbishop nor his proctor, who alone should make report to the King of the proceedings of Convocation. By ancient custom our debate is secret and privileged."

The quick tide of anger that purled about the table ebbed before the King's mirthless, politic smile. "I was forgetting that you are a bishop now, my lord. As you say, the debate of Convocation is by old custom privileged," he agreed with ironic emphasis. "Far be it from us to ask any man to speak against his conscience. We shall wait until to-morrow. But, my lords, what do you advise if this dallying continues even then?"

"As Your Grace has said," the Earl of Wiltshire began testily, "it is too simple a request you have made to justify such scrupulous discussion. Can you not demand agreement to-morrow?"

"But how to enforce the demand?" Thomas Cromwell spoke with so little movement of his thin lips that his thoughts seemed to have revealed themselves without utterance. His scanty eyebrows puckered nervously before he went on. "You must have some potent threat, Your Grace. Parliament grows anxious because there is talk of the plague hereabout. Can you not command that Convocation prorogue to-morrow—till autumn?"

"And have them leave this business conveniently unsettled?" Norfolk interjected.

"By no means, my lord," Cromwell explained patiently. "Let the demand to the clergy to-morrow be a two-handed instrument. If His Majesty would say that the three articles must be acknowledged and the sessions must be ended to-morrow, the business would be speedily done, and the clergy could go comfortably home without fear of carrying the plague with them to spread abroad in the country."

"If Parliament has been talking about such fears, Master Cromwell," Gardiner expostulated, "be assured that Convocation has not; so that will not stand as a pretext for hastening action. The length of time we take for debate is our own concern, for the time and the expense are ours."

"But the matter is the King's," Norfolk insisted as if the application of a little common sense here would end all debate. "We don't care how long Convocation spends on its own affairs."

"After this, it will have none." The bitterness of Gardiner's rejoinder had suffered no dilution from his accustomed urbanity and tact. But with that sharp utterance he seemed to recollect himself; and though his lips were parted as if for continued protest, he said no more.

The half-dozen unguarded words, however, had penetrated the King's armor of composure as had none of the earlier debate. In a long silence he sat frowning at the jewels on his puffy, clenched hand, while about the table the stillness broke in the score of tiny sounds that rise and fall unnoticed in the normal noise of a company. Finally, Henry spoke as angrily as if the pause had been nourishing, not mitigating, his wrath:

"If there be any doubt of the justice of our articles submitted to the clergy, we must deal with that doubt now. You, my Lord of Winchester, I excuse from further comment on them, for they concern your order, and I do not question that you have spoken eloquently on them in Convocation." Quick to the elaborate irony in his voice the sneers gathered on the faces of Gardiner's enemies. Mildly the King continued, "But what have the rest of you to say?"

"Sire," said the Marquis of Exeter, who had frowned at Cromwell's dictatorial speaking, "I for one have only heard about these articles—not that I am objecting to them."

"You were absent on Thursday, my lord," Cromwell replied; then he added hastily, for Exeter resented the imputation of the half-truth, "though we all know that you and the Chancellor were engaged in His Majesty's business."

"And you have read and approved them, have you not, my Lord Chancellor?" The King turned to More.

"They were brought to me, Sire, as business concluded; so there was no question of my approval." More held himself to answering the question, though his pulse leaped at the possibility of such an opening of discussion as would permit the protest that he had been meditating.

If Henry recognized the drift of this answer, he contented himself with an exculpating lift of his thin brows. "Since there is some uncertainty among our councilors as to exactly what we are about, let us review the matter. My Lord of Winchester, you need not stay if this repetition will weary you; but do as you wish."

Though Gardiner murmured his thanks, he evidently refused to take the royal permission as a command; so the King turned to Cromwell:

"Master Cromwell, will you read the articles?"

The latter had already pulled a paper from the sheaf which stood beside him in the ample seat of his chair. As he read, his voice was harsh and perfunctory in resentment of what must seem to him a needless concession to the scruples of some of his fellow-councilors. In accordance with a practice that always struck More as quaint, the very words of compliment with which the clergy were to preface their submission had been dictated in the framing of the demands. Then followed in all the superfluity of unctuous wording the three items of the required surrender: that the clergy would make no new canons, constitutions, or ordinances without the King's license and royal assent and authority; that they would commit the whole body of existing canons to the examination of the King and of a commission of thirty-two members, half lay and half clerical, of the King's appointing; and that canons ruled obnoxious by this body should be abrogated.

As he followed the reading of these items, More remembered his amazement of a few days past when the document had been offered to him to read; then, even though he had recalled the grievous surrender of Convocation in the year before, he had said to himself, "This is too much. Convocation will not yield its centuries-old freedom of action." Now, however, as he listened to Cromwell's rehearsal of the demands thrust upon the clergy, he wondered whether there would be the natural resistance which he had assumed. Twice already, it seemed, Convocation had discussed the matter; and though there had been no startlingly abject acceptance of the proposals, neither had there been the prompt, united rejection that More had thought inevitable. But had he really thought it inevitable, he now asked himself, or had he only hoped for a hopeless action?

The papers crackled in Cromwell's hands, and he was through. The Marquis of Exeter coughed apologetically.

"My Lord Marquis?" the King said quietly, looking at him.

"Oh, no, Your Grace, I have no objection. Perfectly clear."

Though the King was staring at Gardiner, as if he had not really expected any protest from the Marquis, the Bishop's face was unrevealingly composed. Bold as he had been to disregard the King's suggestion that he leave the Council Chamber, he was not rash enough to ignore the command expressed in His Majesty's "You I excuse from further comment."

"Then, saving my Lord of Winchester's privilege reserved," said the King with the dismissing smile of the moment when a worry has not been realized, "we are agreed."

Though it was an assertion and no question, it was the opening for what More knew to be a final step. Were he a man of no imagination, his secret consciousness was telling itself, he would not hear panic knocking at his heart now as he said, "Your Grace, since what I would say does not come too late, as I had feared till this afternoon it would, may I speak as though this matter were newly proposed in Council?"

The dryness of his throat eased a little at the King's astonished nod, so that he did not hear his next words cracking harshly in the echo of the starry-vaulted chamber. Since the King had nodded, he could observe as unimportant the subtle expressions of vexation the table round; only Norfolk's gesture of restraint—a slant-wise lifted hand—did he notice with full appreciation of its meaning. It was kind of the Duke to try to give the only advice the moment allowed, but unavailing, for here Norfolk's and his own understanding had diverged irreconcilably.

"Sire, these articles strike at something so central and so ancient in the rights of the Church that the clergy seem to me to do well in debating them thoroughly. Even were they to dissent from this request, Your Grace, that action would not be necessarily disloyal, for we should respect the loyalty of Convocation to its responsibility. The liberties of the Church in England, we all remember, have been one of the glories of our country. And though I am no political philosopher, I cannot help thinking that the scheme of the Christian state as we have known it in England, wherein the different orders of society coöperate with mutual respect, yet keep their several independencies and their freedom of action, is a scheme not to be disturbed except at grave hazard. And though Convocation may rely on the fair-dealing wisdom of Your Highness, what is laid aside on a sunny day cannot be easily recovered on a stormy one, if it chance to come, as it may in the inscrutable fullness of time. This is a solemn matter; and I should be a recreant councilor did I not say, 'Had I been here at the first proposal of these articles, I should have urged against them.' So now if Convocation, weighing the precious rights of which they are trustees and holding their fealty thereto as a loyalty fully compatible with their high duty to you, plead to be relieved from this demand, I urge, Your Grace, that you be still their magnanimous and kindly lord."

In the moment of his ceasing to speak, the room felt strangely empty as if, having swum through dark and angry waters, he had come ashore in a hostile waste. The men around him did not speak—it would have been easier to bear their crying out against him—but they were retreating so far from him in their judgment of what he had just said that he knew that no more than two of them would keep even the pretense of friendship with him henceforth. And Gardiner's friendship, thought cried out in the moment when shame strove to silence it, he did not greatly depend on; for though the Bishop had framed the creditably "unsatisfactory" reply of the Ordinaries to the complaints of the Commons and had showed his mettle to-day, he gave little promise of being a rock of shade and refreshment in a weary land. He had till this year been almost culpably pliant. Yet Gardiner alone of all the Council would have comprehended what he was talking about; Wiltshire and Cromwell and some of the others, caring nothing for the Church or for the State, would cherish his opposition in just its bare externals; Norfolk, caring as little as they for Church and State, would shake his head uncomprehendingly and say—what were his words?—"Thomas, Thomas, I used to think I could make a diplomat out of you." But unless the gathering anger were too fierce, the Duke would stand by him as one would stand by a child or a fool caught in a fault for which he was not to be held wilfully responsible. That was not understanding, however. No, only Gardiner knew what he was talking about, what counted far beyond all considerations of personal fortune—the principles of justice and righteousness and good order in this earthly kingdom; only Gardiner and King Henry. And with the latter, this comprehension—whether, indeed, he would ever admit it or not

—was the end, not the seal, of friendship. How still he was sitting! Though More had heard much recently of Henry's glowering, he could read now on his face merely a deliberating, somewhat hurt amazement. Forthright anger, free of ambiguity, would have been easier to bear.

Perhaps a full minute had passed when the King, stirred it seemed by the accidental clinking of his golden collar against the table, looked up and down the silent rank of his councilors before he said with an unreasonably exasperating calm:

"It is the part of a faithful councilor to give what he feels to be just counsel, however unwelcome he may fear it to be." Such copy-book sententiousness was like Henry in his most leonine—or should that be feline?—moments; but its unction bewildered More. Had he accomplished nothing in this last time when he could speak as one of the King's Council? He had heard of gamblers staking everything on a single cast, and, having lost it, desperately flinging life and their hope of salvation itself away. In this instant he felt that he could understand their temptation, though by the grace of God it did not assail him.

"If this be just counsel," Wiltshire growled, "Your Grace is right to complain that the clergy are but half your subjects. And some of the laity are no better, it seems."

A deprecating glance from the King, however, interrupted the tirade that Wiltshire was launching. "Remember, my lord, that the Council is one of the privileged bodies of our realm." Though the rebuke was spoken almost laughingly, More wondered whether he had missed the ironic intonation that had pointed the King's remarks earlier in the session. "If there is no more to be said, you may go, my lords," the King remarked good-humoredly. And straightway, with a lightness amazing in one of his bulk, he was on his feet ready to acknowledge their tardier rising and their bowing for his departure.

Oblivious of the rival movements of Cromwell and Exeter

towards him, the King swept through the door behind the great chair whence he had risen; and straightway the decorums imposed by his presence broke in revelation of their brittle unsubstantiality. More had just heard Cromwell's caustic, "My Lord of Winchester," arresting Gardiner when Wiltshire fronted him.

"I wonder, Master Chancellor, that you are so keen to fight the priests' battles."

"Not battles, my lord, if this be no war. But it is perilous to attack and humiliate one order in the state."

"Look at all the mischief they have caused—this recent division and disorder in the realm," the Earl insisted truculently.

The ominous words of the Commons' petition and the treatise he had been reading the night before sounded freshly significant in this echo. "It is the way of nature, my lord," More answered with a calm he did not entirely feel, "that where there is division, there are two parties, generally both somewhat at fault. Or when you place all blame on the clergy, for example, my lord, do you mean that you would hold the rich and the powerful wholly responsible for the murmurings against them of every sturdy, idle beggar, or that you think every king to blame whom any of his subjects find a hard master? Is it not fair to inquire what lies behind disaffection and division? Else we may fall into the political heresy that whoever rebels and protests is *ipso facto* right. Abrogate every discipline in State or Church to which some man objects, and how far are you, then, from anarchy?"

Wiltshire looked almost comically perplexed, as if to inject any questions of principle into practical matters were a gross violation of debate, but he took refuge in repetition of his first attack. "You ought to be a priest yourself, the way you support them. You certainly are their man."

"No, my lord, I am the King's man. And I see no better way to serve the King than to strive that justice may be done to all his subjects. And I am a layman beyond all possibility of being a clerk. Twice-wedded as I have been, I can never be a priest."

"A dispensation could remedy that," Wiltshire snarled so vehemently that More set a guard upon his own tongue.

Before he could make a properly pacific rejoinder, the Marquis of Exeter, unaware of what he was interrupting, had plucked the Earl away to talk of apparently more congenial matters.

That last taunt came back in thought as he sat at night in his office at the Chancery. Yes, he could see that the Boleyns would feel bitterly about dispensations; yet his equanimity had to struggle against admitting the insult to feed upon his heart. By chance—or design, the half-drowned sensitivity interjected—Gardiner and Norfolk had both been otherwise occupied as they left the Council Chamber, and he had come away with a sneer as the Council's farewell. That fact could not weigh with him now, however, for what was said to him as a man was unimportant beside his responsibility as a councilor; and what he must do now, he was doing, he prayed, not out of the personal resentment of a single man defeated but out of the conviction that he could no longer in his office serve the King and his conscience, the comprehension which God had given him of the values and the principles with which the expediencies of temporal rule had come to clash. For a little more than two years and a half he had held his post in neither pride nor joy. He had been persuaded that there was work to do which he could further. And what had he done? Staring into the clear heart of the candle-flame before him, he told himself that he had made the King's high court of Chancery a power to be respected, a tribunal as free as his conscience could keep it of venality, fear, and favor; and that his successor would find no tangle of unheard or prolonged pleas such as had troubled his own first months in office.

But those were small matters of routine honesty and good order that did not deserve to be reckoned as merits. How little they could weigh against the failures! For more than a year now he had had no voice in policies which, since his plea to be released from office had been refused, he seemed, nevertheless, to support; again and again he had suffered the personal mortification of hearing of some new measure only after it had been determined. Yet he had held on in the belief—perhaps delusion—that he could in little ways help good counsel to prevail or mitigate evil.

He had seen the Commons abandon their freedom and servilely accept as their voice documents emanating from the Court; he had seen the Church in England driven to renunciation of its liberties and its autonomy. He had seen the dignified plea for the redress of grievances against ecclesiastical exactions made in the Parliament's first meeting in 1529 degenerate into the wild generalized attack on the Ordinaries of this spring of 1532. He had seen Convocation go earnestly to work in acknowledgment of the sincerity of the first bill of complaints, only to have their two-years' labor thrust aside as if they had been unwilling or unable to effect the reforms which they now asked only time to make operative. How bitter it must be to set one's house in order only to be told that one no longer owns it! Ironically, he thought of a man who has swept and garnished his house coming home to find it held by wicked spirits—not the man of the parable, but one whose predicament took coloring therefrom. And above all, he had seen this happen by the will of Henry, whose proudest title had once been "Defender of the Faith," and whose profession was still unmitigatingly severe on heresy, as if by some magnificent illogicality he could at the same time maintain the faith and subvert the proper custodians thereof.

From the swaying of the candle-flame before him, which

wrote the shadows back and forth across the blank paper under his hand, as if they were time-driven scribes, More realized suddenly that a wind had risen. Looking through the dim glass behind his chair, he could see the topmost branches of the lime trees without, black against the almost black sky, heaving and rearing like panicky horses; and he remembered irrelevantly a fierce dramatic representation of Pharaoh's horses struggling against the overwhelming Red Sea—he must have seen it more than forty years before, a woodcut in a German book in Cardinal Morton's library. With that recollection the May-leafed treetops, beautiful and wild in the night, became suddenly an unbearable pain. He must go out into the wind and walk away this sense of defeat and failure that had drugged his spirit; but first he must write the letter for which the blank paper was waiting. Seizing his pen, he wrote swiftly with none of the elaboration of a more courtly mood:

"Right worshipful, my very good lord and favorer—will you stand my good friend in this one request, please: that you win me leave to speak with His gracious Majesty and to deliver to him the Great Seal? You have long known my anxiety to be freed of my office because of my health and other weighty reasons familiar to you and to our lord the King. Help me to make these prevail, and be assured I am your most faithful, humble bedesman. At Westminster, this fourteenth day of May. Tho. More, K."

As he watched the words dry under the sand, he thought, "With so little it is ended." Then quickly he folded the sheet and let the hot wax fall on the exposed edge to bear the imprint of his seal. Now, with a strange elation spurring him, he endorsed the paper for Thomas, Duke of Norfolk, and cried out to John a Wood, waiting in the antechamber.

The sun of mid-afternoon edged the wind-plowed waves with

silver and turned the whole broad Thames between Westminster and the Surrey shore to a rough, molten plain. Were not the wind running cool about them, the heat would have been for May as intolerable as was the glare on the water; for very relief, More fixed his eyes under a level hand on the far green shore, where horses and men, small as a child's toys, scarcely moved—so far were they—in the methodical pattern of the fields. Yet he was looking still half into the sun, and his hand grew weary. The Duke of Norfolk beside him had been unwontedly gentle and quiet from the time of their meeting at Westminster; now, it seemed, at the end of the sad experiment of this Chancellorship the Duke had nothing to say in expostulation or reproof. Recognizing his withholding of comment, More saw that he had dreaded the necessity of making still plea upon plea; for all that dread, however, he had been sure that this time, in speaking the truth as he saw it, he had made himself unwelcome at the Council board.

The bright colors of Norfolk's livery caught the sun anew as the rowers trimmed their barge towards the water steps of York Place. With the little change in direction, an odd item flashed into More's thought, such a one as he could mention casually to the Duke.

"Your Grace, I began as Chancellor with a barge you lent me; so it is appropriate that I'm riding with you now."

"Eh, so you did," the Duke's answer was but half-attentive to the remark. But his absentness, seemingly the abstraction of some prior concern, had nothing offensive about it. "You never have made much provision for sudden state yourself, have you?"

It was no true question, however, and its utterance seemed to have cleared the Duke's thought completely of the matter, for he was staring at the landing stage as hard as if he hoped to draw it towards him by concentration.

"Damn!" The explosion of the syllable, instead of one of

Norfolk's ordinarily picturesque oaths, sounded amazingly unprovoked and cold-blooded.

Though More looked his most questioning, the Duke vouchsafed no explanation for a few minutes. He could not long postpone it, however, because they were maneuvering surely towards the steps. Already, though, another barge heaved and thudded at its moorings there, and as Norfolk's rowers held their oars in anticipation of orders, the wind streaked a pennant full length before their eyes—the ensign of Canterbury. Norfolk's gaze met his frankly.

"Yes," he said indignantly, "the Archbishop's with the King. Of all the tact—to set your two appointments close together. Thorough, all right!" More was grateful for this apposite phrasing of his own thought when he caught the significance of Warham's presence at York Place. He did not need Norfolk's calmer explanation: "His Grace was to bring the paper from Convocation to-day. You know they agreed to the articles and prorogued yesterday?"

More had guessed as much. Parliament had been excused, Convocation had been brought to heel and dismissed, and the Chancellor had resigned—though More was sure that the rumor would spread that he had been removed. It was, as Norfolk had suggested, a clean sweep.

"Do you mind waiting?" The Duke looked at him critically; then at his nod, he ordered the rowers: "Stand off till that other barge pulls away, but keep us moving."

When they had backed obliquely offshore, Norfolk spoke almost apologetically, "I'd rather not seem to see the Archbishop come out." To the rough decency that prompted this move, More could heartily say "Amen."

The King was waiting for them at the end of a long path in the fragrant garden of the palace. Though there were subdued voices and music among the shrubbery, he stood alone in his most familiar and genial attitude as if he could see the magnificent picture he made. Once in their approach, More dared to glance at him fully, and again when they were almost close enough to speak. He had not changed his heavy stance on feet wide-placed, with his hands thrust behind him, nor had the relaxed muscles of his face altered. In the afternoon sun the gold of his doublet plucked the red-gold of his hair and beard into a brilliant gamut of light and jeweled color. He might almost be, More told himself with a pang of grief for the unrealized hopes of that time, the King of a dozen years before, when he had entertained the Emperor, or met the King of France on the Field of the Cloth of Gold.

"Well-timed to your appointment," Henry was saying more to Norfolk than to him as More knelt to kiss the heavy hand that still wore Wolsey's ring. Probably he would never remark that actually they had been late and had thus avoided passing the humbled, aged Archbishop. More felt in the bosom of his gown for the velvet bag wherein lay the white leather one enclosing the Great Seal.

"Sire, may I return to you with humble thanks for the trust which you have placed in me the Great Seal of the realm, with which I surrender all the duties and privileges of your Chancellor?" More heard his voice break a little queerly. So hard was it to abandon what could no longer mean peace or honor to him?

The King accepted the pouch soberly, held it on the palm of his hand as if he were testing its weight, and scrutinized More's seal in the lead closing its mouth. "You vouch for the sealing, my Lord Treasurer?" he asked Norfolk. Then he laughed softly, "So it is brought to us this time? No such pains as we had in getting it from the Cardinal."

It was a callous thing to say here in the precincts of the palace, whence the Cardinal had once repulsed the two Dukes by his demand for Henry's warrant before he would surrender the

Seal; but it was like the King to remember such details. And though Norfolk had been Wolsey's avowed enemy, he was silent in the face of the King's jest.

Still with the crimson bag poised in his hand, like a sinister stain against his wide chest, Henry spoke solicitously: "Sir Thomas More, though I know you have been reluctant now for a long time to keep your office, we have not been able to spare you; but I shall never be so cruel as to force a man to the endangering of his health. Even a less grateful prince could not overlook your worthy service and devotion; so believe that I will cherish you henceforth as a good and thankful lord should and stand your favorer in any suit that may concern either your honor or your profit."

Though, when the first pang of renunciation had passed, More had no grief in relinquishing his office, he was deeply touched at this gracious promise of the King, which seemed to chide him for his own evil thought. He had fully expected to find the King sullen or stormy, who was now all generous solicitude.

"May I prove not unworthy Your Highness's favor!" he said simply, rising as the King turned away with a curt, dismissing nod.

So briefly was it ended in the hawthorn-sweet garden. He could have sung straightway with the exultant starling overhead, but the undivining perplexity of Norfolk held him to a more sober mien. "Ended, ended, ended"—their steps crunched out his pæan for him.

III

"THOU MORTAL TIME"

CHAPTER I

"Te rogamus, audi nos." As he spoke the petitions of the litany, More heard the treble of the children's voices rise more loudly in the volume of the responses than they had done before. Yes, the little ones formed a larger proportion of the household now with the departure of the attendants of his high estate; but he was not sorry, for the straitening of his circumstances had intensified the feeling that he was with his own in a simple integrity of relationship that fortune alone could not destroy. So in the moments for silent prayer in the family matins, he gave thanks for the mercy of God, which in the winnowing of worldly adversity had kept them together like sound grain, and he prayed for them all—himself and his wife, his children, and his children's children—the grace little by little to set only its proper store by the prosperity of this world. Sometimes he had thought that the world into which these children were coming would be a better one than that his generation had known; but recently the long-unadmitted darkness seemed to be closing in as the fog of the North Sea night invades the coastal hamlets, still westwardly sunny. Westwardly bright with a setting sun—when the eye of man and the mind of man dwell on that setting, how far is the dawn! Rightly, then, did even the childish voices lift up the ancient petition, "And let my cry come unto thee." With a heartfelt weighting of the words, he prayed the last "Dominus vobiscum" and bowed before the answering suffrage, "Et cum spiritu tuo."

As they passed a few minutes later from the dimness of the

chapel into the golden June sunlight, More repeated to himself the *magnificat* of the Psalmist: "Let all that seek thee rejoice and be glad in thee: and let such as love thy salvation say always: The Lord be magnified." In the somberness of his thought, he had not given due honor to the beauty of the Lord's handiwork and the rejoicing that is part of the whole hard duty of the Christian spirit. That he must keep in mind now as they held a family conference after breakfast: there must be no darkening of worry among them.

Easy as was the high resolution, however, he had to struggle to prevent its surrender to his solicitude for his children and a natural yearning over the vexation of his wife, who had neither questioned nor chided his decision but who must have found it, he knew, a great trial of her patience. So he sat thoughtfully silent at breakfast, half-aware of the sounds and the activity of the meal, the gentle thud of the pewter and wooden mugs on the table, the gurgling of little Thomas More in his mother's lap, the watchfulness of Dame Alice lest the wheaten loaf be wasted, the low-keyed discussion between William Roper and Giles Heron on some intricate question of law. As phrases of their conversation strayed to him, he felt that if he would listen and comprehend, he might aid in solving the problem, but to do so would be to turn the years backwards; whereas his present need was to lay hold indisputably of the life they must make for themselves now.

When their many hands, for even the children helped to carry what could be trusted to their strength, had cleared the table of food and dishes, and the children had been sent scampering into the sunny garden, the elders drew together in the hall.

"Now we might think ourselves monks or soldiers," jested William Daunce, wiping butter from his fingertips on a finer handkerchief than either would have boasted. "Not that it's bad fun waiting on ourselves for a change."

That was what made this conference so necessary, More told himself as he laughed with the rest: for a little while the novelty of narrow living would amuse them all and enable them to carry their restricted state with a high spirit. But the simplicity that was congenial to him would grow irksome to the young. Before the plain food grew monotonous, and the reduced staff of the household converted self-respecting help with the chores into an inescapable grind, and the now fresh clothes that they were all resolved to wear till the end of their serviceableness turned dull and dispiriting, they must make provision for a new scheme of life.

But keeping the more serious challenge to himself, he said, "Either gives us a good example. So are you a council of captains or the daily chapter of monks? And shall we sit here round the table or go into the garden?"

"We're more likely to tend to business indoors," said his wife with a good sense that no one could deny, though a couple of the young people had looked ready to suggest the garden.

Seated at their council table, they were straightway silent and serious to consider their common problem. As dispassionately and realistically as possible, More set it before them. Even though they had found places for the extra servants and the boys of the household so that they had turned none out of doors unprovided for, he could count now on little more than a hundred pounds a year. John a Wood had pleaded to forego his wages, he reported with a little huskiness in his voice, for with that thought had come the picture of some of Wolsey's servitors trudging the winter through in the search for new masters, a plight which, by the grace of God, he had been able to spare his retainers. Close as they might cut expenses, however, their household could be but the ghost of its former comfortable self.

Was it not better, then, he proposed, that each of the young families should withdraw to create its own modest establishment with its own income?

"None of you is rich," he said, "but you all have some property in your own right, and you should have, on the one hand, the experience of depending on it and, on the other, the freedom to devote it all to your own and your children's needs."

"And leave you and Mother with less?" asked Will Roper. "That sounds as if you would preach selfishness to us."

"No, it is only fair to let others be generous, within reason, I know," More protested. "But you have your young families to think about for years yet; whereas mine, you see, are all grown to fair, strong manhood and womanhood. You will not see us want, but our needs are simpler than yours and, however long life God may grant us, we have fewer years ahead than you."

He smiled at his wife to win her confirmation of his own feeling, but she sat with head averted as if she would offer neither approval nor objection. She grew always uncomfortable, he remembered with a prick of remorse, when his conversation looked at death too familiarly: not that she was afraid—perhaps with a woman's sensitiveness she felt a needless shadow invoked by such freedom with the finalities of human existence.

"Families lived together with all things in common—was not that the way of life in Amaurote?" Will Roper asked in a voice just barely tinged with reproof.

"That was in Utopia, however, not England. Don't pretend that your geography is so faulty, Son Roper, that you cannot tell the difference between them."

"But, Father," exclaimed Margaret in defense of her husband's idea, "if it were a good plan for Utopia, why not for England? Maybe, if we can show how well it will work, it will cease to seem just a fantastic notion."

More shook his head as undiscouragingly as possible, for he

liked this ardor. "There are a great many of the Utopians' ideas that the world may some day accept; meanwhile, though, if they are good ideas, it does them no harm to make their way slowly. Nothing is gained, and much may be lost, by forcing them on men. Poor things! then they are like tender little cabbages transplanted to a shadeless field in a season of drouth. Suppose you generously pool all your resources, where will your daughters find Utopian husbands caring nothing about the dowries you have honestly spent or your landless sons find well-dowried wives who will not think themselves wed only for their money?"

"We don't have to go so far as absolute communism, though," said John quietly. "We can pool our incomes, but leave the properties intact so that our children won't be taken for eccentrics. And then, Father, there is plate, for example, that can be sold—to bring us nearer our new station." The addition had no bitterness in it, only a calm facing of fact.

"Plate!" exclaimed Dame Alice, taking a milder but similar protest out of More's own mouth. "Where have we enough to repay the effort of trussing it up and the goldsmith's commission?"

She did not, in her charity, add, as More could not have blamed her for doing, that in the last few years they had seen gifts of rich plate returned to their donors on account of what she held mere scruples of conscience.

"Maybe if we sold our jewels," began Anne, hesitantly enough after the rebuff her husband had suffered, "that would help."

"Bless you, my dear! But how much are all your jewels put together worth?" As he asked the question, his thought went back to the time when Anne had begged for pearls and he had chided her vanity with a trinket set with peas. Now when she was thus generous with what little she did own, he was sorry for the tears she had shed that day. "No, my dears," he added gently, "we are not in such sad condition, thanks to your mother's management and the goodness of God, that we need to think yet of selling the few baubles and ornaments you have. They are not precious enough to endanger your souls, I know, but merely pretty, harmless things. If we go looking for valuables to sell, the costliest treasure we have, I wager, is in our book presses. And they would bring us too little to warrant the selling," he added to drive the look of anxiety from Margaret's forehead.

"If only your father could have foreseen this situation and left his property differently," sighed Dame Alice, more willing to enter into the discussion now than she had been at first.

"But he had no reason to think that I should not go on till death in the same affluence. I'm glad he did not have to live to see me now, for"—he heard his voice catch in a little husky sob—"if he is concerned at all about my fortunes in eternity, he understands, I think, as he might not have understood here. After all, he kept his judgeship till he died."

"But some of that property was your mother's," she insisted, not to be distracted from the main issue.

"Yes, and some of it was my first stepmother's, and some of it my second stepmother's, and some of it is your namesake's very own. It would be hard for the other Mistress Alice More to make all the proper distinctions. Besides, my dear, I should not be the only heir, you know, even if the division were feasible. But if you are all brave enough to try the plan of our keeping on together, I shall divide up what property I have and deed it to you straightway so that it will be secured to each of you, whatever happens."

"You must not talk so desperately, sir," protested William Daunce, who had been listening somewhat diffidently as if he felt that these matters did not really concern the sons-in-law.

"You have years ahead of you, and we can make our estates as you made yours." The earnest seconding of this stand on the faces of all his children warmed More's heart; yet he was not to be dissuaded.

"It is not desperate thinking at all for us to consider such things while we have health and strength and time. In the last minutes, a man's thought is ill-given to the things of this world."

"But your will is provision enough, Father, unless you don't trust us to respect it and carry out your wishes," Will Roper insisted.

"No, on my faith, I am not thinking anything like that." More wondered sadly whether Will were remembering his own father's unjust will and the long struggle he had had to redress the wrong. "In fact, I don't know just why I feel that this is the right provision to make, but of the feeling itself I have no doubt. So I shall ask you, Will, to help me with the deeds. In a way, I shall be trusting you very greatly, you see, for, if practically everything is in your mother's and your names, you could turn me out of doors with impunity."

The shocked exclamation of the whole council confirmed More's trust; so he laughed quietly enough to let the shock wear off and make them all laugh with him.

"These things are best seen to, I'm sure, while we can take them in this spirit without haste or grief or regret," he went on when the tension had relaxed. "So then, if we are agreed to be contributors together, let us think of how to manage for a while till you are all established elsewhere. I've had more varieties of living than any of you, for I have had that of Oxford, of an Inn of Chancery, of Lincoln's Inn, and also of the King's Court —from the lowest degree, you see, to the highest. But we need not fall to the lowest first. We'll not, then, descend to Oxford fare, nor that of New Inn, but we'll start with the diet of Lincoln's Inn, where many worshipful men and those of good years live very well. And if we do not find ourselves able to maintain this the first year, then the next year we'll go one step down to New Inn fare, with which many an honest man is well contented. If that exceed our ability, too, then the next year after we'll descend to the fare of Oxford, where many grave, learned, and elderly scholars manage to live. If our purse will not stretch to maintain this either, then may we yet, like poor scholars, go begging with our bags and wallets, and sing *Salve Regina* at rich men's doors, where for pity some good folks will give us their merciful charity; and so may we still keep company and go forth and be merry together."

As he had hoped, the absurdity of the picture which the words and a bit of pantomime evoked routed the somberness settling over them like the shadow of some of the thoughts sprung from covert by their discussion. The whirring of the wings was stilled in their laughter.

Yet when a man of fifty-four, who has been active and much occupied in the affairs of the world and who is still hale, despite some weariness and pain, finds himself suddenly cut off from the habits of business, he can scarcely help listening for the whir of the wings. Through four weeks since his surrender of the Great Seal, More had been planning readjustments, seeing friends about the placing of his servants, writing letters on their behalf, severing the quasi-official ties that had not parted at the central resignation, and without briefs or authority giving advice gratuitously to suitors who had journeyed to Chelsea before they remembered that he was no longer Lord Chancellor. Now that was all done, it seemed, and were he to die to-morrow, he would not be greatly rushed about the affairs of this world. That emptiness in the cabinets of memoranda was a strange sensation, he reflected as he gazed from his terrace towards the Thames—as colorless, seen thus at almost eye-level, as pale glass—a strange sensation for one who had known the exhilaration and sometimes the despair of having always something more to do.

Occasionally when he had been very tired and the goad of others' needs entrusted to him for relief had pricked the merely mortal nag of nerve and sinew to such exhaustion that even will was nearly powerless to drive it on, he had thought in a state acutely like panic, "Suppose I die to-night and leave this undone, that unsaid." That alarm, which he had come to regard as a flood-gauge of weariness, had little admixture of what seemed the most common fear of death—the shrinking from the lonely, unpredictable experience and the terror of judgment; for much as he loved life, he had so long reflected on the naturalness of death that it seemed the last high adventure in man's pilgrimage to eternity, and he had tried by all the disciplines of life's fullness and its austerity within his compass to keep himself shod, caped, and staffed for his call to that pilgrimage. Not that he would go without trembling before the great tribunal—such stoutness of heart rested not in his mortality—but that he would go not without love and hope and yearning for God. No, rather the alarm had some taint, he used to chide himself in calmer moments, of mundane pride, for he was concerned about his reputation for good order, thoroughness, care, and the decent doing of his duty and somewhat more; sometimes when he did penance for that pride he wondered that he should so greatly care for the few decades of memory that the world would hold of him. Yet, too, another element dwelt in that alarm, for he thought sincerely—surely he was not deceiving himself in reading his own thought—of the real pain, grief, perplexity, and loss, however transitory, that the things undone might mean to the living. In eternity an unwritten letter may be nothing—less than a sigh to the night wind on the edge of a chartless sea, but in mortality it may mean years of anguish, for in this world men must live with the sensitivities of the flesh. So he had tried—and often he had failed, God knew!—to live by the seer's rule: "to plan as if one were to live forever; to live as if one were to die to-morrow." Perhaps in the trying—it was cold enough comfort he could give himself—he had left a little less undone than the sloth of his nature, undriven, might have neglected.

And now, strangely, much of his business had discarded its spurs. Oh, there were a hundred things he would do—things soon ended like the plans for their tomb in the Church of All Saints, the letter to Erasmus that he had been meditating for a day or two, or the reading of a new play by John Heywood, which he had promised to criticize. And there were matters demanding longer patience than such things—the answer he had been turning over in thought to the *Treatise of Division* and further such useful writing, and that more congenial to his dreams, the devotional books which had been tarrying in his secret thoughts with the patience of the work that is oneself, that cannot be forgotten or marred by long deferring. More lasting than all the individual tasks he had set himself was the high, difficult one of finding, by incessant search, study, good works, prayer, and meditation, the things of God.

Across the line of his inattentive vision a barge drew towards his river steps. So abstracted had he been from things round him that he needed a moment to realize that some one was coming ashore; his little start at this fact amused him, for no more than a month before the coming of visitors at any time had been a matter of course; but now, like a countryman who saw strangers but twice in a year, he was surprised. The nearer approach of the visitor, as he walked down among the roses to greet him, doubled his surprise, for this was Thomas Cromwell. In the instant of his recognition, More felt a stir of excitement such as messengers from the King had roused for nearly twenty years, but straightway the sober sense that matters were now irremediably altered throttled his anticipation. So hard is it, though, he chided himself, for old habits to surrender. He did not doubt, however, that Cromwell came from the King.

Perhaps he had not in other days regarded Cromwell very closely or perhaps the rising councilor had altered in the last month; at any rate, as they exchanged the formal courtesies of their meeting, he noticed the fine velvet of the dark green, simply elegant gown and the curious Italianate setting of the emerald ring which he wore as his only jewel. Years before, he remembered, Thomas Cromwell had seemed an awkward, uncourtierlike figure in the elegance of the Cardinal's household, which had little polished his soldier's or trader's demeanor; now, however, the King's service was achieving evidently what the Cardinal's had not effected. These changes fascinated More —the delicate shadowings of success, confidence, and power: why, the man might be a courtier yet and bear a title not unbecomingly.

"I have not seen such roses this year," Cromwell exclaimed cordially, as if flowers were a great enthusiasm with him, "not even in the King's gardens. Is it the Chelsea air and soil or good husbandry that makes them bloom so richly?"

"Probably each should have its fraction of credit, Master Cromwell, but I like to give most of it to my household, whose husbandry is responsible for much of the delight the garden gives me."

Cromwell nodded with a roguish, sidelong glance as if he fancied himself complimenting Mistress More on her flowers. "And rosemary running wild here!" he exclaimed. "What does the poetry of flowers say about it? 'Rosemary for remembrance,' isn't it? How like you to think of that and spread remembrance so generously here!"

"Flattery" was More's first response in thought to this unfamiliar and, for Cromwell, almost monstrous prodigality of exclamation; but straightway he reproved himself for this uncharitable verdict by the reminder that no sane man—and his visitor was eminently that—with his way to win ever wasted his flattery on such as he, a fallen, useless servant. Not even for practice, which he could obtain on lesser courtlings, could Cromwell be flattering him; so he must count this admiration sincere.

"Shall we go in?" he asked in a more cordial manner in very atonement for his suspicions. "This morning sun is growing hot for June."

When they were seated in the cool oriel of the hall, and old David had brought a glass of wine for the guest, Cromwell began his errand.

"His Grace is concerned about these rumors that you were forced from your office by his displeasure; and thinking that you may not have heard in your retirement here how often he has spoken in regret for your ill-health, he asked me to bring you assurance of his favor."

"Thank you, Master Cromwell. I am grateful to His Majesty for this solicitude and to you for your troubling to bring me word of it. As you see, I am living quietly and meddling little with things of my old state; so I had not heard the rumors. But now I shall remember the King's good will when they trickle down here."

"Did you hear of the Duke's praise of you when Sir Thomas Audley was installed at Westminster?" The anxiety in Cromwell's voice puzzled More again into, he felt, an unjust suspicion that Cromwell did not relish his immunity to gossip.

"Yes, my sons-in-law repeated it to me. It was generously said and clearly enough, I thought, for everybody to believe that I had several times urged His Grace to relieve me of office. So I have not been worried at all about what the world may be thinking. But I appreciate the warning."

"You are wise to be philosophic, Sir Thomas," Cromwell remarked with unbecoming unction. "Yet few men can hope to escape the world's calumny. Do not the poets and the philosophers make the danger of the lofty head a frequent theme?"

"Yes. The figure I remember offhand is Horace's. Well, I for one," More felt gay enough to laugh at the thought, "seem to have escaped the danger. I don't remember in the Bestiaries any creatures capable of pulling their heads down to safety, but nature gives us plenty of warrant in the turtles for pulling them in."

"Say from Westminster to Chelsea?" Cromwell chuckled with a sudden amazing transformation of his heavy countenance.

"Not that I am boasting at all"—More wondered at the little cautionary chill that prompted the addition—"nor that I've had any reason for such fears."

"You're right in that, for everyone knows that you have never sought honors and advancement. Take a man like me—he's more likely to need cautionary advice. You've known His Grace many years longer than I have. Haven't you some good advice to give me?"

This burst of confidence struck More as almost indecently garrulous; half-relevantly, he wondered how potent had been the wine that David had served a few minutes before. Yet, he chided himself for this distrust, Cromwell had no reason to trap him with insincerities and pretense.

"I am a sorry one to give such advice, Master Cromwell." He was resolved to speak generously but not unwarily. "You are now entered into the service of a most noble, wise, and liberal Prince; if you will follow my poor advice, you shall, in giving counsel to His Grace, always tell him what he ought to do, but never what he is able to do. So may you show yourself a true and faithful servant and a worthy councilor; for if a lion knew his own strength, hard were it for any man to rule him.

But your own discretion, Master Cromwell, can read the nature of our lord the King far more justly than I can interpret it."

"Your analogy hits very close the mark, Sir Thomas." Cromwell seemed to tuck it away in some pocket of thought before he added, "Your courtesy is very beguiling here, but I am due back in Westminster by noon; so I must go. By the way, though, you were busy for a while, weren't you, on the King's foundation at Oxford? You'll be glad to know, then, that it's coming along swiftly."

"Thank you, yes. Bishop Gardiner and I worked together to encourage His Grace to make the Cardinal's project his own." As More chose his words carefully, he wondered whether the shadow of Wolsey's greatness and his tragic fall ever troubled Cromwell's spirit. In the months of the Cardinal's chief anxiety, he remembered, his erstwhile retainer seemed to serve his master's interests in Westminster; but there had been men to doubt his motives. Even Gardiner, who was not one to malign an enemy, had said then, "For Cromwell 'devotion' is a meaningless word without the prefix 'self'; so long as it serves his interest to serve the Cardinal's, very well." At the time, that had seemed an amazing commentary on both the former protégés of Wolsey. But Gardiner had interceded for the colleges out of true respect for the good which the Cardinal had thought to do and for the cause of learning. What, however, were Cromwell's motives, More asked himself as he watched the close-set gray eyes narrow at the mention of Wolsey? So long ago?

"Is Dean Higdon to be retained?" was all he said.

"You have a good memory, Sir Thomas." The tension relaxed in a smile with the seemingly irrelevant compliment, which had in it, however, something sinister, More felt, as if Cromwell had been thieving from his thoughts. "Yes, and Robert Wakefield, the Hebraist, and John Cheke are to be canons. You know them both, I think?"

"Indeed, yes," More could answer heartily. "But as for my memory, it would not be easy to forget so important a matter."

"Well, for myself, I keep memoranda to make sure. Do you at all? I dislike having too much in mind at once."

"With what little I have to remember, I never find things jostling each other out. No, I can't say I've ever put much store by notes or memoranda. I keep the drafts of my letters usually, but that's as far as I have ever gone with such methodical habits."

"You had more thorough training as a lawyer than I; that would help you." With this compliment, Cromwell seemed to recollect the haste of which he had already spoken; so he rose abruptly. "I am glad to see you looking so well," he said earnestly as they moved towards the door. "I can make a good report to the King."

"Do, please, and thank His Grace most heartily for his concern about me. And believe me, Master Cromwell, I shall remember your kindness in coming hither yourself." When they had reached the end of the garden path, he added, "If you weary of the town and crave a little relaxation in the country, think of my poor hospitality as yours for the coming. At least, the air is good."

Cromwell smiled as warm a smile as his cold face seemed capable of, murmured his thanks, and trudged on to his barge. A man who had been leaning against the gunwale pulled away respectfully and turned up the path, John a Wood, with a flagon in his hand; thoughtful of their hospitality, More noted approvingly, he must have taken ale down to Cromwell's rowers.

After dinner he said to himself, "If those resolutions of work mean anything, you had better set about it." So he gathered his papers and found a shady spot in the garden. He had not, however, been working so strenuously that he missed the sweet blend of the children's voices from beyond the shrubbery or the chuckle of the blackbirds and the thrushes in the cherries. The monkey, which had ridden out to the garden on his shoulder and then had grubbed for a while among the pebbles and the grass at his feet, had disappeared. Hardly had More noted the fact and added in thought that probably he had gone in search of livelier play with the children than he heard Meg's laughter behind him.

"Have you missed Master Devil, Father?" she asked solemnly. "I'm remembering your good moral lessons from my youth accurately, am I not?"

She let the wiggling little antic slip to the ground and run away while she sat in a favorite seat, the low crotch of the apple tree beneath which More had set his stool. "He was still finding mischief," she said in reference to the fugitive monkey; "this time he was just about to track over the linen Mother has set to bleach."

"So you picked him up to mar your pretty new frock with his dusty paws?"

"New frock! It was two years ago. Where are your eyes, Father? What a vexation you would be to a truly vain woman! Unless it's true as some moralist says that women dress gayly and deck themselves out for other women's unhappy sakes."

"Doesn't your Will notice pretty things on you? I'm no sample of all men, Meg, for I'm notoriously bad at noticing things. Perhaps that's why the world always has something new and charming for me; even if I've passed it a dozen times unseeingly, its beauty is there when I finally mend my observation. So let an old man like your old gown."

The shadows in her sensitive eyes rebuked his levity. "Father," she said softly, "have you been feeling worse? This morning after breakfast, and a few things you said at dinner about Master Cromwell's visit, and now this insisting that you're old. You really are not—unless you want to go back to the Roman reckoning, you know."

"And if I do that, I shall remember the autumnal sunniness of *Cato Maior de Senectute*. No, Meg, I am not ill, not nearly so ill as in the winter. But in some ways I am old. Don't you suppose some people call a courtier old when he loses his suppleness?"

"Then were you not born old?" she laughed. "Surely you never had that kind of suppleness." The teasing quality of her voice belied the demureness of her posture, for she was sitting with her hands folded in her lap as she used to do in childhood.

More affected to consider the suggestion very seriously. "Yes, maybe I was born old; so it is no wonder if I have grown older still. For one thing, a man seems to me to be old when he stops the activity of his mature years, when he feels that there is more behind him in one sense than before. Years haven't much to do with that; rather it's the sense of failure—"

"Father!" The distress of her protest made him repent the unwary utterance; yet he could undo much of its evil by explanation.

"Wait a minute, my dear. I'm not thinking of failure in many of the ordinary senses—not, for example, in the way in which your mother means it, as that time she charged me with being no more ambitious than to sit making goslings in the ashes with a stick as children do. Yes," he nodded at her incipient defense of Dame Alice, "it is her way, I know, and the picture she conjured up has often amused me since. But I'm not thinking of failure in the sense that hurts, but in another sense that really doesn't at all. It is a great grief to have to admit to one's elders that he has failed, for that means their hopes are gone with his own. That's why it is better, I think, that my father did not live to know—this change, as we know it; for it would be bitter for him to see how little I have done with all he valued for me."

Though his explanation was not succeeding in routing her pain, he must try to make it clear. "Now a man doesn't feel that way in admitting his failure to the young: they may learn from his mistakes, you see, or they may begin where he is ending. The young are his hope that the dream he could not realize may yet be fulfilled in them, that the wrong he could not right may fall before their assaults, that the imperfection may be through the alchemy of their youth and strength transmuted to perfection."

"But this is earth, Father," her rebuke now shone with the light of comprehension in her gray eyes.

"I know," he nodded as if that were the point of the whole discourse, "and so those young people will grow old and have the sense of failure, but they will not be discouraged either, for they will look to a new generation to bear their own hope nearer fruition."

"That could be a very pessimistic view of life, but it doesn't seem so as we talk of it," Margaret seemed to debate with herself.

"It would be pessimistic only if we said, 'So many dreams to this dust!' and stopped there in thought, or if we saw mankind in the figure of the poor caged squirrel or the horse on his treadmill, or if the young began life disheartened. If there were no outward swing in the cycles, however little one circle slip by the preceding one, the picture would be a doleful one. But I do believe that man progresses—slowly sometimes, to be sure; and sometimes," he added in inescapable estimate of this present England, "there seems even to be a falling back. In the fullness of God's time, however, the falling back must be the tiniest of episodes."

"Does it help much, though, to believe that, if one goes down himself in one of those dark periods, 'one of the tiniest of episodes'?"

"Perhaps not to his limited, mortal judgment, but the going

down, Meg, even into the valley of the shadow of death, is a little thing by the measures of eternity, and soon—how soon, we cannot guess—we have passed through the valley and come to a place whence we look back with new eyes and new understanding of what has been and is to be. Then we see our own little earthly episode in its due proportions and are, God grant, at peace about it."

She sat very still for a moment, drawing her heavy skirt tight over her knees as he had seen the drapery of a primitive wooden Virgin carved. "God grant! I think I see what you mean by failure; I shall try to remember it when I am old, Father, and tell it to my children for their heartening. But what did I interrupt?"

Dare he tell her? It had seemed so natural an occupation that he had not thought of his family's being perturbed over it. "You will not be alarmed again?" He seemed to be echoing the question of years before when she had come to him through the dark to sob out a tale of night-terrors that had turned all four little ones in the nursery sick with fright.

"Not even if it be your will or your epitaph," she promised smiling and stooping for the papers he had dropped.

"You sorceress!" he laughed as he drew from the sheets that which held his draft of the inscription for the new tomb. Her smile faded a little, however, as she saw how near the mark she had hit. To give her time and not to spy on her reading, he turned to other matters among his papers; but his ear was sharp for the little murmurs of a sensitive reader.

Close to the beginning she chuckled; twice she said softly, "I like that"; and once between, an inarticulate sound had the force of a frown.

When the papers rustled in her hand, with the finality of those which have been read through, he ventured to look at her. She sat meditating, but not dejected, with the close-written lines in her lap. Realizing that he was waiting, too, she smiled through misty, untearful eyes.

"What did you not like? And what did you?"

"For the first, the part about your being hard on thieves, murderers, and heretics. Some day—people reading that might not understand."

That had not occurred to him; so he considered the objection for a moment. "It is perhaps not strictly true, but a tomb has to be fairly brief." They smiled together at the length of inscription he had already devised. "I know that's almost an autobiography; it would be longer still to explain that I harried the thieves, the murderers, and the heretics for the crimes themselves and not for any malice I bore the men. Any Christian will make that distinction for me, though. Is that what troubles you, Meg?"

"No, I'm thinking this: suppose there comes a time when the crimes don't exist any more?"

"Meg, Meg, who is forgetting now that this is earth?"

"There may always be thieves, perhaps even murderers, but surely not always heretics."

"I'll say, 'Amen,' heartily enough, my dear. Maybe that's one of the hopes to hand down to youth. We'll think about that phrase; it isn't going to be carved to-day. Then, what did you like?"

"Vanity?" She tilted a saucy eyebrow at him. Her occasional archness always delighted him, because from time to time he seemed to have forgotten it completely in her normal seriousness. "The first place was what you say about the Treaty of Cambrai and the way you bring in the verse. It fits beautifully —'Peace everlasting.' The other is the very ending—'that he may find not utterly death but the doorway of a happier life.' An echo of what we were talking about before I— But, Father, it is still hard for the living, for the door seems to close inexorably."

"Do we not know that, sooner or later, it will swing wide again and that ultimately we all go through? So it is not parting forever, but only until the living come after. Where, then, as Saint Paul has asked, is the sting?"

She sat so still, however, that More could see that he not yet wholly exorcised the shadow. Together they watched the bright damasking of the grass by the now slanting sunlight through the trees. The late afternoon beauty of the long June days was both a pain and a very great joy.

"What is it, Meg?"

"No rebellious thought, Father. Only this seems to draw—something nearer than it has ever been before. Perhaps, I am a little—afraid, as a child is even though he understands that there is no fear."

"My dear! Years from now we shall still be kneeling together by the tomb and praying for your little mother—'Chara Ioanna Uxorcula.' This is but foresight, not premonition, for I have years ahead of me. And to prove that to you, my doubter, I'll write a letter to Erasmus to-morrow and be thoroughly alive to get his answer, though he owe it to me as long as I have owed him."

So finally he was rewarded with a whole-hearted laugh, on the heels of which tripped his frivolous question: "And what amused you at the very beginning?"

"Your imitation of Erasmus in your using 'invictissimo' for the King. I was startled, too, by your comment on his title 'Defender of the Faith.' "

"A reminder there, Meg, will do no harm."

CHAPTER II

Oh, this weary writing! Not the writing only vexed More this morning: though it was but mid-September, such a damp, chilly air was creeping into the house that his hands were blue and stiff and the letters they formed were shaky as a schoolboy's exercises. He had labored through a page and a half since the last forced relinquishing of the pen to chafe control back into the numbed fingers. With time out every page and a half, how long would it take him to finish this book in answer to the "Pacifier's" *Treatise Concerning the Division between the Spiritualty and the Temporalty?* And this was still summer by the almanac; so not for weeks yet could he think of a fire here in his study. There were no more than enough logs for the great fireplaces in the kitchen and the hall to see them through the winter; and even with all diligence in picking up dead branches after the windy rains they had had, the men and the boys had gathered only a little brush to be used in the many small fireplaces. So, as long as he could do even a page or half a page at one spell, he would work out here in the new building without a fire and warm himself by pacing the floor or the terrace.

He chose the latter for the present interval. By contrast with the air of the sunless room, the open air was warming for all the grayness that dulled the now brown fields. Responsive to the motion, the cramping and the pricking of his hands and feet relaxed; and with the passing of the stiffness went some of his dissatisfaction with his writing. It was not a bad plan of work, this racing against the cold—it recalled tales he had heard of peasants racing from wolves in fearful times when famine drove the beasts close to villages—and then this warming up again while he thought out the next passage. It was good not to sit all day with the white pages sliding to black before him, but sometimes to send the eyes to some far scene like the shining place in Surrey above which the clouds had broken. After such a little excursion into beauty, he could return to his somber thoughts somewhat more patiently than he had left them.

At best, this was an ungracious business he was about this morning—the formulating of a defense against the lies about him, spreading like weeds in the garden. Not much over two months before—or was it nearer three now?—he had not heard the rumors about his having been dismissed from the Chancellorship on which Cromwell had reassured him; but even when they had reached him, they had seemed unimportant as touching only pride, which a man was a fool to try to defend. Lies in such matters—he remembered a jingle of his childhood: "Sticks and stones may break my bones, but words can never hurt me!" Childhood may not have laid hold on all the wisdom of life; yet the jingle had its truth. An adult, however, must sometimes heed malicious words when they are starting what some men will believe and what will hurt others besides the first victim. So, though he would not be troubled by the tales of how he had left the King's service, he could not ignore these lies which assailed not only his honor and his humanity but through him the cause he was trying to serve. If these tales of his robbing and torturing heretics here in his house in Chelsea grew in their traveling, as the way of rumor is, and passed unchallenged, then others worse would thrive on the credence the first had won. And not tales about him alone, but about all men in responsible places to whom it fell to deal not only with conscientious heretics, but also with all the riffraff who tried to distract attention from their plain crimes by the cry, "Persecution." He could almost pity the sincere heretics who were encumbered, and sometimes deceived into sympathy, by plausible rogues quick to make capital of any disaffection.

By the time his fingers were serviceable again, More had thus reasoned himself out of some of his hesitancy over this present chapter of self-vindication. It might be the tragic labor of Tantalus or Sisyphus—what a strange, powerful imagination had that seer who first visioned eternal frustration among the torments of the damned!—but he must attempt it. With the better courage for the task, he turned to go indoors. He would be explicit in his testimony to what had happened to heretics held in his charge, he would name the men, and then he would await the impugning of his word if any man felt he could refute him. Were it all set forth thus in print now, directly after the events that gossip had distorted, when a crowd of witnesses could without fear of his power—though God knew he had never used his office to intimidate any man—denounce him as a liar for the least deviation from the facts, the ugly rumors might be forever confounded, and neither he nor any apologist for him would need to say year after year, "Unhappily you have heard a false tale; not so, but thus."

To recapture the sequence of his writing, he scanned the first sheets of the chapter; and methodically, in part to restrain the passionate disturbance of his thought, he altered the draft as he read. Surely this was categorical challenge enough: "The lies are neither few nor small that many of the blessed brethren have made and daily make about me. Divers of them have said that such as were in my house while I was Chancellor I used to examine with torments, causing them to be bound to a tree in my garden and there piteously beaten. . . ."

That night, not two weeks before, when Antonio Bonvisi had disclosed reluctantly these tales spreading in the London of their shared affection, came back as vividly as if they two were sitting now before the thin, ashing fire in Crosby Hall. Bonvisi, more anxious to redress the wrong than he could have been were he its now repentant agent, had pleaded that he ask the intervention of the King to silence the libelers.

"At least," he had insisted, "I shall ask Thomas Cromwell to do what he can. I'll have him to dinner straightway, and see if he cannot quiet these tongues."

But he himself had protested that dealing with men's tongues accomplished little, and that little sometimes pernicious, because what was merely silenced could live in men's minds only to spring forth later in full-grown monstrosity. Threats and writs and repressive laws could master tongues, but no more; reason and demonstration of error and truth were needed to alter belief. And that was what he must alter. That, ironically, was what he had been trying to change when he had held some heretics in preliminary safe-keeping at his house instead of committing them straightway to their ordinaries, who alone had judicial power over them; for he had thought some of them amenable to reason.

Though he was sitting with his hands thrust up his sleeves, he warned himself that they would be chilled again before he had written much more unless he set about it; so he continued his reading: "Saving only their sure keeping, I never caused anything to be done to any of them in all my life, except only two, of which the one was a child and a servant of mine in my own house. . . ." Poor little Dick Purser! He had disobeyed the command not to share with the other boys the ideas that had been forced into his own mind, and he had had to be whipped for disobedience like any other boy in the household. But even Dick had understood why he was being punished. How was he faring now? What kind of household had his father put him in? In his very recollection of the pale, difficult, tense child, More's anger rose against the men who had planted their doctrine in him: it was cowardly to corrupt little ones. And this other who had been whipped by his order—if the heretics claimed as a fellow this poor perverted bedlamite who had been indecently annoying women in church until the neighbors pleaded for his arrest, he could not say much for their taste; certainly, he would never insult the serious-minded among them by charging them with the rascal's vicious actions. Those two explanations should be clear enough for even the most prejudiced reader to understand.

Thoughtfully he wrote on: "And of all that ever came into my hands for heresy—so help me God—saving, as I said, the sure keeping of them, and yet not so sure either but that George Constantine could steal away, otherwise had never one of them stripe or stroke given him, so much as a fillip on the forehead."

A knock light enough to sound merely experimental interrupted his pen. "Come in," he said, thriftily tucking up his hands to save their warmth. Before the door had swung wide, he knew who was coming by the savory odor and the little cloud of steam which preceded her.

"Meg! Not again!" He reached quickly to hold the door, for it was no easy work to balance the steaming pan in which a mug staggered uncertainly.

"I put too much water in the pan to-day," she laughed, "but the draft is really a sober one."

"Thank you, my dear. You must not do it, though, for you make me feel guilty." But he sniffed the steam appreciatively. "You have enough to do in your own house."

Undoubtedly, though, the warmth of the pan was welcome. Together they laughed at his hugging its sides as if its ministrations were meant to be no more than surface ones.

"No, no," Margaret chided, "that's not the way. The milk's to be drunk."

"Why, so it is. Will you sit down?" he asked between swallows, as the grateful warmth tingled in his throat.

"And keep you from working when your thoughts are melted to flow like butter? That would be considerate of me, Father. How does it go?" Her merry eye appraised the spread papers and pens.

He tipped the mug well over his head to drain the last drop. "Better than I feared, if only people will believe me now."

"They must, dear," she said compassionately, reclaiming the mug. "Don't worry about that. Do these pens need mending?"

"Yes; but, Meg, I am already so deeply in your debt. Well, if you insist, thank you for doing them as well as for the milk."

Hugging the oddly assorted utensils to her, Margaret raised a hand in a gesture that was both disclaimer and farewell, and she was gone.

With more spirit for the task than he had felt all morning, he set his pen racing: "And some have said that when Constantine was gotten away, I was fallen for anger into a wonderful rage. But surely, though I would not have suffered him to go had it pleased him to tarry still in the stocks, yet when he was neither so feeble for lack of meat but that he was strong enough to break the stocks, nor grown so lame in his legs with lying but that he was light enough to leap the walls, nor by any mishandling of his head so dulled or dazed in his brain but that he had wit enough when he was once out wisely to walk his way; neither was I then so heavy for the loss but that I had youth enough left me to wear it out, nor so angry with any man of mine that I spoke him any evil word for the matter beyond telling my porter that he should see the stocks mended and locked fast so that the prisoner might not steal in again."

True as that last was, would it strike some readers as too frivolous a comment? Far from expecting to be charged with cruelty to Constantine, at the time of his escape, he had laughed over not blaming a man for rising when sitting had grown uncomfortable; and seriously, he had hoped that, fugitive or not, Constantine had been weaned from his heretical activities.

A knock that was too confident and masculine to announce Margaret's return brought him suddenly to his feet. As he opened the door with pen still in hand, two black-hooded figures against the greater light in the gallery startled him.

"Good morning, Sir Thomas." He could not identify that familiar voice as the nearer of the monks spoke. "They told us at the house that you were here."

At his stepping back to let them in, however, he saw the white face in profile—Hugh Marchaunt, now of Christchurch, Canterbury. "Brother Hugh!"

The latter smiled at his host's exclamation. "Yes, and this is Brother John Corl."

With an inclination of his round head, the second monk, a wiry, rough-surfaced man, acknowledged the introduction and turned his incongruously gentle, weak eyes away.

As he set chairs for his guests in the little bay that looked out towards the river, More wondered whether their serge habits were as warm as his own robe or whether it would be kinder to take them back to the house, where the early morning fires might have mitigated the chill. Since, however, the monks seemed unconscious of any discomfort, he felt inclined to chide himself for his softness.

"I haven't seen you for so long, Sir Thomas," Brother Hugh was saying as they sat down, "that it seemed churlish to ride close by and not stop. We've just ridden over from Westminster for a few minutes. You may guess how grateful I have been to you these eighteen months; but I didn't like to miss a chance of telling you."

Though he spoke cheerfully enough, something in the stillness of his face that was neither peace nor composure troubled More.

"Have you been well?" Insipid question though it was, it might elicit the cause of Marchaunt's strange expression.

"Well? Yes. I'm tired just now from all the riding I've done in the last few weeks. A month ago some of us were at St. Peter's at Gloucester on business, when they sent us word from Christchurch that the Archbishop was ill and we should hurry home. He died before we got back. God rest his soul!"

"Amen. He was an old man," More said, remembering how death had been their theme in his last conversation with Hugh Marchaunt. "Had he been ill long?"

"He came home from Convocation a dying man," Brother Hugh exclaimed with a passion that suggested indignant discussion among the monks at Canterbury and Gloucester; at the indiscretion of tone—rather than of words—Brother John shot a covert glance at his companion. The look troubled More vaguely, for it was not truly a communicative and warning one such as would have been meaningful. And the thought that not age alone had hurried the Archbishop to his grave was no extraordinary one; he himself had heard it uttered many times in the three weeks since news of Warham's death had reached London. Remembering the Duke of Norfolk's reluctance to see the humbled Archbishop come away from York Place, he reflected that through these bitter last years most men had spoken compassionately of the aged primate. It was a moving tribute to him that he had incurred little hatred, one of the freest commodities of the age.

"Yes, he was an old man," Marchaunt resumed slowly, "nearly eighty, they say. But you didn't think of age with him till just recently. You knew him a long time, didn't you? Were you in his household as a boy?"

"No, Morton's. You forget how old I am."

"That's right." He smiled shamefacedly at being caught in such simplicity. "I've heard you mentioned since I've been at Canterbury as having been reared in the Archbishop's household, and I just didn't think of any other."

"Though I was never that closely associated with him, we were good friends for thirty years or more. I can understand your feeling that, till recently, he seemed not really old. He was a fine, generous soul." More's thought went out especially to the Archbishop's kindness to Erasmus through years when the latter's more spectacular and noble patrons had defaulted on their promises or turned cold at the conservative's outcry against him.

"Too fine in many ways for these times," Marchaunt sighed. "His going will probably mean a good many changes."

Again More was aware of the shifty look that Brother John cast at his companion. Whom did he mistrust? Or was he merely ill at ease?

"They will come slowly," More said restrainingly. "Much will depend on who succeeds him."

"We shall have to wait; that's true." He gazed through the window; now in the full light his face had a gentle dignity More had never associated with the courtier Marchaunt. After a long pause, he began almost abruptly: "I still can't believe that it's only a little more than two years ago that Elizabeth died. Not that she seems far away—sometimes she is very near." He spoke simply without cant or self-consciousness. "No, but I've found so much in myself that I hadn't realized. I don't mean that I'll ever be a shining example of a monk—just a middling specimen. I'm always feeling ashamed of myself beside some of my brothers. So far as I have seen, the average is really very high in the Benedictine houses, higher than you'd think possible."

The very earnestness of this expostulation prevented More's own amused protest that *he* had never pitched his estimate of the monks so low as had the imagined detractors whom Brother Hugh was confuting; but he would not interrupt.

"It has restored my faith in human nature—that's a queer way to say it perhaps—to belong to something men have kept orderly and meaningful for a thousand years, and that will go on and on. I've never felt like that about life before. Doesn't sound much like a contemplative, does it?"

Since he was smiling at himself, More could join in his amusement. Simple as Hugh Marchaunt thought his discovery now that he had made it, it was a moving one for him to bring to the man who, with some misgivings, had helped him to the monastery.

Still smiling, Brother Hugh turned to his silent companion, "It was here, right in this room, that Sir Thomas suggested Christchurch when I was thinking about becoming a monk. And then, as soon as I could arrange things, I came riding down on you hard as if I had stolen the King's crown."

Brother John's laugh was so pleasant that More felt sorry for his vague uneasiness; naturally enough, as a stranger and an uncouth, plain man, he showed to disadvantage beside the former courtier, whose graces could not hide utterly beneath his habit.

Marchaunt's face saddened: "And do you remember, sir? That time we talked of the Cardinal's death. It was more tragic, I think."

The real tragedy for either Wolsey or Warham, More was reflecting, would have been to live on: the one to come to trial for treason, the other to preside at the next impotent Convocation.

A premonitory click in Brother John's throat was almost startling. "There can't be anybody else saw both the Archbishops buried. That's a distinction." He nodded with a solemnity to match the awe in his voice. No doubt, some of his Christchurch brethren marveled at the range of experience that had been Marchaunt's.

"True," More said.

Brother Hugh was studying the book-lined wall opposite him; without change in his somber expression, he said: "How different those two ceremonies were!" and lapsed into silence.

More had heard of them both—the hurried interment in Leicester Abbey attended by no more than the monks, the small, faithful retinue that had ridden this sad journey with their master, and the men who would start south directly without their prisoner; and the full obsequies of his estate, ended but a few days before, with which Warham had been entombed in his cathedral church.

"We ought to be going," Brother John apologized suddenly as if he were prompting recollection of a prior agreement.

"Will you not stay to dinner? It should be ready very soon, and really not delay you much." In his reflection, More had almost forgotten his hospitality.

"No, thank you." Brother Hugh shook his head. "We promised to be back at Westminster by noon."

After dinner, John a Wood, who had been tagging More's movements anxiously during the clearing away, came up beside him in the oriel of the hall. He wore the worried look with which he was used to reporting a poacher's snare discovered in the wood or a weasel's depredations in the hen-yard, matters that he took with the seriousness due to the fall of dynasties.

"Might I have a word with you, Master?"

"Surely, John."

"Well, the two monks that were here this morning—one of them was a regular prier, sir. Not the gentleman, the other one."

With his ambiguous feeling about Brother John still fresh in thought, More was curious about this discrepant, but equally unfavorable, impression. He said only, "It may have been just his odd manner, John. He's a very different sort of person from Master Marchaunt."

"No, it wasn't that, sir," John insisted doggedly. "He asked regular questions. While the gentleman was talking to my lady, this one came out to me. He wanted to know how we did—*now*, sir, and whether many people came to see you. He didn't think I'd see through him, but he couldn't fool a baby."

"That probably proves that there was nothing but idle curiosity behind the questions, John; otherwise, he'd have been more careful and subtle."

"I don't know, Master. He may have thought I didn't know much."

While More could imagine a courtier's making a low estimate of John a Wood's wit, he could not believe that this monk, seemingly the product of much the same humble background, would misjudge him so.

Pushing back a wisp of gray hair with the same gesture with which he used to threaten the brown unruly shock, forever in his eyes, John returned to his information: "Besides, he isn't the first one, sir. Ever since Master Cromwell's visit, back in June, when his barge-men asked some mighty queer questions, there've been strangers round here every once in a while, just asking this and that, like this fellow to-day. I don't like it, sir. Do you think he is really a monk?"

"I'm sure he is. Why, John, this is modern England, not Robin Hood's. Do you think he'd be traveling with Brother Hugh Marchaunt if he weren't a real monk? So long as you tell them no lies, don't worry about the questioners. Most of us meddle in all sorts of things that don't concern us; and some men just never have learned the distinction between mine and thine in personal matters."

"I'm afraid there's more than that to it, sir. You know my cousin down in Rochester? Well, he was saying how many strangers there are round nowadays that nobody can account for."

"That makes two honest men who've been troubled—perhaps just coincidence, John. Still, if you're worried about any stranger, just send him to me. I'm not too busy now, you know, to take time out if need be. And keep this to yourself, will you please?"

"Yes, sir. Thank you, sir." John moved off with a pride of bearing proper to the man who has made a discovery.

Spies? No, the thought was absurd; there was no motive for anyone to set spies on him. A similar worry, however, at Rochester—but John's cousin was not in the Bishop's service—was disturbing, especially after Fisher's half-jesting comments in the winter before. At least, More was thankful that John a Wood seemed not to recall the time when Cromwell had been, he himself felt sure, spying in the Chancery. And though John might share his alarms with his cousin over a can of small ale, he was no loose-tongued tippler. Spies? He could see to it that they drove an unprofitable trade; but beyond that, he could not admit this terror walking in the noonday. For, once acknowledged, such a fear could make a man jump at his own shadow, till his very nervousness seemed to confess guilt.

CHAPTER III

When autumn had truly come, More had no choice but to work in the hall except when he was laboring a passage that meant frequent reference to his books; then a fire of brush in his study warmed a little arc in front of the hearth, where he sat crouched over his writing. There was discipline for the lazy flesh in this small allowance of heat, he sometimes mused, for it discouraged browsing among the books out in the chill spaces of the room: speedily he found what he needed and came home to the hearth to read. He had laid aside temporarily the not yet fully planned *Apology*, of which he had drafted isolated chapters, in order to do a more swiftly organizable and in prospect—though he knew his prolixity—a shorter piece, an answer to John Frith's letter on the Sacrament.

He was loath to work in the hall because, in spite of his assurance that the natural stirring of the family about him was no distraction, he realized that at his coming all activity was keyed low. The very solicitude manifest in the whispered conversation of the women, the hushing of the children, and the delicate stepping back and forth of all the household was a sharper distraction than would have been the normal unconcern of the daytime noises. In this paradoxical awareness of the efforts toward consideration, he did not intend to be ungrateful, but he could not repress the amused consciousness of it.

So in the gathering light of an early December morning he sat withdrawn into the oriel. Despite the urging of his family, he had refused to monopolize the hearth here, for in sheer numbers the women and children would give it more appreciative use than he. With the few books that he had foreseen use for this morning and the sheets that his writing had already covered spread before him, he was reading in the King's *Assertio Septem Sacramentorum* to find just the right passage to uphold his own contention. It was a brilliant book. His old admiration for its polemic subtleties breathed again in undiminished vigor: the recent shadowings could not dim the clarity of Henry's confession of faith a dozen years before. Defender of the Faith! Yet there had been murmurings that the King was not now averse to compounding with some of the heretics for aid in his cause—would that such rumors, charity urged, were as false as the ones circulating about the late Chancellor! He had little reason to credit hearsay about any man. Having found the presently apposite passage of his search, he began to translate it: " 'Then you do yourself grant that there is no peril in our belief, but all the Church believes that in your opinion is undoubted damnation. Therefore if you will, as wisdom would have you, deal surely for yourself, you should rather leave your unsure way of belief and come yourself and counsel all others whom you wish well to believe as we do.' "

With thought thus primed, he resumed his own argument: "Lo, this reason of the King's Grace clearly proves that unless this young man leave his belief which all good Christians hold so damnable and come home again to his old faith, the common faith of all the Church, in which as he himself agrees there is no peril, I will not for courtesy say he is stark mad, but surely I will say that for his own soul the young man plays a very young, foolish pageant."

As he pondered the next step in his effort to pierce the willful confidence of youth, he felt suddenly oppressed, perhaps as much by the closeness of the air in the room as by his concern for John Frith. A little walk would ease the double discomfort.

He glanced across the oriel to Anne, who was rocking little Thomas More gently.

"How is he, dear?"

"Less feverish, I think; but he doesn't fall truly asleep; every time I think he's going to, he's restless again."

"Poor little chap!" He crossed to her side and stroked the hot forehead. "And poor little mother! When I come back, I'll take him for a while till you get some sleep yourself. I'll not be long, Anne."

How the old habit of thinking that there might come messages for him persisted! He teased himself as he put on his kersey cloak and pulled the lappets of his cap about his ears. The first impact of the frosty air was tonic; so he breathed deeply with the exhilarating sense of stretching that the fresh wintry wind gives one before its cold ambushes the body's heat. Much as, for this quick walk, he wanted to free his mind from thought of Frith, the problem of how to cope with him was not to be outpaced.

What More had heard about him since his return to England late in July had been disturbing, for he could not forget that Frith had been as a boy in Stephen Gardiner's service and that later, after his first falling into trouble at Oxford, Wolsey had interceded for him; in spite of his obstinacy in error and his breaking his word by his flight to Holland, the young scholar had notable gifts. It seemed tragic that he should nullify all these with the heresy that meant imprisonment now and that might mean eternal damnation. More's hope of his redemption, however, drew strength from the example of Simon Fish, who had been a fierce ranter and calumniator, and who had, nevertheless, been reconciled to the Church. To be sure, the evil he had done yet lingered, for some men were still quoting *A Supplication for the Beggars* as though it stood unrecanted; but the mercy of God, which had turned the wayward spirit, would in time destroy the influence of its evil work. Of Frith there seemed even better hope, in his temper and his learning, than there had once been of Fish.

So occupied had he been in thought that he had not noticed his surroundings in the mechanical exercise of crunching his way along the frosty path. The appeal of a thin voice to his left startled him into realization that he was opposite All Saints' Church, in the porch of which the beggar must be huddled.

"For the love of Christ and our Lady, spare a poor man a farthing." The whining plea sounded cold and sick.

Abstracted as he was, More felt for his purse and tried at the same time to recall thought to take counsel on this man's need; then he remembered that he had come out without his purse. As he began that explanation, a little breathlessly because of the cold and the strain of his walking, the beggar interrupted him with a shriek:

"The devil fry you and all proud misers in hell!"

The violence of the curse jerked More into recognition of the man whom he had seen hitherto as only a gray bulk in the shadows.

"Blind Rob! What are you doing here?"

"Oh, Master More, I didn't know your voice." The change in the old man's tone would have justified distrust of a beggar one did not know. "The good God forgive me, sir!"

"Nor did I recognize you at first, Rob; but it's true, I have no money with me. Anyway, I was going to suggest that you walk home with me. This is no place for any man on such a day."

As the blind man scrambled out into the daylight, More was shocked at his filthy, thin rags, through which his shins and chest showed blue-gray with dirt and cold, far different from the decent, warm apparel that was his due as a pensioner at their Chelsea almshouse. Slipping out of his cloak—he was not chilled enough to take any harm if they walked quickly back—More laid it on the quivering shoulders.

"Your worship, I can't take it. Please, sir!" the old man's self-respect protested, even while he clutched the rough wool round him.

"We're both too cold to argue about it here; so come home with me." More took Rob's arm to guide him. "I'm warmly dressed underneath. Don't worry on that score." For the time being, he would not ask the meaning of this amazing transformation, but the blind man was eager to justify himself.

"Master More, I can't go back. Here I ran away yesterday to take myself off your hands. I've been thinking for a long time how you haven't enough for your family without trying to keep us. Then yesterday somebody who'd been to the Great House came back and told us how you and your lady and all the young ladies and gentlemen have to go to bed cold without any fire."

"Oh, Rob!" More could have wept over the picture of some simple gossip, thoughtless of how his listeners would take it, regaling the almshouse with the pitiful tale. "We are a little pinched, but you must not believe every story you hear. We are still living more comfortably, I dare say, than half of England. What were you hoping to do—not beg the winter through?"

"If that was the best I could do, sir. But I was hoping to get back to Tonbridge soon. I was a servant of the Austin Canons before the Cardinal turned us out. Did I ever tell you, sir?"

"Yes, I remember, Rob."

"Well, I figured, sir, I hadn't any call to be living on you when I belonged back there."

"But, Rob, if we couldn't keep the house here, there are plenty of good Christian people in Chelsea to help out. They will make up what I can no longer provide." Wolsey's suppressions, *A Supplication for the Beggars,* and other inflammatory tracts, and now this poor scrupulous pensioner trying to make his way home. God keep the roads of England from being overrun as the result of this disruption of society!

"Tell me, sir, do I look very bad?" The old man's tone was so honestly bewildered that, though his question revived More's first shocked suspicion that the blind man had been trusting to impose the better on charity by his disreputable appearance, he knew there must be some explanation forthcoming.

"To be frank, yes. What happened?"

"Well, sir, when I walked out yesterday afternoon, I met another—traveler. And he said he was going the same way and we'd better join forces." Not chidden as he had evidently feared to be, he warmed to his tale. "We walked a while, and I had sixpence; so we had a can of ale. Then we walked some more, and he said we had got to Westminster. Then he found a byre, where we slept. But this morning I couldn't find my four pence, what I had left after the ale, sir, but he said I must have dropped them. And of course, I may have. Anyway, he got angry at me for thinking him a thief, and he made me change clothes with him; and he laughed at me when I said these didn't feel as good as mine at all. And he told me to wait for him there at the church— Was that honestly just All Saints', sir?"

"Honestly." Sensing that the story was not quite told, More contented himself with the one word.

"The liar he was! And he told me to beg if any one came by."

"Did he teach you the curse, too?" Since Blind Rob had not suffered much from exposure—and that, inscrutably, because John Frith was a perplexing soul to deal with—he could bear a mild teasing.

"No—no, sir. I was scared, I guess. I hadn't heard anybody all morning. Maybe the good angels weren't listening."

"But it's the bad ones we should be worried about. You didn't commit me to the good ones, did you?"

"Now, you're joking, sir." The old man's laugh ended, however, in such a chattering of teeth as made More glad they were on the terrace. "I'm all right," he added between clicks. "I was frightened, though, sir; that's all."

They must warm him and find him clothes and see that he got safely back to the almshouse. Furthermore, they must try to track the able-bodied thief in a Chelsea coat; perhaps John a Wood could ride out straightway. Busy with these plans, he had not noticed, as they came in, the luxurious blaze on the hearth or the company seated before it.

"Thomas!" Dame Alice's cry was absurd in its very alarm. Had she mistaken the ragged figure for him?

But when More had peered round Blind Rob, he could understand her dismay, for three men sat by the fire. He stepped far enough towards them to find to his delight that he had three old friends, Bishops Veysey, Clerke, and Tunstall, as guests. Letting the warmth of his greeting compensate for its brevity, he asked to be excused for a moment to start the provision he must make for his pensioner. His first contact with the heat of the house had warned him, too, how cold he had grown: it would be sensible not to go back to the fire for a few minutes. In the kitchen he found the Bishops' men in high conversation with his own slim household. But there was no spying here, he thought with an assurance that sent him back to the hall reflecting on how much joy friends bring into even the most self-sufficient family.

"My lords," he exclaimed, "count all the handsome phrases spoken and put me out of the pain of my curiosity. What new rite demands three bishops? Or have you lost your way and taken my humble house for some hall of Convocation?"

"Not quite," chuckled Bishop Veysey, leaning forward confidentially with his hands poised on his knees, "but there's a grain of truth in both your guesses. First of all, though, you owe us an explanation: we come to call on an estimable citizen living in retirement, and we find him abroad—very much abroad, it seems—picking up beggars. What's the tale?"

In spite of his own curiosity, More was not unwilling to tell of his encounter with Blind Rob while the incident was fresh in mind and while his wife, who would carry on his work in the kitchen, was still with them. The rest of the family had already retreated to other quarters; noting how they had heaped the fireplace here for their guests, he hoped they had ventured to be at least a little generous with themselves, too. Had Anne coaxed her toddler to sleep and been able to lie down herself?

Though he passed as lightly as possible over his fugitive's motive for leaving Chelsea, all four of his auditors found the episode a strange and touching one. When it was ended, even to a few inevitable questions to lighten dark corners of the incident, Dame Alice excused herself to see what she could do for their "unwilling guest," as she put it with the aptness of phrase she could command.

His "willing guests," as More in turn dubbed them, after a few minutes spent in the exchange of such trifles of interest as friends for months unmet have to share, fell awkwardly silent. Finally Tunstall, the youngest of them, gave his colleagues an odd glance as if to say, "Are you with me?" and began a little tremulously:

"You may think we suborned old Rob; but really you couldn't ask for a clearer parable, a text as it were for our errand. For a long time we have all felt—the clergy, I mean—how heavy a debt we owe you for your work in defense of us and of God's cause here in England. There is not one of us all, who would seem the natural champions of that cause, who has carried as much as you have of the hard, often thankless-seeming labor against heresy. And we know you of old, Thomas—those of us who've had you for a friend: that you never have been rich and that you never have profited in even the customary ways from your offices."

Having at Tunstall's opening wondered at his pulpit-style, More felt himself grow faint and confused in the face of the revelation at which he could now guess; but, though he gazed at him solicitously, the Bishop gave no sign of recognizing any change in him.

"And since your retirement," he went on somewhat more confidently, "we have been considering, not how to repay you as you deserve—that we must leave to the goodness of God—but how to show you in some serviceable way our deep sense of obligation. So we have finally made up this chest, to which every bishop and abbot in the realm and many another clerk"—he looked anxiously at his colleagues, who were acting on their cue—"has given as much or little as he could. And believe us, this has been given with a whole heart. We ask you to accept it in the spirit in which it was gathered together."

From its hiding place between them, the other bishops had drawn a stout little wooden chest, brass bound and formidably hasped. Flushed with the exertion and, he could well believe, with friendly pleasure in the gift, they looked at him pleadingly.

"My lords!" He could not go on. Yet he must make them understand why he shook his head in refusal. The invading perturbation a little mastered, he said finally, "You should not. Believe me, I am touched. And I'm grateful to you all. But you must not think of any reward for whatever I may have done. Your thanks and mine are due to God alone if I've accomplished anything by this writing. Your bounty is very comforting to me"—he thought of the innuendoes and sneers and lies of months now that made this expression of gratitude almost incredible—"you cannot really guess how comforting; but I cannot take the gift, my lords, deeply grateful though I am."

"We are not trying to make it a payment, a reward, Thomas; it is just a token of gratitude," urged Bishop Clerke, "a free will offering of appreciation."

Yes, his was one of the most gently persuasive voices More knew; and he had had hardly a word with him since, both opposed to the King's divorce, they had agreed to hold no further communication till that unhappy business should be ended, and More had come home to burn his copy of the Bishop's treatise on the subject, at Clerke's own request. The leaping firelight turned the brass of the chest red before More's eyes, but he could not offer his guests the similitude shaping in his own fevered thought.

"I am grateful," he repeated, "more grateful than I can possibly say."

"Then what is the matter?" Tunstall spoke as to a frightened child.

The patience of the question gave More courage to try to explain the horror in his thought. "You remember, for one thing, what some people are already saying about me." There was no time to shape this explication tactfully. "They say in print and they spread it by word of mouth that I have had great rewards and subsidies from the clergy for my writing, which is, therefore, partial, dishonest writing."

"But as subsidies go, this is a very modest one—not much over four thousand pounds," protested Bishop Veysey, missing delightfully, as he had a habit of doing, the real point of More's objection. Perhaps he was thinking of the more than a hundred thousand pounds Convocation was in process of paying the King.

In almost the same instant Bishop Clerke returned to the attack. "None of us ever held the heretics wrong in everything. Maybe here their doctrine's sound: they think that men should pay their just debts, and they recognize our debt to you."

More groaned: "No; they charge me with corruption, you see. And if people believe the charge, it destroys everything I've tried to do through these books, everything you value in them."

"I think More is right on Tyndale's and the other's meaning," Tunstall admitted. "But this gift comes after the false charge, and it isn't the kind of thing they're talking about. We are not buying your pen. We should be sorry, of course, if you felt you couldn't go on with such writing now, but we should not feel resentful nor unfairly treated even if you wrote not another word."

"Maybe you oughtn't to write any more books for us; we've been worried about your health as well as your wealth," Clerke added.

"And we honestly mean every word we say, and more, when we insist that this is a gift in appreciation of things past and not a retainer for the future," Tunstall reiterated. "I don't mean to pry into what we've no right to know, but no churchman can miss the significance in the time of your resignation. You don't need to show whether I'm right or wrong—let it just stand as guesswork. And I've heard, and not from the Bishop of Winchester, that you dared to defend the rights of Convocation in the Council just before that day. It is not a complicated problem in arithmetic and logic, Thomas. I believe absolutely everything that was announced about your resignation —your illness and your desire to be released. And I'm sorry for both those causes. But I know more than just so much. And the more I know, the prouder I am of being your friend. It's in pure friendship and esteem we want you to take this gift."

"But it's because whatever I've done for the clergy, I've done in loyalty and the conviction of right, that I can't take anything in return." Would they not see the peril in giving color to the calumny that would injure not him alone, not them, but the cause of truth that was more precious than all its human agents?

"We do respect your scruples," Tunstall spoke with the patient assurance of ultimate success that was one of his major gifts. "But there is another way to look at the question. It's nearly five years since I personally drew you into this work on heresy. I was thinking then, I admit, more of the general welfare than of your own good."

"You could not make the distinction," More tried to comfort the self-accusation of his friend, "any more than a man can withhold his thoughts because to record them is to destroy his pen. My pen seemed able to serve the need."

"It was the best, I knew. And it has done valiantly. But perhaps I was wrong not to do with weaker ones. In these five years you might have been using your gifts far otherwise. I can guess the hours and hours of your labor over this writing, and I know you never stinted on the demands of your offices. So you have sacrificed, for there is only so much time in a day or a year, probably all the private satisfactions of life this long time. Think of the other writing you might have done."

"This is what I did. We all know how vain is thought of what we might have done. We cannot recapture the spent time. I don't deny that the writing has been joyless enough sometimes; but that may mean only that, without it to do, I should have grown fat in idleness." Hearing his own little laugh at that prospect, More took new courage of resistance.

"One thing is sure, though, you didn't grow rich in those years," Bishop Veysey, whose gaze had been straying humorously about the hall, asserted as if this were the final argument. "If you hadn't been doing the books, you might have done more in a material way for yourself."

"And for your family. It's on their account I blame myself now." Tunstall's earnestness seized on his colleague's contention. "I've come to see that it was not fair to involve a man with a family in the sacrifices this business has meant. We should have used clerks, for they have no such ties of responsibility as laymen and it is most of all their battle to maintain the faith."

"It is true"—there was no harm in a small concession—"that the man with a wife and children has given hostages to fortune—haven't we said that before, my lord?—but he cannot be timorous for their sake or the bare fear of hurting them will paralyze him. And then he may destroy them more quickly by venturing nothing than he would have done by risking a great deal. Yet, begging your pardon, I cannot agree that the battle for the unity of Christendom belongs to the clerks alone. So I have had as clear a duty to serve God's cause with what powers I could command as to serve the King. What use is there in talking about rewards for the simple doing of duty?"

Bishop Clerke had been smiling artfully in the last few minutes. "Since you will not take it, at least let us give it to your wife and children."

It was a not unworthy stratagem, More laughed to himself, but the Bishop of Bath should have remembered how stubborn he could be: they had been a pair of sturdy resistants to the royal will. "No, my lords. I had rather see it all cast into the Thames than let myself or any of mine take one penny of it. Perhaps it's the old Adam in me, but I am both too proud and too slothful to be hired to undertake half the labor I've had in this writing."

"You proud and lazy!" groaned Tunstall. "Oh, Thomas, when you begin to talk about secret sins, there is no dealing with you. If you were to call yourself stiff-necked, I should agree. We are old friends enough, we three, not to be called meddlers, and certainly we respect indifference to wealth; but is it kind of you to deny us when we know that you are close to poverty, with little abatement of the old demands on your charity?"

"Is it kind of you, my lords, to seek to deprive us of the merits of Christian poverty?" More could jest now that Tunstall's reproaches admitted their defeat. "How much wealth did His Grace of Canterbury leave? Was it not a mere thirty pounds? And did he not say to his steward, 'It is allowance enough for the journey'? Surely, we can believe that his soul rests the easier therefor. Do not worry lest we be poor; for, even if worse come to worst, we are agreed to sing on rich men's steps."

"Sing!" laughed Tunstall. "And I suppose you will pitch the tune."

More looked at him gravely. "Isn't that my duty as head of the family? And, my Lord of Exeter, do not be surprised if we appear on your doorstep, for once you sent Margaret a gold piece—"

"Eh? When was that?" Bishop Veysey seized the opening as if here might be a fresh opportunity for persuasion.

"I showed you one of her letters and some Latin verses of hers once, and you insisted that I send her the gold piece as a token of your pleasure. The worst of that was, my lord," More chuckled partly at the setback to his vanity years before, partly at Bishop Veysey's quizzical look, "that then I couldn't show you what my other daughters had written, too."

They all laughed at the proud father's predicament.

"And it is always the habit of beggars, I have heard," More went on gayly, "to return to the doors where they have received alms."

"But not the habit of the needy, if we take you and your blind pensioner as examples." Tunstall shook his head ruefully. "Our parable still fits—with a difference. You've eluded us more skillfully than he did you."

"You see, I have still the sight that the kind Lord gave me." This time, their laughter was full admission of defeat.

When the Bishops had rowed away after dinner, with the chest wrapped shapeless in sacking and lashed to one of the thwarts of the barge, More stood on the hearth in the hall. The great fire was nearly burned out—so much wrath come to this flaky grayness. Well, the room had been warm for their guests, and the meal had been a generous one for all its simplicity. His wife's step behind him made him turn quickly.

"Alice, you did nobly with that dinner."

"We mustn't complain, though, if to-morrow's is slim—not that you will, I know." She seized the hearth brush to sweep back the scattered ash.

"Alice, it was money they had in that chest." She nodded in a matter-of-fact way he could not quite interpret. "They meant it for us. I couldn't take it."

"I told them beforehand to save their energy." Her equanimity surprised him, for he had feared her not understanding. As if the matter were merely one of current interest, she added, "Do you know how much they had?"

"More than four thousand pounds." Would the chiding come now?

"Four thousand pounds!" She studied the masonry of the chimney as if she had never really observed it before. "They said they had a gift for you; that's more than a gift."

The edging of indignation in her tone reminded More of an ally he had not reckoned on—her pride.

"They meant it as a friendly gift, Alice; it was a general

collection to show how the clergy have appreciated my writing. Thoughtful and generous of them, wasn't it?"

"Yes." She spoke without enthusiasm. For a minute or two she was busy raking back into the center of the fire the half-charred bits of wood that had fallen clear of the blaze. "Well," she added finally, "you used your own time and energy on the writing. I guess you ought to know what it's worth."

More could have whooped in delight at this implied appraisal of his books; but it was evident that Alice was through with the matter.

"How is the littlest Thomas?" he asked instead. "When I went out this morning, I was coming right back to relieve Anne for a while."

"He's much better; so she can get some rest now, too."

"And Blind Rob?" The old and the young of the day's anxiety drew together in thought.

"He'll be all right." She shook the ash from the scraper and the brush, and stood them in place. "Of all the foolish ideas, his is the limit! John is back with the thief. He persuaded him to come along."

They smiled together at the thought of the probable persuasion. After all, no one could have stripped him and left him on the highway in midwinter.

"What kind of fellow is he?"

"Not a bad sort, but dirty and hungry and scared. What is the world coming to, Thomas, when a man like him—really half-decent and gentle-spoken—will rob a blind man? He begged me to let him work to prove he's not just a thief. What shall we do about him?"

"We'll see. I'll talk with him." Not a bad sort? More remembered John Frith, whom he must try to persuade from his errors while there was time.

CHAPTER IV

THE stir of the city, as More came along Fleet Street towards St. Bride's Church and William Rastell's printing shop wakened his old excitement and joy in London. Now in early April, when cleansing winds swept between the houses and spring worked in the gardens and the bustle of apprentices and housewives livened the narrow streets, he liked his city best. This morning, Monday of Holy Week, the tokens of housecleaning and of approaching festival everywhere in his path reminded him that he had been little away from home through the winter. Dodging an apparently self-trundling barrow of rubbish, from behind which his warning summoned a tousled, impudent head, he turned into the churchyard, where his nephew's shop, on the ground floor of John Heywood's house, elbowed its crowded neighbors. Through the open door the familiar creak of the press and the thick odors of ink and wet paper welcomed him; in its bustle and its congestion of furniture—great press and little, stools, benches, forms, type cases, stacks of paper, and damp sheets drying on wires—the main shop was as busy a place as he had glimpsed since his landing at the Blackfriars' steps. Another stage in the making of books, he thought, while his lifelong delight in the mysteries of print leaped to attention.

As he crossed the threshold, an apprentice carrying a form of type towards the press smiled his recognition and called out, "Master Rastell."

"Just a minute, sir; be right with you." Speaking smartly, the master of the shop peered through the room, at the rear of which he was in conference with one of his men. With some last directions to him, he passed round the press into clear view of the door.

"Uncle!" The young face glowed with pleasure. "It's a long time since we've seen you here. I'm sorry to have kept you waiting like—"

"Like a mere author? When they were out yesterday, Margaret Clement was saying that you wanted to see me; so I came in this morning with Will Roper. Is anything wrong?"

"About the book? No, that's going splendidly. The sheets are ready for the binder. Want to see some of them?"

More admired the craftsman's dexterity with which Rastell spread a couple of the sheets on a near-by table. The little blocks of print on the wide sheet, for the pages would be no larger than those of a prayer book, reminded him of a tessellated floor. Having stood off an instant for this effect of the whole sheet, he bent to examine the text.

"Good clean presswork. And your device of the different types helps immensely; now the most careless reader should see at a glance where I am quoting the 'Pacifier' and where myself."

"It shows up well, doesn't it?" Though he spoke modestly, Rastell had a proper pride in the work of his shop. With a swing of one of the sheets, he brought the title-page right side up before them. "Do you like it?"

The simple title stared arrestingly from between the ornamental pillars—or were they maces?—supporting at the top of the page a design of Christ preaching and at the bottom breaking into one of His giving Peter a key.

"Yes, I like it. How much the artist has crowded into his little space—the way that head is poised and the backward look of just one of the apostles! Where do you think the others are going in their very positive separatism? William," he fixed a stern eye on his nephew, "are you sure this wasn't devised for some subversive book?"

Rastell laughed with him. "Hardly. Do you think Saint Peter would then be getting so heavy a key? I imagine the artist was thinking more about his design here than his theology, Uncle."

"Undoubtedly. He's put in plenty of odd detail. Yes, you've done very well by my *Apology*."

"It's going to make a fat little book, a great deal thicker than this." Rastell reached for a slim volume from a near-by stack.

"John Heywood's play!"

"Yes, we both want you to have a copy. It's just done."

"Thank you. I'll have to congratulate John. Trade secret maybe—but why doesn't it have his name?"

"You've read it, haven't you? He thought it better published anonymously, the way things are. He doesn't want some people claiming him as an ally."

"Hem! Yes, I can see that. When he wrote this a dozen years ago for Court, we could all laugh at it as good innocent fun. But the people who take Erasmus's *Encomium Moriae* for sober opinion may overlook the fact that the play is a jest, too. His new one, *Wether*, though, doesn't need such caution."

"No, we'll put his name on that, but I guess it's just as well left off this one."

"We don't want John to have to write an apology." More sighed at thought of his own unhappy labor.

"Yours ought to end the detraction once and for all, Uncle." Rastell picked up the sheets again.

"God grant it may! I'm not sanguine enough to be disappointed if it changes nothing. You think me too pessimistic?"

"Not exactly that; too modest, rather. Your book's so clear and reasonable that I don't see how any one could fail to be convinced."

Having returned the sheets to their place, Rastell motioned

towards his tiny stall of an office, where, with the transfer of books from the chairs to an already perilously heaped chest, he made room for them to sit down.

"But you were convinced anyway, William, before you read a word. No, much as I believe in reason still, I think I have lost my superstitious faith in it."

Rastell laughed. "That's what it amounts to with some men, isn't it? At times, when I listen to the solemnities of logic round me, I decide I began my study of the law too late ever to develop a proper respect for mere human subtlety. But I'm enjoying myself immensely at Lincoln's Inn."

"More than here?"

"At least, it looks more certain for a career, Uncle. I like all this dearly." He made a wide gesture that implied not only the crowded cell of his office but also the busy, many-odored shop beyond. "But it seems to me a question how long it will be a very comfortable business. Well, you know my worries on that score already. It's something connected with that I want to ask you about—not that I expected you to come to me when I mentioned it to Margaret Clement. I should know the way to Chelsea by this time."

"But it's good for me to come into the city once in a while; I've been away from home very little in months—to Sion and Sheen a couple of times, hardly anywhere else. I must have forgotten how much I enjoy London. This isn't getting to your serious business, however, William."

The young man looked sharply past his door into the shop. Noting the intensity of his expression, More said involuntarily to himself, "Fear!" And he thought of the spying suggested recently, rather than proved, by trivial happenings. Then, he reassured himself with the reminder that absent-mindedness can fix as sharp, though unseeing, a gaze as concentration itself. The first thought came back, however, with his nephew's question, spoken, despite all the noise of the shop, in hardly more than a whisper.

"I remember your telling a while back of a nun who was visiting at Sion. Is she the one they call the Holy Maid?" At More's nod, he asked, "What do you think of her?"

More hesitated, wondering just what focus Rastell's concern with her needed; finally he began, "She is a gentle, pious soul. Considering how she has been sought after, I thought her very humble and sensible in her speech."

His nephew nodded as if to indicate that he had heard the same report from others. "Did she prophesy for you?"

So that was the point! Yet, were he to help William, More told himself, he must not give way to alarm too easily. "Hardly in a conversation as matter-of-fact as ours—not much more than that I had heard of her and she of me. When we talked a little about visions, because she had warned a girl we know, who had them, that they might be rather of the devil than of God, she spoke very meekly about the dangers in what one may think to be revelations. I liked her much better then than I had expected to after some of the tales I've heard; and I decided that perhaps some of them had grown in the telling."

"That's interesting. She really understands, then, that not all so-called revelations are from God? That sounds as if she were neither self-deceived nor consciously deceiving others. Some of the reports stretch credulity pretty far."

"I agree—at least so far as I can judge from what I've listened to. One thing I've noticed: I've never met a man who could vouch that he had the marvel first-hand from her. So I discount the tales as having sprung up to feed our human appetite for wonders that many a holy reputation suffers from. They are no essential part of our faith, as I was bold enough to tell Father Rich once in the winter."

"One of her advisers, isn't he? An Observant at Canterbury?"

"No, Richmond. From Canterbury it would probably be Father Risby."

"That's right. Some of the monks of Christchurch are interested in her, too, I understand. But tell me, Uncle: when you said a minute ago, 'from what I've listened to,' were you making any distinction, or was it just accident?"

"A real distinction, William. I will not hear tales or prophecies that meddle with the King's matters; and it seems to me that the Nun and her counselors are very rash to spread them round." Curious as he was to know how much his sister's son had been listening to, More withheld the direct question.

"Why rash?" William sounded even a little anxious.

"Because, if the Nun has had revelations to make to the King—and we all know she has talked with His Grace—they're of too solemn a nature to be bandied about and distorted by every wonder-monger. Publishing them does not help the peace and order of the realm. But I nearly said, 'Impious,' as well a moment ago. For there's a more serious objection still: a prophet's message is for the ears only of those who are to be warned; it should be as secret as the voice of God to conscience. This babbling about prophecies for the King seems to me, therefore, almost blasphemous."

"I hadn't thought of that." The shadow on Rastell's face lifted as this second aspect of More's scruple commended itself to him. "Yes, that is the way to look at it. And if they be not of God, it is sinful to spread these prophecies. So there is every reason against disseminating them. You probably wonder what's the point of all this. I haven't heard the prophecies in detail—just generalizations about them; but I've been approached about printing a pamphlet or some sort of little book of the Nun's visions. The more I've thought about it, the less I've liked the idea. At first, I was skeptical as I would be of any seven-day wonder; but the fact that upright and honorable men took her

seriously made me doubt my own judgment. And I've even been thinking that, though there may be little merit in the visions, there may be no harm either. You've settled it, though: I'll not print the book."

"You're right, William, I think, and wise. Yes, I mean a distinction there, too. The farther you go in law, the more you will realize that legally as well as morally we are bound to stop slander, or that which may give rise to slander, not only by refusing to repeat it but even by refusing to listen to it. And what might become slander of the King has, you know, a more serious name."

"Yes. You've set me quite straight on the matter, Uncle. Thank you. Things are moving so dizzily now with the new Archbishop and the decisions of Parliament last week and the arrest of the Bishop of Rochester yesterday—"

"Bishop Fisher!"

"Hadn't you heard, Uncle?"

"On what charge?"

"Nobody knows. Strange to seize him on Palm Sunday, wasn't it? Unless the reason were very heinous, and that's incredible."

More shook his head slowly. "Words change with the times, William. Perhaps you are right to think of giving up one kind of traffic in them; but the law will commit you to another. I am not sure there will be much use for law in the old sense very soon. But there! I've fallen into my dark habit of foreboding, for which Will Roper chides me. Perhaps he is half-afraid that talking of things brings them about—that queer, shuddery human sense responsible for *absit omen* and its synonyms. Do you know where the Bishop was taken?"

"The report is that the Bishop of Winchester has him in charge. That sounds more like a cautionary measure than a punitive one, doesn't it?"

The custody of Gardiner would undoubtedly be wholly kind, More knew; but comforting as was the assurance that Fisher would not suffer from inconsiderate treatment, he questioned whether circumstances could much affect the pain of unjust arrest. That it was unjust, he did not for a moment doubt; yet he could not in fairness burden his nephew with the knowledge of his own indignant suspicions.

"At least," he said in commentary on, rather than direct reply to, the question, "we can feel sure that physical hardship will not be added to his anguish. I trust Bishop Gardiner."

For an instant he studied the heaped ledgers and books on the chest opposite him. Perhaps William Rastell was right; it might soon be an unprofitable and even a dangerous business—this dealing with ideas. And even jests like John Heywood's *Pardoner and Frere*, that he was carrying off in his pocket, could be perilous in this topsy-turvy time.

When he had come out into the sunlight and, by contrast, the quiet of St. Bride's Churchyard, More felt the shadow which had invaded the shop still trailing his thoughts. "If only I could lure it away from William like an unwelcome dog!" he thought mirthlessly. A walk through the city might give him time, he considered as he recrossed the Fleet, to sort out the vexing items that had crowded in on him in the last few weeks. Could he have them in a measure quieted by the time he reached his old house in Bucklersbury, where he would find now the peace of the Clements' household? The security of the Christian family was one of the inviolate human values in this world where so many things were falling—that and the sanctity of private conscience; so long as they endured, there would be hope of recreating the more perishable goods of society, as there is hope of germinating seed long dormant.

What had been the vaguest fears, tossing like flotsam, two

years before, when Convocation had yielded the title *Supremum Caput*, or even a year before, when it had surrendered its independence of legislation, had found their direction. The act forbidding appeal to Rome in questions of marriage, among other matters, was leading the whole nation into complicity in the King's flouting of the papal authority. Still, however, Henry was negotiating with the Pope; for, by virtue of bulls duly procured from Rome, Thomas Cranmer had just been consecrated Archbishop of Canterbury on Passion Sunday. With his incomprehensible power of keeping his one hand ignorant of the other's actions, the King had obtained the papal sanction for the elevation of the Boleyns' chaplain to the primacy of England at the very time when he was forcing the Parliament of England to abrogate the effectiveness of papal decrees within the realm. And why? Though Parliament had just declared His Majesty free to marry, rumor had him already secretly married to Anne Boleyn. The first encouragers of the divorce surely had never dreamed of this result, which proved Henry either incomprehensibly obtuse or incredibly perverse. Of the consummation of Queen Katharine's first marriage there were grave doubts; of the King's relations with Mary Boleyn there were none. And Canon Law, which Henry held so absolute that the Pope's dispensation could not avail against it, made no distinction between legitimate and illegitimate unions. So, if the King had gone through the form of marriage with the Lady Anne, he had robbed his earlier scruple of all title to respect.

That was an appalling conclusion to reach about any man—trebly so when that man was King and former patron and friend. The strain of his walking towards Ludgate, combined with the anguish of his thought, tore at More's heart. He was grateful for the brief darkness of the passage through the gate to slow his pace in preparation for the hill. And he would redress the balance of his judgment: this marriage of rumor might be no more than that, the sorely tried loyalty of half a lifetime protested. It was wrong—wrong—to let untoward appearances create their prejudice; if for no more than a day, he must agree with charity in the reproof, "You do not know."

Yet strong as his resolution to forbear judgment might be, he could not still the magnetic activity of thought. Why had Bishop Fisher been seized? Though it was possible that so seemingly cruel and arbitrary a move had some sound reason, and far more likely that a pretext would be alleged, the true motive undoubtedly lay in the Bishop's courageous stand against the King in Parliament and Convocation. In spite of its failure the year before, the device of excusing him from Parliament had been repeated; and again, in the face of the strong suggestion that he was unwelcome, he had come. A pretty farce of Parliamentary government was this, when the few, like Fisher and Tunstall and Clerke, who marred the illusion of unanimity and free consent were either not summoned to the session or pointedly excused from attendance. But this restraint of the Bishop of Rochester must have some further purpose than the silencing of him in parliamentary debate, for there he had already made his brave, if little-availing, stand; it argued the approach of some critical time in the affairs of the King, of some event which must not be marred by embarrassing protest.

The clearer that conclusion became, the more certain grew the feeling that events in the state were moving beyond advice and expostulation, that soon all men must choose among three courses—unthinking subservience, the silence of conscience reserved, or the criticism construable as rebellion. And even in Utopia, though the Prince might be deposed for tyranny, it was death to argue about the affairs of the commonwealth outside of the council or the place of election. What more could reason achieve than such a plan for the preservation of liberty under law, with equal provision against the tyranny of an arbitrary ruler and that of sedition and unrest, even rebellion. For when did men ever, in hatred taking the law into their own hands, keep it law? Was it not a ruler's and a counselor's first duty to understand that, freedom of debate and advice under law denied, the true fomenter of disaffection might come to be government itself?

In the intentness of his thought, he found himself—prematurely, it seemed—at the gatehouse of St. Paul's. A momentary abridgment of time in imagination brought the dead and the absent together in the curious, brilliantly outlined unreality of abstraction: he should be able to find Dean Colet in his precincts here and to talk with Tunstall as well. They understood the greatness and the littleness of the state devisable by human reason alone; loving scholars of history, they knew how little an opening the forces of disorder needed to lay all the world waste. Once he had stood with a plowman in August on the edge of what should have been a field of gold ready for the harvest, which was instead a waste of browning stubble. "Do you know what did it, sir?" The farmer had stooped to feel along a half-devoured stalk and risen to show a speckled mite: "Him and his kind, sir!" At the time More had been uncertain which was the more pitiful—the loss that the man had suffered or the scorn that he felt for his destroyer. "Him and his kind." Too late men might try to move against the devourers of peace and good order in their world—materialism and oppression and selfishness. The large dialectical names could not conceal the fact that these were some of the deadly sins of plain morality.

The casual greeting of two men, caught almost too slowly for true exchange, hinted that he had been walking unseeingly along a crowded thoroughfare. He could not go back to apologize to men he had slighted, but he could consider his way hence more circumspectly. Instead of turning right into Creed Lane, however, he accepted the impulse that directed him round to the north of the cathedral. Putting away the reflections that had accompanied him from his nephew's shop, there in the cloister of Pardon Churchyard, he stood to gaze on the painted terror of his childhood, the Dance of Death, that by very familiarity had lost much of its horror and had even taken on a certain power of comforting a soul too much beset by the noonday evils of change. Here was no change—only the insistent warning that the true tyrannicide, whether the tyrant be merciless king or merciless rabble, deals impartially; all the cheating, all the bullying, all the flattery, all the timeserving of which man's fallen nature is capable avail less than a poor man's groat to stay his eviction. Death is not mocked. So this grisly pageant on the walls of the cloister had its edifying truth. A child might shudder at it, as he had once shuddered and as his little ones had when, remembering his own terror, he had brought them to it with some care to make its strangeness, its mystery, master its fearfulness. Odd that men should shrink from the contemplation of death, for early in life they all learn of the corruption that is the latter end of the body's cunning impermanence; a skull is no less natural than a soft-fleshed face. Why, then, should men shudder and turn away and call reflection on death morbid? Or spurning all forethought, would these same men, bidden to a feast in a great man's hall or sent on an embassy, dismiss as morbid all concern about their dress and their jewels and their demeanor?

"Give us all Thy grace, Good Lord," he prayed in the quieting of his agitation, "never to dwell so in the fears or the hopes of this life that we forget their end in death."

CHAPTER V

MORE's forbearance of judgment was not long tried, for the advance of the Paschal season disclosed the fullness of the King's measures. Within a week near the end of May, Archbishop Cranmer pronounced Henry's marriage with Katharine invalid and, without revelation of its date or circumstances, that with Anne Boleyn valid.

As he sat reading in his garden late on the last Thursday afternoon in May, More found himself distracted by the mumbling of a bee at his ear. Turning cautiously enough not to distract it in turn, he watched its nervous indecision—a plump yellow-jacket incongruously heavy for its filmy, opalescent wings. "Why, master bee," he laughed to himself, "you might be a courtier in a panic to prepare for the coronation." And though it sped off—"What! Not angry at the comparison?"—the interruption had started a train of thought too subtly laid to be ignored.

This was a new process in law, to appeal to a recognized tribunal as the King had to the Papal Curia and then, while the matter lay still undetermined by it, to submit the case, prejudged, to another court. That six years of failure had tried Henry's patience, More could well believe; but even then, thought of the grave results of contumacy should have had a sobering influence, unless— The most amazing aspect of the whole tragic farce of this week centered in the gentle, hesitant chaplain who had been consecrated Archbishop of Canterbury two months before. It was comprehensible that, both by temperament and by limitation of experience, he lacked understanding of what his acts might entail in the large drama of world affairs and even the smaller one of English domestic policies; but it was utterly incomprehensible that he should so stultify the oaths of his consecration as to render these decisions, unless— The recollection forced itself upon consciousness: back in 1528 the English ambassador to the Pope at Orvieto—that would have been Gardiner—was said to have threatened Clement with the loss of England's allegiance to the Papacy unless he rendered the decision the King wished. The Princes of Europe were so used to threatening when they could no longer cajole that the violent words must have seemed at the time mere words.

Yet William Roper, reporting the validation of the new marriage—as it probably must be called for convenience—at dinner yesterday, had announced also that the Archbishop was to crown Anne Queen on Sunday—Pentecost of 1533. Was it any wonder that London, though no stronghold of conservative doctrine or of papal loyalty, seethed with protest over this outraging of common morality and the ordinary decencies? So they had had the pretty spectacle of a proclamation that the citizens must silence their wives. What would a Diogenes make of all this tragic obliquity? At any rate, the courtiers must have been bustling all week, like any mumbling bee; and brocade and cloth of gold would be selling at a premium.

Before he was ready to return to his book, his wife's step on the garden path brought him to his feet. She was walking with unusual alacrity, and she was carrying a letter and a packet.

"A messenger from the Bishop of Winchester brought these, though he could not wait," she explained so breathlessly that she ended in a little puff. Evidently, though, she had guessed that the message was too good a one for her to let momentary discomfort mar her pleasure in bringing it. Her anticipation as she balanced the packet on appraising fingers while he opened his note was amusing.

Phrases of the note flashed bewilderingly before him: "bear us company in the procession from the Tower to the Abbey"—"twenty pounds for a new gown to honor the coronation"—"no doubt, the King's Highness will be well pleased." He had not thought to be so beset. Reading the familiar signatures of Tunstall, Gardiner, and Clerke, he was assured that the motive of this invitation and the accompanying gift was whole-hearted generosity, free of guile; and he did not question that they were right in hinting that special significance would attach to presence at the ceremony. It would not be a matter of indifference.

"Read it, Alice." Silently they exchanged note and packet. He studied the seals, for the three friends had marked it individually. From beginning to end, their gift and their request had been thoughtfully devised. That fact touched him deeply; at the same time, their very consideration made the necessary refusal hard. Necessary? Yes, this was a definite test. Which of them had suggested it? "We must persuade Thomas More to be there." That might be John Clerke, with a personal solicitude no greater than the others', to be sure, but with a keener sense of urgency, perhaps, since he had been recently accommodating himself to the changes he had tried to prevent. That was a quaint phrase—"accommodating oneself." "God knows, I cannot judge him, though," More thought, "for he stands in much harder case than I. A bishop cannot ask to be relieved and withdraw from all the problems as I have been allowed to do." It was possible, too that Gardiner's responsibility for the Bishop of Rochester's safe-keeping for a few days in April had sharpened his anxiety for another friend. Tunstall, though he would not have lagged behind the others in concern for his welfare, would have been least confident of success for their appeal. Of the three, he probably understood best what was happening and what it portended. More thought of their effort on his behalf gratefully, unresentfully: they were not trying to compromise him; in the light of the need as they saw it, they were trying to save him from himself. Evidently, they did not recognize in these events the same promptings to fear as he did. And he could foresee the dreaded consequences—schism, terrorism, the triumph of the forces of evil—only in silence, for he was no prophet to proclaim the way for other men. "God grant that I be wrong!" he reflected. "If time prove me so, I will say, 'Mea culpa,' a thousand times in pure joy."

Alice was waiting for him to rouse from his pensive mood. "How generous of them!" she exclaimed warmly.

"And thoughtful, Alice. They are kind friends."

"Then you will go?"

Her question was not eager, More noted with relief: apparently she had not really hoped for his acceptance. Still, it was natural for her to think of the splendor of a coronation and to wish him a sharer in it.

"How can I?" he asked as simply as possible.

"Are you sure the mention of the King does not mean that he is responsible for this?" Her hand moved vaguely above the letter and the money. "He might be hurt. It may mean—something."

More smiled. "Not that, Alice." For he could guess what the desirable "something" was in his wife's esteem. "The King has no use for my services now—for any I can render him; and he has already found my conscience a troublesome counselor. No, I shall be sitting on your hearth a long time yet."

She snorted her half-teasing, whole-earnest rejection of his untimely whim. "If the King had nothing to do with it, the more pity to offend your friends."

"They are generous enough to respect my judgment. Besides, I shall keep their gift, which is the really personal thing about this. It is different from last winter's 'subsidy.' I shall probably not be publishing any more books against the heretics, for I have shot all my bolts. There is no point in going over and over the old arguments, and I do not know what more they can do that words can refute. Do not look so worried, Alice. We'll go to church here on Sunday and think no more about coronations."

"The hussy! Queen indeed!" she exclaimed with a sudden passion that took him aback. "Much satisfaction there would be in seeing her crowned in place of her betters."

More peered exaggeratedly into the shrubbery and the trees as if he expected to find an informer ambushed there. "Tilly-vally, as you say yourself, my dear. Do you not remember what is happening to city wives who let their tongues run their husbands into danger?"

A few weeks later, when the promise of June hung golden in the air and the evenings were lengthening towards midsummer, More had taken three of his grandsons down to the river for a little play between supper and bedtime. They had watched the fish darting in a pool just by the quay and had talked of the miraculous draft of fish on the Lake of Genesareth, which had been the previous Sunday's lesson for the children; they had played at guessing how far away were the men still working in the fields across the river; they had waved to passers-by in their barges far offshore and had told tales of who they might be and whither bound; and—dearest of all the riverside games—they had tossed stones into the water to hear the strange thirsty gurgle of the river as it sucked them down and to watch the widening aftercircles. In and in they came until the last ring flattened itself against the quay with a thin little ghostly slap. Then the children laughed and began to compare their counts of the circles that had spread from the first hole cut by the stone.

"The hole looks like the one Tom made with his ball in the window, doesn't it?" cried Anthony Roper, who had discovered this simile a week before and already had repeated it often enough to disgust his brother. "Only, this one heals itself."

"If we were out in the middle, could we see the rings there? How do they look?" Tom asked in magnificent disdain of his brother's now antiquated observation.

So More showed them with a stick in the dust how the circles would look to the eye of an imaginary bird directly above the hole; then he explained how, because they were circles, they would look the same to watchers on shore or river.

"Why do they look like the rings in the big oak that fell last winter?" asked John Daunce.

"I don't know exactly why. But in a way both show one of God's mysteries. The circles push slowly outward from the tiny center; that is growth. They don't break away so that one circle lies here and another here." The boys chuckled at the palpable absurdity of such a separation as the stick described in the dust. "A man watching only till the stone fell might say as the hole healed itself, 'That's all.' But how wrong he would be! And another man studying the bark on the tenderest sapling might say, 'It's no use; this will never be an oak. See how tight its skin is already.' The end of some tiny action, you see, may be as far away in its scale as would be the end of the circles were Goliath heaving bowlders into the ocean, and the rings it makes in us may be as many as those in a great oak still standing that was young when William the Conqueror landed. When was that?"

"1066," sang Tom and John in unison. Then Tom ventured a new question: "Do you think any of our oaks were here when the Romans landed?"

"I doubt it, Tom."

"Oh, look! Here's a boat," cried Anthony, jumping up and down in his excitement.

Straightway, dusty and tousled as they were, the boys lined up in an awed reception committee. "Who is it?" they whispered with variations of emphasis in their repetition.

"It's the Lord Bishop of Winchester's barge," More explained to them, "and I can see his Lordship of Durham in the stern at this side."

Indeed, not having expected his letters of thanks to silence the natural questions, he had guessed who his visitors were. In what temper were they coming now, he wondered, while he enjoyed the children's absorption in the maneuvers which brought the craft sliding gently broadside to the quay.

"We did not expect a delegation to welcome us," Gardiner laughed as he grasped More's hand to step ashore. So the mood was set, and Tunstall and Clerke accepted it heartily.

When More had presented the still awed youngsters, Tunstall said, "A boy apiece if we leave you out, Thomas. But you have them all the time; so that's only fair."

"And a bishop apiece for them—an event of a lifetime," More added.

The long walk from the river through the garden offered no chance for the taking to task More knew awaited him; rather, they all strolled along like men glad to defer a task in the excuse of the present beauty. The air was restless with gnats and whirring millers and the first glow-worms of the evening, and grass and foliage exhaled the cool scent of moistened verdure. To linger thus, never to come to grips with the finality imminent in this visit—such seemed the delectable invitation of the garden now. As they neared the house, More asked the boys to scamper ahead with the news of their coming. Thus he put himself at the mercy of the three, still reluctant to begin their chiding.

When they had sipped the light wine that Anne More brought out to the terrace and had edged little by little nearer the heart of their intended conversation, Bishop Clerke thrust directly towards it:

"We were worried that you were ill when you did not come to the coronation."

"And you wasted your pity? No, my lords, not ill but most distressed in mind. You have probably guessed that I don't enjoy being churlish with my friends." He waited a moment to study their anxious expressions. "Since I was so willing to grant you one-half of your request, I thought I might be the bolder to deny you the other. And since I took you for no beggars, but kind and thoughtful friends, and knew myself to be no rich man, I was glad to grant the more—intimate part. Even though I shall not spend all your gift for one gown, be sure it will be well used, and believe me deeply grateful."

"We're glad you took it this time," said Bishop Clerke after a glance at his associates, neither of whom seemed inclined to speak. Then he laughed a little uncertainly: "You have a remarkable power of saying, 'No,' Thomas."

"It may be my last poor private treasure." More was surprised at the unsteadiness of his answering laugh. "At least, it helps to have you recognize my 'remarkable power.' I shan't have to explain it to you."

As if to defy this confidence, Tunstall looked up and sighed: "Why couldn't you come to the coronation? Just be present?"

More could understand the emphasis in the second question, for many men he loved and admired had been present and some of them had had parts to play in the whole pageantry—the Bishop of Winchester here, for example, and Giles Alington of his own family. He shook his head sadly.

"May I tell you a story that has recurred to me a few nights recently when I've lain awake thinking? There was an Emperor who had made an edict that whoever, except a virgin, committed a certain offense—what does not matter—should suffer death: such reverence had he for virginity. Now it happened that the first offender was indeed a virgin. The Emperor, hearing this, was in no small perplexity, as you may guess, for he desired by some example to have the law put into execution. When his council had sat long solemnly debating this case, suddenly there arose one of them, a good plain man, who said, 'Why do you make so much ado, my lords, about so small a matter? Let her first be deflowered, and then afterwards may she be devoured.' Does not the dark tale strike close home for us? Take good care, my lords, that in this matter of the marriage you keep your virginity still; for there are some who, by inducing you first to be present at the coronation, and next to preach for the announcement of it, and finally to write books to all the world in defense of it, are desirous to deflower you, and then they will not fail soon after to devour you."

A slight groan from Bishop Clerke, who sat with his head in his hands, was the only answer from the three. It was growing too dark to see their faces distinctly, but the poise of Gardiner's head seemed to say, "I can be strong if the need arises"; it was not the bearing of a man ready to take advice. To be sure, the parable did not wholly fit him, for he had represented the King at Rome in the early negotiations for the divorce; but recently, since his entering on the responsibilities and perhaps the perceptions of the episcopacy, he had seemed to be drawing back from policies to which he had once committed himself. In profile, Tunstall's face was sadder than More had ever seen it; the quietness had fled out of it before the struggle between the will to hope and the understanding that branded such hope delusion. Far on the Surrey shore the battle must be waging, so intently did this friend, who might never see peace again, study the darkening landscape. For all three More grieved that the good in them should be exploited by the invading evil of the time; yet there was distinction to be made in the grief, which cried out especially against the cruelty to Tunstall. His was a richer, more sensitive nature than that of either Clerke or Gardiner, whose limited sturdiness was their defense against such agony as he could know; he was generous and selfless, free from guile, trustful even to disaster that a little promiseful good could be retrieved from the ruin of what he still passionately believed in.

It would be merciless to insist on the application of his parable; so, imperfect though it became in focus, More turned the pitiful tale upon himself: "My lords, I know it does not lie in my power to prevent their devouring me; but, God being my good Lord, I will provide that they shall never deflower me."

"God being my good Lord." Though their conversation strove to return to uncontentious matters, the horror of the innocent child's cry, "What have I done?" echoing across fifteen centuries, beat upon More's spirit; and his friends' silence paced his own.

The dark had come, and with it desultory lights across the landscape to mark man's essential unsubmission to nature. A torch in a passing barge dragged its red planet-tail along the black plain of the river, and the night closed upon it. Upward the air held a luminous quality that denied all but the brightest stars. The hurried talk of the night-creatures round them swelled in volume, but they themselves had no heart for further converse.

Yet, when the rowers, with torches kindled in the kitchen, had come at their summons, the bishops seemed loath to go. As they followed the lights towards the quay, Tunstall hung back with More in the sheltering darkness. As if the continuity of their speech had not lapsed, he said quietly:

"Still, it may not be so bad as we fear. Bishop Fisher was released completely from his rustication on Friday; that is a good sign."

"Beside the very bad one of his arrest?" More kept the question as nearly level as possible, even though he was thinking how, after all, the Bishop of Rochester had been honored by being kept under restraint from the week before Henry's marriage to Anne Boleyn was to be announced till several days after her crowning. Except for a light sigh from his companion, More might have been walking alone.

Then Tunstall said slowly, "But, Thomas, this is Christian England in the sixteenth century."

And More knew that his scholarship, at least, had identified the parable; his own spirit, however, could not share this confidence. Discounting time and space in thought on the devious ways of human nature, he could not grant the remoteness of Tiberius's Rome.

"God keep us all!" he said quietly. "And let us pray for each other."

"That we may find the way and the light," Tunstall added.

They had come into the glow of the torches, which found only grief and perplexity in his face.

CHAPTER VI

"THOUGH it is a lie, Uncle, does that fact help us much if the Council believe it?" While the sharing of his worry had eased it somewhat for William Rastell, he was still nervously tense.

More could well understand why, and the worry became a heavy anxiety to him; for though the charge seemed incredibly frivolous and easy to refute, it was striking not only at him, but at his young kinsman as well. It was clear enough in Rastell's report of Cromwell's conversation with him that the Council thought he had written a reply to their recently published nine articles on the King's marriage. The accusation offended him in its assumption that he so little understood his duty to the King that he would come into open contention with an official pronouncement; but beyond that, he was puzzled to find a motive for their belief. The immediate need now, however, was to clear Rastell as well as himself of the charge; the wonder about its occasion would not die for being laid aside.

"Since our consciences are clear, William, we can strive our best to convince them. And if worse come to worst, they must produce the book which I am supposed to have written, and if they do not find it in my handwriting, they must let impartial judges consider whether its style conforms to that of my known books."

"But you are assuming that this thing would be handled by ordinary process of law," Rastell protested in a dismal voice.

"Why should it not be? Except for the sad fact that exoneration seldom catches up with the first rumors of guilt, a charge without proof is an empty business, not to be trembled over. The law of the realm can not be so lightly put aside, William." His nephew's settled anxiety, however, still furrowing his forehead, troubled More. "What is behind your worry over the law?"

"Well, it may be a poor example, but some of the young lawyers have been debating—secretly enough, you may be sure—how legal has been the treatment of the Nun and her so-called confederates. They haven't been tried yet; so why all this denouncing of them and putting them to public shame?"

More could well picture the young members of Lincoln's Inn matching wits and memories in the citation of the statutes, precedents, and decisions applicable to the Nun's case. It was the proper activity of students, with which he heartily sympathized; yet, if men's recent fears were more than chimeras, it had its dangers.

"For one thing," he began after a moment's deliberation, "if you feel the need of keeping the debate secret, William, may it not be better to let it go on only in each man's thought? I don't want to suggest that you must distrust your fellows, but remember that what others have heard a man say they may be challenged to repeat, to his prejudice and their own honest grief in the reporting. What a man but thinks, only his own conscience and God know truly, and no earthly court can produce a witness against him. That is not merely cautionary counsel; it is not fair for one man to burden another's memory with what may tempt —not malice—but human frailty to unwitting betrayal or for one to involve another in unforeseen evil. As for the Nun and her advisers—hard as it may be to believe, especially of the good fathers—they are said to have confessed the imposture."

"That's the point: some think that those were no real confessions."

"What was told me of the pitiful show at Paul's Cross in November certainly sounded like definite confession."

"I know. I was there. But afterwards some shrewder men than I were pointing out the loopholes in the statements and saying that the poor souls had probably confessed, though innocent, in the hope of escaping with just the humiliation of that spectacle."

"That is possible, I know," More shook his head slowly, "but if a man has once confessed, even under torture, and then retracts, he marks himself as at least once a liar. I'm not being hard and inhuman in saying that, William; for God alone knows how my own weak spirit would bear torture or the threat of it. A man from whom fear has wrung a false confession—we may leave the final judgment of his lie to the mercy of God, Who understands the temptation; but the earthly judge, though he be more patient and more charitable than Pilate, is bewildered to find the truth. I do pity the Nun and Father Rich and Father Risby and the rest, and I am sorry to hear the rumors that Bishop Fisher is suspected. But I dare prophesy that, ill and weak as he is, he will make no confession out of fear."

"Do you think he can be really involved, Uncle?"

"There is no judging without the facts; but I doubt that he ever encouraged her to prophesy. He is too wise and thorough a theologian to be uncritical of visions. Of course, he must have talked with her; but so did many others, including the King himself."

"That's what the lawyers point out: how can there be any treason in the business when the Nun herself told the King her revelations, and these others knew only what he knew about them? It is a real question in law."

"And were you not saying a few minutes ago something to suggest that you have given up hope of the ordinary processes of law, William?"

In thinking about this strange scandal of the Nun of Kent, whether impostor or dupe or victim with her advisers of the powers of evil, Rastell had lost some of his tenseness about their own predicament. He smiled naturally: "A shrewd hit, Uncle. Well, if we assume that truth can prevail, how can we make it in this matter of the book you haven't written and I haven't printed?"

"What you told Master Cromwell sounds to me clearly convincing, and the question over the dating of my answer to the *Book on the Supper of the Lord* is negligible. A little inquiry will show that the book was being sold before Christmas; so 1534 was but a printer's error. And a little reading will show that it has nothing to do with the King's marriage or the Council's articles; so what if it were dated even 1535—except for the fair reputation of your shop?"

"I know that's how it all looks to a reasonable man, Uncle. Maybe I wasn't very convincing, or maybe I sounded too plausible. At any rate, I couldn't help feeling that Master Cromwell had his mind—sort of closed on the matter, that he was just telling me to let me worry about it. I know that sounds horrid. Have you ever felt that way?"

More nodded. He knew that vague, intuitive perception of the mind barred that is one of the most disheartening antagonists to encounter. "Perhaps I had better write him a letter about it, William. We have nothing to help us but the simple truth, and nothing to worry about in it. I'll do that to-day, and I'll try to make unmistakable my view of what I owe to His Grace and his Council. If they understand that I should not dream of writing against their book, they will not again vex you or any other printer on that score."

"Thank you." Rastell rose to go. "Really I am not such a coward on my own account, Uncle, for a search of my shop would exonerate me; but I have been worried for you."

"I appreciate that. Surely, though, they will believe me. And there is no *corpus delicti*. So sleep well to-night, as I shall when the letter is done. I am grateful for your telling me right away, William. God bless you."

"And you, sir." And the young man went out into the gray, midwinter afternoon with a more confident step than had brought him hither. As More listened for the clatter of his horse's hoofs on the frosty path, he was thinking of the letter he must do straightway. Repudiation of this charge would be easy. Less certain, he knew, would be his success on the larger issue, for, though he prayed to be spared the pride of the Pharisees, he had no confidence that all these men he was dealing with would understand what he meant by loyalty and by his sense of duty and of the fitness of public silence for him. Even weaker, he feared, though he must use it, would be his disclaimer of the folly of answering a book that he had read but casually with neither full knowledge of the facts nor curiosity to inform himself on all the intricacies of the law appealed to in the Council's tract. They probably would not credit his resolution to meddle no more in politics and the King's matters.

"You are more pessimistic than William Rastell," he mocked himself as he sat down to draft the letter.

Though his letter to Cromwell had ended that groundless accusation before it had drawn any full breath of life, within a few days More was again reflecting, in the mixed misery of self-respect and the stubborn uncharity of judging others, on how thin an armor against detraction is a man's own sense of integrity. Unless others could believe him—in his youth he had met the philosopher's thesis that nothing exists except in the perceiving consciousness, that we are then, according to the corollary, what we are believed to be—how unavailing with men must be his own poor trust in his honesty! But this abstraction was not the demeanor that the King's Council had a right to expect of one called to a hearing.

And the Lord Chancellor—even after almost two years' absence, it was strange to see the Council from this angle—had found his memorandum. He looked nervously the length of the table to where More stood to speak in his own defense. "Master More," he began in a tart, thin voice, "His Highness the King has been much disturbed by reports that you dishonored his office and cheapened his justice when you were lately his Chancellor. Specifically, the complaint has been that you took bribes. What have you to say for yourself?"

"My lord"—More tried not to see Cromwell's frowning signals to Audley—"the complaint is, as you say, specific; yet I shall need the exact cases recalled to me, for my memory evidently fails me. I do not know to what you are referring."

A slight sound that might have been a cough or a sneer drew More's glance to the left, where the Earl of Wiltshire was sitting; the snarling line of his lips destroyed any doubt about the sound. So vindictive, Thomas Boleyn, you who were once so impatient?

Audley, after studying the document before him for a moment, resumed his indictment: "One John Parnell, citizen of London, has denounced your judgment against him as unjust and extortionate, because when the suit of one Geoffrey Vaughan against him was pending, the said Vaughan, unable to travel because of the gout, sent his wife to you with a valuable gilt cup as a bribe."

"I remember the incident well, my lord." More wondered, with a little tempering of his exuberance, how he himself as a judge might have read the eagerness of his answer. "It was long after the decree, nearly a year, as I recall, that Mistress Vaughan brought me the cup." Out of the tail of his eye, he noted an amazed, compassionate glance from Archbishop Cranmer. "And since the judgment was so long passed and she had come on the journey herself to bring the cup as a New Year's gift, at her importunate pressing, I could not in courtesy refuse to receive it."

Wiltshire's fist thudded on the table. "Did I not tell you, my lords, that you should find this matter true?"

More had not hoped for such easy success—so neatly hooked, Thomas Boleyn? Aloud he said, with as great calm as he could summon, "My lords, since you have courteously heard me tell one part of my tale, will you not in honor listen to the rest impartially?"

The Chancellor, taken aback by the Earl's interruption of More, looked at his fellow-councilors uncertainly.

"It is only fair, my lord, to hear the whole explanation," Norfolk said brusquely, as if he were disgusted with the matter.

"Of course, we are withholding judgment till you have finished," Audley announced too lamely to make his words reassuring to More or chastening to Wiltshire.

"Although I did, after long refusal, receive the cup from Mistress Vaughan, I immediately had my butler fill it with wine, and I drank to her from it. And when she in turn had pledged me, I gave the cup back to her to take to her husband for his New Year's gift. She made as much ado over accepting the cup as I had done in the first place; yet at length I prevailed on her to take it."

When he had finished, Norfolk looked at him in relief so obvious as to be almost funny. Cromwell and Wiltshire seemed both to be glowering at some invisible object halfway between them on the table.

The Chancellor coughed gently. "Is that all you wish to say, Master More?"

"All, thank you, on that case. Are there others?"

Audley affected to study his paper for a moment before he said with admirable ambiguity, "We shall finish with this inquiry now. Will you wait in the anteroom while we hear the other witnesses, Master More?"

Bowing—"demurely enough, I hope," he said to himself—More turned. As he passed through the door which two ushers opened for him, he caught a glimpse of a woman and two or three men waiting at the end of the corridor—Mistress Vaughan, he hoped, and at least the footman who had accompanied her. The prosecution, he reflected, had probably neglected to summon any of his former household.

What were they holding in reserve? For a frivolous moment he was divided in his mind whether to lay a wager with himself that there were no other "cases" on that bill before Audley or to hope that they would charge him with having received the gift of a gold-ornamented walking stick. It would be delightful to say, "Does His Grace the King know that that is in the indictment? If you will send for it, my lords, you will find his own badge upon the head of the stick." But as he weighed this incident seriously, he felt that he had made a distinct gain. Of course, it was vexing to think of the King's Council using their time and his and Mistress Vaughan's on so trivial and insulting a matter—that was one side of it; on the other hand, were there any murmurings about his honesty as a judge, he was grateful for a chance to vindicate himself. In the nearly ten months since the appearance of his *Apology* no one had repeated the libelous accusations of cruelty to heretics or risen up to say, "I am one he abused"; perhaps men were even coming to see that the man who labored to persuade heretics and to answer their arguments desired not their death but their conversion. That charge, at least, he could leave well-answered to the justice of posterity; for he would write no more in disputation. If he were vindicated to-day in this other matter, it would stand as something more ended. Even if he were not, however, his enemies had revealed themselves: without surprise, he had found Wiltshire the head of them, but he had been amazed to note Audley's malice. What more did Thomas Boleyn want? His daughter wore her crown, and his five-months-old granddaughter had the Princess Mary, the granddaughter of a King and a Queen, as a lady-in-waiting. And why was Audley, whom he had never offended to his knowledge, leagued against him? Cranmer and Norfolk were well-disposed. But what of Cromwell?

At that question, which would need pondering because he had not read Cromwell's expression and actions with any positiveness, the sighing of his door on its hinges interrupted his thought. When he had followed one of the ushers into the Star Chamber again, he could sense that mentally the Council had broken rank and stood adjourned, though they kept their places for the formality of whatever announcement he was to hear.

"Master More, we have found that the witnesses' testimony corroborates yours." But Audley's manner and voice had drawn no honey from the discovery. "I shall be glad to report as much to His Grace. That is all we care to inquire about at present."

"Thank you, my lord." ("No jesting, no irony, now," More warned himself.) "May I ask one question? Do I understand, my lord, that there are other headings to this charge of bribery? Or am I clearly discharged of all such abuses?"

Audley would neither meet his gaze nor answer the question directly. "We find no ground for accusing you of bribery during your Chancellorship," he said finally with unabated tartness.

What of Cromwell? The interrupted question returned with heightened importunity a week later. More had been sitting by the fire in the hall with his book before him, for recently he had been too uncomfortable with the pain in his chest to risk the draughts of his library. Here William Roper found him. He was home very early, More thought, for there was no need yet of lights to lengthen out the brief February afternoon; nor was his earliness alone disturbing. He had some perplexing news. As he sat down opposite, More noted the passivity of his expression, always a sign of a struggle to subdue worry which drew all the reserves of liveliness inward.

"How is the pain to-day, Father?" Roper began.

"Less sharp, thank you, but cramping enough to make me sit up; so I chose a little book that doesn't have to be hunched over —Erasmus's *De unitate ecclesiae*."

"Oh! That sounds definite on his part. What's it like?" Though the comment spoke an honest interest, More knew, its tone was that of a man too preoccupied to loose his hold on the main matter.

"You will like it, I think, for it keeps the middle of the road more honestly than some of our 'pacifying' here in England. Remember I have it when you want to look at it." He let the little volume slip to the seat of his chair. "What's the matter, Son Roper?"

Though there was no one else in the room, the young man spoke cautiously, as if even his thought had looked to its shutters. "Did you ever have much to do with the Nun of Canterbury, Father?"

"Almost nothing. Why?" More's first anxious thought turned to the Ropers' connection with Canterbury. Had any of them become involved in the scandal which had endangered many there?

Roper's answering sigh sounded like one half of relief, half of irremediable despair; with it, however, his retreated energy came back to his face. "Let me tell you the whole story, Father. I'd like you to judge it as much as possible for yourself, for you know I don't greatly admire Master Cromwell. He sent for me this morning at Westminster, and began with professions of his concern for you and his anxiety to serve your interests. You can imagine how well he would carry out the part. Yes, I am thoroughly ashamed of being so suspicious," he supplied his own commentary in a matter-of-fact, unrepentant tone. "Then between statement and question he tried to search me pretty thoroughly about your relations with the Nun. At first I was afraid that some of my family down in Kent had meddled with the matter, for this is how he began: 'This business of the Nun spreads out distressingly, Master Roper; there must be many people sleeping uneasily lest their share in it be discovered—the most unexpected people to be deluded by such an ignorant, superstitious woman.' 'I am sorry to hear that, Master Cromwell,' was all I could say after so blind a lead into the matter; indeed, I wanted to add the hope that many who had been drawn to the Nun by her reputation for holiness could be proved innocent of any political implication. But I was walking into no traps. So with that look of his which plucks out one's thoughts he went on, 'Your father-in-law has been so often mentioned by those who specially encouraged the Nun that I am concerned lest they try to involve him beyond the truth—not that they would mean to lie, but they stand in such a desperate danger that they might try to clear themselves by exaggerating the influence that wiser and more notable men than they had had with the Nun.' Then I ventured to say, 'That is a caution we lawyers must always remember when we listen to witnesses, isn't it, Master Cromwell?' But he flicked the thought away and went on: 'We have one letter which Sir Thomas wrote her, which the Nun had evidently treasured as a wise piece of counsel.' "

"Had he read it?" More asked jubilantly enough to startle Roper.

"I don't know. Why?"

"If he has read it, he knows that it's wise counsel. I advised her against meddling with politics. But I'm sorry to interrupt you, Will."

"He went on, 'This letter suggests that he may have written her others or been frequently in conference with her. Thinking you might know the facts, Master Roper, I thought we could save your father-in-law inconvenience by my asking you about these letters and visits that he paid to her or she to him.' You know how quick I am to anger, Father; but I think I held on to myself fairly well while I explained that for all I knew you had written not even that one letter and that, though I had heard you mention seeing the Nun once at Sion, I knew she had never been to consult you at Chelsea. I lost some of my heat when he nodded and smiled over that information as though it were what he most wanted to hear. He thanked me and wound up with a suggestion: 'Much as I respect Master More's wisdom and loyalty, it may happen that others in judging this matter will feel more doubtful; therefore, if he were to write as full an account as possible of all that he ever heard, or did, or said, in the affair of the Nun, we should have it on hand to quiet any questions. Will you ask him to write me about it—freely and fully as to a friend?' When he thanked me again for my help, I felt half-ashamed of my innate distrust of him."

"Only half? He seems to me to have spoken very openly." More would not conceal the fact that this new attempt to inculpate him sounded very grave, for during nearly three months now the terrifying charge of treason had hung over the Nun and her associates, and there had been the methodical leakage of official action calculated to torment the scores of people who had had some innocent intercourse with her and to invite the panicky to inform against others. It was a very serious matter to be even named in such a case. Before they considered his course of action, however, he was anxious to have Will Roper's full estimate of Cromwell's attitude. The latter smiled sheepishly at the challenge to his repentance.

"Grant I don't like his general manner; the special thing about him I distrust is his air of thinking when one has made the most casual, unpremeditated remark, 'Is that so? We will check on that.' I couldn't ever unburden myself to him."

Ludicrous as was the thought of anyone's unburdening himself to Thomas Cromwell, More said with but the faintest smile, "In a way, that's what I must do, however, isn't it? The sooner I start, the better, too."

"I wish there were some other way, Father. I don't like the idea of your writing after these vague accusations."

"Spoken like a cautious lawyer, Will. But there is no shade of evidence against me in the truth, and the more circumstantial my account of the facts, the more completely can it be verified. Father Risby and Father Rich are the two who gave me fullest reports of the Nun. And, though they may have been foolishly credulous of her visions and revelations, they are honest men, and I trust them to bear me out in my testimony that I refused to listen to anything from them that concerned the King. I had better set about writing the letter now, for it will have to be a long one."

Roper looked newly perturbed. "But, Father, the bending over will make you worse. You ought not to try to write it yourself. Let me be your secretary."

It was true, More had forgotten, that so long a letter as this must be would overtax his strength in the mere physical labor of it; yet he must make the attempt, for he was determined not to be devoured in vulgar, causeless, ignominious quarrels such as these his enemies were raising against him. If they would destroy him for the truth, he prayed that he might be steadfast in it; but he could not give them the satisfaction of cloaking the truth in these dishonoring lies.

"You tempt me, Son Roper. That is generous of you, but you are a busy man in your own right."

"Not so busy as not to do you one small service. Where shall we work—right here? I can bring a table over."

"All right, Will; this once I'll run myself headlong into debt to you. But first, I must find my copy of the letter I wrote to the Nun. No, I think I know exactly where it is; so I can find it more easily than you."

"That isn't all I was thinking, Father, though I was going to offer to get it; but if Cromwell has it, since you wrote just the one, why trouble about it?"

"Is there any telling what may happen to letters, Will?" More was startled to find himself echoing a comment of Bishop Fisher two years before. "I want Master Cromwell to have that letter just as I wrote it; so we're sending him a copy of it."

After the dispatch of the long letter to Cromwell, there was nothing for them to do, More assured his anxious family, but to rest in the truth. They might never even hear again of the matter, any more than they had of the charge three weeks before of his answering the Council's book. Much as he had believed in their sharing joy and sorrow, he regretted the worry that camped like a sturdy beggar on their hearth. His wife went nervously about her work with, touchingly, no word of complaint or reproach for him; his sons and daughters came anxiously home to inquire for news. It came on a snowy Saturday evening, when they were all gathered at the Great House for Sunday together.

Cloaking a little yawn, Margaret said, "Will is late. We'd better not keep the children up any longer."

Almost at once, they heard a muffled clatter and thudding outside, and they nodded in unison: "This must be he."

The door from the corridor by the chapel cut a shaft of light across the floor towards them, but the man who straddled it was John a Wood, not William Roper.

"Master More," he began in so tragic a voice that More glanced anxiously towards Margaret and the children, "Master Roper asks will you please come out here a minute."

In the entry, Roper leaned against a settle like a man too bewildered to move further; he had not shaken the snow from his shoulders nor removed his wet gloves. Behind the mask that his face had become, More read some bitter pain that had taught John a Wood his cue.

"Father!" Roper's voice died in that one cry.

"What is it, Son Roper? Are you ill?"

With a shake of the head, Roper fought for self-control. Laying his hand tenderly on More's shoulder, he said, "To-day in the Lords the Bill of Attainder—the Nun and the others accused with her." Choked, he could not continue, but More understood.

"Am I in it?" Will nodded. "Anyone else?"

"The Bishop of Rochester." His worst report made, Roper could speak more easily.

"Fisher? That is infamously done! Is the charge misprision of treason?" The charge was a heavy blow, but it was not yet condemnation. "God willing, Son Roper, we shall confound the lie. Warm yourself for a moment. We have been waiting for you to join us in prayers before the children go to bed. Then directly after, I shall write to Master Cromwell to request a copy of the bill. That is but common justice."

CHAPTER VII

THROUGH almost two weeks of anxiety, More waited an opportunity to defend himself before the House of Lords. At length, the King seemed to make some acknowledgment of his plea by appointing a group of the Council to hear him. The Duke of Norfolk, the Archbishop of Canterbury, the Chancellor, Master Cromwell—their names sang in his thought like phrases in a chant to accompany the rhythmic sloshing of the oars this warm March morning. Beneath the main chant ran the minor one of Will Roper's imploring: "Win their help to free you from the Parliament Bill." Yes, that was important, but the thing that sent such a tingle of excitement through his veins as made him feel able to front all the world's malice with the humble courage of the truth was the fact that at last he could speak before those whose report, whether grudging or not, must bear him witness to the King. Half, at least, of the little commission empowered to hear him, the Duke and the Archbishop, would listen fairly: that was a generous allowance of favor, for which he gave thanks. What of Cromwell? In proportion to the power attributed to him, he had been ineffectual in his promised friendship; but More reminded himself that the overbearing forces and false evidence might have been too strong for even his influence to withstand. He would not judge Cromwell by the fact that his own name had come to a second reading of the Bill of Attainder before the Lords.

When he had waited only a little while in their antechamber —not the enfeebling hours that turn a suitor's courage key-cold and beat his spirit to the pulp of supplication—the Lords of the Council sent for him. Sitting in easy informality about a small table, where a fifth chair waited, Cranmer, Audley and Norfolk were laughing lightly as if at some sally of Cromwell's, for he wore the smile of the man who is being appreciated. At More's entrance they checked, but did not retract, their mirth to greet him with disarming graciousness; Cromwell's "Good morning" was the warmest of all.

With a better grace than he had expected, Sir Thomas Audley bade him be seated, and the nods of the others seconded the invitation.

"Thank you, my lords," he answered, deeply touched by all this affability which seemed to be turning the clock back to days almost forgotten in this recent beleaguering. "But it is not fitting that I, who have come here to be examined, should sit now among you."

"As you prefer, Master More," said Audley, "for it is your own doing that you are not sitting among us in as great honor as anyone." Then, with a quick glance at his colleagues, he began to speak stiffly as if he were rehearsing a declamation: "To no man has our gracious Lord the King showed greater love and favor than to you, both in offices and in private trust and friendship, which it would be only common gratitude for you to repay as His Majesty wishes. Nothing would have made him happier than to continue you in your office and to heap more benefits and honors upon you; even now, in spite of your stiff-necked resistance to his pleasure, it is not likely that His Grace would deny you any worldly honor or profit you could ask, in the proper spirit, at His Highness's hands. In his bounty all that he asks of you is that you add your open consent to those matters already passed and ratified in the Parliament and by the bishops and the universities, for it is a great grief to His Highness that you set your judgment against that of so many wise and reverend men."

As the Chancellor's tone announced the end of his reproaches, More wondered a little dizzily what he, who had expected to plead his innocence of complicity in the case of the Nun, could say now. What the King had attempted hitherto as most private solicitation he had delegated to his Council. Yet did His Majesty think that they could succeed where he himself had failed?

"There is no man living, my lords," he heard his voice speaking more calmly than his heart beat, "who would more willingly do the things that should be acceptable to the King's Highness than I, who do heartily acknowledge his manifold goodness and benefits bestowed upon me. Nevertheless, I had hoped not to hear of this matter again, considering that I have from time to time from the beginning of it so plainly declared my opinion to His Grace. His Highness always seemed to accept my views like a most gracious prince, never intending, as he said, to molest me with the matter again. Since that time, my lords, I have not been able to find anything further that could move me to change my mind. And if I could, there is no one in all the world that would have been gladder of it than I."

"Master More," Archbishop Cranmer's voice was almost incredibly gentle after the not unkind hardness of Audley's, "when I recall how earnestly you listened to me while I reasoned the matter out for you—it must be about four years ago, is it not?—I cannot but believe some of the arguments for His Grace would be convincing to you. It is not as if you held your opinion contentiously in despite of reason and even of your own conviction. Indeed, I have assured His Highness that I have never found truer meekness and willingness to be persuaded in any man I have reasoned with."

"I am humbly grateful, Your Grace, for your good report of me and the patience I remember you showed me. Yet, without setting my judgment against others' or my conscience in condemnation of them, I have found nothing to change the belief that I have always confided to His Majesty when he has consulted me."

"You wrote me that you had read the Council's book, Master More," began Cromwell. "Did not that persuade you?"

"It offers no argument, Master Cromwell, that I have not met before. And I read it only once, and then not critically."

"Did it not deserve more careful consideration than that?" Audley asked in undisguised virulence.

"Surely, my lord, from those still concerned with the matter, for its articles are very learnedly and subtly drawn, far beyond my poor knowledge of the law and the facts. But I read it only once because the matter has become one of indifference to me, who never argued with any man about it, or revealed my reasoning to anyone except His Grace at his own earnest request, or sought to persuade anyone to my way of thinking."

"If it be a matter of indifference to you, Master More," the Archbishop resumed, "can you not safely subordinate your judgment to that of the King's many learned doctors? It is right for you to trust your conscience to the guidance of others in matters wherein you can honestly say that neither your knowledge of the law nor your acquaintance with the facts permits you to judge finally. You have only to say, 'I am content to abide by the decision of those who know.' "

"That is kindly urged, Your Grace, I know; but I cannot take that position when my 'abiding' would be read as approval."

"Then we are dealing with sheer stubbornness," cried Audley.

"Just a minute, my lord," interrupted Norfolk, who had been mumbling his upper lip, "before we jump to any conclusions. Can you not just say that the matter is ended, Sir Thomas, and you are willing to accept things as they are and go on from there?"

"In one sense that is what I am doing, my lord; as you know, when His Highness granted me leave to retire, I planned to meddle no more in politics, and I have kept that resolution. But beyond that silence I cannot go."

When the Chancellor glanced at Norfolk to see whether he would protest further, the Duke shrugged his shoulders in so scarcely perceptible a motion that More wondered whether it existed outside his own imagination. Thus left to follow his course, Audley drew himself up and began bitterly:

"If we should find you obdurate and unwilling to be moved by gentle persuasion, as you have fully proved yourself, the King commanded us to charge you with the basest ingratitude. Never was there a servant so villainous to his prince as you have been."

These words spoken as with Henry's authority cut More to the quick. If they were the King's—and four of his councilors would not have banded together in such a lie—they meant the end of any expectation of justice. But perhaps, hope challenged, here was his opportunity to repudiate the charge of treason, which this attack must be prefacing.

"By your subtle and sinister tricks," Audley was saying, "most unnaturally persuading and provoking His Grace to write his book of the Seven Sacraments and the maintenance of the Pope's authority, you caused him, to his dishonor throughout all Christendom, to put a sword into the Pope's hand to use against His Highness. Therefore, all the trouble that has arisen between our gracious Lord and the Pope, who is more properly called the Bishop of Rome, can be laid to the charge of your delicate conscience."

More could have laughed at the sheer delirium of intimidation in this accusation; but open laughter was hardly the decorous answer to these councilors or to the King. After the moment due to the enormity of the Chancellor's revelation, he said, "My lords, these terrors are for children, not for me." The picture of Warden Elstowe facing down the wrath of young

Boleyn flashed before him. Alas! he had no such courage as the calm Observant. "To answer that with which you chiefly burden me, however, I believe the King's Highness of his honor will never lay that to my charge; for there is no one who can on that point say more to exonerate me than His Grace himself, who knows right well that I was never the persuader nor the counselor of His Majesty to undertake that book. After it was finished, by His Grace's appointment I merely sorted out and arranged the principal matters contained in it." He could feel his examiners listening as if to something they had been long curious to know.

"And when I found the Pope's authority highly exalted and powerfully defended with strong arguments in the book, I said to His Grace: 'I must put Your Grace in remembrance of one thing: the Pope, as Your Grace knows, is a prince as you are, and in league with other Christian princes. Hereafter it may happen that Your Grace and he may disagree on some points of the league, and that there may come a breach of friendship between you and even war. I think it best, therefore, that that passage be amended and his authority be touched on more lightly.'

" 'No,' said His Grace, 'that shall it not be. We are so much bound to the See of Rome that we cannot do too much honor to it.'

"Then I further reminded him of the Statute of Praemunire, whereby a good part of the Pope's pastoral authority here in England was pared away. To that objection His Highness answered, 'Whatever impediment there may be to the contrary, we will set forth that authority to the uttermost; for we received from that see our crown imperial,' which I had never heard till His Grace told me of it with his own mouth. So I trust, my lords, that when His Grace shall be truly informed of this and shall recall to his gracious remembrance my action in the matter, he will never speak of it again, but will clear me thoroughly on that score himself."

"Though you speak very plausibly, Master More, these are proud words," the Chancellor scolded him. "You would make the King a liar."

"By no means, my lord! His Grace must have forgotten the circumstances of his writing the book. I, who have less to remember, recall them vividly. All I have said is that His Highness, when he reconsiders the matter, will exonerate me of any effort to influence his attitude towards the Pope, except as I urged that he use milder terms in reference to the Pope's temporal authority."

"It is your word against His Majesty's." For a simple remark, Cromwell's was unmitigatedly sinister.

"When His Majesty remembers—" More was beginning.

"You say you did not write the book," the Archbishop interjected. "Who did?"

"It was published as His Majesty's, and I for one never doubted, Your Grace, that he had the skill and the knowledge to compose it himself, though he did, I believe, consult some theologians on the subtlest points of his argument."

"Do you remember whom he consulted?" Cranmer insisted gently. "The Bishop of Rochester, for example?"

"Your Grace, only His Majesty can answer that question," More said as quietly as his indignation at such sounding permitted.

"What you said about your attitude towards the Pope's authority interested me," Cromwell remarked. "I am not sure I understand what you meant; so I should appreciate your telling us just what you think about his primacy."

"That is a somewhat different question, Master Cromwell,

for His Majesty was in the passage I questioned exalting the Pope's temporal authority; his spiritual primacy I hold to be indisputable."

"Concerning it," the Archbishop broke in eagerly, "do you hold it instituted by God or agreed upon by men simply as a matter of expediency? It seems to me I have heard you cited as one who held the latter view."

"Your Grace, I do not presume to dispute such questions, for again I feel I am not adequately instructed. It is true that, having given the matter little study, I once was not convinced that the primacy of the Apostolic See was of divine institution until I read the King's book against Martin Luther. Then I began to read in the Doctors from Saint Ignatius to our own day, both Latins and Greeks, and I found them so unanimous on that point that, after these seven years and more of study, I should think it perilous to conscience to hold otherwise than that the primacy is of divine ordinance."

"Ah, but there is weighty authority for disputing that conclusion, Master More, and holding the primacy of the Bishop of Rome but a usurpation which the rest of Christendom may redress by refusing allegiance to that see," the Archbishop explained patiently. "There is a phase of the question you should study."

"To what profit, Your Grace? For, at the least, the primacy was instituted by the whole body of Christendom to prevent schism, and it has been corroborated by continual succession over more than a thousand years. If the question is one of England's refusing fealty to the Apostolic See, I cannot perceive, Your Grace, how any member of the body of Christendom may without the common assent of that body depart from the common head. So in this connection, Your Grace, I cannot see that the arguments about the institution of the primacy are truly relevant. But, honestly, my lords, I have not much meddled with such questions in the past except in private study, nor do I intend to meddle with them henceforth."

"But were you to inform yourself, you could be useful to the King's Highness," Cranmer still urged.

"No longer, Your Grace, as His Majesty is, I believe, convinced." More shook his head sadly.

All but the Archbishop had so long given him up, he felt, that Audley's impatient glance at the former was not unjustified. "Master More," he said dismissingly, "I am sorry that we can make no better report to His Highness than you are forcing upon us. He will not take it in good part that you have spurned his generous and loving offer of favor, such as never any other prince condescended to try to force on an ungrateful and wicked servant. There is no more to be said in the matter."

So ominous a dismissal should have terrified any reasonable man, his own good sense strove to convince More, though his spirit exulted almost riotously in the face of the rebuke. Now he knew not only who the chief of his enemies were, but why they sought his life, for he recognized the ultimate motive of these machinations with a curious, impersonal light-heartedness. It was a problem in logic neatly solved, and he could write *Q. E. D.* at the close of a perfect demonstration.

The still piercing wind of early March made conversation unwise as they traveled homeward from Westminster; but Will Roper's studious examination of his face suggested that, in thought of his interview, he must be grimacing like a monkey. A little later, if need be, he could assure Will that he had not lost his wits. Now he would reflect on his recently confirmed knowledge: the Duke of Norfolk was not unfriendly, but he could do no more than shrug off concern for a fool; the Archbishop was definitely solicitous to win him to compliance with Henry's will—though not ill-disposed, he was only a reed in the wind of the King's desire; Chancellor Audley had reiterated his hostility, and it seemed no longer possible to doubt that, as befitted his office, he spoke the mind and the conscience of the King; and Cromwell—"It is your word against His Majesty's." He could not blame the councilors; in fact, much as he ought to have trembled, he was glad that the quarrel had found its true terms and had broken thus into the open.

It might be his word against the King's in the sense that men ordinarily attach to such a phrase; but more truly than anyone except Henry and him could realize it was the word of the King whom he honored and whom he had served against that of a King transformed. Resolved not even to attempt characterization of this usurping personality, he must in loyalty to the Henry who had been superlatively his friend and patron try to make him prevail. He had been a King who respected private conscience, who kept promises, who said to his counselors, "In my service look first to God, and afterwards to the King." To that King he had sworn fealty, and he would recognize no other; so he must fix all his thought and devotion, his hope and his prayer, on him. "First to God, and afterwards to the King"—that was an irrevocable command.

Before he had perceived they were so near, the rowers had pulled over to the quay at Chelsea, and Will Roper, sprung ashore, was holding his hand out to him. Straightening, as much from the preoccupation of his thought as from the physical strain of his cramped position in the boat, More took a deep breath.

"Strange, isn't it, Son Roper," he laughed, "that, near as we are to Westminster, we breathe a different air?"

"Is it the freshness of the wind here?" Roper hesitated; then, a little shamefaced, he added, "Or are you thinking of moral atmosphere?"

"You may read the riddle, O Daniel."

As they came up through the garden, he noticed with the

year's first delight in the observation that the twigs of sunward, sheltered bushes were swelling to bud and overlaying the winter's dun with the warming shades of life. This was the beginning of the spring tinges in the landscape that, with the impudence of youth, for a few days mimicked the autumn's coloring.

The strange intensity of gaze, the wordless questioning, had crept back into Roper's face; so between their two curiosities they must reach the question.

"What is it, Will? Am I changed into some queer creature for a menagerie?"

"It's just that I haven't seen you feeling thus for a long time, Father. I trust, sir, that all is well because you are so merry."

"It is so, indeed, Son Roper, I thank God!"

"Are you, then, put out of the Parliament Bill?"

The question shook him to an awareness in which for an instant he seemed dreamwise to lose his experience with the King's councilors. That had been no dream, however; and till the examination was well started he had thought to exculpate himself from the charge of misprision of treason, and in the course of the session he had utterly forgotten it. He was sorry as a child might be at being caught, not at the fault itself.

"On my word, Son Roper, I never remembered it."

"Never remembered it, sir?" Were he capable of being chided into realization of his folly, Roper's consternation, he knew, should have sobered him. "A case that touches yourself so near, and us all for your sake! I am very sorry to hear it, for when I saw you so merry I was truly confident that all was well."

Yes, it had been selfish of him to exult so; yet the exultation was a precious thing that he could in part share, even though he could not tell all the grounds for his rejoicing.

"Will you know, Son Roper, why I was so merry?"

"Gladly, sir."

"In good faith, Son, I rejoiced that I had given the devil a foul fall, and that I had gone so far with those lords that I could never without great shame go back again."

In spite of all the conviction of his words, however, he saw that Roper could not share his rejoicing, and his heart sank; for if he could not prevail with the King on the one hand, he must with his family on the other. It was hopeless to try to tell which would be the harder task. Not even that sobering challenge, though, could quiet the surging thanksgiving in his heart. God being his good Lord, he would prevail.

To erase the lines of anxiety from Roper's sensitive brow, he said heartily, "The bill is not yet passed; so help me, please, to save the rest from needless worry. I mean to write Master Cromwell a full statement of my stand on all the issues they would raise against me. It shall be unmistakable and final, even if I must make it a book. And if need be, the Lords may still hear me in my own defense."

Before the letter, which had grown into a little book, as he had feared it might need to grow, was dispatched the next day, however, his hope seemed well-justified, for Cromwell had spoken hearteningly to Will Roper about his intercession with the King. So, though he could make it no fuller nor more open than it already was in its exposition of his views, More sent the letter in profound gratitude and confidence. There was even a fair likelihood that this long explanation, as well as his short appeal to him personally, would reach the King. Surely, then, after the years of their friendship, Henry would read believingly the words that were as sincere as his most secret prayers. Some one had been afraid that he would write and speak against the King's new policies, he told himself: that was all. Now, with assurance that he had renounced such matters, they had no reason to harry him. Moreover, there were still in the House of Lords men who meant to withstand injustice, for they had asked the King that he be heard in his own defense.

Nevertheless, among all the news from Westminster in the next week, there came one item that concerned his hope and almost throttled it. Not Cromwell this time but Norfolk, who was not unwilling still to expostulate with More, had told Roper a little of what had happened in the Council Chamber when all the Lords of Council had knelt before the King to dissuade him from risking defeat in the Lords by going thither personally to overbear resistance. Not that all the Council had turned his friends, he knew too well, but that the case against him as an accomplice of the Nun's had no show of equity in it. "Had knelt before the King to dissuade him"—even the Cardinal had so knelt and failed.

Though his exhilaration in knowing the terms of the battle from which he could make no retreat had persisted through this week of uncertainty, it had grown sometimes faint in the presence of grave thoughts. And these were his chief company as he walked for a few turns on the terrace in the midday sunshine of March the twelfth. Far in the orchard a chaffinch was singing, and back and forth below him half a dozen winter-fattened robins gleaned greedily in the dried grass and round the shrubs. The beauty of God's world seemed to plead for undistracted appreciation—"Rest in this peace, be glad, and fear not." But the mind that God had given him would not be stilled by such solicitations. Back and back it went, seeking through all the strands in the maze of his knowledge, his conjecture, his hope, and his fear the one that should, like Ariadne's silk, deliver it from the labyrinth and the devouring Minotaur.

If he must stand condemned, one advocate reasoned, there was no man whose company could be a greater honor and consolation in undeserved ignominy than the Bishop of Rochester's. Indeed, firm as was his own assurance of innocence, he felt that his claims were poorer in connotation than Bishop Fisher's. The sanctity of his office, in which he had been a true shepherd and no mitered hireling of a politician, should have exonerated him; his age and his feebleness should have pleaded for him; above all, his long spiritual service to the King's grandmother, to his father, and to him should have silenced the obloquy crying against him. What had he himself, More's grief for his friend despaired, to witness so powerfully for him, who had been a worldly servant and councilor, proud of honor paid him, enthralled by joy in his work and his family? But these good things of his life, another advocate contended, had been of God, the trusts given him in his station. Thought of his family might not plead for him in Parliament, but now it pleaded mightily with him. Had he any right to bring to these loved ones pain and grief and infamy? Then, he cried shame upon the cowardice that would cloak itself in such an argument. As when the question roused him in the night, he prayed, "Give me Thy grace, Good Lord, to hold these earthly affections in but their proper dearness." How simple it would be, he groaned to himself, if from this crisp wind over the Thames a voice could speak as from the whirlwind! But not thus in these latter days did the voice of God come to men.

As he strove with himself, he saw Margaret hurrying from her own house towards him. What could be the matter? In the instant of admitting the question, he remembered with a start that such a note of alarm was the recent response of all of them to anything new. They must learn to quiet these quick-springing fears. While Meg was still too far off for him to read her face, his sanguine fancy leaped ahead to interpret her errand as good by the buoyancy of her gait.

"Father!" She was panting from haste and excitement, and smiling at him through tear-bright lashes. "Your name is out of the bill."

Out! For an instant he feared that she might grow hysterical with the joyous relief of her news, revealing such a past anxiety as it hurt him to think of; but Meg's control was too strong to yield easily. She wiped her eyes with a suspiciously moist handkerchief and laughed naturally. It was the glorious laughter that might welcome a soul to heaven, More told himself with the ghost of a sigh for these dear earthly affections of his.

"Isn't it splendid?" Her voice danced as her feet had done years before at some childish delight.

"That depends on what it means, Meg," his somberness forced the words with which he was sorry to blight her joy. "Tell me about it."

"Ned Cowper has just come with the news from Will. He had promised to dine in the city, but he couldn't let us wait till he came home; so he sent just the word that Master Cromwell had told him you were out of the bill. We'll hear more to-night, but this is the heart of it—the best news imaginable. Aren't you happy, Father?"

"Indeed, I thank God for this release for us all, but I cannot be light-hearted over it." The reproach in her eyes and the cruel necessity of his thought made explanation painful; but the picture of the Council kneeling before their angry sovereign held his inward eye inexorably. He took her hand very gently: "In faith, Meg, quod differtur, non aufertur."

That picture of Henry in his Council recurred often in the next few days, when rumors bloomed and wilted and William Roper's nightly homecoming was a family occasion. Yet there was no definite news as to what had happened or what was to follow. More tried little by little to win his family from any expectation of complete security and to turn their thought to Bishop Fisher, whose name had not been stricken from the bill, now passed by both the Lords and the Commons. Though they all knew that neither the imprisonment nor the forfeiture to which he stood condemned could in material senses grieve the saintly Bishop, they could well read in the pitiful injustice that had befallen him the dangers that threatened men who had angered the King.

Near proof of that unremitting anger came soon in a visit from the Duke of Norfolk, who had rowed up to Chelsea in midafternoon. More had brought his guest to sit in the spring sunlight in the oriel, where they talked briefly of their health and their families and the prospect for crops. Then for a moment embarrassment fell between them.

Finally the Duke said with his habitual bluntness: "I'm glad you have a good sensible farm here, not one of these gingerbread show places some people are going in for. Have you been much pinched the last two years?"

The direct challenge touched More's pride, for poverty is a tender subject even between friends; yet this was no shameful, wastrel's poverty to justify embarrassment.

"We have managed, Your Grace, and we are not yet threadbare or out at toe. I could wish for a smaller estate to maintain, but this has not devoured us yet."

"I could wish you had more rents," the Duke said with a business man's confidence in his values. "I am worried about you, for His Majesty swears you shall not have your annuity any longer."

Though he hoped the blow left no outward smart, More was grateful to the rough courtesy of the Duke, who was staring resolutely across the hall. In the instant of a very simple calculation, he grieved for the strain this deprivation of nearly two-thirds of their income would put on his wife's skill in managing.

"I am sorry that seems necessary, my lord." More hoped that his voice sounded not too limp. "But I have had the money these many years by His Majesty's free gift; so he is only taking back what he granted me."

"Gad, though, Thomas, how much has it been?"

"A hundred pounds."

"A hundred pounds! And by our Lady, I wager you have not that much left."

"I'm afraid you're right, Your Grace."

Norfolk clenched his thin lips as if to keep from uttering some impatient rebuke and, leaning forward, surveyed the hall. Was he too thinking arithmetically? He straightened suddenly in his chair.

"And why? By the Mass, it is perilous striving with princes. Therefore, I urge you to incline somewhat to the King's pleasure. By God's body, Master More, 'Indignatio principis mors est.' "

Though he could not echo the terror that spoke in Norfolk's words, their anxiety touched him; after all, faint-hearted as they were, they were the words of many men in these dark days, and they were generously meant and sincere in this utterance.

"Is that all, my lord? Then, in good faith, there is no more difference between Your Grace and me but that I shall die to-day and you to-morrow."

Norfolk stared at him unanswering. With a pang, More thought of three other old friends whom he had not seen in the nine months since they had come here likewise to expostulate with him. A willfully friendless man had always seemed to him somehow God's enemy.

CHAPTER VIII

"I LIKE this one best," little Winifred Clement declared after the solemn appraisal proper to a seven-year-old. More and she had been studying and comparing the printers' devices that made the last pages of books as fascinating as the more intricate title-pages. And her father's library was a good hunting ground for the strange beasts, birds, and reptiles that swarmed between the covers of the soberest volumes; so they had drawn out a collection of tailpieces—one to a printer unless he had changed his heraldry.

Well-trained little girl as she was, Winifred methodically closed the volumes of the rejected colophons and piled them against his chair, where they leaned in somewhat crazy insecurity. Still, if the big ones toppled off the little, they could not be much hurt in so short a fall as the child's arms could cause them. With distractions thus removed, she sat down again on her hassock at More's feet and propped Theodric Martin's *Utopia* against the impromptu lectern of his knees. In the full seriousness of her years, she studied the page; then she broke into a rippling chuckle as she turned the book round for him.

"Look, Grandfather. Aren't they funny? They ought to look alike, but they don't." Though More knew well, after seventeen years of acquaintance with them, that the lion on the left was a sharp-looking beast while his fellow on the right wore an anxious, or perhaps bored, expression, he delighted to match his own seriousness with Winifred's. These heraldic creatures with the almost human countenances and their peers were a source of unfailing delight to children, his experience with his grandchildren and with young visitors at Chelsea had taught him.

"Why are they standing up like that?"

"To hold this shield in the middle. See?"

"Oh. Could Tip do that?"

The picture of the child's devoted terrier attempting such a pose was an alarming one. "It would be painful for him to try. Nature meant him to go on four feet, you know."

"Why?" The girl's clear, sweet voice rang suddenly loud in the room, for her question caught a moment of silence in the earnest conversation of her father and mother and William Roper.

"Little question mark!" Margaret Clement teased. "She'll wear you out if you humor her, Father."

"You are a fine one to rebuke a questioner, Margaret, especially any child of yours, who comes by the gift naturally," More laughed.

"And I guess, if children's questions could have worn you out, you'd have been frazzled long ago," John Clement added.

"Why does Tip go on four feet, Winifred? The best answer I know, my dear, is that it is God's plan. You have two and the beasts have four—"

"How many does your fly have?"

That was a thoroughly nonplusing question until Margaret, who had been half-listening, explained, "The amber heart, I think."

"Oh. The fly shut up in amber, Winifred? Once he had as many feet as the sauciest fly on your windowpane. Next time you come to Chelsea, we'll have the heart out to look at."

"Will you look at my bestiary with me now, please, Grandfather?" Winifred was evidently well-satisfied on the score of feet; so at his smiling nod she was away to find this favorite book in the nursery.

"I wish all the whys could be answered so briefly," John Clement sighed, as his gaze followed his daughter from view. "Have you been listening to our comments on the sermon today?"

"No, but I listened to it; so I can guess."

"Paul's Cross has heard strange doctrines attacked," Will Roper mused, "but this must be the strangest ever defended there. Denying the Pope's authority in the country—what does that make England, Father?"

"Schismatical, at least. This is willful contumacy." And three years before, More thought with heavy heart, men had quieted this fear with "A few words—what do they change?" To-day's preacher, almost frothing in his abusive denunciation of the head of Christendom, gave answer.

"From what you've said, Will, if that sort of rant can be called a godly sermon, it's well we didn't go. I might have cried shame on the preacher and been arrested," said Margaret, with so determined a toss of her head that More smiled in spite of his somber thoughts.

"I don't doubt your courage, Margaret," he said, "but prison is, they say, a swift cooler of hot heads. And what should your family gain by having you shut up?"

"Not advices of caution from you, Sir Thomas!" John Clement exclaimed with gentle irony. "As we were just listening to Will's account of that sermon, I was thinking of your old instruction: 'If you live to the time when no man will give you good counsel or good example, when you shall see virtue punished and vice rewarded—' Do you remember?"

As if he were speaking a response, Roper completed the quotation more to himself than aloud, but the words were familiar enough to come home in thought whether truly heard or not: " 'If you will then stand fast and firmly stick to God, though you be but half good, God will allow you for whole good.' "

"You remember accurately. And I do not take back one word of the lesson. But to be arrested for sheer bad manners in interrupting the preacher in his pulpit might confuse the issue, Margaret, and bring God little honor. And I can take you so seriously, my dear, because I know you would never do it."

"With things going as they are, there's no knowing what I may do," she insisted. "In whole earnest, though, Father, was there ever anywhere in history an irony like this of the Pope's just pronouncing His Majesty's marriage to Queen Katharine valid and binding when Parliament has passed this new Act of Succession? After all these years!"

"And they say that the two actions occurred on the very same day," John Clement added.

"But why has there had to be all this grief and confusion when the end leaves things just as they were?" In the insistence of her question, Margaret leaned forward with the fine, stubborn inclination of her head which marked her reflective moods.

"That is such a *why* as John was thinking of, I imagine, harder to answer than the ones the children bring us. Yet, Margaret, you are the most hopeful among us, for you speak as if the confusion and the grief were all ended." More saw their cry of protest at his own gloom shaping itself; but the appearance of Winifred on the threshold hushed them all.

As the child danced towards him, hugging her book under her chin, More wondered whether she had noticed their perturbation. There flashed into memory his own vividly recalled experience of coming so into a council of his elders and hearing of the death of King Edward the Fourth and of the rash prophecy of a man named Pottier: "Then will my master the Duke of Gloucester be King."

"Are you ready, Grandfather?" Winifred had found her place; so he could not postpone their survey of the bestiary. In the next minutes, as they were enjoying the pictures together, he was aware of Margaret's leaving the library probably to busy herself in household matters and John's and Will's moving to a far corner to examine some new books on which he himself had had his eye. Scarcely noticing it, he heard a pounding on the street door and saw one of the maids bring in the lights and another come to summon her master. In one nook of consciousness he entertained the hope that the message was not one of illness to summon Doctor John away from them.

Only as he looked up into Clement's face when the latter, having returned, stood over them, did he realize that something was amiss. The young friend, whom for twenty years he had guided and watched grow, was a man suddenly aged by anxiety.

"Will you come downstairs a moment, sir, please? There is a man asking for you." His tone pleaded for forgiveness in bringing the message. He laid his hand on his daughter's curls: "No more this afternoon, dear."

"Mayn't I hold the place?" she begged as, rising, More laid the book in her lap. But quietly, at her father's shaking of his head, she closed the book, and the leaves clapped softly together.

Westward the sky was bright with the almost tintless clarity of a spring sunset, too soft to be called a glow, too definitely washed with the faintest of greens and lime yellows to be merely colorless. In the ordinary barrier of the sky belling down to the horizon, this light opened a corridor, a luminous avenue to tempt the imagination beyond the simple bounds of space and time. Whither? The question hurled thought back to that which More had hoped momentarily to escape by this concentration of the outward eye on the ephemeral track into the pathless heavens. Whither?

Lambeth—now peacefully gray on their left across the wide water—to-morrow morning. "You to appear before His Majesty's Commissioners to take your oath to the statute lately enacted in Parliament—" The words of the summons he had read there in his old house marched back and forth in thought as if by the mere harboring of them he could come to full perception of his duty. They had not surprised him, for on one level of consciousness as he had fronted the officer with his paper he had said to himself, "You have been expecting this"; and to himself he had added, after passing it silently to Will and Margaret and John, "Of course, it was only a question of the precise time. Now even that is set." If only consciousness had no other levels than the one chief stage of any moment! For nearly a year he had seen this coming—yes, Queen Anne had worn her crown almost a year; so it must have been close to last Whitsunday that he had angered Will Roper, sitting now so dejected beside him, by uttering the hope that the whole travesty of order and morality be not in time confirmed by oaths. Far back there in June, had the oath been set for the next day—instead of for to-morrow, the thirteenth of April—he would have been intellectually forewarned. And since then he had had the preparation made by the birth of the Princess Elizabeth in September and by this few-weeks-old act establishing the succession, with its provision that all subjects might be summoned to their oath at the King's will.

As if, however, it were his first lesson in all his fifty-six years, he recognized sadly that a great gulf stretched between rational prevision and emotional. In how little a time now must he bridge that chasm where the tides of human attachments surged, as he had seen the stormy tides of ocean churn in a cliff-rimmed pool. As yet his engineers had strung but their guys. Long as he had been trying to school his heart to accept thought of the perhaps imminent parting, it had been a stupid pupil. And, were the heavy countenances of John and Margaret Clement and Will Roper fair index of what he had achieved, the hearts of his family were no more apt pupils of his philosophy than was his own. He saw the three again in that instant when, the summons scanned, they had dared to look at him—the white, still horror of their faces against the darkening room. On a wild impulse he thought of turning the boat back. That must not be his farewell to his own first, in many ways his dearest, house. But the impulse died in the correcting comfort that all the segment of his life in Bucklersbury, with its thousand pictures of family and friends, of the joy he had had in his first wife, Jane, and their four little ones, and of the sorrow of her death, was an unalterably whole possession. When he thought of the Barge, he had so many tender associations to summon that this last dark picture need not grieve him unduly; and in that fair, crowded, early pageant John and Margaret Clement had their places as young members of his household.

Thus musing, he came into a certain gladness that the officer with the summons had found him in the city instead of at Chelsea: he and Will Roper were prepared. Together they might be able to stand off the legions of consternation that beset a household whither bad news has come and where, like a contagion, panic spreads from face to face and heart to heart. As their boat drew towards the landing, he prayed for strength to bear the hours between now and the time of testing with only the heaviness of spirit due to a solemn need. "Give me Thy grace, good Lord, to keep myself Thy servant." His aspiration dwelt on the words of Saint Paul: "In all things let us show ourselves as the servants of God in much patience, in tribulations, in necessities, in distresses—" Patience and a sober cheerfulness—they were so little to achieve, and for him so hard!

The feebleness of words weighed upon More's spirit when he saw tears shining in the eyes before him: he had tried to tell his family that the morrow was a day of testing, but that they were not unprepared, not unfortified. He had spoken of how greatly they had been spared—three generations of them who had scarcely known suffering or the shadow of death—spared till they might have to fear that their souls had grown soft with sojourning in the sunny felicity of their life. How little they had known of the bleakness the human spirit can make for itself or of the misery that has forgone all faith save unbelief, all hope save that in despair, all charity save the nursing of its own cankering sores! So greatly had the mercy of God spared them that they must see the present as a time of trial not beyond their strength provided they remembered that they had nothing of themselves—no goods, no gifts, no honor among men, not life itself—but all things held in trust, inscrutably bestowed, inscrutably reclaimed, by God. "The Lord has given, and the Lord has taken away: as it has pleased the Lord, so it is done: blessed be the name of the Lord." He had meant it to be a heartening little discourse; and instead, he had made them weep.

In the chastening of that defeat, he said, "Let us say compline, and keep afterwards the silence of hearts composed for the rest and refreshment the night gives." The quiet rustling as they knelt and found the place in their books brought him a pang of the unregenerate foreboding he had tried to mortify—if he were never again to keep his devotions in this dear, strengthening company! The deeper, then, must be his thanksgiving for the long, long time of his joy.

As they read and prayed and sang together, their voices grew stronger in the strength of God's certitudes—rest and peace, trust and safe-keeping, and joyful blessing. Noiselessly, while they went on with psalm or prayer, the glorious words already uttered stole back in consciousness to be a secret choir in More's heart. "A quiet night and a perfect end . . . In peace I will sleep and I will rest . . . Love the Lord, all you His saints: for the Lord will require truth . . . Do manfully, and let your heart be strengthened, all you who hope in the Lord . . . His truth shall compass thee with a shield: thou shalt not be afraid of the terror by night, nor of the arrow flying by day . . . In the nights lift up your hands to the holy places, and bless the Lord . . . Now dost Thou dismiss Thy servant, O Lord, in peace according to Thy word, for my eyes have seen Thy salvation . . . He has risen as He said, Alleluia." As befitted these last hours of the octave of Easter, the glad cry echoed and reëchoed in their worship: no man could keep his private sorrow now when all Christendom was commemorating for the fifteen hundredth time the great joyous mystery of sorrow and suffering vanquished in the Resurrection. "I will go before you into Galilee. Alleluia."

According to their custom, they fell to silent prayer, from which each would steal away in his own time. "Peace be with you"—if he could lay hold of that peace, More meditated, it would quiet all the rebellion, all the dissension of his impatient spirit; for it was the peace of triumph beyond defeat, made secure against all pride of victory, all despair of failure. The saints had won it by long-suffering and vigilance, by pain and sorrow and the fierce spending of all the strength of man; poor, naked, maimed, they had brought their struggling and their failure home and had seen them made glorious in the infinite love and the infinite pity of God. It was easy to obey His will and to say, "Thine be the honor and the glory!" when glory and honor abounded; but hard, hard, hard, to consume all one's gifts and powers in the battle and still to say, "Thine be the glory!" "Give me the grace, good Lord," he prayed, "to remember that Thou hast never promised that the way shall be smooth or the burdens light, and the strength to understand that peace which Thou hast promised to those who travail and are heavy-laden."

When he had climbed by his prayer to the high, still plain whence even the saddest day looks but its small, insignificant self, he was ready for his last thanksgiving of the night. At a little stir that he made in shifting his position, he heard some one rise behind him, and he knew that save for him the chapel was for this last moment empty; but he had not watched and striven alone. Then, as he blessed the companioning strength of his dear ones, his eyes were blind with glad tears.

The curious exaltation that had waked him in the gray of the morning and brought him straightway into the whole consciousness of those who fear they have slept too long stayed with him as he let himself out to the terrace. This was the day. Involuntarily, he shivered in the almost frosty air, but the body would be shamed to have no discomfort when its tenant the spirit was restless. Restless? He groaned. Was it all to be labored over again because this was a new day? All things yielded and went their way—this hoarlike dew, the web of mist above the river, the low-hanging great star, these busy birds that had slept no more than half the night—all things but the stubborn spirit of man. For there had risen again in his heart the cry for these he loved. He must align them—these antagonists in him that would keep no armistice. Suppose the oath proposed to him were one that he could honorably swear and then come home again, all this panic would seem a coward's folly. But that hope was a fool's weakness, for the whole purpose of these oaths must be to enforce the presumption, the outrage, already perpetrated; the oath would be but a farce did it not, explicitly or implicitly, demand approval of the severance of the Church in England from the unity of Christendom. If it be only implicit approval, the secret devil prompted, must you sacrifice all the wholesome joy in life that you find in your family, your friends, your studies, your devotions, for—what? A few words. "A few words. What do they change?" The King who had asked that more than three years before knew how much they were meant to change. No, the defenses of his conscience lunged at the enemy, there must be no compromising such as would turn the blessings of life to a curse. Though he believed that Parliament could make whom it would ruler or heir to the throne, he believed, too, that it could not alter the spiritual jurisdiction of Christendom. There was the true Palladium in this warfare. If all the private beauty and glory of life died in the conflict, the issue could yet be victory.

Poor frail spirit! Here a full month past he had exulted in the fall he had given the devil, and now it had risen up against him again. If he could hold this better mind only till he reached Lambeth—no, only till he took boat from Chelsea and passed out of sight of home, he could hope to be no more afraid. For so small a grace would he pray in his Communion, he who, like a fearful child, must see his way in little steps. Now, by God's grace, he would set an armistice for the warring passions in his heart in order to compose his thoughts for his confession. As he turned back along the terrace, he began attentively, slowly, his prayers of preparation.

The rowers sat in their places, and Will Roper, ever thoughtful, ever generous, had gone ahead to the boat so that he might have these moments of farewell alone with his wife and children. In the fullness of his heart he could say no more: Dame Alice and Margaret, Cicely, Elizabeth, John, and Anne needed no practical counsel. And for spiritual—what could he say in any time he had now except "Trust God and fear not. And pray for me as I shall for all of you"?

At the garden gate he stopped them—from the quay it would be too far for them to go back remembering this travesty on their thousand cheerful partings; and in spite of all the strengthening he had been vouchsafed, he could not trust himself to be still calm to kiss them there at the river's edge as had been his wont. Better here, as it had been better to say good-by to the little ones at the door.

Gently he thrust them back and pulled the wicket to. "God bless and keep you all!"

Without a word, Will Roper helped him into the barge and straightened the collar on his gown to lie evenly and warmly on his shoulders. Thoughtful and generous and loving—all of them.

Behind him all the good of many years, except for the memory of them that was his forever—behind him Chelsea. And soon on the left, as they beat away from it for the Surrey shore, the gray of Westminster, whither he had come thirty years before to his first Parliament: burgess, lawyer, diplomat, councilor, Speaker of the Commons, Chancellor, he had known Westminster well. And since his father was not sitting there in the Court of King's Bench to be distressed by this last failure, he did not grieve that he was leaving Westminster, too, behind him.

And now, by the irony of life, he was coming home to Lambeth, where as a boy of twelve he had first glimpsed the complexity and the splendor of the world, and something, also, of its hard, shrewd dealing. Chelsea, Westminster, Lambeth—not all his life, but how much of its beauty and its pain and its joy! Suddenly, it all had for him the arrested peace of the wise, ungrieving memory of the dead that abides with the living.

And he was aware of how sadly Will Roper was sitting beside him. He laid his arm across Will's shoulder and drew him closer to whisper what he could now trust himself to say:

"Son Roper, I thank our Lord the field is won."

Will's lips parted in the smile of one who does not wholly understand; but he said only, "Sir, I am very glad."

And the quay at Lambeth was close on them.

CHAPTER IX

No other layman—were there any distinction in that fact, More reflected as he watched the anteroom filling with clerks, he should be a proud man. They came by twos and threes, talking quietly among themselves, nodding good morning to him, passing trivial comments on the weather; yet under all this ostensible ease ran a current of nervousness. It was no small matter to appear before the King's Commissioners to take an oath the exact tenor of which no one seemed to know beforehand. As one of the first to come, More had taken his place in the elbow of a window: no station for a man in haste, who might be passed over for those hugging the door, but it suited him well in its light, airy semi-privacy. His thought was idling with the promise of warmth in the morning when he noticed Dr. Nicholas Wilson approaching him.

They had seen little of each other since those of the King's advisers who opposed the divorce, of whom this royal confessor had been one of the stanchest, had agreed not to confer lest they invite the charge of conspiracy in their resistance. So their first conversation followed the natural personal inquiries, beneath which, however, More felt the stirring of his friend's anxiety; the deeply circled eyes and the settled frown of self-debate could have served as mirror to any thoughtful man.

"How restless they are," the priest exclaimed suddenly, "in spite of their show of calm! We'll all feel better, I suppose, when we see just where we stand." He studied their companions with a gently melancholy gaze. "How do you feel about this oath, Sir Thomas?"

Utterly sincere and guileless as the question was, More felt he must refuse a direct answer, "We must wait till we see it, Reverend Doctor, before any of us can be sure. Yet I prefer—I do not mean this unkindly, as you know from experience—not to know your intention or any other man's, and I will reveal my own to no man. Our old counsels of caution, perhaps."

"I understand." The tension eased a little as Wilson spoke. "I grant you're right; but sometimes it helps to know that one is not standing absolutely alone."

"God guide us all!"

The subdued murmur in the room, rich in the overtones of voices used to the pulpit, stilled suddenly before one of the Archbishop's secretaries, standing in the doorway. From the paper in his hand, he read:

"Sir Thomas More."

Dr. Wilson pressed his hand encouragingly, and the rest made way for him—the one layman. No doubt, it seemed convenient to have the odd person disposed of before the others.

At the far end of the great hall the Commission sat behind the high table. In the Archbishop's chair that should be Morton, ready to hear the reckoning of his household's demeanor, or Warham, welcoming Erasmus, Colet and him; instead, it was Cranmer, and he himself was approaching the paper-strewn table and the men behind it alone. As he stood before the dais, they gave him a moment in which to appraise them and be awed: the Lord Chancellor seated beside the Archbishop, with Thomas Cromwell beyond on the right and Abbot William Benson of Westminster on the left. New men, all of them, he noted. Yes, there had been a clean sweep, for, he remembered, on the day when Archbishop Warham and he had spoken last with the King, Abbot Islip had been laid in his tomb in the Abbey. With the formality of men who have weighty business to dispatch and who feel the pressure of time, they looked at him impersonally—the first to be dealt with to-day.

In a kindlier voice than he had sometimes used, Audley began the preliminary explanation: "In pursuance of His Majesty's commission to us to register the oaths of his subjects to the Act of Succession recently ordained in Parliament, you are summoned, Sir Thomas More, to subscribe to that Act under oath. Are you ready to be sworn?"

"May I see the oath, my lord?"

Freely, as if only through an oversight had he not been shown it before, Audley turned the paper he was holding, heavy with the great seal, and handed it across the table. With an inclination of thanks, More accepted it to read: stripped of its necessary legal verbiage, it was simple enough—"to bear . . . faith, truth, and obedience only to the King's Majesty, and to the heirs of his body . . . according to the limitation . . . within this statute of succession . . . and not to any other within this realm, nor foreign authority, prince, or potentate." In addition, any who had taken such oaths as were incompatible with this were to repudiate them through this superseding one. Save for the implicit rejection of papal jurisdiction, this oath might seem only a proper one for a loyal subject to swear; yet it supposed full knowledge of the statute.

When he looked up, the eyes of the Commissioners seemed to reach through his to seize his opinion, unbetrayed in his face, he trusted, as he laid the paper on the table.

"Since this rests, my lord, on the very wording and intention of the statute, may I read that, too?"

Though a shadow of impatience darkened Thomas Cromwell's face, the Chancellor and the Archbishop agreed in a heartening equanimity; the Abbot sat just beyond the line of direct vision. Again as if he had made the most reasonable of requests, the Chancellor extended a printed roll towards him. It was indeed a formidable document in length. In the flicker of recognizing that fact, he remembered the men in the antechamber; but Lambeth was a commodious palace, and this oath could be neither lightly sworn nor lightly refused.

As quickly as his practiced eye could find the significant phrases, he read the statute, of which he found he had had accurate report: the plea for the fixing of the succession to avoid ambiguity and division; the preamble declaring the King's first marriage void, affirming that with Queen Anne, and specifically denying to any man, "of what estate, degree, or condition soever he be," power to dispense for marriage within the prohibited degrees of consanguinity; then the Act itself declaring all such unlawful marriages void and the judgment thereon of the English ordinaries "definitive, firm, good, and effectual," forbidding appeal to the Court of Rome, reaffirming the legitimacy of the King's children by Queen Anne, fixing the succession on them, setting the penalty for acting, writing or talking against the Act from the first day of May, and requiring an oath, without form specified, however, "to observe, fulfil, maintain, defend, and keep . . . the whole effects and contents of this present Act."

Very slowly he read the second last paragraph: "And if any person or persons, being commanded by authority of this Act to take the said oath afore limited, obstinately refuse that to do, in contempt of this Act, that then every such person so doing, to be taken and accepted for offender in misprision of high treason; and that every such refusal shall be deemed and adjudged misprision of high treason; and the offender therein to suffer such pains and imprisonment, losses and forfeitures, and also lose privileges of sanctuaries, in like manner and form as is above mentioned for the misprisions of treasons afore limited by this Act." Though, after that, he read the final brief paragraph with a certain irrelevant amusement, he put it out of thought for the present: that could wait.

With all the Act thus in mind, he looked again at the oath and laid them both on the table.

"Are you content to swear?" The words were Audley's, but the eyes of all four men were asking the question.

"My lords, I do not intend to impute any fault"—he must say this carefully enough to keep it free from any confusing issue—"to the Act or to any man that made it, or to the oath or to any man that has sworn it; nor do I presume to condemn the conscience of any other man." He could feel the patience of the Commissioners cracking. "But as for myself, though I will not refuse to swear to the succession, I cannot in conscience swear to this oath without jeopardy of my soul to perpetual damnation."

It was said. The others stirred in silent irritation, but the Archbishop leaned forward.

"May not this be some excessive scrupulosity, Sir Thomas, the aberration of a good and honorable conscience?" he said with his wonted gentleness of voice and manner.

"Nc, Your Grace, for I have given these matters long thought. But, my lords, if you think that my refusal springs from mere eccentricity or from some delusion, I am ready to satisfy you by oath that the reason for my refusal is so deep-seated in conscience that I cannot take this oath without peril to my soul."

"What use would such an oath be?" Audley asked more in bewilderment than in the distrust the words suggested. "It could cloak many motives."

More fought off the thought that the Chancellor was thus avowing a genuine expectation of perjury on the part of this Commission. Oaths! What do they change?

"If you could not trust me to swear truly in this matter of my scruple, my lords," he said with forced calm, "of what use would it be to give me any oath? And if you believe that I will swear truly in this, then I trust you will not of your goodness urge me to swear the oath you have offered me since you perceive that the swearing of it is against my conscience."

The Chancellor glowered down the hall as if he could see the huge company that must by now be waiting without. "Master More," he said huskily, and More remembered the picture of Audley kneeling before the angry King to plead for him, "we are all very sorry to hear you speak thus and to see you refuse the oath. On our faith, you are the very first one who has refused it. Is not that true, my lords?" A murmur of grieved assent ran among them. "This will, I fear, cause the King's Highness to feel great suspicion of you and great indignation towards you."

"Look," Cromwell said abruptly, extending a roll of close-set signatures; "here are the names of the Lords and the Commons who have already sworn to the Act and subscribed their names without fear or scruple. You are not having to stand alone."

There were many names, but More would not lean close enough to read them: it would be no encouragement to find his friends' signatures there.

"My lords, what other men have sworn I leave freely to their own consciences; I am judging only for myself." He recognized how hard it must be not to think him stubborn in this iteration.

Audley looked uncertainly at the others; obviously they could not debate what to do with him while he stood thus before them. The Archbishop murmured something about time to reconsider; and the Chancellor, seizing eagerly upon the suggestion, said, "Go down into the garden till we have sworn these others who are waiting, Sir Thomas. We will send for you again."

Considering that the heat of the advancing morning made the sunny gardens for the present uncomfortable and that the Chancellor's command meant no more than that he should tarry within call, More turned instead into the shell of the old burned chamber that looked out upon the garden. Here he could sit in the shadows on a blackened jut of stone and enjoy the bright beauty outside through the unglazed windows. There was something about the unchanging ruin that he found congenial to his present mood and that, without effort to analyze it, he could accept gratefully. As his eye located the vein of lead seared into the stone, which his boyish observation had marveled over years before, his thought was busy with other matters.

He had told the Commissioners that he would impute no fault to the Act and he meant to keep that resolution; but the lawyer in him was already dissecting the measure. An Act for the Succession: yet it tried, implicitly or explicitly, to be a compendium of the statutes enacted in this Parliament. If one would, he could make an appeal on that score, for it was a muddling sort of lay legislation that pronounced on what belonged to the jurisdiction of spiritual courts and that made repudiation of the papal power a corollary to the establishment of the succession. Its own words refuted those who, willfully ignoring them, denied that the Act meddled with dangerous matters. In the face of the Pope's verdict that the marriage of Henry and Katharine was true and valid, it would be, as he saw it, sheer contumacy to swear to this preamble setting forth the nullity of that marriage and the illegitimacy of the Princess Mary. It was unavailing to plead that the Act antedated the announcement of the Pope's decree in England. Parliament could settle the succession—a temporal matter; but to pit its judgment against that of the Pope in a spiritual question was, at the least, to deny the sacramental nature of matrimony. It seemed to him so plain; yet he had resolved not to argue, not to presume to instruct the doctors and the theologians.

On another score the old legalist in him stood aghast: here was a statute which all men must observe on pain of being judged in misprision of treason, or even—who could tell?—of being accused of treason; yet it failed to decree the wording of the oath on which lives might come to depend. As things stood, men might swear to one oath, only to find themselves in time declared subscribers to a very different one. To say that, of course, would be to insult the King and his councilors; but not to see the danger of irregularity was to confess oneself over-simple. That the Act required the oath offered him was by no means apparent, nor was it evident that those who had already sworn had subscribed to it. Indeed, Roper and others had reported the oath of the Commons as a more direct and plainer form than this. Wild as was the conjecture, it was even possible that men swearing to this extra-legal oath might find themselves, by some unpredictable spin of events, accused of violating the law in the very oath by which they thought to accept it. Christian decency cried out against so base a supposition; but legal knowledge stood its ground: that oath was not in the Act. He would dearly like to hear the matter pleaded; yet for him to plead it would be casuistry, for even the oath implied in this statute offended his conscience. Here was a pretty quandary: he would be imprisoned, he did not doubt, illegally; and he could demonstrate the illegality only by a quibble which would merely insure his being imprisoned legally. The lawyer in him argued for the demonstration, but another voice urged that he cease, so far as conscience would permit, to give offense. Justice and injustice, legality and illegality, he could leave to other tribunals than the earthly ones before which he was likely to plead henceforth.

So clear did all this seem that he could even smile at two minor aspects of the present travesty of law. Of course, it did not much matter that he was refusing the oath on this thirteenth day of April though the penalties of the Act were to apply from the first of May. What should he have been doing between now and two weeks from Friday? Yet he had heard of men turning over to sleep another hour on the morning of execution. The other ironical bit lay in that last brief paragraph of the statute, with its saving clause that the prohibition of marriages within the forbidden degrees applied only to those solemnized and consummated. On the one hand, then, the King was by the ruling of his own Parliament a bigamist, for one of the premises for the defense of his marriage with Katharine was the improbability that her first marriage had been consummated. On the other hand, of course, the union of Henry and Mary Boleyn had never been solemnized. As he read the list of the forbidden degrees of consanguinity, More had wondered whether the one that, by the understanding of canon law, applied here, "his wife's sister," would be cited; and finding it, he had wondered how the impediment to this second marriage could be explained away. And there was the explanation at the very end of the whole Act—truly an afterthought, it seemed, for it stood without any appropriate context. Very seriously, he speculated whether the framers of this statute had meant the abrogation of the safeguards to decency and morality provided by canon law, with its recognition of the impediment arising from extra-marital relations. He meant to keep his resolution never to talk or to write of the King's marriages; but the *cacoethes arguendi* vexed him sorely. No, the tragedy would have to play itself out without his telling the monstrous jest he had discerned in it, for he had promised the King almost seven years before to talk of the matter to no man else. And that promise held despite all the changes of the seven years between. It might be different—at least in the necessity of attempting to warn the King privately—were Henry a less learned man; but he knew what he was doing.

And so did he himself, More thanked God. He wondered how other men were faring, and whether Bishop Fisher had been summoned for to-day. When laughter in the garden made him straighten from the slump in which his aching body had relaxed, he realized that there had been much coming and going as if men swore easily and went their ways with little heaviness of heart. "May they never wish the morning's work undone!" was the kindest thought he could have. The laughter that had roused him came from a little group walking close beneath the wall of his shelter; of all these doctors and chaplains, Hugh Latimer was the one whose name came first to him when he sought to identify them. By his side walked a Black Monk, looking a little out of place among the secular clerks, no doubt one of the Archbishop's secretaries, or perhaps one of the Abbot's company. He was forgetting that Westminster had reason to be represented here to-day. But this monk was from Christchurch, after all, More saw with a certain sense of shock when he turned to laugh with some of his companions: he was the Brother John who had come to Chelsea once with Hugh Marchaunt. And he had been also, according to report, one of the chief informers in the case of the Nun: perhaps John a Wood had been right about his spying. Now, however, he was amazingly jovial for so taciturn a man. By straining, More might have heard some of the conversation that made them so gay; but eavesdropping had no interest for him. To his somber eye, though, the dumb show of their posture and manner was fascinating. There could be men so merry and unconcerned on such a day? At one moment he almost laughed himself, for Dr. Latimer had flung his arms over Brother John's shoulder and drawn him sidewise as a courtier might have embraced a not unwilling maid of honor, or a boy have played at courtship forty years before in the mumming upstairs in the great hall, where now—he must not forget—the King's Commissioners sat registering oaths.

Even in his amusement at the pleasant bit of drama—he did not grudge men their happy moments—he rose from his hard seat, turned away from the garden, and strolled towards the door by which he had entered the burned chamber. How long ago had he been worried for Dr. Latimer, who now stood high in favor at Court? Four years back, that must have been. From where he stood in the doorway, he could see the corridor by which men went timidly and came again cheerfully like boys from school. Not all of them, however, for Dr. Wilson came from the hall between two gentlemen and moved directly off towards the river-gate. Under escort—that fact had but one meaning. Though he had glanced hither, More could not be sure he had made him out in the doorway; yet he hoped so for the sake of whatever heartening his own detention might give the King's chaplain. What had Dr. Wilson said a few hours before? "Sometimes it helps to know one is not standing absolutely alone."

Yes, he recognized that he had been treated with extraordinary favor in being remanded to think the matter through again. In one way, then, he was sorry that the Commissioners had so misplaced their kindness as to weary themselves with him a second time. The garden had grown shady and the sociable noises of men had died away before a gentleman of the Archbishop's summoned him—the first one heard and the last evidently for this day. In the hall the paths of the sunlight on the flagging had shifted, and the Commissioners sat in half-shadow. They had had a good day's work, the pens and the open roll of signatures testified; but they looked worn with the weariness of dealing with many people.

"Have you reconsidered your refusal, Sir Thomas?" the Chancellor asked, still more patiently than More should have expected. "See how many men have signed gladly without any qualms since you were here before." He motioned towards the roll, which now ran diagonally across the table, but he did not say that all had signed.

"I do not question what they have done, my lord, but I cannot for all their number change my opinion."

"Do you not see that this refusal looks like sheer obstinacy, Master More?" Cromwell began urgently. "Though you say you cannot swear, you give no reason that can carry weight with others, nor do you point out any part of the oath that definitely offends your conscience. Why will you not swear?"

"My lords, I have feared that, as you yourselves have already said, the King's Highness would be displeased enough with me for simply refusing the oath, and that, were I to show my reasons, I should only exasperate His Highness further. That I will not under any circumstances do; rather will I abide whatever danger and harm may befall me than give His Grace any cause for anger beyond what the offering of the oath has of pure necessity forced me to."

"I cannot see that," reasoned the Abbot, who had not entered the discussion before. "You feel that you have good reasons for your scruples; yet you fear they will anger the King. The two do not hold together unless you mean to impugn His Highness's fairness in dealing with truly good reasons. This secrecy of yours reveals either an unworthy suspiciousness or sheer obstinacy."

"When a man is assured of a fair hearing for his scruples and he still will not disclose them, he cannot help seeming stubborn," Archbishop Cranmer seconded his colleague's deduction reluctantly.

How could he allay this charge and yet not be blinded by blandishments and taunts to the risk in confiding his reasons? "My lords," he began slowly, "I know how my refusal must look to you. And I have already offered to affirm on my oath that my objections are not frivolous ones. May I make one other suggestion?" He accepted their tired inclination as permission. "Rather than be considered obstinate, if I receive the King's gracious license—or rather his gracious command—to assure me sufficiently that my declaration shall not offend His Highness nor put me in danger from any other statute, I will declare the causes for my refusal in writing. Moreover, I will take my oath beforehand that, if I find my causes so answered by any man that I may think my conscience satisfied by him, I will then with all my heart swear the principal oath, too."

Though Cromwell frowned—and he was the one among these men who stood closest to the King's counsels—the others seemed to see some merit in the suggestion.

"It is a novel situation for a subject to suggest terms thus," Audley said deliberatively. "We must weigh it for a moment." His nod dismissed More out of earshot.

Walking halfway down the hall in contemplation of the trunkless tree-tops that the high windows revealed, More reflected that he might be inviting that very argument which he had in debate with himself renounced. Let him once give his reasons and the same demand at every item—"Why? why? why?"—would thrust itself upon him till he should have offended the King beyond all endurance. What had the Duke of Norfolk said? "Indignatio principis mors est." And it was better to die for a simple indignation than to fight and fight till the angers had fused in a conglomerate of rage and still to die with the responsibility for provoking that futile wrath on one's soul. What a coward this flesh was! After all his efforts at discipline he had been troubled at being called stubborn and obstinate.

A sudden silencing of the voices on the dais made him turn to see the Chancellor beckoning him.

"Master More," he said, when More stood again before them, "we can assure you that you shall have the King's license to state your reasons under his letters patent; but the statute is absolute. If you run into danger from it, the King's license will not serve to protect you."

This, then, More reflected, was a new definition of obstinacy, for, if a man may not declare his reasons for an action without imperiling himself, he would hardly seem stubborn in his silence. Still, he had been called suspicious and untrusting as well as stiff-necked; so he must take what risks might come. "My lords, if I may have His Grace's command under his letters patent, I will trust his honor for the rest."

That they were not very sanguine of what might be thus achieved showed in the indifference with which they accepted this submission. They were not done, however, with efforts to break his determination; for while his colleagues were busy with their papers, Archbishop Cranmer leaned forward to speak.

"Sir Thomas, you have several times spoken of not condemning the consciences of men who have sworn to the oath. It seems clear, then, that you do not believe surely that you may not lawfully take the oath, but rather that you regard it as an uncertain and doubtful matter." Cranmer fixed on him the same earnest, compassionate gaze with which he had been used to wait an argument's taking effect when he had exhorted More to accept the King's view of the divorce four years and more past. "But you know for a certainty, a thing beyond doubt, that you are bound to obey your sovereign lord your King. And, therefore, you are bound to give up this doubt of unsure conscience for which you refuse the oath and to take the sure way of obeying your Prince and swearing to it."

So amazing was this chain of reasoning that More felt genuinely perplexed. It was subtly pleaded. Could it be possible, however, that Cranmer, wise and skillful and sincere, as More believed him to be, by reason of his office the advocate of conscience against all worldly counsels of prudence and compliance, did not see the logical conclusion of his argument? In true debate a quick *reductio ad absurdum* would expose the fallacy; but he believed the Archbishop his friend in this crisis, and he would not gratuitously make him his enemy.

"Thank you, Your Grace. But I myself think I may not do

that, because to my conscience this seems one of the cases in which I am bound not to obey my Prince, since, whatever others think about the matter—whose conscience or learning I will not condemn nor take upon myself to judge—in my conscience the truth seems to stand on the other side. Believe me, Your Grace, I have not settled this with my conscience suddenly or frivolously, but only after long and leisurely and diligent search for the right. And in truth"—he was trying to keep his expostulation as temperate as possible, but he must add this—"if that reasoning may hold, we have a ready way to avoid all perplexity; for in whatever matters the doctors stand in great doubt, the King's commandment, given upon whichever side he pleases, will settle all doubts."

When it was said, he could not be sure that it had any real effect, for Abbot William Benson was waiting an opening to speak. He, too, began like a man laboring to save a stupid objector from the consequences of his pertinacity: "Master More, however this matter looks to your own mind, you have cause to fear that your mind errs here when you see that the great Council of the realm has determined the opposite of your opinion. For that reason, if no other, you ought to reject this conscientious scruple."

"It is true, my lord, that, were there none but me on one side and the whole Parliament on the other, I should be sore afraid to depend only on my own conviction against so many. But on the other hand, if it be that in some of the reasons for which I refuse the oath I have, as I think I have, as great a council on my side and a greater, too, then I am not bound to change my conscience and conform it to the Council of one realm against the General Council of Christendom."

With the old thrill of disputation rising in him, he saw that they all had listened to that statement. The King's license granted or not, if they wanted to read in those words the chief reason for his refusing the oath, he would be well pleased to abide the danger to follow.

Cromwell, who had been making notes for some time, had rested his pen to listen to the last score or so of words. "By God's body, Master More," he cried with an explosiveness that could be startling in a man so reticent as he, "I would rather that my only son had lost his head than that you should thus have refused the oath. Surely now the King cannot help suspecting you deeply, and even thinking you wholly responsible for this business of the Nun of Canterbury."

And she and her closest advisers were under sentence of death! More stiffened himself against the natural shiver accompanying that thought. "In that business, sir, the contrary is well known for the truth. But in this, it does not lie in my power to avoid whatever may happen to me without peril to my soul."

Chancellor Audley, who had reason enough, More granted, to feel that they were spending their time in vain, said a little sharply, "We shall have to report your refusal to His Highness the King through Master Cromwell. His Grace is to understand, then, that you refuse the oath proffered to you, for reasons of conscience which you are willing, however, to declare to him in writing on license given you under his letters patent; and further that you have not refused but are willing to swear to the Succession itself."

So fairly spoken was this summary that More was reluctant to interject the condition upon which, however, experience warned him to insist. "My lord, may I make one qualification there? I am willing to swear to the Succession provided I may see my oath so worded as will agree with my conscience."

"Marry! Master Secretary, mark that, too," Audley's long patience gave way in a testy exclamation. "He will not swear that, either, except in some certain manner."

"Truly, no, my lord!" More could not throw away all the

fruits of their forbearance in misunderstanding now. "My point is that I wish to see the oath so phrased beforehand that I shall neither be forsworn in taking it nor swear against my conscience."

"Well, let that pass for now. Do you have the distinctions recorded, Master Secretary?" At Cromwell's nod, as he began assembling his papers, the Chancellor glanced at his colleagues for their scarcely perceptible assent on the unspoken question. "Master More, until we know the King's pleasure in this matter of your oaths, you must stay in the custody of my Lord Abbot at Westminster."

There was no more to say. Waiting now, at the end of the afternoon, in the antechamber whence he had been called first that morning, More reflected on the consideration he had been shown. It all touched him deeply—from the patience of men who had sometimes been short with him to this detention at the Abbey. He might have been sent straightway to the Tower. But the right of sanctuary at Westminster, he recalled, was, according to the Act, not to save anyone from its penalties. How many other non-jurors had there been? And what had happened to them? "Master Secretary!" But that should have been Bishop Gardiner. Was Audley's giving Cromwell the title only an informal way of speaking, or was there a new man in that post, too? Henceforth, he smiled to himself, he was likely to be asking many questions without learning their answers.

CHAPTER X

TURN . . . and turn. To the sunlight and the good warmth of May and the wide blue of heaven. It was a niggardly segment of the earth's beauty that his chamber in the Tower looked upon; yet it had served to busy thought many times in these three weeks More had been thus shut away from the world. The high window that gave him this morning brightness faced east; and often, when anxiety for news from his family threatened to overwhelm his spirit with the heaviness he knew to be the deadly sin of sloth, he had reinforced his prayer against sorrow by active remembrance of his experiences that lay eastward and southward. The King's officers might be making inquisition about his property—he knew they had a disconcerting habit of acting prematurely in cases like his—but they could never lay hold of all the personal treasure he had brought with him to this bare cell. It was worldly enough meditation, he sometimes chided himself, but not ungodly, coupled as it always was with deep thanksgiving for the joy and the richness of life that God had given him. "You cannot hope to leap lightly over heaven's walls with the little exercise you have given your sinews," he answered the impatient anchorite in him. So he found help against despair in recreating the beauty past, which he could look upon without grief for its ending or desire of its renewal. Though it was, by the miracle of memory, still his, all this experience had achieved the immunity to envy of the things a man delights in but does not covet. Seeking to define that feeling—for he would have much time for such precision—he had likened it to the freedom from desire to own with which a man could roam Westminster Abbey, as he had done in his four days' sojourn with Abbot William last month, or Canterbury Cathedral, or the glorious Eternal City that he was never to see now, except in the mind's eye as he pieced together what Colet and Linacre and Erasmus and Gardiner had told him of its magnificence.

Gardiner . . . and Erasmus. His narrow walk back and forth across his room concluded, he drew the one oak stool of his cell into the sunlight. He must think out a distinction. Coward that he was, he had shrunk from thought of the living, who were somehow tangled, as was he himself, in the pain and confusion of the present; they came to mind as subjects of wonder or anxiety or compassion, not yet to be viewed in ungrieving contemplation. Colet and Linacre and even Erasmus dwelt in that bright Canaan of memory; but Gardiner, like his other friends and his family, was struggling in this wilderness of the present. Strange, he had never before recognized the evidently long-held tacit conclusion that he would not again see Erasmus, who a little more than seventeen years past had made his last, uncomfortable crossing to the Continent. He at least could always turn his sufferings into literary gold so that the very delight of dramatizing the experience for his friends must have assuaged somewhat its hardship and danger. Though there had been the brief exhilarating visits during More's embassies in Flanders, the last in 1520, he himself had thought of them even then as sheer gratuities in life—the more precious in their accidental, tangential occurrence. Erasmus had had, in the years between, his vexations and anxieties; but deeply as they had stirred him, More mused now, his Erasmus belonged to the long chapter of intimacy that the diptych portrait by Quentin Matsys had sealed. His habit of almost seventeen years of studying the living faces and posture of Erasmus and Peter Gilles through the likenesses had fixed them in his affectionate memory. And though concern for Erasmus could move over into this area of immediate pain, his recollection, like an expert scout in a new-found land, could skirt the morasses of distress.

That was the secret of all this eastward-lying experience—the unassailable serenity of what a man has known. That way and southward lay Kent. And he was riding again in a frosty twilight through the gray gate of Canterbury, surprised in his boyish excitement at the sudden clatter of hoofs on the cobbles and the admiring stare of people crowding the narrow street and leaning from gables to greet the Archbishop's entry. Probably he had seen the shrine of Saint Thomas first that evening, but he could not separate his first view of it from the overlying memories of other times. In the single sharpest picture of that stirring scene, a boy his own size, ragged, thin, thrust back with a gaunt, unsmiling man against the abutment of a bridge, cried out and pointed at him; and the man, speaking surlily, struck down the child's arm. For an instant, More remembered now, he had tasted the heady wine of importance, but it had turned to vinegar on his lips with his own ill-defined, lingering wonder at the pitiful child. He had seen poverty before that, of course; but he had not before recognized envy and bitterness as he identified them then, though the noise of the cavalcade had drowned the words of the boy and the man with him. Did that child, probably not privileged to read the philosophers, come ever to a true understanding of the mere pageantry of fortune, who deals men out their apparel, their ornaments, and their nags, and—temperamental playwright that she is—sometimes shifts the rôles in the very middle of the spectacle? Then, little brother, he mused, the actor—however sorrowfully—lays aside his gold-banded robe, his mask, and his buskins, and is a poor and humble man again—no longer Agamemnon, son of Atreus.

A poor, humble man? Perhaps even a prisoner keeping company with his shadow—his most faithful, life-long attendant—

and his thoughts. And they were treacherous comrades, for here he had been riding off through Kent with them and they had brought him home to this strong, stone room in the Tower. It would be warm outside this morning, he noted, as he moved out of the sunny track athwart his floor and drew his shadow back into himself—warm, and the Thames would be running at brim past Chelsea, and the children. . . . He groaned. His poor, rebel mind needed books and paper to sharpen and guide this dull, wavering meditativeness. If only he had news from outside! Faithful John a Wood, consorting with other servants within the Tower, picked up crumbs of rumor and, like a nervous thrush with a hedge nest of fledglings, came flying to cram him with them. But the walls were thick and high, and the Lieutenant's lodge was a narrow filter for news.

Yes, he needed occupation for this thought that leaped thus persistently from the smoke into the flame. Even work with his hands might steady it. So he drew his bucket of coals towards him to select a likely charcoal to serve as a pencil when he should have paper again; sharpening it was a slow enough task to discipline his flightiness. It was, too, a minor act of faith—he would be allowed some paper again.

When he had been about this quieting work for many minutes, the grumble of the keys at his thick oak door came as a not unwelcome interruption. The tall, soldierly presence of Sir Edmund Walsingham filled the doorway.

"Good morning, Master Lieutenant," More exclaimed, rising to offer his visitor the stool. "Like a wise governor, surveying your domain?"

"In part." Walsingham took the seat of honor while More placed himself on his mattress. "But you know, too, Sir Thomas, that I enjoy a visit with you for its own sake, and I've had no such opportunities as this for years."

"I wish I could give you a more luxurious welcome, Sir Edmund." More affected to examine his apartment ruefully. "You understand, though, that I have moved recently and am not yet well settled."

"Now that is what I should be wishing," Walsingham said with genuine concern. "When I remember your hospitality at Crosby Place and out at Chelsea, and your kindness to me, I feel like an ungrateful wretch to be entertaining you no better. It may be, however, sir, that things will change for you. I've had orders before to keep people very close and then after a while orders to let them go into the garden and to the church, and they've even been allowed visitors. To-day's state here doesn't argue to-morrow's."

"Then mine is a very hopeful uncertainty," More laughed, "though I can imagine some of your prisoners think none too cheerfully about changing their state. I can make no complaint, however, of anything that lies within your control. And I have been a councilor long enough to understand whence the orders come. If you have the opportunity, will you ask one favor for me, please?"

"If it will not offend the King."

"This should not. Did he not send me here to improve my mind? And if I might have some of my books and paper and pens, I should be more likely to spend the time profitably. Do you not agree?"

"It sounds reasonable; so I see no harm in asking Master Cromwell. I'm afraid I have no books you'd like." Walsingham seemed to be running through the catalogue of, More remembered, a not extensive library. "I suppose they're afraid that you'll write letters if you have paper."

"I've done only the three, to my wife and my daughter, in all the time I've been here, Sir Edmund. That doesn't sound much like disturbing the peace of the realm with my agitation, does it?"

"I should say not. You say 'all the time I've been here' as if it had dragged for you. Again I am more sorry than I can say to offer you no better hospitality, though I'm glad to find you so cheerful." Walsingham rose to continue his rounds.

"Master Lieutenant, I have no reason to grumble. Indeed I believe that, if you could, you would entertain me in your best fashion; and for that I thank you heartily. And assure yourself that I do not dislike your hospitality; but whenever I do, you may thrust me out of doors."

"That's fair enough," Walsingham laughed as he drew the door shut.

The triumphs were so few these days that More felt he could be forgiven a little gloating, for after all the foe he was vanquishing was his own affection: the great moment of this visit had come with Walsingham's casual mention of Chelsea. The pang of the beloved name had thrust at him far more gently this time than hitherto. Chelsea, Chelsea—he tested it as a man tests his knife edge gingerly; in time he might be able to say and think and hear it without pain.

The longed-for paper came with startling promptitude, for early in the afternoon, when he had cleared away after dinner, John a Wood puffed into the room with a letter and a few sheets of paper.

"And Master Lieutenant, he says he'll hunt up some pens if you want to answer this. Master Cromwell sent word he might."

"Thank you, John. It's Mistress Roper's writing." More could have laughed at the tremor in his voice as he unfolded the letter. It did not matter that its seal had been broken already.

He only half-heard John say, "Now that's fine, sir," and shut the door softly.

"Margaret!" he cried out in spite of himself, and in the last flicker of the joy with which he had opened the letter, he was glad that she could not hear him. As he read—it was no long letter in its pain and its pleading—the room went black and cold round him, though the sun shone blindingly when he tried to look up from the blinding words. Now, at last, beyond all jesting, he knew he was in prison, and he and all his—even the friends whom the idle finger might point to: "Behold! these also were with him"—stood in nameless dangers.

What had happened? The first half-comprehending reading over, he let the pitiful sheet lie on his knee. For a moment, though his eyes were dry, the lines had become an undecipherable blur on the page. The hand was Margaret's—indisputably hers; so the first wild thought of a forgery fled away—but the voice was the voice of an interloper. Unless. . . . The maddening question taunted him. What had happened?

Though he could have flung himself on the floor like a Bedlamite to dull the anguish of his mind with physical pain, he prayed for strength to fight off unjust judgments, reproach, fear, and, most of all, the temptation to yield in this fresh despair. If Margaret thought his scruples fantastic—no, that was not her word, but it was hard not to read it into the letter—how could he hope for any understanding, anywhere in all the world, of his decision? But now, passion aside, he must try to comprehend what lay behind her writing. Had the letter come from Dame Alice, it would have been natural, though distressing: she had so often thought him foolishly scrupulous that once more would be a bearable grief. But Margaret. . . .

He would think it through very carefully and believe it all meant in loving concern for him; so he read slowly the anxious phrases about his health and peace of mind. The pity of seeming ungrateful to the love that would save him from himself beleaguered his heart: this was the last of temptations. Gladly would he give life itself to save these dear ones from the pain that spoke here—unselfish anxiety for him; but it demanded, surely unwittingly, more than life for its assuagement. In that bitter reflection he took some hope. Margaret had been always so quick a pupil, so sensitive a spirit, that, if words could once serve his need faithfully, she would understand that the pure necessity of self-respect—respect for the integrity of his soul—had compelled him to the decisions that had brought him here. With all his explanation hitherto, he had failed to make that one important fact clear. It was comforting to see that the fault must be his, for now he could try to correct it. And Margaret would understand and cease to plead that he reconsider the oath.

The Commissioners had doubted the worth of his oath to objections deeply rooted in conscience: they had asked, "Why? Why?" In Margaret's echo of the question, he sensed in a slow rereading to weigh the key-phrases, she was speaking less as herself alone than as attorney for the defense. And the defense included his family and the families his children had married into and other kinsmen and friends who had looked to him for guidance. Would he be responsible before God for the suffering—even the destruction, he no longer doubted—into which they would run if blindly, without instruction as to the reasons for his own refusal, they followed him? "Some one has been urging on William Rastell that it is a grievous sin, very perilous to the soul, to resist the King; and the words of Scripture on that point seem very weighty. We have wondered how you have read them, good Father, in respect to this oath." They were not trying to trap him, he knew; yet his answer was for no one's ears but the King's. And he was by no means so confident of his judgment as to feel that others should hazard their souls by unquestioning compliance with his decisions. God knew how he had studied and watched and prayed to find his own course. Yet for others, without his knowledge or with more than he had, a different course might be the way of salvation: he could not tell. He could but pray that in the registers of God the oaths of men were entered according to the light they had been vouchsafed.

Another of Margaret's echoes of "some say"—was she not become as great a victim of rumor as the Pacifier with whom he had contended in that remote time when controversy had absorbed him?—refreshed the wonder he had first entertained in the burned chamber at Lambeth. "Many report, dear Father, that any man may take the oath with such reservations as respect his conscience. Surely then, if we add, 'so far as God's law allows,' what harm is there in the oath?" Since the Statute had not specified the form of the oath, it was evidently being administered under varying forms, and no one would know to what his neighbor had subscribed. The illegality and the obliquity of the proceeding alike revolted him. Only one thing he knew for certain: the oath offered to him had permitted no safeguard of conscience. And now, if such a reservation were offered him, knowing what had already happened, he could not accept it.

"Dear Daughter Margaret, do you not see the result?" he pleaded in thought. "It is no inordinate pride that makes me think they would gloat over my taking the oath. Many men's reservations they may honestly respect; but mine, I fear, since I have resisted, they might suppress, making capital only of the fact that I have yielded. You say that I have many years to live. Suppose that be true, by God's mercy: how happily shall I spend them if I be forever trying to catch up with a spurring lie about my oath or forever sinning in secret anger at calumny? For I fear, beloved Daughter, that I should be sworn not only to the oath but also—God forgive my suspicion!—to silence about its wording."

Still Margaret had one more shaft in her quiver—one to inflict a mortal wound. "Many have told us of the King's anger against you, for now they say that you show in the true colors of an ingrate—which is, you may guess, a grievous charge for your friends to listen to, though to attempt to refute it is for them to run into grave danger. Sad is it, too, to know that they are saying at Court that now you are unmasked; for they talk of you as one who professed not to meddle with the matter, who yet secretly wrote and spoke against the King's cause and perverted other men to your malicious opinion. We who know your spirit to be without malice, dear Father, wonder how you can refute this calumny save by complying with the King's will."

He could well imagine that threat and fear and covert insult were hounding William Roper, Giles Heron, Giles Alington, and William Daunce, who must often have to listen to such attacks on him. They had courage, he knew, but they must not squander it in vain battling for him. Since they had taken the oath according to their consciences, he must not let them grow suspect for his sake. They stood in danger enough of property loss, he read between the lines, for Margaret wrote almost gayly: "Do you remember how worried John a Wood used to be about idle questioners in the house? He would have cause enough now to be vexed."

How could he cope with all the danger his agile imagination descried for these young people who were so dear? The sure way looked so easy. And he heard again the Archbishop of Canterbury urging that way gently, insinuatingly, as the shadows fell in Lambeth Hall. No wonder that Secretary Cromwell had sent word that he might have paper! The thought was less compounded with resentment than he had expected; rather its chief ingredient was awe before the pitiful irony of human motives and actions. It was even painfully and inscrutably right that Margaret should be the agent of this bitterest temptation. Adam would not have fallen had not Mother Eve been very dear to him and very unselfish and greatly devoted.

With a knock, John a Wood came bringing the pens and a much-dabbled pot of ink. When their spirits were low some day, More decided, as he thanked John, he would tell him of Margaret's jest about spies and questioners—not now, for he must keep hold of such calmness as he had won in these heavy minutes of meditation.

Four sheets of paper—not encouragement to prolixity, he smiled a little wryly as he spread them on his rough table and then gathered them together to cushion the top one. It was awkward to have the pen puncturing the sheet when it rode over a hole or the unplaned grain of the oak.

Slowly he wrote across the top of the sheet, "Our Lord Bless You." Then he thought he saw her opening the letter anxiously as he had opened hers to-day—eagerly, perhaps, and hopefully. He could not begin with reproaches or careful reasonings. The pain surged back in his heart as he had seen the tempestuous sea break over walls men had labored all night to strengthen; and they who could stand again when the wave had seeped off across their fields fled from the ones to follow. Fled. He hid his face in his hands while the pen scuttled across the floor. "Whither can I fly, my God, but to Thee? Lord, strengthen Thou me."

The paroxysm drained away. "If it be Thy will—Thy will!" his thought sobbed. "Oh, weak, babbling soul! Can you even pray to be spared temptation when your high Savior Christ, humbling Himself to this bondage of flesh, suffered all pain for you. Good Lord, give me the grace in all my fear and agony, to have recourse to that great fear and wonderful agony that Thou, my sweet Savior, hadst on the Mount of Olivet before Thy most bitter passion, and in the meditation thereof to conceive ghostly comfort and consolation for my soul."

Gently memory ministered to the pain of his temptation. "God is faithful, Who suffers you not to be tempted above that you may bear, but gives also with the temptation a way out." Well could Saint Paul speak, as one having knowledge and authority through suffering.

He lifted his head and sat gazing at the sheet before him—"Our Lord Bless You." Hard as it would be to refuse Margaret and yet not chide her, he must go on. Having found the fallen pen, he began: "If I had not been, my dearly beloved daughter, at a firm and fast point, I trust in God's great mercy, this good great while before, your lamentable letter had not a little abashed me—"

CHAPTER XI

"Exaudiat nos omnipotens et misericors Dominus."

"Amen."

"Et fidelium animae per misericordiam Dei requiescant in pace."

"Amen."

The voice was Margaret's and the bowed head was hers; yet it seemed as if she would be gone when he rose and walked about the room again. Beneath the seven psalms and the litany had run the cry of his thanksgiving that she had come; but had the responses ceased and left him alone in his prayer, he could not have felt startled. She had risen from her knees; she was by the window. He ventured to lift his head.

"What is the matter, Father?" Her gray eyes were worried beneath their smiling. "You look sad."

"If I do, Meg," he said, rising, "it is for pure gladness. Or maybe for my lack of faith: I can hardly believe that you are here—that you will not slip away through the wall in an instant."

She gave the masonry an appraising pat. "It is substantial, and I am no magician from the East or it should have been whisked away long ago. Besides, the moat is deep. But, Father, we do not trouble you in dreams—or visions?" Her face was suddenly anxious.

"Bless you, no, Meg!" He could almost laugh. "I am too prosaic for that. I think of you all often and often, but I know my thoughts for no more than they are. Come, sit on my best chair, for all it is a wobbly stool. And do not worry because I let myself be carried away by joy in your coming. God hears the good prayer of your last letter, the one where you joined old pagan Juvenal to the most proper Christian words—'preserve you both body and soul *ut sit mens sana in corpore sano.*' Don't you remember what you wrote, my dear?"

"Indeed, yes. I was only surprised at your remembering my words so."

"Surely, Meg, you do not pride yourself on being the only one to cherish 'fruitful and delectable' words, as you called my heavy-hearted ones. I do not get so many letters that by very excess of correspondence I miss any precious words."

"There are many who would like to write to you, Father, if they felt sure you would receive the letters. And they would send you gifts, too. They have asked and asked what you need."

"I'm grateful to them. Antonio Bonvisi has already had leave to send me delicacies, and I'm afraid I shall be overwhelmed by his generosity beyond all power of thanks."

"I should think that a comfortable kind of fear, Father. Yes, he has been asking indefatigably about you. And when I could tell him that we had had your first letter and you were surely here, he seemed ready to weep, as much in relief at some news as in distress over your suffering. It was very touching to see him. Do you think he is as close to Master Cromwell as he used to be?"

"I don't know, Margaret. Of course, the Secretary is a very busy man; so he may have little time for his old friends in the city. Still, it may be through him that Master Bonvisi has permission to put me so deeply in debt as I already am. And our years of friendship warn me I shall not escape from it save by complete bankruptcy, unless he will take my thanks and my prayers in payment."

"I'm sure he counts them good coin. And Master Thorne—that's right, isn't it?—came to see us last week; he was sadly concerned for you."

"How is he?"

A slight frown of hesitation answered for her. "When he heard that no one could see you—my permission came only last night—he was downcast and talked pitifully of falling into some old temptation from which you have helped him in the past. I could only urge him to pray, as he said you used to do together; for I had no certainty then of being allowed to see you."

"If he comes again, Meg— No, send him a note by Master Bonvisi right away, please, to assure him that I will pray for him as well here as I ever did elsewhere. Perhaps better. For, though I am denied a church to pray in, I grow by little and little more able, by God's grace, to make my weak spirit a lowly chapel for His coming to comfort me. I must be long a-building, I know, Meg, but it is as good a work as I have ever undertaken. And when it is time for our family prayers or the harmless prisoners here are gone to Mass, or all the bells of London clamor round my tower, I beg to be admitted to the company of worshipers, and I pray our Lord to count my desire as my presence. Sometimes, too, when there are no bells ringing and no candles burning anywhere, my soul and I keep our vigil, for we count mightily on Christ's good promise: 'Ubi sunt duo vel tres congregati in nomine meo, ibi et ego sum in medio eorum.' And we draw you and all our dear ones and friends to us in thought so that we are a vast company in prayer."

In the outpouring of the pent-up longing and pain of deprivation, More had forgotten to set a watch on the secret of his wakefulness until a cry from Margaret reminded him.

"Father! You cannot sleep?"

"I'm sorry, Margaret; but you mustn't be troubled. You know how often I have waked and watched at night. Now, by

God's mercy, I have greater peace at such times than once, when my mind was beset by division. Do not tell the others, dear, for they would suffer needless anxiety. Perhaps it is only now that this tyrant the body is beginning to yield to its master without too fierce struggling to retain such luxuries as sleep."

"But if you are ill, this narrow room is no place for you." Her affection, allied with her expert knowledge as a mother and a director of their almsgiving, made a formidable attempt to conquer him.

"Really, I am not ill. See how healthily my beard is growing. In all seriousness, Meg, I have had whole days without a twinge. This is a snug house, and the roof is sound."

Though her eyes darkened as he remembered them when some childish plight had brought her to the edge of tears, she smiled in spite of herself.

"You are incorrigible!"

"Now still seriously, my dear, does it much matter where we are sick? Does a headache wring your brows less cruelly because it catches you in a dainty room? Or death put on better manners for the rich worldling's chamber than for the cell of the anchorite? I believe, Meg, that they who have put me here think that they have done me a high displeasure. But, on my faith, my own dear daughter, had it not been for my wife and you that are my children, whom I account the chief part of my earthly charge, I should long before this have closed myself in as strait a room, and straiter, too. But since I am come hither undeservingly, I trust that God of His goodness will discharge me of my responsibility and with His gracious help supply my lack among you."

"You must not be concerned about us in material ways, Father. You have taught us too well for that."

"Well, as for just my own welfare, I find no cause, I thank God, to reckon myself in worse case here than in my own house;

for it seems to me God makes me a wanton and sets me upon His lap and dandles me more lovingly than ever I did my beloved children or their children. And you know, Meg, what a fond grandfather I have been."

"I know how the children have missed you. Not more than the rest of us—that would not be possible—but they understand less than we of why you are gone—if that is possible, Father." She knew the drift of her answer, the little catch in her voice confessed.

He must protect the scarfing tissue on the wound her letter of ten days or so before had made; it might be that they could talk again of the scruples that had brought him here, but not to-day, when the comfort of her first visit must be kept unmarred. With a lightness that needed all the encouragement his spirit could advance, he said, "What, Mistress Eve! But if you are to tempt me to talk of why I am here, you must start earlier in your visit; for I am afraid the warders will send you on your way soon. And do not worry that we may lack opportunity for your wiles; for either His Majesty will keep me here a long time for you to practice on, or he will set me free and you will count their cause all won. Will you not believe, dear Daughter, that my reasons are neither fantastic nor ill-considered?"

Her eyes filled with tears, which she fought bravely back. "Father, I'm sure they're neither. It's the injustice of your being here that seems most reasonless. And may it not be wrong to abet injustice like this by letting it prevail against you?"

He studied her face, earnest in love as in disputation. "Did I call you Mistress Eve? Now I remember how your education has been compounded, for Scripture alone would not teach you such sophistry with which to argue like a rhetorician. But, indeed, Meg, I may tell you that they who have committed me hither for refusing this oath, not consistent with the Act, are not able by their own law to justify my imprisonment."

"That is why you ought not to let the injustice go on," she insisted resolutely.

"In theory, I agree with you, Meg. But, in fact, how am I to fight it? If I take the oath, that does not remedy the injustice, but simply tangles me in a wholly different wrongdoing. If I cry out, I try to make public cause against the King. And to what end? Your Will has thought me an inconvenient prophet more than once, but it takes no great gifts of foresight—merely the prophet's ordinary skill in interpreting things as they are—to see that the insufficiency of the law can be remedied when Parliament reconvenes."

Margaret startled so suddenly that he broke off in amazement. With a pretty flush, she apologized: "I'm sorry, Father. I was almost forgetting a message I have for you; that's all. Master Secretary sends you word, as your true friend, to remember that the Parliament still lasts. With all the advice we have had to present to you when we should have a chance, I had not thought of this as particularly important before. What are you and Master Cromwell both thinking about in this concern over Parliament?"

He had hardly expected this sudden confirmation of his own surmise; yet he had not thought, either, that the King's councilors would long leave the legal loophole unplugged. From the beginning he had regarded it with indifference because, for him, escape by it was unthinkable: the letter of the law could not blind him to its spirit.

"I am grateful to Master Cromwell," he said slowly, "for he has been my good friend more than once, I believe, so far as he could be in the light of what he sees as his duty to the King. And I quarrel with no man for maintaining an honest loyalty to His Grace. But surely, it is a great pity that any Christian Prince should be so shamefully abused with flattery by a flexible Council ready to follow his affections and by a weak clergy lacking grace to stand constantly to their learning. This isn't answering your question about Parliament, though. What may be in Master Secretary's thought, I can only guess, but what I foresee is that the oath to which everyone will be presumed to have sworn will be formulated some day in Parliament. Surely, by every standard of worldly wisdom, it would be incredible folly for those who want these changes to leave the oath ambiguous as it now is. And then many good men may regret too late—God grant I prophesy too darkly!—that they have sworn. Yet I dare hope that God will count their lack of opportunity to foresee the evils to come as extenuation of their oath. For myself, Meg, since I have had the opportunity to study the direction of these policies for many years, I could not swear innocently; therefore, I cannot swear at all. But another day, my dear, you may summon all your arguments against me; for it is not fair to you, either, to leave you feeling that all might have been different if only I could have seen some point eye to eye with my family and my friends."

"Is this a commission for me to gather ideas to play the advocate?" she asked in a flash of her old mischief.

"Even the devil's? That is a dangerous rôle, Meg, for men may misunderstand it, as the simple countryman once misunderstood the Corpus Christi play. He was for climbing up on the stage and denouncing Judas before he should carry out his villainy. And when the other spectators tried to quiet him, he cried out that they were no true Christians to let their Lord be betrayed like that. So you must be very careful to ticket the arguments with your 'Some say.'"

The noise of some one wanting to be heard in the corridor brought them the warning More had expected. He started up.

"Meg," he said in a sudden matter-of-factness, "I am going to give you a little letter for all my good friends, asking them to respect your requests for me as if they were my own. Now we need not fear any question of bribery if we accept favors."

Quickly he found in one of his books a small piece of paper treasured for such use and drew his pencil of charcoal from the bucket on the hearth. While Margaret busied herself to arrange some of the things she had been allowed to bring him, he drove the thick point forward: "To all my loving friends."

By summer, however, the days that passed without a twinge of pain in chest or back—and often no mere twinge, either—had become so few that the physical anguish took on almost a separate companioning existence for him, and on the rare free days his cell seemed more lonely than on the afflicted ones. In Margaret's visits the books and other comforts had accumulated rapidly, and he had even been allowed to purchase straw to alleviate somewhat the chilliness of the stone room, through which the warm, drying winds of summer were never able to blow. Little by little, the alarms from without had so diminished that More, adream over his book or his papers, or waking to walk away the night-cramp, to meditate, and to pray, wondered often whether he was not knowing in mere imprisonment the worst that was to befall him. He might continue long the tolerated, half-forgotten prisoner with his many privileges and the hope of securing still others. One morning, Sir Edmund Walsingham had brought him the news that he would probably soon be allowed to walk in the garden and to go to Mass.

The anticipation wakened by this report was still singing in his heart when John a Wood escorted Dame Alice and Margaret into the room. Gladly as he welcomed them, this first visit of his wife seemed as incredible in its way as had Margaret's first one two months before. But Dame Alice's gingerly care of his new bench—it was rough for her finest gown—and her obvious disgust at the squalor of his apartment were reassuringly real. While they talked of family affairs and the welfare of the many they could call theirs, her eyes went searching busily about the room, missing not even the gnawed corner of the door or the lamed leg of his stool, and Margaret's humorous gaze kept pace with hers. They might be, More laughed to himself as his own look followed theirs, a monkey stalking a cat that was stalking a bird intent on the lively, darting insects in the garden. There was no more for her to discover when she exclaimed sharply—but that was her way:

"I marvel, Husband, that you who have always been taken for a wise man will so play the fool now as to lie here in this close, filthy prison, and be content to be shut up among mice and rats, when you might be abroad at your liberty with the favor and good will of both the King and his Council if you would but do as all the bishops and the most learned men of this realm have done." Margaret's nervousness at this tirade amused More: here evidently was a subject that was not to have come up during this visit. Unnoticingly, however, Dame Alice went on: "Seeing that you have at Chelsea a very fair house, your library, your books, your gallery, your garden, your orchard, and all sorts of other comforts about you, where you might be merry in the company of all of us, I wonder what in God's name you mean by staying here so foolishly."

When his wife paused, he asked in his mildest, most judicial manner, "I pray you, Alice, tell me one thing."

"What is that?" She was more than a little on guard.

"Is not this house as nigh heaven as my own?"

Irritated by so unseemly a question, she exclaimed only, "Tilly-vally! Tilly-vally!"

"What do you say, Alice? Is it not so?"

"Good Lord, man, will you never leave off this nonsense?"

"Well, then," he urged, taking her exclamations for sign of surrender, "if it be so, very well. For I see no great cause for me to take much joy either in my gay house or in anything belonging to it, when, were I to lie only seven years buried under the ground, I should not fail to find some others living there who would bid me get out of doors and tell me it was none of mine. What cause have I, then, to like such a house as would so soon forget its master?"

With magnificent disregard of this last point, she returned to her chief complaint: "What I most wonder at, Thomas, is your making so much ado about words, for God reads all men's thoughts; so if men say one thing while they think the opposite, God surely pays more heed to their hearts than to their tongues. Therefore, an oath goes according to what a man thinks and not according to what he says."

"Subtly argued, my dear; yet that is a very dangerous doctrine. For such a man knows surely that he is lying in tongue or in spirit. And though a man may under sudden fear of torture or death swear falsely and still afterwards hope for God's mercy, the man who willfully encourages himself to sin with the hope that God will afterwards forgive him stands, it seems to me, in very perilous case. This kind of presumption, I fear, draws close on the one side, as despair does on the other, to the abominable sin of blasphemy against the Holy Ghost."

"Blasphemy?" She was more truly cowed than he had meant her to be. "Yet a man might take comfort from Saint Peter, who swore falsely and was afterwards forgiven; and if that be true for a great saint—"

"Saint Peter!" he murmured gently, not intending to interrupt her, but she broke off at the sound. "I've heard him mentioned a great deal lately. Has he become the patron saint of this new England of ours? But don't men read their Gospels carelessly, for you remember that Peter denied our Lord only in bitter fear and that he repented with bitter weeping? In the calm moments when he was merely thinking about danger, he could not conceive of his swearing falsely. And if these same men read on in the Book of Acts and the Lives of the Saints, they will find that he suffered much, finally even to the death of the cross. And are they who are ready to lay the unction of Saint Peter's example to the comforting of their false faith ready to follow him in his bitter repentance and steadfastness thenceforth? Truly, I should think them wiser to use his example as a warning and to pray for grace to withstand the first temptation; for falling once, they could have little assurance of rising afterwards to the courage of Saint Peter. Failing in a deadly terror is a different sin, surely, from premeditated tempting of God's mercy."

"Well, if you will talk your theological subtleties, Thomas, I grant I can do nothing with you," Dame Alice said with a good-humored smile that robbed her words of their asperity. As, their time up, she and silent, twinkling Margaret rose to go, she added with a delightful flouncing of her skirts: "But you might think sometimes, too, of what God meant us to do with His good common sense."

Between them Dame Alice and Margaret proved, More thought more than once after a visit, excellent respondents to help him, as in their disputations one student helps another, see his own best reasons. To do their love full justice, however, he recognized that their intentions were far from academic; yet, touching as he found their devotion in returning time after time to persuasion, he could not admit any argument as truly effectual against his scruples. There was comfort, nevertheless, in feeling their discussions shave over old, once-tender scars without making him wince. No longer did they have to fear a subject as painful. And everyone was so generous that he needed to be afraid lest his luxury make him slothful again. Now, when this thought came to him, he remembered contritely Margaret's telling him that Dame Alice was wearing the fine rich gown of New Year's, 1532, because she had sold most of her others to pay for his keep here. His jesting that he had thought the best gown was to do him honor had not deceived Margaret. It promised to be a long serviceable one, this that had once pinched her waist; she was thinner now. The homely fact that his wife was thus patiently mortifying her vanity by selling her finery reminded him that he was a poor prisoner dependent on her alms.

More than four full months had he been here now, when the humid air of August grew acrid with the reek of brewing. The odors and the sounds of the city and the winged things, heedless of moats, came and went freely in the precincts of the Tower. Watching the dragon flies, More found himself enjoying their liberty without envy, for this enlargement of his that let him, after close confinement, walk in the courtyard and the church was commensurate liberty.

Margaret should be here soon, and the warders had promised to send her into the courtyard instead of up the dark stairs to his cell. Strange—it seemed more definitely prison when he was away thus than when he had settled again into its narrow hospitality. This time he had something for her after all the times she had come with full hands and gone with empty ones, and he felt like a boy who has been allowed for the first time to lay out his own money for a New Year's gift or a trinket at the fair. How would she like it? Would she guess how absorbing it had been in the making? He brushed his arm against the bosom of his gown to hear the muffled crinkle of the paper. And there she was!

When they had come out again into the sunshine from the Chapel of Saint Peter ad Vincula, whither they had gone for their devotions together, More was secretly blessing the restored richness of his life. Perhaps the deprivations had been only a chastening so that his gratitude might be the more abundant. For a time they talked of the family—of each one excellent report. "Good! Good! Good!"—the private litany sang in thanksgiving.

"And the boys are racing each other on their irregular verbs," Margaret said, for the children's studies had their place in these summaries of family activity. "I am to set them an examination next week."

"Good! And as a special prize from me, Meg, let the high scholar have"—he had to think for a moment, he had so little that was properly his to give away—"the reddest apple in the orchard."

She laughed. "The little rascal, whichever he is, will like that, if he hasn't eaten it already. And, Father, let me give you my most important message now. Always when I look back at the gate outside, it seems, I remember something that I meant particularly to tell you. Master Bonvisi was at the Clements' yesterday when we were. He wonders whether you recall meeting his cousin at Cambrai."

"Indeed, yes. He's like Master Antonio, not so much in looks as in manner and speech—the things that are the breeding of a family. That was in August, too, earlier in the month, five years ago."

The name and the recollection of the quiet deference of the Italian merchant-diplomat brought back with a little access of pain the bright beauty of the day when they had made the Peace of Cambrai, and he had wondered whether it could be a lasting peace on the earth. And now—he had not thought of it just so before—there was a fiercer war impending, for the temporal power was warring on the spiritual and the State on individual conscience. And five years before, he had dreamed of a lasting peace, wherein men would find together the order of Christ.

They had paced one length of the courtyard before Margaret, whose gray eyes saddened to his mood, resumed her message: "Master Bonvisi had written his cousin of your being here, and he has just had a letter mostly about you, we gathered. It has assurances of his concern and regret and hope. He plans to visit

Master Antonio next summer, and he counts on seeing you restored, he writes, to liberty and honor."

"That is kind of him, Meg, but overoptimistic."

With a reproachful glance, she went on: "The most interesting part, though, was his lamenting that you had not left England in time. It's strange that nobody here thought of that. He says that all Europe would have welcomed you."

"He is indeed a sanguine man. I fear a good many places in Germany would have given me no kinder welcome than this." More's smile won an answering one from her. "And it is very kind of him to suggest that somewhere in Europe I should have found friendly harborage; but it's not strange that none of us here thought of exile. Yes, that's what it would have been, dear. And think of how often men speak pityingly of Reginald Pole, who may not come home in safety. We are very insular and deeply rooted, we English. We live by the thousand associations in our lives—our manners and speech and family affections. It is strange that we have this settled sense of possession that makes us talk about our country when we are all pilgrims and wayfarers in this world."

"But even the constant pilgrim has his favorite inns, I fancy, Father."

"True, Meg. And this England has been mine. There is, too, another personal reason why I could not have gone. Technically, you see, I was one of the King's Council almost till I came here; I'm sure I'd not have won leave to go away, and flight would have been treason. But I'm grateful to Master Bonvisi's cousin for his concern. You will tell our friend? Don't say too much of how I feel about the suggestion: in spite of the long time he has lived with us, he himself is far from home."

Margaret nodded understandingly, but a cloud lingered on her forehead. After a little silence, she said, "Still, Father, we were talking about it later—Margaret and John Clement and

William Rastell and Will and I. Suppose life became impossible, dangerous to life and liberty for conscience' sake, in one's own country, wouldn't he be justified in going away?"

"If he could go and find life possible elsewhere, surely. Wide as the whole earth is, a man so going—for conscience' sake—would not have to feel himself gone far from home, for it is God's earth and God would know always where to find him."

"It might be better than going to prison."

"Honestly, Meg, does there seem to you much to choose between exile and prison?"

"Between liberty and restraint?" She sounded genuinely puzzled.

"Between a wide prison and a narrow one, Meg; that is all. Between my room upstairs and the same room with my present extension into the courtyard and the chapel. Is not the world a prison, for all it is broad and beautiful and subtly built? Do you see?" Her face had lighted in sympathetic comprehension of the figure. "And though it lies open on every side, Meg, with no visible wall or moat, the earth is so sure a prison that no man, woman, or child has found the gateway by which to steal out quietly. There is no way off the earth, though a man sail ten times as far as your Uncle Will meant to do when he set out for the New Found Land, save the violent, mortal jail-delivery of death."

"Then who is out of prison?" In her pensiveness, it was not a question but a response.

"And the only difference is that some of us know, and some of us do not—yet." The appearance of a warder at the door of the Lieutenant's house suggested that their time was nearly up. And More had almost forgotten something; so he said more lightly, "This time, Meg, I have a present for you."

"A present. What?"

"Guess. But there, I'm afraid you never would before Sir

Edmund himself would have to come to put you out. I have been entertaining myself with a report of our talk last week when you brought me Alice Alington's good letter. See." He brought the little sheaf of papers from his gown and had the swift reward of her eager, grateful smile. "There may be a bit added by invention, but most of it follows what we said."

"And the rest is what we should have said? No, I mean that seriously, Father. I am always thinking afterwards of what I should have said."

"Ho! That's because your case is bad."

"Maybe it's because it is good and I am frightened of my responsibility. But this is a regular dialogue, Father! Just like one of your books or Plato's."

"Thank you, my partial, injudicious daughter." He made her a grave bow in appreciation of the compliment. "We'll make allowances for your bias. There are some places, you'll see, where your part isn't very full, and I hope you'll complete it. So I turn it over to you for your emendations and additions. Then we'll read it together—next time, maybe."

"I like it"—she had skimmed a page—"and I shall enjoy finding fault with it." They were gently teasing words. "But how does the real book come along, the one about the Grand Turk and the Christians in Hungary?"

"I am enjoying it thoroughly. Perhaps that's the wrong tone of voice in which to talk of a devotional book. Your father is a poor light-minded fellow, I fear, Meg, for he is forever letting a trivial tale break into the serious thought. But you see, it is a dialogue, too, since my mind seems to work best when I am imagining people in conversation; and then, unless I set a strong guard on my fancy, they run away with it and lure me off on some idle, merry stories. When I am deep in this book, it doesn't seem remote at all; rather, sometimes, uncomfortably close. So I find it very absorbing. Maybe, though, Tyndale and the brethren were right, and I am no more than a jesting poet, when I had hoped God could make me a sober recluse with his thought fixed on devotion."

"If anyone objects to laughter, he must be a new kind of heretic, Father. Surely God gave us that gift, too."

"I believe so myself, Meg, but I know that I have shocked some of the unimpeachably orthodox by my levity. Do you remember how some people took me to task for making the poor souls in purgatory talk lightly? Yet—who knows?—since they are not in hell, they may have their merry moments."

Margaret's eyes were shining as when, years before, she had had the right answer to a problem. "Do you remember in turn, Father, the tale you brought us back from France once about the monk who had been a juggler and who knew no other way to show the full fervor of his devotion than by offering our Lady his one high skill with his balls and his tricks? Other things he might have done meanly for her, but that he did perfectly."

"Yes, Meg, it is a comforting story for my *Dialogue of Comfort*. I shall not do so well, though, I fear, as did our Lady's juggler; but I trust God will accept my writing as devoutly meant. He is making me over little by little, though He has not mended my wit yet."

CHAPTER XII

"FATHER, what moved them to shut you up again, we can nothing hear. But surely I conjecture that when they considered that you were of so temperate mind, that you were contented to abide there all your life with such liberty, they thought it were never possible to incline you to their will except it were by restraining you from the church and the company of my good mother, your dear wife, and us your children—" In the grayness of this late October Sunday, More read and reread Margaret's anxious yet exalted letter, the first communication to reach him from outside in the two dark, confused weeks since his liberties had been abruptly suspended. He did not dare ask John a Wood how this letter, brought to him secretly, had penetrated their prison. "I'd keep it hid, sir," he had said with a mysteriousness that might have branded them as arch-conspirators. Yet there was not a word in it that—saving his modesty—the King and his Council might not have seen.

It was a richly comforting letter, though he grieved for the anxiety that he could imagine had descended over the houses of his children and his friends. Now at length, it seemed, they had abandoned the futile effort to turn him from his resolution, for Margaret closed the letter with her prayer, "That our Lord of His infinite mercy give you of His heavenly comfort, and so assist you with His special grace, that you never in anything decline from His blessed will, but live and die His true, obedient servant." So loving a prayer would long be for him spiritual fortification, he reflected, so that he would have less need to fear the weakening of his own frail will. Still, physical pain weighed upon him as a burden which put him to shame. That he was no stronger master than this of these old ailments and their new fellows induced by the cold, the dampness, and the narrowness of his room had become an increasing grief. His susceptibility to pain, which could drive away his joy in his devotions, seemed to him unworthy the name of Christian; so he took it now as the chief of his enemies.

This bodily fear was his true prison, he knew as he meditated how all men, whether they dwelt in one prison or two externally, lay closely pinioned in some invisible prison of mind or heart. Only the few high spirits, who proved always what man could aspire to, were able to convert that inmost dungeon—for poor sinners very like the pit of Dante's Hell—into a citadel secure against all siege, meet shelter for the grace of God. In a measure, reason could cope with pain by weighing the greater and the lesser advantages of it; yet it could never alone make it cease to be or change its nature, for, were it not felt, pain had no being. Faith, however, could rear pain up to be an obedient servant, forever quick to garnish and sweep the inner chamber against the coming of the Spirit of God. Sometimes it seemed easy to think thus of some great heroic suffering; whereas these ugly, commonplace rackings and cramps and cutting strokes were only inglorious reminders of the prison house. Sad, sad error, he rebuked himself, unless a man could think it a smaller pain to have the knife thrust from within outward than from his skin inward. The flesh was capable of but so much pain, whether glorious or inglorious in the eyes of the world; and many a man had suffered as fierce a martyrdom in his bed as another in the arena or the market place. In thinking thus, he did not mean to detract at all from the honor of those whom men reverence as martyrs, for he recognized that they, foreseeing torment, had chosen it as the better way, while in the hundred natural pains of the flesh—fevers and aches and sores, palsy, gout, and stone—men had little thought of incurring them for love of Christ.

For love of Christ! And for the reverencing afar off—like the sorrowing women of Galilee—of the passion of Christ, the one utterly unmerited, utterly voluntary suffering of mortal body. He could hold his awkward, cramping pencil again, and he remembered the place where he had broken off in his *Dialogue*. Swiftly as the coal could form the letters he wrote: "Our Savior was Himself taken prisoner for our sake, and prisoner was He carried, and prisoner was He kept, and prisoner was He brought forth before Annas, and prisoner from Annas carried unto Caiaphas; then prisoner was He carried from Caiaphas unto Pilate, and prisoner was He sent from Pilate to King Herod, prisoner from Herod unto Pilate again, and so kept as prisoner to the end of His passion. . . ."

As November and December wore on, report of the measures intended in this Parliament leaked even into the close precincts of the Tower. The oath was confirmed, as he had feared it would be, under a form written into the Statutes as the one all who had sworn were presumed to have meant, and there was now no doubt that the King considered himself Supreme Head on earth of the Church of England. Forgotten was the safeguarding phrase for which Convocation had struggled nearly four years before. Finally to justify his imprisonment, seven months late an act of attainder was passed against More for having refused the oath just now written on the Statute Rolls. In calm, daylight moments, reflection on these actions of Parliament left him not greatly moved: he had foreseen them and had, therefore, balked some of their horror. He could even smile at the methodical release of the news that seemed to come to them so casually. It was a refined policy, calculated by degrees to break the spirit of men thus shut away.

In the night, however, when he waked at the scuttling of some creature in the straw or the marrow-chilling cold of his bed or the tightening of his muscles, anxious thoughts still kept company with his physical pain. Then the danger of his family laid siege to his heart, for history taught all too clearly that attainder was not only a cruel instrument, but a rapacious and undiscriminating one; and he remembered how the houses of his children had been searched and inventoried as well as the Great House at Chelsea. They might be beggared for his sake; and the lot that had no terrors for him alone became, in the thought of it for his children and his grandchildren, a heavy grief.

Between midnight and dawn on the Feast of the Circumcision, he woke thus in worried restlessness. O weak, frail spirit that could not use whole-heartedly the peace God had given! He could not tell by these cold brilliant stars of winter how long he had slept since with the bells of midnight he had given thanks for the approach of the New Year. But now he was awake with a full consciousness that was no less the gift of God than was the ease of dreamless sleep. Setting his coarse gown straight and close round him, he drew his stool to the window so that he might watch the stars pass in the unspectacular waning of the frosty night. The Wise Men were drawing near the end of their long journey, by day and by night padding tirelessly on to bring their gifts to the King; but they had many miles yet to go, he mused as for a moment in his mind's eye he saw them watering their camels at an oasis in the desert. To-day the Babe was to receive His name, which the angel had spoken to Joseph in his sleep: "Thou shalt call His name Jesus; For He shall save His people from their sins." Only eight days past was the beautiful, undimmed mystery of the birth of Christ, incarnate God. And now on the octave of the high feast of joy was beginning the brief subjection of the divine to the human order, of eternity to mortality, that from the old law the new might spring. So He was to receive His name according to the ritual of the people He had come to save. God had put on mortality that He might show men how to live within its prison and how at length to free themselves from the bondage of the flesh. Already, in the octave of Christmas, the eye of meditation was fixed on the dark mystery of Passiontide and the unending, sequent glory of Easter, sealing forevermore the victory over the frailty of flesh and sin and death of Jesus Christ and of mankind in Him.

"Sweet Savior, who didst take on Thee the pain of our humanity by Thy glorious incarnation, grant the strengthening of Thy example to all those who grow faint through tribulation. In Thy mercy and long-suffering, save us from temptation and trial beyond our strength, which is as nothing unless Thou art with us. And if it be Thy will, bring us to Thy peace after this sorrow. Amen.

"Almighty God, have mercy on Thy suffering servant, John, Bishop of Rochester. Comfort him in his loneliness and affliction, and let his holiness convert the hearts of his enemies for Thy name's sake. Amen."

How gentle had been his own imprisonment, he reflected, beside that of Bishop Fisher, who had deserved infinitely more compassion from the King than he. Yet all these nine months and more, the Bishop had had none of the precious liberties that had been his—leave to go into the garden, to attend Mass, to have his books; though some of these liberties were lost now, he had had them and the solace they had brought.

The stars had faded, and the first flutter of sunrise streaked the sky desolately as if it were a ribbon dropped from the frosty sunset of the night before. The year 1535 by the continental reckoning. Soon people would be hurrying through the still half-dark streets with their merry greetings and their gifts; whereas here it would be only a wintry day for the poor prisoners. He tripped the thought and laughed at it in its ignominious tumble:

unwittingly he had thought of prisoners without remembering that he himself was one. Of such delicate stuff are the victories spun.

Well, if he were but half a prisoner, he would celebrate the holy day by sending at least one gift like any free man. Gray as the room still was, he found two pieces of paper in his books. Yes, by the window he could see that he had hit on the right ones—a little picture of the Wise Men offering their gifts to the Christ Child and a small blank sheet. Carefully he wrote with his charcoal: "To my Reverend Father in Christ, my Lord of Rochester: My most humble and heartfelt greetings for the New Year! And because I am detained from saluting you in person to present my gift of the season, I pray you accept and expend for your comfort and the enlargement somewhat of your estate the enclosed token of my esteem." How much should he make it? A thousand pounds were as possible as one, and likely to be many times more entertaining. So like a spendthrift he added his order for two thousand pounds in gold—with the picture a respectable gift to a beloved friend.

Two men were talking close by his door—but outside, he thought; and he did not have curiosity enough to turn towards them or to try to hear what they were saying. He had had a little fever, he remembered vaguely, and evidently the old pain in his chest, where it felt dull and heavy now; but he could not remember that. He was warm, and the sunlight in the room seemed nearly as bright as the fire in his grate, and he wanted to go to sleep. That was a foolish thing to do, however, for those voices had just wakened him; and vaguely he knew that a long time had passed since he had drowsed off. What day was it? The passion to know waxed so strong that he could have laughed at himself were that not too much effort. Easier was it, since there was no one in sight and it was strangely hard to turn, to identify the last day he remembered; then he would ask John a Wood later about to-day. New Year's? No; the next day he had received Bishop Fisher's note thanking him for the gifts and a gift in exchange of some jelly. But he had not eaten the jelly. John was to save it till they had finished some on hand. There was something about the day after that—the third of January—but he could not recall what. The third of January—that was definite anyway. So thought veered back to the problem of this day's date.

"... regain consciousness to-day," one of the voices outside was saying, an unfamiliar voice.

The murmur of the other voice concealed its words, but the quality of it suggested Sir Edmund Walsingham's. Then he had been sick, and the first speaker must be a doctor.

"No," the louder voice grew heavy as if with laughter. "No, I shouldn't worry about that. They won't need to use force with him; he hasn't the strength to bear up against even the threat of it."

That was it! On the third of January, John a Wood had come in, green with pallor under his prison-faded tan, with the news that George Golde had heard talk of torture in the Lieutenant's house between his master and visitors unknown. What had happened? The first wild thought that he had already been subjected to "force" and the accompanying fear as to what he had said or done under it fled away: surely he would remember it. He had been writing that day, though his eyes had been heavy with fever and the dull pains had been playing hide-and-go-seek all over his body. He had tried to make light of John's fears—had doing so been really an admission of fear on his own part?—and had asked him not to listen to idle tales. But John had insisted that George Golde had given a very circumstantial report of talk in which the first of February figured; and that was the day from which the penalties in the new Statutes were effective.

What was the key-word in the Statute which made the penalties operative? But the search for it was too difficult now.

Had his body and his frail will played him false at the mere mention of stray words overheard by one servant and passed on to another, perhaps with elaborations and the conversion of guesswork into affirmations? The shame of that charge tried now to hale him out of bed; but, whatever its cause, his weakness was indisputable. Then, he remembered that he had gone on writing after that conversation and that he had got up the next morning still with his will set on work: that brought him to the fourth of January for the beginning of the blackness from which he was just emerging.

Though the voices had continued outside his door, he had not tried to hear more of what they were saying after the cruel doubt assailed him.

He must even have slept again, for, when he woke, John was sitting by the hearth, and the sunlight came only in an arrow across the room from one of the westward loopholes.

"John," he said tentatively, and was surprised at the sound of his own voice.

More surprising still was the startled movement he had provoked; the stool toppled over as John jumped.

"Master! Glory be—you know me now!" The stolid face was working strangely, and the familiar voice blurred a little with emotion.

"Yes, John. How long haven't I?"

Standing over the bed, only a dark figure because of the narrow light behind him, John hesitated a moment before he said, "I don't suppose you ought to talk, sir. The doctor wouldn't like it."

"Faithful nurse!" After all, he did not feel like insisting; still he would try one more question: "What day is to-day, John?"

That must have seemed a properly innocuous query, for, busy

about the covers of the bed, John answered promptly, "Lord love you, sir, it's the twelfth."

"Of January?"

John laughed, "Well, you have been sick, sir! Yes, of January. What did you think, sir?" As he lifted him awkwardly to adjust the pillow, More could feel the continuing chuckle. Eight days?

The next day, when he could be propped up in bed, Sir Edmund Walsingham, having come to congratulate him on his recovery, left a little packet of letters—"to cheer you up," he said. After his departure, More turned them over eagerly: none from home. He had had so few letters in months that this accumulation in scarcely more than a week puzzled him. But it was foolish just to look at them like this; so he began to read. Congratulations? The first one was phrased so guardedly that he really could not understand its drift. Surely, word of his illness had not gone abroad to warrant so early felicitations on his recovery from his brother-in-law, John Rastell. It was a kind and hearty letter, though, considering that there had been some coolness between them recently. The next one from Master William Leder was more revealing. Congratulations on his having been reconciled to the King's Grace and on his impending release! For now, he could not read the others, which he doubted not were of the same tenor. What had happened? Had they come to him in his fever and offered him the oath again?

"John!" Perhaps he was, as often, just outside the door.

"Yes, Master?"

As soon as the clipped head came round the door, he cried, "Who was here while I was sick?" He fought back the panic that he feared his voice revealed.

"Mostly me, sir. The Lieutenant came in often, and George Golde sometimes, and the doctor."

"What's his name?" If there had been none of the King's Commissioners, he felt reassured.

John scratched his head so slowly as to be at once exasperating and funny. "Albertson, I think, sir. Something like that. I didn't pay much attention to him, sir."

"Halburton, probably; he's one of the King's physicians. No one else?"

"No, sir."

"Thank you, John. That's all I wanted."

It was a groundless rumor, then, that had brought the pressure of these letters. He was grateful for the solicitude of the writers, whom he could not for a moment think insincere. But what had they heard? He skimmed the others to see if they disclosed any more. No, only that his surrender "to good sense" had been given out in such a way as—if he could judge by this evidence—to reach these well-wishers who were not of the closest circle of his friends. What had his family and his more intimate friends heard? Since there was no fact behind the rumor, however, it would be soon refuted.

"But what started it?" anxiety insisted. Of course, the report of his illness might conceivably have led to discussion of possible release for him, and that in turn to speculation about his taking the oath. Then, by the same process to which he had attributed the talk about torture, speculation might have been metamorphosed into fact. Comforting as that bit of reasoning was, it was notably disconcerting in its linking of two kinds of force. However sincere they were, these letters were a sort of pressure to bring to pass what they assumed had happened, and the officials who had so thoughtfully let them reach him must have calculated their power to serve that end. Unless he were vilely suspicious, there was method in the delivery of the letters just now.

Was there, after all, a possibility of the other kind of force?

He knew to his sorrow how weak his physical courage was, how little pain had succeeded, year in and year out, in schooling him to bear it in anticipation. When it had actually laid hold of him, he could be quiet under it, but that was all he had learned; and even that was a kind of cowardice, for unresisted, the pain seemed to speed away the faster. It was like a willful child, finding no fun in another's refusal to be teased. What was torture? Twisting and racking, binding and cutting. After all, it was pain and only pain—and perhaps death the sooner therefore. Only pain—unless a man were to think it less painful—he had been writing something about this before the lost days—to have a knife cut from within outward in his tender flesh than to have it begin at the skin and cut inward. Then he remembered that in thinking about the glory of martyrdom and the mere inglorious suffering of illness, he had otherwise applied the figure.

This fear of torment was one of the last of the devil's weapons against weak flesh. Of so much he felt sure as weariness laid him back upon his pillow. "If he threaten us that we are too weak," his busy thought began, "let us tell him that our Captain Christ is with us. And let us fence ourselves with faith, and comfort us with hope, and smite the devil in the face with a firebrand of charity. . . ." And he could sleep again.

CHAPTER XIII

DEATH! At his writing, early in the afternoon of the thirtieth of April, More felt the shadow fall again and again across his meditation. All through the Tower evidently the word had spread that yesterday the Prior of the Charterhouse and Dr. Reynolds of Sion and three others had been sentenced to the traitor's death. So much the rest of the prisoners were allowed to know; but the specific charges and the evidence against the condemned lay concealed behind a shrugging silence calculated to chill the heart. The Carthusians were all suspect, he had heard; with that recollection came the thought of two men—the courtier Sebastian Newdigate, who had exchanged the King's favor for the impartial stillness of the Charterhouse, and the courtier Hugh Marchaunt, who had thought of the Charterhouse but had gone, instead, to Christchurch. Yes, he had found there personal peace, it was true; yet, he had seen political terrorism pluck two of his brothers from the cloister in the case of the Nun and cast its shadow over the whole monastery.

Death! He must not think of it thus unprofitably. The forty-first verse of the twenty-sixth chapter of Saint Matthew, the thirty-eighth verse of the fourteenth in Saint Mark, the forty-sixth verse of the twenty-second of Saint Luke—he turned the pages of his New Testament back and forth, to mark the repeated command: "Orate, ut non intretis in tentationem." Again and again Christ had taught that one truth: prayer is the comforter of the tempted, the strengthening against temptation. He reached for his Homilies of Saint Chrysostom to see whether he had any comment on the passage in Saint Matthew, but though he lifted the book to the table, a new reflection stopped his hand.

He seemed to be walking again in the cloister of the Charterhouse, meditating on the peace that dwelt here, not far out of the city as the foot of man measured it, but in another world by the surveying of the spirit; more than thirty years before, watching the monks moving in the tiny orbit of their lives—from cell to chapel to cell—he had marveled at the completeness with which the tides of worldly care ebbed away from these gates. And now Prior Houghton and his brother Priors of Axholm and Beauvale were among the first condemned to death because worldly pride and passion had ruled that there should be no longer any sanctuary from them. More did not know on what evidence they had been convicted, but he knew the rule of their order and he knew Dr. Richard Reynolds, scholar, preacher, and friend. That they should have spoken maliciously—that was the word of the new Act—against the King's supremacy was unthinkable; so there was no safety in that supposedly saving limitation. "Pray that you enter not into temptation"—the safety that the world could offer, if it condemned its holiest men, was only vanity and delusion.

As he opened his Saint Chrysostom, a knock at the door again stopped his hand. Before Sir Edmund Walsingham, who always observed this—for a jailer—quaint courtesy of warning, spoke, his anxious expression told of an unpleasant errand.

"Master Secretary Cromwell wishes to see you in the Council Chamber, Sir Thomas," he said without preliminary.

More rose. "May I change my gown?" He looked down the worn, coal-smutched front of the old one in which he had been sitting. At a nod from Walsingham, who seemed loath to say more or to come fully into the light of the room, he shifted into the camlet one that Bonvisi had sent him. Surely, this was an occasion important enough to warrant his wearing the fine gown, which he had been saving for high feast days; as he set it straight, he realized that he had almost forgotten how light and soft silk could be.

Behind the narrow table in the Council Chamber sat the Secretary—now the King's Vicar-General, More remembered hearing, for the administration of his headship of the Church—and four others: the King's Attorney, Christopher Hales, who had seen him receive the Great Seal; the new Solicitor-General, Richard Rich; Thomas Bedyll, Clerk of Council; and Dr. Tregonwell. As More ticked them off in thought, he wondered a little at the composition of this board to examine him: the character of the King's Commission had changed greatly in a little more than a year. In the same instant, an even more interesting idea occurred to him—this was the sort of Commission which would draw up an indictment; no doubt, there was economy in sending the legal experts thus instead of having them work afterwards from the testimony of less professional investigators.

"Ah, Master More," Cromwell spoke with unwonted alacrity. "Will you be seated?" He motioned towards the extra chair before the table.

"Thank you, Master Secretary; but I do not forget that I am a prisoner, who should not be treated as your free equal."

Letting the excuse pass, Cromwell began directly: "I do not doubt, Master More, that you have seen the new statutes enacted at the last sitting of Parliament. Some one visiting here has brought them to you?"

"Yes, that is true."

"And you have studied them?"

"Not especially. Since I am shut away here from intercourse with other people, I thought there was little need for me to bestow much time on them; therefore, I returned the book shortly after, and I made no effort to mark the statutes closely or to remember them."

Cromwell seemed to study this answer for a moment. "You have read the first statute, however, that concerning the King's headship of the Church?"

"Yes."

The simple affirmative seemed to give the Secretary just the opening he sought, for he nodded as if to say that More had saved them much trouble.

"Master More," he resumed confidently, "since it is now by Act of Parliament ordained that His Highness and his heirs be, and ever rightfully have been, and perpetually shall be, Supreme Head on earth of the Church of England under Christ, the King's pleasure is that we of his Council assembled here demand your opinion of the Act and learn your attitude towards it."

No oath this time, but a demand for an expressed opinion on the title? A quick way, certainly, to obtain a denial of it from the unwary. Did they forget that he had been a lawyer? But More restrained what could easily have been a scornful answer.

"In good faith, Master Secretary, I have trusted that the King's Highness would never command any such question to be put to me, since from the beginning I have always on occasion truly declared my mind to His Majesty. Since that time I have also declared my purpose to you both by word of mouth and in writing. And now, in good faith, I have discharged all such matters from mind, and I will dispute neither King's titles nor Pope's. But I am and will be the King's true, faithful subject, and I pray daily for him and all his, and for all of you who are of his honorable Council, and for all the realm. Beyond this, I intend never again to meddle with affairs of policy or state."

Though there were five men sitting here, there seemed but one mind among them, for a common frown lowered on their brows and the same delicate shadow—almost too faint to be called a sneer—passed across their faces. And More remembered that there were men whom talk of prayer made uncomfortable. Obviously, they had but one voice—Cromwell's. He smiled in a mirthless drawing back of his upper lip.

"This sort of answer, Master More, will not, I think, either satisfy or please the King's Highness; His Grace will undoubtedly exact a fuller one." For an instant he studied the bright world beyond the windows, and imperceptibly his face softened till it seemed that of an enthusiast in contemplation of his devotion. "Remember, Master More, that the King's Highness is a Prince, not of rigor, but of mercy and pity. And even though he has found obstinacy at some time in any of his subjects, yet if he should find them later conformable and submissive, His Grace would not fail to show them mercy. As for you, His Highness would be glad to see you adopt such conformable ways as might bring you abroad again among other men as you were once."

"I am not ungrateful, Master Secretary, but, in truth, were I to have the world given to me, I would never meddle with its affairs again. My utmost concern with them is prayer that God guide and keep all those who are busied in them. I am determined neither to study nor to meddle further with any business of this world, but to make my whole study the Passion of Christ and my own passage out of this world."

Something in this answer must have offended Cromwell, for he said curtly, "Well! Wait in the gallery outside till we send for you."

At one end a warder, and at the other. More had seldom had so complete an awareness of the human agents of safe-keeping as now while he awaited the result of the Commissioners' conference on his stubbornness. In some ways, he reflected, he liked this frankly hostile Cromwell better than the wily man who had sworn at Lambeth that he would prefer seeing his only son lose his head to hearing More himself refuse the oath. Yet, there had been that moment of gentleness to-day. Was that an echo of some word of compassion from the King? At the thought he noted with a certain sober gladness that he was beyond even hope on that score, for the possibility of Henry's relenting could not quicken his pulse.

At the creaking of the door behind him, he turned to see Thomas Bedyll's pale face peering out for him. Yes, he was the serviceable investigator who had hunted out the associates of the Nun of Canterbury. Without a word, they returned to the hearing.

Again Cromwell launched his attack directly: "Though you are a prisoner, Master More, condemned to lifelong imprisonment, you are not therefore discharged of your obedience and allegiance to the King's Highness. Do you not think, then, that the King's Grace may exact from you such admissions and recognitions as are contained in the Act on the very same pains as apply to other men?"

"I will not say that he may not."

"Now, just as the King's Highness will be gracious to those whom he finds amenable, so will His Grace follow the course of his laws against such as he finds obstinate. Furthermore, for all your meek speech, your conduct in connection with the oath is probably what has made others so stiff-necked in the matter as they are."

After his resolute silence as to his reasons for refusing the oath, More could have regarded this charge as ridiculous were it not deadly serious. He thought pityingly of the men who had pleaded for his advice, even some of his fellow-prisoners in this long year past. Had Dr. Wilson, who had finally resolved to swear the oath, been released yet? But such yearning over his friends was not answering the charge laid against him.

"Master Secretary," he began slowly, "I give no man occasion to hold any opinion one way or the other; and I have never given any man advice or counsel on the matter. Whatever penalties may come of it, I can go no farther than this silence. I am the King's true and faithful subject. I do no one any harm, I say no harm, I think no harm; but I wish everybody good. If this be not enough to keep a man alive, in good faith I do not long to live. And I am dying already; and since I came here, I have been at different times so ill that I thought to die within the hour. I thank our Lord I was not sorry then, but, rather, sorry when I saw the pang past. Therefore, my poor body is at the King's pleasure. Would God my death might do him good!"

A fine tremor through his whole frame pleaded the body's weakness against the intensity of his spirit. He hoped they would not notice it and discount his words as mere bravado. He need not fear, however, for they sat with gaze averted as if he had, in this passionate speaking, embarrassed them by some indecency. In the prolonged silence he tried to steady his quivering nerves. Finally, Cromwell puckered his thin brows and coughed dryly.

"Well, you find no fault in that statute. Do you find any in the following statutes?"

"Sir, whatever might seem to me otherwise than good in any of the statutes, I would not declare what fault I found in it, nor would I talk of it at all."

Again like something remembered barely in time, the gentleness drifted back into Cromwell's face as he said quietly, "Whatever you have said this afternoon, Master More, rest assured there will no advantage be taken of it. We shall report to the King's Highness and learn his gracious pleasure." He shuffled his papers together absently, his gaze concentrated on More's face. Perhaps His Majesty's interest in his prisoners extended beyond their words. Then Cromwell added, "Will you ask the warder to call the Lieutenant, Master Bedyll?"

He had still heard nothing of that "gracious pleasure" four days later when Margaret was ushered in unexpectedly early.

His joy in seeing her after their long separation could not blind him to her pallor, which he considered anxiously. Though he had been concerned about her health, this disturbance seemed to be due to some immediate nervous shock rather than only to her being with child. Watching her steadily during their brief greeting, he thought that his imprisonment had put its cruelest strain on her, and the inscrutability of suffering that rewarded devotion like Margaret's with new pain beat upon his heart. He who would give her all things for her peace could not free her from sorrow over him. It had ever been part of the satanic wisdom of tyrants to double the torture of parents in that of their children; and that torment could be of other sorts than the physical atrocities devised by a King Antiochus.

When they had finished the litany, he added one brief prayer: "Good Lord, grant us in our weakness and fear and pain the understanding to lay hold of the mystery of Thy comfort to Saint Paul, 'Sufficit tibi gratia mea'; and through that grace keep ever before our eyes Thy sacred passion, remembering which no man can be confounded by his frailty. Amen."

Margaret's low echo had a reassuring vibrancy: the worst of to-day's fear had passed. But the heaviness of her tired eyes and the tautness of every muscle in her face showed the toll that her anguish was exacting. An unidentified noise that he had heard before this morning—a rattling, scraping clatter in the courtyard—forestalled a question he had been going to ask. She shuddered and the little color that had been seeping back into her cheeks fled away precipitately. She might faint. He caught her round the shoulders to steady her against him.

"What is it, Margaret?"

In spite of her agitation, she was not yielding easily. Leaning against his arm, she braced herself by the wall with her white left hand.

"Father!" The one word seemed to help her; after a moment

she went on. "Do you know—what is happening to-day? The Priors and Dr. Reynolds—"

At that—all she could say at the instant—the unfamiliar noise had meaning, and he understood to what Margaret had been subjected. She had come into the Tower in time to view the preparations for the death which, they could not doubt, he was himself to die when the King's forbearance should run out. Had it been merely cruel chance that had dictated the setting of the unusually early hour for her visit, or had some refinement of torture appointed it that she might see and be unnerved by horror? What had she seen? One symbol of the traitor's death, however, he well knew, could evoke the full picture of the suffering that stretched between a Tower cell and the last conscious gasp at Tyburn. After that, by God's mercy, what befell the mutilated body did not matter.

"It will not be long for them, Margaret," he said softly. "Our Lord will strengthen them."

Her passionate clinging relaxed a little, and she let him seat her on the edge of the bed, where she could lean back against the wall. She looked wan and frail, a little figure in gray and white; her hands clasped and unclasped in her lap, but her eyes were unflinchingly steady.

"You knew?" she asked after a long time. "I meant not to show—anything."

He shook his head. "Not till you spoke, dear; but it's well I should know. Probably, they were not told till this morning. After the sentence the exact time is set by the King. Sometimes it is no later than before dinner that very day, you remember from the example of Lord Hastings. It has been five days now for these holy fathers. Did you see them as you came in?"

"No; but the crowd was gathering all along the road. I—I could hardly reach the gate to show my order. And then, in the courtyard the—hurdles were being pulled out. That is what we heard just now?"

"I think so, Meg, though I did not know the sound at first." He went to the window to discover how much of the preparations they could see from there. Men oddly stunted by the height from which he looked moved about the courtyard; he could not see the hurdles, but the jutting doorway through which the sufferers must pass lay within view. When he realized that, a resolution shaped itself swiftly.

"It must be nearly time, Margaret. Let us watch them come out."

She shuddered.

"I'm not being cruel or morbid, dear. This is what I am thinking: there is no terror that man can devise or comprehend to which the mind of man cannot likewise be reconciled after meditation on it. We look at the horror with the eyes of the spirit as well as those of the body, and gradually, perhaps like the once ugly face of him who becomes a friend, it is transformed."

In the fixity of a sleepwalker, she came to him. They had stood thus, gazing down into the sunny yard, only a few silent moments when shouts arose below them. Margaret's arm, linked within his, stiffened a little, but her face was unflinching. Her courage, which was no callousness to fear, was a beautiful thing. The cries hushed. A white-robed monk, accompanied by his useless-seeming guards, stood for an instant in the doorway and was gone. Another. And another. Then, the Brigittine, Dr. Reynolds in his black robe. And the unknown secular priest, who took on distinction from his association with these four. Though the last two could be known from the Carthusians by the accidents of their appearance, in demeanor the five were at one, erect, serene in the commotion about them. Looking into the sunlight as they were, More and Margaret could not read the faces of the priests, but the exaltation of their bearing was unmistakable. He blessed the strengthening grace of God to which they bore witness.

"In their habits?" Margaret asked, and her voice was almost natural. The strangest aspect of this execution had come to her, mercifully, in the guise of a problem for the reason to ponder.

"How could they be degraded, Meg? Can the Church admit that they are criminals who die for her liberty and integrity? They die as priests—that is the new dispensation." All the way to Tyburn, he reflected, the watchers would be asking her question and drawing his conclusion.

The place where they had passed lay bare and empty as the sunny corner of a cloister-garth at service time. The quiet of the priests had robbed the scene of its potential terror, More reflected as they continued to gaze into the peaceful courtyard. One could not fear for men so fortified; indeed, one could hardly pray for them except in thanksgiving and praise to God for their example.

"Do you not see, Meg," he began softly as if their conversation on the vulnerable nature of horror had been only lightly interrupted, "that these blessed fathers are going now as cheerfully to their death as bridegrooms to their marriage? So we may see, my own good daughter, what a great difference there is between such men as have spent practically all their days religiously in a strait, hard, penitential, and painful life and such as have in the world consumed all their time like worldly wretches in pleasure and ease licentiously—as your poor father has done. For God, considering their long-continuing hard life in most grievous penance, will no longer suffer them to remain here in this vale of misery and iniquity, but speedily He takes them hence to the fruition of His everlasting godhead; whereas your foolish, sinful father—God, thinking him not worthy to come so soon to that eternal felicity, leaves him still here in the world, further to be plunged into turmoil and misery."

For the first time there were tears in Margaret's eyes—perhaps a good sign, for the tension in her face had eased. The noise, even outside the Tower, had retreated so that, when they turned back to the dimmer light of the room, there was nothing beyond their own mental pictures to suggest what they had witnessed. The inevitable thought would never again be so hard to front.

"You must not judge the facts that way, Father," she protested patiently.

"And I may not have long to wait? If my yearning to go may be acceptable in His sight, Meg, I shall go most gladly, though in my sins I be but half-ready."

So definite had his premonitions become in the last few days that he busied himself in the little chest where his books and papers lay. "Will you take these away with you to-day, dear? They will not be very heavy." He had piled two sheafs of paper and his Book of Hours together; he smiled a little at her unspoken question. "I ought to know the offices by now, and there are some writings in it I should like my children to have. These sheets are the end of my Hungarians' book—I am not sure that everyone who might chance to read it, were it to stay here longer, would find it palatable fare. The rest of the writing is some of a treatise on the Passion I've been doing recently; I'll have more of it ready next time."

But he felt not at all confident that Margaret would be allowed to visit him again. His heart longed for some power to comfort her in the days of strain he foresaw, and his love blessed the grandchild he told himself he would never look upon with mortal eyes. The unborn—and the dying. It was good to fix thought on them both. So, when he should be alone, for they would summon Margaret away soon, he would say the office of commendation—unworthy sinner as he was—for the five who were drawing towards their death: "Set free, O Lord, the souls of Thy servants—"

"Sir, I thank you heartily. You have reported my words and my meaning faithfully to His Grace." Having heard Cromwell's summary of the report he had given the King of the previous hearing, More bowed and waited what this new Commission—the Archbishop of Canterbury, the Chancellor, the Duke of Suffolk, the Earl of Wiltshire, and the Secretary—had to demand of him. The appearance of so many of the powerful members of the King's Council here in the Tower bore an ominous finality.

"The King's Highness was by no means satisfied or content with your answer," Cromwell continued sternly. "He believes that by your demeanor you have been the occasion of much disaffection and harm in the realm, and he cannot help thinking you obstinate and ill-disposed towards him. His Grace holds it is your duty as his subject to answer plainly and finally whether you think the statute in question lawful or not. Now he has sent us of his Council to demand in his name that you, on your allegiance and your duty to him as your only sovereign lord, answer this question. You must either acknowledge and confess that it is lawful for His Highness to be Supreme Head of the Church of England or else plainly declare your malignity. There can be no further delay."

"My lords, I have no malignity in this matter; therefore, I can declare none. To this demand, moreover, I can make no other answer than I have already done—the answer, Master Secretary, which you repeated a few minutes ago. I am deeply grieved that the King's Highness should have so bad an opinion of me. Were anyone to speak evil of me falsely to His Highness and win his credence, I should be sorry to have him hold that opinion of me for even one day; yet were I sure that another, coming to him on the morrow, would convince His Grace of my innocence, I should in the meantime comfort myself with that thought. So now, though it is a cause of great heaviness to me that His Highness holds such an opinion of me for the time being, I have no way to help that except to comfort myself with the assurance that the time will come when God shall declare my truth towards His Grace before him and all the world. And though that may seem to be but small cause for comfort, because I may suffer harm here first, I thank God that I so stand in this matter, in the clearness of my own conscience, that, though I may suffer pain, I can have no real harm. For in such a case a man may lose his head and have no harm. I am very sure that I have had no corrupt motive for my decision, but that from the beginning of my service to His Highness I have conducted myself loyally, looking first to God and afterwards to the King, according to the lesson that His Highness himself taught me on my first coming into his noble service—the most virtuous lesson that ever prince taught a servant. I do regret deeply that His Highness thinks ill of me now; but I have no means of changing his opinion. Meanwhile, I comfort myself only in the hope of that joyful day when my faithfulness to him shall be known. Beyond that I cannot go in this matter, nor can I make any other answer to your demand."

In the same instant Audley and Cromwell began to speak, but the latter withdrew deferentially.

"Master More," said the Chancellor after a pretty exchange of amenities with the Secretary, "the King may by law compel you to answer definitely one way or the other."

"I was about to make the same observation," remarked Cromwell in answer to Audley's questioning glance.

Again the threat of torture! "I will neither dispute the King's authority, nor question what he may do in such a case," More said in as quiet a tone as he could command. He noticed the hitherto silent councilors take on a more alert air than they had worn. "But truly, my lords, it seems to me—subject to correction though I am—that this is somewhat a hard measure. For were it true—I am not declaring it so—that my conscience opposed the statute and yet I did nothing and said nothing against it, why should I stand in danger? But, if the statute be like a sword with two edges, so that a man is compelled to agree precisely to it against his conscience to the loss of his soul, or to speak precisely against it to the destruction of his body, I cannot see how he is to conduct himself."

For simple words, these last provoked an extraordinary response among the Commissioners. More could not interpret the exchange of glances—what had he said to cause such exultation as this seemed?—but he could not miss the scratching of a pen in Audley's cramped fist. Whatever it was, it would be recorded against him.

"When you were Chancellor, Master More," Cromwell began with such alacrity as suggested his waiting for just this opening, "you used to examine heretics and thieves and other malefactors very thoroughly and justly, and you were most laudably vigilant to see the laws of the realm truly enforced. At that time, I think, you used—or at least the bishops used—to examine heretics as to whether they believed the Pope to be head of the Church and used to compel them to make a precise answer. Why, then, since it has been made law here that the King is head of the Church in England, should not His Grace compel you by the same token to speak precisely on the law?"

More wished for time to study the Chancellor's and the Archbishop's expressions after this parallel from the treatment of heretics: they, at least, knew that such examinations were the bishops' business. But he must answer Cromwell, who looked thoroughly assured of a scoring argument.

"My lords, I do not intend to defend my position or to enter into contention. There is a difference, however, between the two cases, because at the time Master Secretary refers to—very graciously giving me more credit for vigilance than I deserve—the Pope's power was recognized as undoubted here as well as elsewhere through the whole body of Christendom—a different situation from that in which one thing is believed in this realm and the opposite is held the truth in other realms."

"Well," Cromwell interjected, "the parallel seems to me good, because the heretics were burned for the denying of that supremacy as traitors are beheaded for denying the King's. Therefore, there is as good reason for compelling men to make a precise answer to the one as to the other."

"In matters touching belief"—More felt they must see the distinction—"a man is not so bound in conscience by the law of one realm when there is a law of the whole of Christendom to the contrary, as he is bound by the law of the whole body even though somewhere an opposing local law is made; therefore, the reasonableness or the unreasonableness of compelling a man to give a precise answer does not depend on the difference between beheading and burning. But, because the difference rests in conscience, it is the difference between beheading and hell."

"I wonder, Master More," Audley urged, "that you stand so precisely on your conscience while, at the utmost, you have no assurance that you are right therein."

"My lord, I am very sure that my own conscience, informed as it is by the diligent study I have given these matters, may stand with my own salvation. I do not meddle with the consciences of those who think otherwise. Every man 'suo damno stat aut cadit.' I am no man's judge."

"Is not this a new tune you are piping since you were Chancellor?" Cromwell's question was an open sneer.

"I was then in public office administering the laws of the realm, Master Secretary. At that, you give me credit that is due the bishops. Never did I, however, or any bishop I know force men to speak their secret opinions on the Pope's supremacy or any other question unless they had first, by speech, writing, or action, incurred suspicion. Good, honest Christian men have lived and died without ever expressing a sworn opinion on such matters. They have been assumed to be loyal and orthodox until they have proved themselves otherwise. Then and only then, have they been questioned as to their beliefs. By no law of Church or State have all men been put to their oath on matters of conscience wherein they have refrained from contention and disorder or actions conducive to them."

Feeling the old spirit of debate quickened within him, More wanted to point out also that no heretic he had ever heard of in England had limited himself to denial of the Pope's supremacy—indeed, so far as he could remember, that matter had not figured significantly in inquiry or polemics in England till the Defender of the Faith had flung his challenge—and, therefore, no heretic had been burned for such a denial, much less for refusing to affirm or deny. That distinction, however, was likely to do no more than prolong fruitless discussion.

For a moment they were all silent; then Cromwell echoed More's last words: "Conducive to disorder? That is exactly what His Grace considers your refusal to be. You have disturbed the peace of the realm."

"When I have been held a close prisoner for nearly fourteen months and this Act of Supremacy, as an openly enacted law, is no more than seven months old, sir? I have persuaded no man to take my position. As you well know, I have refused to discuss the King's matter with anyone but His Grace." Now More secretly blessed the failure of his proposal at Lambeth to write the reasons for his scruples at the King's command; at that time he had spoken of trusting himself to His Highness's honor.

"That may be," Audley snapped, "but the mere fact of your obstinacy gives others a bad example."

"How can I prevent that, my lord? I have not pinned my soul to anyone's back, nor have I asked any man to pin his to mine."

"But your reputation influences others," the Chancellor admitted grudgingly.

"Such as it is, my lord, I cannot unmake it. I can only trust that God will keep other men from any danger on my account and guide them with His own high wisdom. And I trust further that I shall not have to answer for the destruction of any other man's soul when I come to His judgment bar. How to face that tribunal has been my chief study of late."

Cromwell chuckled in a cruel distortion of laughter: "If, as you have said, you had as lief be out of the world as in it, why do you not speak out plainly against the Act? Though you say so, it seems that you are not willing to die."

Deeply as the taunt hurt, More fought back the cry of the outraged spirit. Patience, patience!

"Sir, I have not been a man of such holy living that I may be bold to offer myself to death, lest God suffer me to fall for my presumption. Therefore, I do not put myself forward, but rather draw back. Nevertheless, if God Himself draw me to death, then I trust in His great mercy that He will not fail to give me grace and strength."

Embarrassment hung over the little group: the Duke of Suffolk shifted in his chair as he used to do at the Council board when the sessions dragged; the Archbishop coughed discreetly; Wiltshire sat glowering only a little more fiercely than he had done since the beginning of the session.

Finally, the Chancellor spoke in the hollow tone of a man who feels that he has somehow lost control of the direction of discourse for which he is responsible: "Here is a simple oath to which we will swear you." At his nod, Cromwell laid the Bible straight on the table before him. "You shall swear to answer truly such questions as are asked you on the King's behalf concerning the King's own person."

"My lord, I purpose never again while I live to swear any book oath."

"You are very obstinate if you refuse so plain an oath," the Chancellor insisted. "It is no more than every man swears in the Star Chamber or any other court."

The others added the weight of frown and confirming nod to the Chancellor's rebuke.

"That is true, my lords." More felt that for once they were all agreed. "But I do not have so little foresight that I cannot well conjecture what will be part of the questions put to me; and it is as well to refuse them at the first as afterwards."

Audley laughed a shrewd laugh, to which the Earl of Wiltshire contributed a sinister undertone.

"I think you have guessed the truth, Master More, for you shall see the questions." As he spoke, the Chancellor handed a small paper across the table.

To More's surprise, and almost amusement at the simplicity of the trick, there were only two questions, the old ones: had he seen the statute? did he believe it lawfully made or not? In thought he added a third: had they really hoped to trap him so foolishly? He handed the paper back. He could feel the five men waiting.

"My lords, I will not take the oath. I have already answered the first of these questions and acknowledged seeing the statute; to the second I will make no answer."

The Chancellor looked from one to another of his colleagues, all obviously—and excusably—weary of this business; then he said dully, "There is nothing else since you are so stubborn."

As he approached the door, where the Lieutenant was waiting, Cromwell came up with him. "Master More," he said peremptorily, "I've liked your attitude to-day much less than I did last time. I pitied you greatly then, but now I think you do not mean well."

"God knows—" More began, distressed by the tone of personal grievance; but his notice of favor ended, Cromwell had turned away with a curt nod to Sir Edmund Walsingham. He could have his prisoner.

CHAPTER XIV

THE edge of the axe away from him, swerving a little in the hold of the guard who bore it, caught the sunlight like a wind-whetted wave on the Thames. There was a certain mercy in making a man's thought dwell on the instruments of his suffering, as he had tried to convince Margaret. She would be watching somewhere, praying for him. Together they had seen the first five go out to death. And now nine had come thus to trial under the Act; and they were dead.

Leaning on his staff, he had finally—two years after refusing to join the triumph of a coronation—come in a procession from the Tower to Westminster. So he stood at the bar of the court where his father had sat. Strange and not strange that he should think of that rather than of his own presiding in Chancery, across the hall at the right: life had turned backward, and he had come into his father's court—to ask a blessing. As consciousness admitted the throng in Westminster Hall, restless as the surf on a rough shore, the richly robed Commissioners, the colorless jury, some taut nerve snapped. But the irony of the remembrance saved him from its cruelty. To ask a blessing. While the heralds cried the opening of the court, he prayed silently for grace to stand in courage not too far below God's servants who had preceded him.

"Thomas More, late of Chelsea, in the county of Middlesex, Knight."

He held up his right hand: he was come to judgment.

So he listened to his indictment: the rehearsal of the statute and its penalties—how often they had asked him whether he had seen it!—and the four articles alleged against him. He fixed them in thought: they must be answered. Finally, the prolix document drew to its conclusion that he had "falsely, evilly, maliciously, and artfully imagined, invented, practiced, and attempted to deprive the King of his due title."

Then the Lord Chancellor, pale from the solemnity on which he was entering, spoke in measured, deliberate words: "You see well, Sir Thomas More, that you have gravely offended the King's Majesty. Notwithstanding, we so trust in his clemency and benignity that we believe, if you will repent and withdraw from the obstinate opinion in which you have so rashly persisted, you will obtain his grace and pardon."

As if his were the same voice, the Duke of Norfolk, leaning forward a little, continued the exhortation: "Truly, Sir Thomas More, such is the King's bounty that we have good hope that, if you retract the willful error you have so long dwelt in, you shall taste of his gracious pardon."

Did the Duke at that moment remember the warning he had spoken at his last visit to Chelsea? At least, though with no joy, More could believe this offer of pardon more than a perfunctory detail of a state trial.

"My lords, I thank you most heartily for your good will," he said with the feeling that these were the last neutral words he might speak to these former associates, who bore him personally, he would believe, no malice. "I pray only that it may please Almighty God to maintain me in this my just opinion even to death. As for the accusations charged against me, I doubt that my understanding or my memory or my words can suffice to reply to such detailed and serious articles, especially in view of my long detention in prison, my grievous malady, and the weakness from which I suffer."

After a whispered conference among the Commissioners, an

attendant of the court set a chair for him that he might answer to the charges. This once, he must accept the concession he had hitherto refused.

"As for the first article," he began, "charging that, to utter and show my malice against the King in his second marriage, I have ever attacked and resisted it, I can say nothing but this: I have never spoken maliciously against it, and whatever I have spoken in that matter has never been otherwise than according to my true mind, opinion, and conscience. Had I not acted as I have in this, for the discharge of my conscience to God and my duty to my Prince, I might well count myself an evil, unfaithful, and disloyal subject. And for this error of mine—if it ought to be called an error—I have not gone untouched, for my goods and chattels have been confiscated and I have been condemned to lifelong prison, where I have now been shut up about fifteen months.

"I shall answer only to the chief matter, wherein you charge that I have incurred the danger and penalty of the last Act of Parliament touching the King's supremacy, made since I was imprisoned, and that I have as a traitor robbed the King of the title, honor, and dignity accorded him by the said Parliament. Specifically, I am challenged because I would not answer the King's Secretary and others of His Majesty's honorable Council, when they demanded what I thought of the said statute, except thus: that, being dead and mortified to the world, I gave no thought to such matters but fixed all my attention on the Passion of Christ and my passing out of the world. Touching all this accusation, I answer that for this silence neither your law nor all the laws of the world can justly punish me unless you lay to my charge, besides, some word or some deed."

Immediately, the King's Attorney rose to answer: "This very silence is a sure demonstration of a perverse nature, maligning and resenting the statute. There is, in faith, no true and faithful subject to His Majesty who, being questioned as to his opinion on the said statute, is not deeply and utterly bound to confess categorically, without dissimulation, that the statute is good, just, and lawful."

Thus, More reflected, was a new definition of loyalty formulated, but he would not invite any rebuke for frivolity. "Truly," he resumed, "if the maxim of the civil law, 'qui tacet, consentire videtur,' be good and allowable, my silence implies rather a ratification than any condemnation of your statute. As for the statement that every faithful subject is obliged to answer to the question, in things touching conscience every true subject is more bound to respect his conscience and his soul than anything of this world—especially when his conscience is such as mine, giving no occasion for scandal or for sedition against his Prince. For I assure you that I have not up to this hour opened my conscience to any person living."

As he paused for breath, the Chancellor—perhaps misinterpreting the break, perhaps trying to help him—interrupted: "What do you wish to say on the second article: that you carried on a treasonous correspondence with the Bishop of Rochester in the Tower?"

"Would that those letters were now produced and openly read; but inasmuch as the Bishop, as you say, burned them, I will explain as briefly as possible their tenor. Some of them contained nothing in the world but certain familiar talk such as was suitable to our long friendship. One other contained the answer I made to the Bishop's question as to what I had answered at my first examination on the statute in the Tower. To that question I replied only that I had informed and settled my conscience and that he should inform and settle his." He was sorry that brevity made the words harsh as they had not been in his excuses to his dead friend. "On my soul, I made no other answer. For these letters I cannot be by your law condemned to death.

"As to the next article—when the Lords of the Council questioned me on the third of June, I did not precisely, but only conditionally, use the simile of the two-edged sword: that is, were the statute to prove to be like a two-edged sword, so that the man who would obey it might lose his soul and he who would oppose it would destroy his body, I could not tell how a man could so conduct himself as not to fall into one of the two dangers. Nor do I know what answer the Bishop made. If his answer chanced to correspond to mine, that accident is due rather to the resemblance between our minds, our knowledge, and our doctrine than to any agreement on the phrase between us. Nor has there, at any time, any word or deed maliciously escaped or proceeded from me against your statute, though it may well be that my words have been wrongfully and maliciously reported to the King's Majesty.

"My lords, I should not have spoken thus fully, but should rather have abided by the indictment in law, were it not that by so doing I should have been driven to confess as a fact the denial of the King's supremacy, which is not true. If only these terms, 'maliciously, traitorously, and diabolically,' were stricken out of the indictment, I see nothing therein to set as a charge against me. And to them, as to all the articles, I plead not guilty."

This effort of sustained speech had so exhausted More's strength that, as he leaned back in his chair, he thought with a pang, "And it is but started!" In spite of the lofty coolness of the great hall, the heat of the July day was bearing in upon them.

Attorney-General Hales rose to address the Commission: "My lords, since the prisoner at the bar has denied the fourth charge in a generalization, may we swear His Majesty's Solicitor-General as a witness, even though his testimony is embodied in the indictment? The jury should have the opportunity to judge this all-important testimony repeated here before them."

At permission given, Solicitor Rich left his place and was sworn as a witness. More was eager to check his story in more detail than the perfunctory reading of the indictment had permitted. Richard Rich! In his chief answer—already too long—More had thought a general denial enough because the accusation based on Rich's evidence seemed palpably absurd. Were he to repeat it now, however, on oath, it would become very serious. What an innocent looking, plausible person he was on the stand!

"Why did you go to the Tower on June the twelfth?" the King's Attorney asked his colleague.

"I was instructed to remove Master More's books."

"Were you alone?"

"No, Sir Richard Southwell and Master Palmer were there."

"Will you tell us what you and the prisoner said?"

"While his books were being packed, I drew Master More one side, and I tried to persuade him to conform to the recent laws. He answered rather shortly, 'Your conscience will save you; my conscience will save me.' I then explained that I had no commission or instructions to talk with him and that this was a purely informal, friendly conversation; and I asked him, 'If it were enacted by Parliament that I, Richard Rich, should be King and that anyone who denied this would be guilty of treason, how would it be wrong for you to say that I was King? Rather, indeed, since it would be no offense in conscience and since it would be obligatory in law, you would be bound to accept me thus.' Then he said, 'If this were set by law, I should be obliged to accept you. But that case is a trivial one. Let us consider a more serious and lofty one. Suppose it were enacted by Parliament that God should not be God and that, if anyone impugned that law, his act should be treason. If the question were asked of you, Richard Rich, should you want to say that God could not be God according to the statute, and were you to say thus, would you not offend?' Then I answered, 'Indeed, it would be impossible to legislate that God should not be God; and because your case is thus lofty, I shall propose a middle one. You know that our Lord the King has been constituted Supreme Head on earth of the Church of England. Why should you not, Master More, as much acknowledge and accept him as you would accept me were I named King, in which case you agreed that you would be obliged to acknowledge and accept me as King?' Master More answered that the two cases were not the same because, as he said, 'the King can be made by Parliament and deprived by Parliament,' to which act he would feel himself bound to submit; but in the case of the supremacy, he felt he was not bound to submit because that could not be settled by Parliament, and though the King be thus accepted in England, many foreign parts would not accept him. That was all we said."

When Rich, with his narrow eyes diffidently averted, had returned to his place among the prosecutors, a heavy silence hung in the hall. What he had said was cleverly contrived, for it seemed too crass and obvious to be an invention: people might well reason, "It must be true, for false evidence would be more subtle." Yet this tale of a snare too stupidly laid for a half-wit to walk into it was the crucial evidence.

"Have you anything to say now specifically on the fourth article, Master More?" The Chancellor's question was so perfunctory as to suggest that he expected either silence or an abject admission.

More pulled himself to his feet this time and stood braced on his staff: not merely the close-set Commissioners and the jury and the King's prosecutors, but every spectator—even those who, straining, had been unable to hear the mealy-mouthed testimony of the Solicitor-General—and, if need be, the impartial angels of the hammer beams far in the roof, must hear his answer.

"My lords, were I a man who did not value an oath, I need

not, as is well known, stand here in this place, at this time, in this case, as an accused person. And if this oath of yours, Master Rich, be true, then I pray that I never see God in the face, which I would not say—were it otherwise—to win the whole world.

"Here is what happened, my lords, that day when my books and papers were taken from me. Master Rich, pretending friendly talk with me, as indeed he says, began flatteringly thus: 'Inasmuch as it is well known, Master More, that you are a wise and well-learned man, as well in the laws of the realm as otherwise, I beg you, sir, let me so bold as to put to you this case: suppose there were an act of Parliament that all the realm should take me for King, would you not now take me for King?' To that I agreed, as he has truthfully said; but there his truth ends. Then Master Rich said, 'I put as a further case that there were an act of Parliament that all the realm should take me for Pope: would you not then take me for Pope?' On that I said, 'As for your first case, Master Rich, the Parliament may well meddle with the state of temporal princes; but as for the other, I will put you a case. Suppose the Parliament were to make a law that God should not be God; would you, then, Master Rich, say that God is not God?' 'No, sir,' he answered directly, 'that would I not, since no Parliament may make such a law.' With that I turned away, for we had said enough I thought, and that day I had too much to think about to give more time to clumsy, dangerous supposes. So my things being packed, the men took them and went away.

"In good faith, Master Rich, I am more sorry for your perjury than for my own danger." It was hard to decide whether the expression on Rich's plump face were brazen or indignant; but the ambiguity must be erased by the facts. Now, however, he could speak in a lower voice, for what he would say next needed to be heard by no more than Rich and the men who, knowing his character, had accepted his services. "And you shall understand that neither I nor any other man to my knowledge ever took you to be a man of such credit as to deign to communicate with you in any matter of importance. And as you know, I have been acquainted with you and your reputation no little while, for I have known you from your youth. We long dwelt in the same parish, where, as you yourself can well testify, you were esteemed—I am sorry you compel me to say so—very light of tongue, a common liar, a great dicer, a man of no commendable fame. So were you considered, too, in your house at the Temple, where you had your chief education.

"Can it, therefore, seem likely to your honorable lordships that I would in so weighty a case so unadvisedly overshoot myself as to trust Master Rich, a man whom I have always reputed worthy of little trust, as you have heard, so far above my sovereign Lord the King or any of his noble councilors as to utter to him the secrets of my conscience touching the King's supremacy, the special point and only admission so long sought from me: a thing which I never would and never did reveal, after the making of the statute, either to the King's Highness himself or to any of his honorable councilors several times, as is not unknown to your honors, sent to me in the Tower from His Grace's own person for no other purpose? Can this in your judgment, my lords, seem credible?

"Yet, if I had indeed so said as Master Rich has sworn, seeing that it would have been spoken in familiar, secret talk, and only in the putting of suppositions, without affirmation and without any offensive circumstances, it could not justly be taken as spoken maliciously; for where there is no malice, there can be no malicious offense." There was neither interest nor sympathy on the faces of his judges; still he must make these distinctions that, however unavailing to him now, some one might remember and apply in some poor successor's case. "Never think, my lords, that so many worthy bishops, so many honorable nobles, and so many worshipful, virtuous, and wise burgesses as were at the making of that law assembled in Parliament ever meant to have any man punished by death in whom there could be found no malice, taking 'malitia' for 'malevolentia'; for, if 'malitia' be taken in its general sense of 'sin', there is then no man who can excuse himself: 'Quia si dixerimus quod peccatum non habemus, nosmet ipsos seducimus, et veritas in nobis non est.' And only this word 'maliciously' is material in this statute, as the term 'forcibly' is in the statute of forcible entry. By that statute, if a man enter peaceably and do not put his adversary out forcibly, it is no offense; but if he put him out forcibly, then by the statute it is an offense, and so shall he be punished by this term 'forcibly.'

"Besides this, the manifold goodness of the King's Highness himself, who has been so many ways my singular good Lord and gracious sovereign, who has so dearly loved and trusted me—even at my first coming into his noble service admitting me to the dignity of his honorable privy Council—as to advance me to offices of great credit and worship, and finally, as he never did a temporal man before, to honor me above my merits or abilities with the weighty office of His Grace's High Chancellor, and who for twenty years and more has showed his continual favor towards me until at my own poor humble suit it pleased His Highness, giving me license to bestow the rest of my life for the provision of my soul in the service of God, of his special goodness to discharge and disburden me of my office—all this His Highness's goodness, I say, so long thus bountifully extended towards me, were in my mind sufficient reason to refute this slanderous surmise so wrongfully imagined against me by this man."

That they had heard, he was sure, for as he had spoken of the King's bounty—with what fear of breaking beneath the weight of passionate memory, he could only now admit—the impersonality of their faces had colored subtly to the hue of each man's thinking. If some one would bear him honest witness to the King—his mind was still working feverishly as he lowered his quivering body to the chair again—Henry, realizing that he was dying without malice, could perhaps believe that he had so lived.

Was Rich going to undertake his vindication? He, who had been sitting much of the time since More's denunciation of him in moody scorn, rose to address the court. "Will Master Palmer take the stand?"

Of course, that was why three of them had come to take away his books. If the conspiracy would bear him down by sheer volume of perjury, he could not hope for justice, More tried to teach himself while he listened to the preliminary questions and answers to establish Palmer's presence in his room on the twelfth of June.

"Will you tell us what conversation passed between Master Rich and the defendant on that occasion?" Attorney-General Hales asked confidently.

Sullen, hard, ill-favored, Palmer hesitated a long moment: "I was so busy tying up Sir Thomas More's books and thrusting them in a sack, I paid no attention to any talk that was going on."

Incredible. The haste with which he was dismissed from the stand suggested that this honest regard for his oath had not been expected of him. Less sadly, then, More heard Sir Richard Southwell, the very pattern of a smooth scoundrel, summoned: there might be no more than two voices agreed against him.

To the same question, Southwell replied, "I was instructed only to see to the removal of his books and papers; so I did not pay attention to anything else."

Doubly incredible. Too vague to evoke the anger of the Commissioners, yet definite as the release of held breath, a murmur stirred in the great hall. Men might count too much on this, More told himself, for the murmur was obviously one of sympathetic relief. While the jury was receiving its routine instructions, he reviewed this new turn in events. First of all, he apologized in thought to Palmer and Southwell for his cynical expectation that they would perjure themselves; at least they were men who respected an oath—indeed, they were almost men after his own heart—and he could believe that they had told the strict truth in disclaiming any knowledge of what had passed between Rich and him.

Of course, the help their testimony had given him had been wholly negative: during the deliberations of the jury some one would be sure to point out that the failure of the two men to hear the conversation was no proof it had not occurred. Then, it would be a question whether the jurors were to believe the King's Solicitor-General under oath or the defendant, allowed to speak for himself, to be sure, but permitted neither counsel nor the right to be sworn on his own behalf. Perhaps, a stubborn hope asserted, some one else on the jury would ask why Rich had not made sure that these handy potential witnesses should hear the prisoner's "malicious words." Certainly, it had been very careless of a spy to let an all-important episode pass unconfirmed when those who could attest it were at his service only a few feet away.

Would this jury, however, ask such questions? His lawyer's eye, which would probably function as long as he stayed in this world that tempted it, had already warned him not to expect much independence of inquiry from these twelve "good men and true." During the reading of the indictment and the subsequent proceedings, they had looked, perhaps not consciously hostile, but, rather, comfortably determined in their opinion. One of them—he could not recall his name, though that face was memorable—had been troublesome, even contumacious, in a case some years back in Chancery; still, that was all too remote and indefinite to consider now. More interesting was the fact that among these jurors there had been, at the failure of Palmer and Southwell to support Rich, no such show of surprise as had fluttered in the audience or as he should have expected a normal jury to evince. Too often to be deceived by the apathy of this jury he had seen men wearied by the formalities of a trial wake to sudden curiosity at some unforeseen turn of testimony such as this had been, for the two men would not have been sworn as witnesses save on the expectation of their supporting Rich. How the prosecution had bungled—he had to check his scorn at the flimsiness and the ineptitude of the whole case—and perhaps overreached itself! But he felt no great hope in spite of his own assurance of innocence and his belief that what he had said should in any normal trial lead to his acquittal. No, the one cause for rejoicing in all that had happened so far lay in the respect two men had had for their oath: it was an eloquent commentary on the order that was coming to prevail in the world that a commonplace virtue, like truthfulness, should take on such distinction. Now, however, it meant this: were he condemned—and he had no real expectation of acquittal, he repeated to quiet the still springing hope—only one man had burdened himself with perjury to compass his death; and for one man's sin there was no need to despair of the race.

A sudden silence in the hall interrupted his thought—the jurymen were returning. "No hope, no hope, since they come back so soon," he told his throbbing heart, "and you know all that can happen."

As he stood again, braced on his staff, to hear the verdict, he prayed passionately, "Dear Lord, keep me unafraid; let me not shame Thy servants who have gone before."

"Guilty."

However the word may have echoed in the hall, in More's

own hearing it was translated "Free." Beyond fear, beyond hope, beyond regret, he recognized the word that—by the King's action, not his—absolved him from the scruple that had held him silent. He was to die—he had known that almost since his birth; but since he was to die by this process of court, not of law, he must show why beyond all chance of misrepresentation. He would have this one last opportunity to speak before the sentence that they all knew would be pronounced. But when he lifted his head, expecting the question as to what he would still say, he saw the Chancellor standing and heard him begin:

"Having by due process been found guilty of high treason, you, Thomas More, Knight, shall be—"

"My lord"—no time for courtesy were he to escape collusion in this iniquity—"when I was at the law, the manner in such a case was to ask the prisoner, before judgment, why judgment should not be given against him."

For an instant Audley stared at him—he was not cruel certainly, but frightened and confused; perhaps he and his colleagues had not really expected this conviction. The Lord Chancellor seemed to bring his judicial poise back from a great distance as he asked in a quavering voice:

"Have you, Thomas More, any reason to allege why judgment should not be pronounced upon you?"

"Thank you, my lord." He studied the splendid, wretched Commission empowered to end his silence. "My lords, seeing that you are determined to condemn me—God knows how—I will now speak plainly and freely about my indictment and your statute, also, in order to discharge my conscience.

"Inasmuch as this indictment is grounded upon an Act of Parliament directly repugnant to the laws of God and His Holy Church, the supreme government of which, or of any part thereof, no temporal prince may presume by any law to take upon himself, as rightfully belonging to the See of Rome, a spiritual preëminence by special prerogative granted by our Savior Himself, personally present upon earth, only to Saint Peter and his successors, bishops of the same See, this indictment is therefore in law, among Christian men, insufficient charge on which to condemn any man. This realm, being but one member and part of the Church, may not make a particular law contrary to the general law of Christ's universal Church any more than the City of London, being but one member in respect of the whole realm, may make a law contrary to an Act of Parliament intended to bind the whole realm.

"Furthermore, this Act is contrary to the laws and statutes of our own realm as yet unrepealed, as you may clearly perceive from Magna Charta: 'Quod ecclesia Anglicana libera sit, et habeat omnia iura sua integra et libertates suas illaesas.' It is, besides"—this was one of his most secret reasons, but now his remonstrance could reach Henry only through public utterance—"contrary to the sacred oath which the King's Highness himself received with great solemnity at his coronation, as every other Christian Prince always has done."

Surely, he was not the only man there who remembered that coronation oath, he told himself while he waited the quieting of the agitation among the Commissioners he was fronting and out in the vast concourse, whose excitement he could feel.

"Moreover, my lords, this realm of England may no more refuse obedience to the See of Rome than may a child refuse obedience to his natural father. For, as Saint Paul said of the Corinthians, 'I have regenerated you, my children in Christ,' so might Saint Gregory, Pope of Rome, of whom, by Saint Augustine, his messenger, we first received the Christian faith, truly say of us Englishmen, 'You are my children because I have given to you everlasting salvation, a far higher and better inheritance than any carnal father can leave to his children, and by regeneration made you my spiritual children in Christ.'"

Audley was frowning as if in the effort to remember something that would be potent reasoning here; then the frown cleared. "It is very strange," he said dryly, "seeing that all the bishops, the universities, and the learned men of the realm have agreed to this Act, that you alone stand so obstinately against them all and would be thought wiser than so many."

Was he then alone? Even if they could say that honestly, they could not destroy the fact that nine wise and learned and holy men had already died in the same belief on which he stood. As for this contention of Audley's, More had heard it before, on the day that had begun his imprisonment, and he had answered it in part then as he would answer it more explicitly now.

"My lords, these seven years I have seriously and earnestly fixed my study and meditation on such matters as touched the King's policies and will and, among others, chiefly on this question of the Pope's authority. And not yet have I chanced on any ancient writer or doctor who advances, as does your statute, the supremacy of any secular and temporal prince. Were there no others but me upon my side, and the whole Parliament on the other, I should be sore afraid to rely on my own mind alone against so many. But if the number of bishops and universities be so material as your lordship seems to regard it, then I see little reason why that consideration should change my conscience. For I do not doubt that—though not in this realm, yet round about us in Christendom—not the smaller part of learned bishops and virtuous men now living are of my mind in this. But if I should speak of those who are already dead, of whom many are now holy saints in heaven, I am very sure that the greater part of them, all the while they lived, thought on this question as I think now. Therefore, my lord, I am not bound to conform my conscience to the Council of one realm against the general Council of Christendom. For every bishop of yours I have of the aforesaid holy bishops over one hundred; and for one Council or Parliament of yours—God knows what manner of one—I have all the Councils held these thousand years; and for this one kingdom, I have all other Christian realms."

Such amazement had been gathering on the Duke of Norfolk's face—had he not heard these arguments hitherto?—that his angry outburst seemed natural enough: "Now we plainly see that you are maliciously bent."

"No, my lord, absolute necessity forces me, for the discharge of my conscience, to speak thus much, wherein I appeal to God, Whose sight alone pierces into the very depth of a man's heart, to be my witness.

"And finally, my lords, I think your statute to be an evil one because you have made a contract and taken an oath to do nothing against the Church, which is in all Christendom single and whole, not divided, and you alone have no authority, without the consent of all other Christians, to make a law against the unity of Christendom. Nevertheless, it is not so much for this supremacy that you seek my blood as because I would not condescend to the marriage."

He would reason no more: the King knew why he opposed the marriage. If Queen Anne's father and brother and uncle, sitting on this Commission to condemn him, wished to know, let them ask His Grace, whose matter it properly was.

The Chancellor, though somewhat more composed than in that panicky moment when he had begun sentence, seemed more timorous than ever. Unable to dismiss More, as he had done at mere hearings, to take counsel with his colleagues, in his confusion Audley turned to Lord Chief Justice Fitz James, who was undoubtedly the most thorough jurist present here in the Court of the King's Bench.

"My Lord Chief Justice, do you hold the indictment sufficient or not?"

The Chief Justice frowned judicially before he declared: "My lords, by Saint Julian, I must confess that, if the Act of Parliament be lawful, then the indictment is good enough."

Sagely and unenthusiastically spoken!—If the Act be lawful? That was the whole question; and thus were they begging it. Such as it was, however, this opinion sufficiently bolstered the Lord Chancellor's hesitant courage.

"My lords," he said with a last glance at his colleagues, "you have heard what my Lord Chief Justice has said." He faced More again: "Having been found guilty of high treason, you, Thomas More, Knight, shall be brought back to the Tower by William Kingston, Sheriff, and thence drawn on a hurdle through the City of London to Tyburn—"

He had no need to listen: he had weighed all the horror of the sentence long before. Eight men had just borne that pain, commuted to mere beheading for Cardinal Fisher. They, all nine, however, had been some of God's saintliest servants. "Far as I stand below them in life, dear Lord, grant me strength not to shame those who have gone before."

"—And God have mercy on thy soul. Amen." Audley's voice had sunk to a tremulous whisper on the grim judicial benediction.

"Sir Thomas More," Norfolk's voice reached anxiously through the silence that was closing in, "we, the King's Commissioners, should be sorry not to hear all that you may wish to say to-day."

More bowed—his last salute to an old friend, who had tried, with all the wisdom vouchsafed to him, to prevent his coming thus to jeopardy. "I have no more to say, my lords, but that, as the blessed Apostle Saint Paul was present and consented to the death of Saint Stephen, and kept the clothes of them who stoned him to death, and yet they are now both holy saints in heaven and shall continue there friends together forever, so I trust, and shall right heartily pray, that, though your lordships have now here in earth been judges to my condemnation, we may yet hereafter all meet merrily together in heaven to our everlasting salvation. And I desire Almighty God to preserve and defend the King's Majesty and to send him good counsel."

As his escort closed round him, he looked upon the axe, its edge towards him.

CHAPTER XV

Beyond the dun roofs of Southwark the fields stretched lush and green in the sunlight of July, and the tawny road ran Kentward. This was a new view of the familiar scene, the restless mind was thinking while it strove to bring back from experience a time when it had dwelt long on its associations with Kent. Here on the battlements of the gate it was oddly silent, though the mind knew how the noises funneled to the entrance to the bridge—the crunch of wagon wheels on the cobbles, the lirrup of dainty hoofs, shouts and songs and oaths and the cries of beasts being driven to the slaughter; silent, though the eyes could see the wind flailing the far fields of grain and the rooks whirling blindingly close. Suddenly, recklessly, in the midst of the thronging traffic of the bridge a boy and a woman had halted. The child was pointing upward and seeming to shout, though no sound came, but the woman had covered her face with her hands. These lips had been stubborn before, but now they must cry out to warn the two below—and to comfort. Now, now—

In the agony of the effort, the mind won, not speech, but waking consciousness. It was day—dawn of the Vigil of Saint Thomas and the octave of Saint Peter—the fifth day since the trial. And More had waked in good time. For a moment, though, the dream lingered in thought. The two had been Margaret and his oldest grandson. Poor little Thomas! He had been about the same age himself when he had first seen the withered heads above the gate.

"Peace, restless mind! Do you forget that you will be gone away, and that what befalls the body will not matter? And weary head! In time you shall have a soft pillow on the river bottom, where the ooze cuddles many a proud skull. Do not fear: as if this scattered dust lay decently in its tomb at Chelsea, the Angel of the Resurrection will gather it from its ignominious corners and breathe upon it. O fearful spirit, on the journey whither you set out to-day, if it be the King's will, no man starts headless, for our head is Christ, Who said, 'I am the way, the truth, and the life. No man cometh to the Father but by me.' And no man coming in His name, though he lag far off like one unworthy, can come all unwelcome.

"Accept my longing, good Lord, to fill out the measure of my preparation, from which my worldly prides, ambitions, and affections too long detained me. In Thy infinite mercy bless and make whole the imperfect good that I can offer Thee, though I, sinful wretch, am not worthy to lift up my hands to Thee."

So quieted in, he hoped, the last access of the body's rebellion, he began a litany of recollection to repeat the blessings he had tried to write in haste last night in the little farewell notes to Dame Alice and Margaret, whom he had heavily charged with messages to the rest—his friends, those whom he had fostered, his children, his grandchildren, and the unborn who should be his. As he had prayed for them before and as he would pray for them when he knelt beyond the gate, he began: "Almighty God, have mercy on—"

With daylight the first church bells began to ring, and he had reached the end of the long list of those who, in kinship or friendship, had claim upon his love. Had he forgotten anyone, at the next such prayer he would remember him with a memory set free from the frailty and the distractions of the flesh. Now, on this day, he could not call any man his enemy; yet there might be some not satisfied that he had meant them no harm.

"Almighty God, have mercy on all that bear me evil will and would harm me, and their faults and mine together, by such easy, tender, merciful means as Thy infinite wisdom can best devise, vouchsafe to amend and redress, and make us saved souls in heaven together, where we may ever live and love together with Thee and Thy blessed saints, O glorious Trinity, for the bitter passion of our sweet Savior Christ. Amen."

Again the bells were ringing for the first Mass of the morning. "Domine, non sum dignus." He fixed all the fervor of his aspiration on the Sacrament that he might come to it spiritually now, though denied the right to share in it before any earthly altar.

How long he had been kneeling in this passionate meditation he could not have told. The knock he recognized and the turning of his key summoned him back. He understood. Rising, he saw Sir Edmund Walsingham and young Thomas Pope in the doorway, which only the latter passed. The soberness of his darkly shadowed eyes spoke for him: the final message had come.

"Welcome, Master Pope, whatever your tidings." More pitied the distress of this young friend, whose coming instead of some stranger or enemy was a generous act.

"Sir Thomas, it is the will of the King's Highness and his Council that you die this morning before nine o'clock." Pope's voice was faint with strain. "In his gracious mercy His Majesty commutes your sentence to beheading on Tower Hill. Therefore, sir, I am sent to bid you prepare yourself."

A simpler death—so little the cowardly flesh could hope to bear. He must comfort the messenger, unschooled by his few years' service in Chancery to a legal impassivity; and he must speak the last words he could be sure would be scrupulously reported to the King.

"Master Pope, I thank you most heartily for your good tidings. I have always been much beholden to the King's Highness for the benefits and honors that he has most bountifully heaped upon me; and yet I am more beholden to His Grace for putting me into this place, where I have had convenient time and space to have remembrance of my end. And so help me God, Master Pope, most of all am I beholden to His Highness that it pleases him so shortly to rid me of the miseries of this wretched world; therefore, I will not fail earnestly to pray for His Grace, both here and also in another world."

Pope could speak more easily the remnant of his message: "The King's pleasure is further that at your execution you shall not use many words."

"You do well to warn me of His Grace's pleasure, for otherwise I had intended to speak somewhat, but nothing with which His Grace or any other could have had cause to be offended." More could almost smile at the thought of how thoroughly his old love of words was being mortified—for nearly a month no books, no paper except the fugitive bits of last night's letters, no one to talk to; so the day of his trial had seemed half a holiday. "Nevertheless, whatever I intended, I am ready to conform myself obediently to His Grace's commandment."

"Is there anything I can do for you, Sir Thomas? Any message?" Pope looked about the almost empty cell, from which, remembering that those before him had had five days, More had sent yesterday his last intimate possessions.

Since with this commutation of sentence his corpse could have Christian burial, there was one request. Margaret's long devotion in visiting and comforting him made him bold to ask leave for her to perform one last daughterly office. For an instant the pictures of her and John and the others only less dear invading the unreality of his journey back to the Tower with the intense verity of their love dimmed his thought.

"Good Master Pope, be my intermediary to His Highness that my daughter Margaret may be at my burial."

"I should have told you, sir: the King is content already that your wife and children and any of your friends shall have liberty to be present thereat."

"How much am I beholden, then, to His Grace, that he vouchsafes to have such gracious consideration even to my poor burial."

"If there is nothing else, then, Sir Thomas, you will not remember me unkindly for bringing you—" The catch in the young voice had given way to unabashed tears.

Quickly More held out his hand for their farewell: "Quiet yourself, good Master Pope, and be not discomforted; for I trust that we shall, once in heaven, see each other full merrily and live and love together in eternal bliss. God bless you!"

When the key had turned again in the lock, More thought of the King's injunction that he say little on the scaffold. Three or four sentences would suffice him to explain to the people what he would have them understand: that he died for his faith in a united Christendom and the Church that was its spiritual authority, and that he died, as he had striven to live, the King's good servant but God's first. If they would remember so much, it would not matter what else they judged of him.

"Let me not forget, good Lord, Thy long and fearful agony. Let not my strength fail. . . . Thy servant, Lord. . . ." With gaze concentrated on the crucifix he carried, he scarcely perceived that they had passed the gate of the Tower till the jostling thrust of the bystanders warned him how short was the journey. "Thy servant, Lord. . . ." A quivering hand and the glow of wine lipping its cup. He lifted his eyes to the pale, compassionate face of a woman.

"Our Lord bless you! I will not drink now. My Master had vinegar and gall, not wine, given Him to drink."

Ahead a thin, high voice shrilled above the murmur of the people: "Do you remember, Master More, that when you were Chancellor you did me great injury by giving wrong judgment against me?"

With an effort—the affairs of earth had the right still to enter their claims—his eyes sought the woman. Poor soul! Yes, he remembered her envy-bitten, vindictive face, and he could only reiterate the old judgment.

"Woman, I am going to my death. I remember well the whole matter; if now I were to give sentence again, I assure you I would not alter it. You had no injury; so be content, and trouble me not."

"Master More, do you know me?" Yet another voice assailed him—the cry of a pain he could medicine, for in spite of the glare on the road he made out the distraught face of William Thorne. "I pray you for our Lord's sake, help me: I am as ill-troubled as ever I was."

"Friend, I remember you full well. Go your ways in peace and pray for me, and I will not fail to pray for you."

Still earth would have its due—the few last words. The hill taxed the weary heart, but dark in the summer sunlight More could see the scaffold at the top and them who awaited him. God had given him strength to find the unseen gate, and the keys were in the words he must yet speak: "The faith of Christ's Holy Catholic Church . . . the King's good servant but God's first."

THE DIRECTION OF HUMAN DEVELOPMENT

BOOKS BY ASHLEY MONTAGU

Adolescent Sterility
The American Way of Life
The Anatomy of Swearing
Anthropology and Human Nature
The Biosocial Nature of Man
Coming into Being among the Australian Aborigines
The Cultured Man
Darwin, Competition, and Cooperation
The Direction of Human Development
Education and Human Relations
Edward Tyson, M.D., F.R.S. (1650-1708): And the Rise of Human and Comparative Anatomy in England
Handbook of Anthropometry
Human Heredity
The Human Revolution
The Humanization of Man
The Idea of Race
Immortality
Introduction to Physical Anthropology
Life before Birth
Man: His First Two Million Years
Man in Process
Man Observed
Man's Most Dangerous Myth: The Fallacy of Race
The Natural Superiority of Women
On Being Human
On Being Intelligent
Prenatal Influences
Race, Science, and Humanity
The Reproductive Development of the Female
The Science of Man
Sex, Man, and Society
Statement on Race
Up the Ivy
Anatomy and Physiology (2 vols., with Edwin B. Steen)
The Dolphin in History (with John Lilly)
Man's Evolution (with C. L. Brace)
Prevalence of Nonsense (with Edward Darling)
Textbook of Human Genetics (with Max Levitan)

Editor

Atlas of Human Anatomy
The Concept of Race
The Concept of the Primitive
Culture and the Evolution of Man
Culture: Man's Adaptive Dimension
Genetic Mechanisms in Human Disease
International Pictorial Treasury of Knowledge
Man and Aggression
The Meaning of Love
Studies and Essays in the History of Science and Learning
Toynbee and History
The Human Dialogue (with Floyd W. Matson)

The Direction of Human Development

New and Revised Edition

by ASHLEY MONTAGU

Hawthorn Books, Inc. Publishers New York

Dedicated to J. C. FLUGEL

THE DIRECTION OF HUMAN DEVELOPMENT

 All inquiries should be addressed to Hawthorn Books, Inc., 70 Fifth Avenue, New York, N. Y. 10011. This book was manufactured in the United States of America and published simultaneously in Canada by Prentice-Hall of Canada, Ltd., 1870 Birchmount Road, Scarborough, Ontario. Library of Congress Catalog Card Number: 72-107636.

New and Revised Edition

1 2 3 4 5 6 7 8 9 10

CONTENTS

Look round our world; behold the chain of love
Combining all below and all above.
See plastic Nature working to this end,
The single atoms each to other tend,
Attract, attracted to, the next in place
Form'd and impell'd its neighbour to embrace.
See Matter next, with various life endued,
Press to one centre still, the general good.
See dying vegetables life sustain,
See life dissolving vegetate again:
All forms that perish other forms supply;
(By turns we catch the vital breath, and die)
Like bubbles on the sea of Matter borne,
They rise, they break, and to that sea return.
Nothing is foreign: parts relate to whole;
One all-extending, all-preserving soul
Connects each being, greatest with the least;
Made beast in aid of man, and man of beast;
All served, all serving: nothing stands alone:
The chain holds on, and where it ends, unknown.

Alexander Pope
Essay On Man (1733)
Epistle III

PREFACE

When this book was first published in June, 1955, among the kind things said about it the one that pleased me most was William Ernest Hocking's comment, "You have made the intangible tangible." Hocking has since departed for the Peirian Springs, where I trust he is reunited with his many Harvard students of long ago. Still are thy pleasant voices. . . . We never met, but in Hocking's remark lay concentrated the essence of at least one part of the book's endeavor. Love had been discussed from virtually every angle, but it had never been examined from the scientific point of view in any adequate manner. In putting the ideas together for this book, that had not been my original intention. That intention was to throw some systematic light upon the foundations of human nature, and *The Foundations of Human Nature* was to have been the original title of the book. But as I began to organize the materials for it, certain forms of behavior began to fall into place in such a manner that their fundamental and basic importance for the healthy development of the person became strikingly and illuminatingly clear. The most consistent of these forms of behavior was love. I found that all the child's needs were oriented in the direction of the growth and development of love and that if those needs were adequately satisfied, the child would grow and develop into a healthy human being—that, indeed, disorganized, destructive behavior, mental illness, and aggressiveness were all the result of a childhood lacking love. Everything I have learned since fully confirms these views.

The evidence of such apparently unrelated branches of knowledge as radiology, dermatology, endocrinology, physiology, biochemistry, and several other fields, as well as the data of comparative biology and evolutionary anthropology, all served to give love a many-faceted series of dimensions that for the first time not only put love in its proper relation to the development of the person but also endowed it with a tangibility that, conceptually at least, it had hitherto lacked. As far as I know, in this matter *The Direction of Human Development* still remains the only book of its kind.

The conclusions to be drawn from the facts and observations discussed in this book seem to me now more than ever to be of the first order of importance. Unless the findings presented in this book become part and parcel of the behavioral equipment of educators, politicians, and parents, there is a real danger that the human enterprise may founder.

It is time we began teaching the facts about the nature of human nature in the schools and preparing children for the tasks of parenthood and humanity. In a technologically advancing society this becomes more than ever necessary if we are to avoid the further technologization and debasement of humanity. The function of human beings is to be humane. Cleverness is no substitute for love or humanity. In a society that justly prides itself upon the accomplishment of so many things, that can send men to the moon, there is always the danger that qualities and values of vital importance will be slighted.

Man's unique evolution has caused him to develop as a highly interdependent, cooperative creature.* This is not a theory, but a fact. Furthermore, we now know that any serious interference with the infant's development as such an interdependent, cooperative creature will seriously and deleteriously affect his subsequent behavioral development. The causes and effects are discussed in the body of this book. Those causes and effects have been thoroughly substantiated

*For detailed discussions of the processes involved in this evolutionary development see Ashley Montagu, *The Human Revolution* (New York: Bantam Books, 1967); Ashley Montagu (ed.), *Culture and the Evolution of Man* (New York: Oxford University Press, 1965) and *Culture: Man's Adaptive Dimension* (New York: Oxford University Press, 1967); Hugh Miller, *Progress and Decline* (Los Angeles: Ward Ritchie Press, 1963); T. Dobzhansky, *Mankind Evolving* (New Haven: Yale University Press, 1962).

by innumerable investigations, the reports of which have been published mainly in the periodical literature, since the original edition of the present volume.

The fundamental category of ethics which philosophers have discussed and debated for centuries is the nature of the "good." Ingenious and interesting as these discussions have been, they have, in my view, failed in every case because the problem has been approached at a level of complexity at which it could not be solved. Goodness is not a matter that can be effectively discussed at the level of "rights" or "tastes" or "desirability" or "values" or the like. Whether they are aware of it or not, philosophers are essentially concerned mainly with the meaning of words. This is important, but it is not enough to throw any real light on the nature of the good. For this purpose what is necessary is a microscopic examination of the physiogenetic and ontogenetic development of man, so that by this double method we may learn what have been the evolutionary pressures that tell us what kind of creature the young of human kind is. For unless we clearly understand the nature of the requirements with which *Homo sapiens* is born, we cannot ever learn to know how to turn him into a healthy human being. I have attempted to provide this knowledge in *The Direction of Human Development.*

A.M.
Princeton, New Jersey
August, 1969

1 INTRODUCTION

Central to the future, as it is of crucial significance for today, is the conception of man, of human nature, the potentialities of the human organism.

—LAWRENCE K. FRANK*

THE PURPOSE OF THIS BOOK

By what means and by what processes does man become socialized, that is to say, a social being? Or, to phrase the question in another way: What is man's original nature and how is that nature influenced and conditioned to assume a socially functional form?

This is the compound question that we will seek to answer in this book. It is perhaps the most fundamental question that the student of human nature and of society can ask—and attempt to answer. For man is not simply a social creature; indeed, he could never have become the kind of social being he is without the unique biological equipment which supplies the potentialities enabling him to undergo socialization. It follows, therefore, that in order to comprehend the nature of the processes whereby man becomes a social being it is essential to understand, as far as possible, not only the nature of these organic potentialities of human behavior but also the nature of their interaction with the socializing process. What, then, we wish to discover is the nature of the reciprocal interaction between the organic and the social, their mutual conditioning or organizational effects upon each other.

* Lawrence K. Frank, *Nature and Human Nature,* New Brunswick, New Jersey, Rutgers University Press, 1951, p. 12.

Socialization Defined

While it has justly been said that definitions are properly meaningful only at the end of an inquiry, it will be useful to give at the outset some definite, though arbitrary, measure of form to our subject by a definition. We may, then, take the term *socialization* to mean *the process of interaction between the organic potentials of the organism and the factors which serve culturally to differentiate and organize those potentials into a socially functioning whole.*

Socialization is a process which commences at birth and proceeds throughout the learning life of the person. Socialization is, indeed, the process by means of which the person acquires social experience and social habits. It is the process by means of which the organism forms social relationships through learning and becomes a person.

Socialization has been defined by Kluckhohn and Murray as the process of inculcating and learning the traditional patterns, until they become "second nature."[1]* Linton has defined the process of socialization as learning what one should do for other people, and what one is entitled to expect from them.[2]

The Learning Life of the Person

Here we may ask a question. How long is the learning life of the person? The evidence of neuropsychology is clear upon that point: As long as the person is capable of learning. Which is to say, as long as he is capable of increasing the strength of any act through training;[3] by training is to be understood more or less ordered repetition.[4] Perhaps, more generally, learning may be defined as the alteration in behavior that results from experience.[5] Making an omelette of these definitions we may say that learning is an increase in the strength of a response that comes about through *repetitions* of stimulus situations appropriate to the evocation of that response.[6] In sum, then, learning is the totality of those processes by which the organism utilizes experience to comprehend and manipulate the environment.[7]

* References for numbered footnotes can be found in Appendix C.

The training capacities of the person endure, albeit with diminishing strength, throughout his life span. For all practical purposes then, socialization is a term which may be taken to describe a process which affects the person throughout the greater part, if not the whole, of his life. In the United States (1954) the average life span of the white male is 66.6 years, of the white female 72.6 years. For nonwhites corresponding figures are 59.4 and 63.7 years respectively. Socialization is, however, not simply a matter of extension, but more particularly of intension. The intensive phases of socialization fall into the earlier period of the organism's development, the period of infancy, of childhood, of adolescence, and of young adulthood. These are the periods during which, with generally increasing ability, the organism learns to become a social being and in the process of which it becomes a person.

Approach

Commencing with the socially undifferentiated state of the newborn we shall follow the process of social differentiation through infancy and childhood. We shall refer to a certain amount of the comparative material from other groups of less complexly organized animals for such light as that material may be capable of throwing upon the relevant data in man. Indeed, before we introduce man upon the stage we shall discuss some of this material, as well as some of the fundamental concepts with which we shall be dealing, some of which have already been mentioned but neither discussed nor defined. Finally, when we have completed this part of our discussion, and before we proceed to consider the newborn, we shall have to discuss his prenatal history; for if it is true that the child is father to the man, it is also probably true that the developing fetus is to some extent father to the child. Without an understanding of the ontogeny of the child there can be no real understanding of the development of the man in all his subsequent sociobiological relationships. We shall therefore discuss the prenatal development of man, and the development of those organically based or biogenic potentialities which prepare him for the process of social differentiation.

The Biological and the Sociocultural

However biological our discussion may at times appear, it is always being conducted with reference to an integral of which society and culture are essential elements. *Human beings function within a framework from which the dynamics of the sociocultural universe cannot be separated.* This is true of fetuses as well as of philosophers. The difference is one of degree. Where man as a functional whole is concerned it is never really possible to dissociate the sociocultural from the organic or biological. When, for the purposes of discussion, this is sometimes done the procedure is arbitrary. For methodological purposes it may be justifiable and, indeed, advisable. It must, however, always be remembered that this procedure is arbitrary, and that man, social man at any rate, is an amalgam or better, an integral of the biological and the sociocultural. The integration of the biological, the social, and the cultural variables yields the functioning person. Kimball Young has expressed this point in a simple formula.[8] If O is the organism, S society or social interactional effects, and C culture, while P is the personality, then the interplay of O, S, and C gives rise to P. Thus, the formula may be written:

$$O\}\ \ S\}\ \ C\} \ = \ P \ \text{ or } P = \int (O, S, C)$$

or more shortly

$$OSC = P$$

More recently Kattsoff has proposed a similar formula for behavior:

$$B = \int (G, C, E)$$

or more shortly:

$$G\,C\,E = B$$

where B is behavior, G is the goals of the organism, C is its capacity, and E its environment. In other words, behavior is a function of G, C, E.[9]

VARIABILITY

In the details of their structure the variates *O, S,* and *C*—or *G, C,* and *E*—must be taken as virtually infinitely variable. That is to say, for all practical purposes, in human organisms in interaction with one another in the universe of the sociocultural and physical environments, there is no measurable limit to the permutations and combinations which the processes of these interactive variates can assume. We do, however, make approximations to the measurement of many human behavioral functions; but with the exception of certain purely physiological functions our measurements are crude and rough approximations, even though they may have definite meaning for us. Such meanings are of a limited nature; our measurements of human behavioral functions are of limited meaningfulness, hence, for almost all human traits we may state this fact in what may be called *the principle of limited meaningful measurability*. This principle implies that in virtue of the enormous number, complexity, and variability of the processes and conditions of human behavior it is at best possible to obtain an approximate résumé of any form of human behavior.

No two organisms, no two societies, no two cultures, and therefore no two persons can ever be identical—not even so-called identical twins, as we shall see later. Practically infinite variability is the rule, and variation is the term which states the fact that no two things are ever exactly alike. The fact of variability is no occasion for despair but rather for congratulation, for variety constitutes not only the spice of life, but also—to the inquiring mind—a challenge to understand its origin and meaning.

POSSIBILITY OF SCIENTIFIC LAWS IN THE BEHAVIORAL AND SOCIAL SCIENCES

Variability constitutes the most advantageous of systems for growth and development and the increase of further variability. The existence of such variability does not mean that the discovery or development of laws of sociobiology, of human behavior, or of sociology are rendered impossible. On the contrary, such laws, while perhaps more difficult to arrive at than in the physical and biological sciences, are not only possible but inevitable if scientific methods are pursued and rigorously utilized.[10] In the realm of the sociobiological there unquestionably exist statistically modal recurring series of phenomena, so that wherever one finds man living in groups, there one can always be sure of discovering certain uniformities of organized behavior as expressed in institutions. Such are, for example, the family, kinship, religion, magic, customary law, language, sexual division of labor, mythology, property, marriage, art, secular knowledge, science, and so on. Where such phenomena occur with the regularity with which they do in the human species the formulation of certain laws of society is not insuperably difficult.

By *law* we mean a generalized statement, verifiable within measurable degrees of accuracy, of the manner in which certain events recur under given conditions, from which a prediction can be made.[11] Thus, for example, we can predict from what we know of human behavior that when a child is born to a married woman within any human social group she will, other things being equal, nurse it and bring it up. We can make this prediction for a particular case from what we know of human behavior under such conditions universally. The possible variability of human behavior is so great as to prohibit the prediction that *all* married women will at all times and in all places behave in this way. But the total range of that variability is limited enough, and within that range constant enough to enable us to predict that *most* women in all cultures will nurse and take care of their children. An aboriginal married woman in Australia, for example, may have had a child ten months before the birth of her most recent one. Her inability to handle two such young children may, with the full approval of the group, cause her to suffocate the newborn infant.[12] This is not a universal pattern of behavior in parturitive married women. On grounds such as these it has been claimed that laws in the social sciences are impossible, at least in the sense of representing the precision and unrestricted universality of physical laws. This is an erroneous claim based, perhaps, upon a misunderstanding or possibly an ignorance of the modifying factors always at work in any social field. Such a modifying factor is present in the example of the Australian aboriginal woman who was forced to dispose of the newborn since she could not adequately take care of the older child with the added burden of the younger one on her hands. The modification of behavior here actually represents no variation from the law of maternal care; on the contrary it reinforces it, for the Australian aboriginal woman acts in this way because of her enculturated feeling of obligation to the older child, and because it is the customary belief that an unsocialized newborn is not really destroyed if it is killed, but will undergo subsequent reincarnation.

An understanding of the particular conditions underlying an apparent aberration from a particular social law often reveals, as in the above example, that it is not a departure at all but a good illustration of the functioning of the law. In most instances, if not in all, where the nature of the modifying factors is understood the resulting behavior is often found to be merely a special case of the law in question.

Because of the greater complexity of social as compared with physical phenomena, social laws should not be expected to be as precise as physical laws.[13] That the formulation of significant social laws is beginning to be possible we shall see later in the present volume. The expression of physical laws in mathematical form is suitable to the phenomena with which the physical sciences deal. Such mathematical expressions are only now beginning to be developed to meet the needs of the social sciences. When those needs become more refined and soundly based there can be little doubt that more refined mathematical methods will become available.[14]

As Miller has said, "Science is not any particular method or set of techniques. It is a way of reasoning. The standards are intellectual rather than procedural. The method of observation, formalization, and testing must vary with the nature of the problem."[15]

It is not its subject matter which makes a science, but the scientific application of efficient methods to the analysis and organization of that subject matter. In the study of human nature the humanity of the scientist is possibly the more important part of his equipment. Self-understanding is the best of all means toward the achievement of the understanding of others. The quality of the investigator is usually more significant than the methods he uses. As D. L. Watson has recently put it:

> Of course, the student may easily be misled by his emotions, but equally by his *lack* of emotion. The road to success in handling human relations does not lie through the inhuman stolidity of the surgeon, but rather—as a first step—through the cultivation of emotional versatility and self-awareness. What is needed is not just participation, but a *critical* participation which holds fast to the thought that our self-regarding emotions deceive us.[16]

The scientific method, in Bridgman's words, is doing one's damndest with one's mind.[17] And as another Harvard physicist puts it, "the great moral which the progress of science teaches its students is: Faith in the marvelous ability of men to arrive eventually at truths by the free and vigorous exchange of intelligence."[18]

The old problem concerning the supposed difference between objective and subjective phenomena no longer exists. Objectivity, as Robert Seashore has pointed out, is simply verifiability, as judged by descriptions of equivalent samples of a given phenomenon.[19] When the subjective becomes measurable it is as objective as any other phenomenon. There is, then, no need to despair of our being able to apply scientific methods to the study of human behavior.

In spite of the tremendous variability and great complexity of the materials with which the social biologist, the anthropologist, and sociologist has to deal, there is every hope that the objective regularities observable in numerous aspects of social functioning will become increasingly more amenable to analysis and eventual statement in the form of laws.

The "Biological" and the "Social"

It has been said that the human being is at once the terminal problem of biology and the initial factor of sociology, and that the last word of biology is the first of sociology.

If such a statement means that where biology ends and no longer plays a significant role in any social process it is unnecessary to consider biological factors but only social ones, then that is the sort of *as if* fiction which one may, for methodological purposes, justifiably accept. For that such a view is a fiction should be evident from the fact that interactive minds in society are functions of organic systems as well as social ones, and that there is therefore more than a doubt whether social phenomena ever occur without bearing to some extent, however imperceptible, the impress of the organic factor. Be that as it may, there are whole areas of social phenomena in which if an organic factor plays any part, that part is so minimal that one can safely proceed to deal with such phenomena as if organic factors played no part at all in their development. For instance, from the point of view of human relations and the organization of society, race prejudice is a social problem to be studied and dealt with by social means. In no way can the social fact of race prejudice be conceived as in any way biologically generated. Nor can the phenomena of bureaucracy, of business ethics, of annuities, of apprenticeship, of zoning, and many similar phenomena be so conceived. This is not to say that any of these phenomena is devoid of biological reference—which is always minds in interaction. But this does mean that such phenomena can be conveniently treated *as if* they were devoid of such a reference with considerable success, and under analysis yield results of great value.[20] The social biologist may be able to round out the value of these results by showing what part, if any, the organic factor plays in the genesis and expression of these phenomena, but at this stage of the development of social biology it must be his task to grapple with problems significantly more fundamental than these. He stands, as it were, in the middle of a continuum at the beginning of which the biologist labors while at the terminus the sociologist strives to reduce his less tractable material to some semblance of order. It is the social biologist's task to establish the most profitable relations between the one and the other. Thus, sociobiology, the study of the sociobiological relations of man, is at once a branch of biology and a branch of sociology. The social biologist is in a position to be able to avoid the occasional extremes of both the pure biologist and the pure sociologist, without himself making an extreme of his intermediate position. He will recognize that the life of man in society is a biological fact, but that that life is characterized by different and more or less interactive aspects, and that methodologically very different scientific techniques may best be utilized in the analysis of these various aspects of human life.

The social biologist recognizes in human culture something unique, but he finds it unnecessary to regard that culture as either superorganic or superpsychic. Here, indeed, he is in a position to supply the corrective to such points of view, and to point out the errors to which they lead. Yet when all this, and much more, has been said he can fully subscribe to the view, so well expressed by Hofstadter:

> . . . that the life of man in society, while it is incidentally a biological fact, has characteristics which are not reducible to biology and must be explained in the distinctive terms of a cultural analysis; that the physical well-being of men is a result of their social organization and not vice versa; that social improvement is a product of advances in technology and social organization, and not of breeding or selective elimination; that judgments as to the value of competition between men or enterprises or nations must be based upon social and not allegedly biological consequences; and finally, that there is nothing in nature or a naturalistic philosophy of life which makes impossible the acceptance of moral sanctions which can be employed for the common good.[21]

The study of man in his sociobiological relations embraces much more than the "merely" social and the "simply" biological. That study embraces also the psychological, the psychoanalytical, the psychosomatic, and the psychiatric analysis of the process of socialization. The social biologist, in short, seeks at once to bring about a unification of the scientific approaches to the study of socialization and an integration of the knowledge thus yielded for the better understanding and the more intelligent control of that process.

Orienting Concepts and Definitions

Before we can proceed much further there are several fundamental concepts the meaning of which must be clearly grasped. These concepts form the matrix or ground of much that we shall be considering. Two of the most immediate and important of these concepts are *social* and *cultural*. These terms are often used interchangeably and are not infrequently regarded as synonymous. Such loose usage should be avoided, for the distinction between the social and the cultural is real and useful, providing us with two helpful interdigitating concepts which, like all good concepts, serve as useful tools. Furthermore, through the medium of the processes for which these two concepts stand, the socialization of man is chiefly brought about.

What, then, do we mean by the "social" and the "cultural," what is the relation of these two processes to each other, and how may they be distinguished? An examination of the comparative material is here indispensable. Indispensable not so much because it is helpful in tracing the evolution of sociocultural behavior in man, but because the comparative simplicity of the more elemental processes in lower organisms gives us the kind of insight it would otherwise be difficult to develop into the nature of the more complex processes in man, and because it helps to confer greater sharpness of definition upon our understanding of those processes.

Origin and Evolution of Social Life

In the early stages of life upon this earth it is probable that the only forms of life were single-celled plants and animals. Such unicellular members of the plant and animal kingdoms are known to biologists as the *Protista*. Those organisms which belong to the plant kingdom are known as *Protophyta,* those belonging to the animal kingdom as *Protozoa*. In all these forms of life the single cell is a complete and self-supporting organism, which performs all the necessary functions for itself by means of the differentiated parts of its protoplasmic body. The amoeba and the paramecium are familiar examples. Such unicellular organisms always originate from a parent cell. In this fact, at this early stage, may be perceived the fundamental ground of social life, in the origin of one cell from another in the process of budding off or cleavage. In amoeba reproduction is achieved by simple fission of the parent body into two single cells. The plant cell haematococcus (which occurs in temporary pools of stagnant rain water or in the resting condition in dried-up mud or dust) multiplies itself by simple fission within the old cell wall, this process almost immediately resulting in the production of four new individuals (the same thing may happen in amoeba). Sometimes, however, another method of multiplication occurs in haematococcus. Instead of dividing into four relatively large zoöspores a restive individual may divide into thirty-two or sixty-four much smaller "microzöoids" which differ from the ordinary active form in the absence of the characteristic cell wall and its underlying vacuole.

The microzöoids freely swim about, propelled by their flagella, and sooner or later form a single individual. In so doing they provide an excellent illustration of sexual reproduction, the essential feature of which is the union or conjunction of two sexual cells or gametes (in this case the microzöoids) to form a single cell, the zygote, which is the starting point of a fresh series of cell generations.

Whether reproduction and multiplication is secured by fission or by conjugation of gametes, the process is always an interacting one between parent and developing organism. The parent organism supplies the vital tissues to the new organism and in the process of fission metabolic and other physiologic exchanges occur before parent and daughter cells become organically independent of each other.[22] This type of relationship in varying degrees is characteristic of all plant and animal life.

The fundamentally social nature of all living things has its origin in the reproductive relationship between parent and offspring; in the fact that the life of either one or the other is at some time dependent upon the potential or actual being of the other. Thus, for example, when the amoeba has reached a certain size the increase in tension becomes so great that it can only avoid death by dividing, and this it does. The original process of reproduction would seem, in part at least, to be a tension-reducing response. The new organism, during the period of division, is entirely dependent upon the proper functioning of its parent. In this dependency, brief as it may appear to our eyes, we may perceive the origins of infant dependency in the higher animals, and the obvious social, and in man cultural, consequences of that dependent relationship. In short, *the universal fact of reproduction constitutes the foundation of the social relationship which characterizes all living organisms.*

Where the offspring are born in a helpless condition and their postnatal care is more or less extended we have a setting for the development of more complex forms of social life. But of this more later. In the nature of the reproductive process we see, then, the basis for the development of social life, and the suggestion is that social life represents the response to organic drives, the expression of functions which are inextricably a part of the life of the organism. The universality of social life would seem to indicate as much.

It is the interstimulation of cells in the reproductive process which is the primordium of that subsequent interstimulation of organisms without which social life is impossible. This interstimulation has been called "trophallaxis."[23] The organism is dependent for its proper development upon other organisms, it being a product of the harmonic functioning of other organisms within the system. Organisms are environmental necessities of one another.[24]

Few living organisms are solitary either in their origin or in their lives. As Allee states: "The growing weight of the evidence indicates that animals are rarely solitary; that they are almost necessarily members of loosely integrated racial and interracial communities, in part woven together by environmental factors and in part by mutual attraction between the individual members of the different communities, no one of which can be affected without changing some or even all the rest, at least to some slight extent."[25] With few if any exceptions every organism from the lowest to the highest is engaged in some sort of social life. The solitary animal is, in most species, an abnormal creature.[26] Dobzhansky tells us that "A solitary individual wholly independent of others is largely a fiction. In reality, most or even all living beings exist in more or less integrated communities, and the ability to maintain these associations entails some cooperation, or at least 'protocooperation.'"[27] And Simpson adds:

"No animal or plant lives alone or is self-sustaining. All live in communities including other members of their own species and also a number, usually a very large variety, of other sorts of animals and plants. The quest to be alone is indeed a futile one, never successfully followed in the history of life."[28]

Animals that have been removed at birth from their mothers and raised apart from others of their kind do not know how to behave toward the members of their own kind when they are placed among them. A sheep so raised by J. P. Scott never became integrated into the group,[29] and a chimpanzee so raised was at first disturbed and aggressive when at nine months of age he was placed with another juvenile chimpanzee, although after several weeks good relations were established.[30] Dr. J. A. Reyniers of the University of Notre Dame has reported to me a similar but even more interesting series of events with respect to a monkey, *Macacus rhesus,* which was raised in isolation:

> One young female which we reared germ-free for over a year and then deliberately contaminated for purposes of study, we eventually removed to the outside world. This animal had been reared alone in the confines of a germ-free cage and consequently had never seen anything of the outside world except a ceiling view and the face and arms, encased in rubber gloves, of the operator. When the animal was brought to the outside world, it seemed to be completely disoriented. If placed on a floor or table, it buried its head in its arms and remained motionless for hours at a time. When the animal was placed in a small container, it seemed to move about freely and to lose these inhibitions. This animal had never learned to make sounds. It was then placed on the opposite side of a glass panel one side of which was occupied by normal monkeys and in the course of several weeks, learned to accept its kind and to make animal noises.

Chickens which have been reared in isolation in a similar manner in Dr. Reyniers' laboratory have often "to be taught to eat." Dr. Reyniers writes, "we routinely in such cases teach it the proper head motions by manual operation."[31]

Certainly, social life is the rule among all mammals, the Class of animals to which man belongs, and no mammal is normally a solitary animal.

If the origin of social life owes its existence to the organic drives arising from the reproductive relationship, it is of more than passing interest to note that physically the multicellular organisms probably owe their origin to the same processes; that originally separate cells developed the habit of remaining attached together after division, as the spores in the encysted envelope of the parent amoeba might do to form a multicellular organism. Such an aggregation of cells would provide the means for the development of the multicellular higher animals. The interactive cells would, by their increasing ability to cooperate, develop specialized functions, and increasingly complex relations. The multicellular organism is therefore to be regarded as the expression of increasing intercellular cooperation, in which the interdependent cooperating activities of its cellular masses work together so that at all times the organism is able to function as a unit and as a whole.

Organism and Society

With the development of this interpretation of the facts we reach the view not that society is an organism, but rather that the organism is a species of society. The organismal conception of society is today generally discarded, yet, while the notion of society as an organism may be difficult to justify, a strong case can be made out for the organism as a form of society. Every word in Cooley's definition of society, for example, can be applied to the definition of an organism:

> Society is a complex of forms or processes each of which is living and growing by interaction with the others, the whole being so unified that what takes place in one part affects all the rest. It is a vast tissue of reciprocal activity, differentiated into innumerable systems, some of them quite distinct, others not readily traceable, and all interwoven to such a degree that you see different systems according to the point of view you take.[32]

The system which a multicellular organism constitutes can also be so defined. But there is considerably more involved in human society than is stated in Cooley's definition, though that definition will do as a description of society in general. It will not do as a definition of human society in particular because it omits explicit reference to the fact that human society represents a development of mind, of interactive consciousnesses and the complex of relationships to which these give rise, in a sense different from that which might be conceived as possessed by the individuals or masses of cells which are the interactive elements constituting the organism. The units which make up human society are free, those constituting the organism are, for the most part, comparatively fixed. The greater part of a society can be destroyed without causing the death of its remaining units, whereas under similar conditions death would generally follow in organisms. A person in human society exercises his will and his being in thought, feeling, and action. This is not the case with regard to the cells which make up the organism. All this is not to say that there is no relation between the society of the organism and human society, but simply that there is a real difference between the two forms of society, and that one must not be identified or confused with the other. The organismal analogy as applied to human society is questionable, but the relationship of the behavior of the cells which in interaction constitute the organism and human society is a phylogenetic one, and this is far from being questionable.

Whatever the nature of the factors involved in the cooperation of cells cohering to form functioning many-celled organisms, such cooperation does exhibit the elements of a protosocial or social act, and our principal purpose has been to indicate the possibility that such acts originally represent the expression of a drive which has its origin in the reproductive-dependency relationship of parent cell and daughter cell, and that the tendency of living things to form aggregations or societies of however primitive a nature is coeval with life itself. Finally, we have tried to show that human society represents the culmination of this evolutionary tendency, and that in virtue of what seems to be the accident of the development of man's remarkable psychic potentialities human society has assumed a unique form: it has become culturalized.[33]

2 THE BIOLOGICAL BASIS OF COOPERATION

So advantageous are all forms of mutual service that the question may be fairly asked, whether after all Co-operation and Sympathy—at first instinctive, afterwards reasoned—are not the greatest facts even in organic Nature? —HENRY DRUMMOND*

THE UNIVERSALITY OF SOCIAL LIFE

The fact that such diverse groups as insects and mammals have developed social life strongly suggests the existence in organic life of deep-seated potentialities toward societization or rather toward what might more properly be called *sociality,* the tendency to be attracted to and exist together with other organisms. This drive toward sociality may be weak in some animal groups and strong in others, but in one form or another it appears to be universally present. Group life offers advantages of many kinds to the members of the group and therefore to the species.[1]

Having postulated an organic drive or basic need for sociality in living organisms, we have now to inquire into the manner in which those drives or needs are expressed in some typical organisms, and further, to discover, if possible, what are the biological advantages, if any, of social as compared with solitary life.

LIFE AND ORGANISM DEFINED AND DESCRIBED

Since we have been speaking about living organisms without having defined either life or organism, let us, before we proceed any

* Henry Drummond, *The Ascent of Man,* London, Hodder & Stoughton, 1894, p. 305.

further, offer a tentative definition of each. A minimum definition of life is that condition in which a body exhibits the functions of *irritability* (response to stimuli), *motility* (movement), *self-regulation* (control), and *reproductivity* (multiplication). An organism or living individual is that organization of interactive elements which displays the functions of life in a self-consistent manner. The activities of the organism constitute its behavior, and that behavior always represents an adjustment to environment. The environment is the totality of energy changes which may stimulate the organism and influence its behavior.[2]

What distinguishes the organism from inorganic matter is its directiveness and creativeness; the purposive building-up and maintenance of its structural-functional organization.

As E. S. Russell has pointed out, the activities of the organism and of its component parts are directed toward living, developing, maintenance, and reproduction. If the organism is to complete this life cycle of processes successfully it must maintain its structural-functional integrity, and satisfy its essential needs and requirements. To do so its environment must be functionally adapted to its needs and requirements for maintenance, development, and reproduction. It must be integrally adapted to its environment or environments, for it is upon its environment that the organism is dependent for the satisfaction of its needs. The organism must be an integrally harmonious structural-functional unity, in which its component parts cooperate to maintain the organism as a whole. Self-maintenance or homeostasis is the dominant drive of the organism, and in the realization of this drive it must cooperate with other organisms.[3] As Russell puts it: "A drive toward the actualization of potentialities, to which self-maintenance is a means, perhaps describes more accurately the essence of individual life—in Aristotelian phraseology, a movement from *δυνάμις* or potentiality to *ἐντελεχεία* or actualization, 'the perfect realization of all that any creature or power is capable of becoming.' " In the words of Tinbergen, the key question is:

How do living things manage to survive, to maintain and reproduce themselves? The purpose, end, or goal of life processes in this restricted sense is maintenance, of the individual, of the group, and of the species. A community of individuals has to be kept going, has to be protected against disintegration just as much as an organism, which, as its name implies, is a community of parts—of organs, of parts of parts of organs. Just as the physiologist asks how the individual, or the organ, or the cell, manages to maintain itself by organized co-operation of its constituents, so the sociologist has to ask how the constituents of the group —the individuals—manage to maintain the group.[4]

The Cooperative Behavior of Living Organisms

From the enormous mass of data which now exists on the behavior of living organisms from the elementary to the complex let us select here a few representative examples of cooperative behavior.[5]

Sponges, which are made up of several different kinds of cells, may have their cells artificially separated and even passed through a muslin filter so that the cells become thoroughly dissociated and eventually form what appears to be a completely disorganized mass of cells. But interestingly enough, if they remain uninjured they will not long remain separated, for they regroup themselves in proper position and reform into a new organism.[6] Similar phenomena have been observed in hydroid, i.e., freshwater polyps.[7] Some of the original investigators of these phenomena have regarded them as due largely to random movements which bring the proper cells into appropriate relation with one another; if the random movements do not bring the cells into proper relation with one another they do not develop into an organism. This is, no doubt, true, but the important point is that the dissociated cells most frequently do establish the proper relations, and this must be due to something more than chance. To account for such behavior Wallin has postulated the principle of *prototaxis,* which is defined as "the innate tendency of one organism or cell to react in a definite manner with another organism or cell."[8] The reaction may be either positive or negative. Whether we regard prototaxis as being due to purely physicochemical factors or to a social appetite will depend largely upon the rigor with which and the degree to which we have made and analyzed our observations. It is easy to read into the behavior of cells purposes and motives which may in fact constitute no part of that behavior; on the other hand the fear of appearing ridiculous may deter some from drawing the clear conclusion. The fact is that no sharp line can be drawn between the behavior of cells forming an organism, the phenomenon of prototaxis, and the behavior of organisms in the process of association.

There most certainly exist the greatest differences in complexity in the relations involved; in these behavioral responses evolution has undoubtedly occurred in much the same manner as evolution has taken place in physical characters as between the simpler and the more complex organisms. Just as the single-celled organism stands physically in ancestral relationship to the human organism of some 60,000,000,000,000 cells, so does the single-celled organism's behavior stand in relationship to the behavior of a human being. Indeed, the physicochemical basis of the behavior of the human being bears the closest relationship to that of the single cell. This we shall clearly see when we come to the analysis of the basic or biogenic needs of the organism, whether it be a single cell or a multicellular organism such as man.

Examples of what has been called "the social appetite" in the lowest organisms have been known for many years. More than half a century ago, in 1894, the distinguished experimental embryologist Wilhelm Roux shook apart the cells of a frog's egg during an early stage of its development, placed the separated cells some distance from one another in water, and watched to see what would happen. The separated cells slowly approached each other until they established contact.

When an experimenter removes individual amebas some distance from a group of their fellows, the separated amebas immediately begin to make their way back to the group.

Deegener, in a series of experiments carried out on the caterpillar *Hyponomeuta,* found that these creatures actively seek out the company of their fellows when separated from them, and that even the isolated larvas tend to seek out their kind. He recognized a distinct need for association among caterpillars and spoke of a social instinct.[9]

When exposed to the toxic colloidal silver the grouped fish shared between them a dose easily fatal for any one of them; the slime they secreted changed much of the silver into a less toxic form. In the experiment as set up the suspension was somewhat too strong for any to survive; with a weaker suspension some or all of the grouped animals would have lived; as it was, the group gained for its members a longer life. In nature they could have had more minutes for rain to have diluted the poison or some other disturbance to have cleared it up and given the fish a chance for complete recovery.[15]

The experiment involving the goldfish illustrates the physicochemical basis of the advantage which lies in numbers, and presumably holds true for all other aquatic organisms. Allee's studies on the rate of cleavage of the fertilized egg of the common sea urchin *Arbacia* show that, with few exceptions, the rate is more rapid in the denser clusters of eggs than in associated but isolated fellow eggs. Protozoans, it has been experimentally shown, grow more rapidly when they are introduced in large numbers into a sterile medium of relatively simple salts than if the cultures are started with only a few organisms. The biological advantages are all in the crowding—not overcrowding—while separation or isolation would appear to be so fatal to the organism that we can be fairly certain that it rarely occurs in nature. The optimal population size for different groups in nature will depend upon the group and its environment, but thus far the evidence strongly indicates that optimal numbers present in a given situation have certain positive survival values and exert positive stimulating effects on the growth of individuals and the increase of population.[16] Thus, for example, Darling has found that among herring gulls the members of large colonies stimulate each other to commence sexual activities earlier than when the colonies are smaller, and furthermore, there tends to be a speeding-up of egg-laying, so that breeding activities are more intense while they last. The survival value of the short spread of time between laying and hatching lies in the fact that a greater number of young gulls survive under such conditions than do so where the colony is small and the spread of hatching time therefore longer.[17] The same holds true for asexual protozoans. It has been

ing behavioral and organic variations which better adjust the organism to its environment. Competition of every kind exists in the state of nature and has, of course, played an important role in the evolution of the varieties of life, but so has cooperation. In the struggle for existence one group may be competitively more successful than another because it is more cooperative. Certainly, so far as the persistence or continuation of every group is concerned, natural selection favors the *cooperative* as opposed to the *disoperative* struggling for survival. As Burkholder has recently stated: "Though struggle, conflict and elimination have long been emphasized by the proponents of the Darwinian school, probably the most important basis for selection of fitness actually is the ability of associated components within organisms and in societies to work together harmoniously among themselves and in conformity to the physical environment."[31]

The modern concept of natural selection is that of differential fertility or reproductive efficiency. The fitness or adaptive value of a group is expressed or measured by its reproductive efficiency, by the number of surviving progeny it produces. In a population containing differences in the distribution of mutant genes (that is to say, in which some types or groups possess such mutant genes and some do not), if for any reason one type or group leaves a greater surviving progeny than others, certain of the hereditary particles, the genes, and associations of these will become more frequent in succeeding generations. To put it in other words, any group of a population which for any reason leaves a greater surviving progeny, will increase while others become fewer in numbers in succeeding generations. This is what is meant by natural selection—*differential fertility,* resulting in the perpetuation of new genotypes.

We have already seen that reproduction is greater in cooperative situations than in noncooperative ones. Social life is, among other things, a means of ensuring reproduction. Familiarity is more likely to breed children than contempt. To the extent, therefore, that any group is less social, less fully integrated than another, it is likely to be differentially less fertile. With all other factors being equal, the group in which its members are closely integrated and are often together is likely to leave a greater surviving progeny than the group whose members are less socially integrated. Compare the numbers of the comparatively solitary lions, tigers, leopards, and jaguars, with those of the more gregarious nonpredatory deer, cattle, rabbits, and the remainder of the harmless gregarious creatures of the land. Consider, in the air, the flocks of swallows, pigeons, ducks, gulls, and other birds; in the water the shoals of herring, cod, and mackerel and the innumerable big and little unarmed fishes; compare the numbers of these with the eagles and hawks of the air and the sharks and alligators of the waters. Those who have most efficiently learned to avoid destructive competition survive better by the association they have developed. The meek shall inherit the earth. It is in the methods of peaceful association that strength is accumulated, and it is in those of competition, struggle, and combat that it is dissipated and wasted. Getting along with one's fellows has great adaptive value, and in the evolution of man there can be little doubt that selective pressures have favored those possessing these adaptive qualities.[32] "In comparative or competitive life the peaceable would benefit more and live longer than the needlessly disputatious, and so among the most unintelligent creatures there would develop a more harmonious life by the operation of the law of survival, without any conscious sense of harmony or of duty."[33] As Gibson says: "the adaptation to closer association, by cultivation of its peculiar methods of cooperative life, will enable a continued increase, by reducing the evils of crowding and developing its benefits.

"Thus association begins to appear as a constructive force, while the mere competition of numbers for survival of the fittest, is a form of destructive contest."[34]

Evolution itself is a process which favors cooperating rather than disoperating groups, and "fitness" is a function of the group as a whole rather than of separate individuals. The fitness of the individual is largely derived from his membership in the group. The more cooperative the group, the greater is the fitness for survival which extends to all its members. Politically such conditions are best realized in a democracy, and most threatened in a totalitarian or "closed society." As A. E. Emerson has concluded, the dominant directional trend in evolution is toward a controlled balance of the important factors within the system. "Human society cooperatively brings the social environment under control for the better survival of the species."[35]

If we would seek for one word which would describe society better than any other that word is cooperation. Cooperation may be defined as interaction between organisms which produces mutual support and enlarging stimulations which confer survival benefits upon the interacting organisms. It is important for us to understand that, contrary to the beliefs of the Social Darwinists, man does not have to make war upon his alleged bestial innate nature by opposing it with a cooperative way of life of his own invention. Not in the least, for man is born with the strongest cooperative impulses, and all that they require is the proper support and cultivation. Man's innate cooperative impulses are notably strong, as might be expected of a species individually so defenseless and weak. With respect to any other kinds of strivings the infant of most birds and mammals is equipped with the ability to compete with the universe for attention, and it generally succeeds in eliciting cooperative behavior, usually from one or both parents. In the process of socialization a certain quantity of the energies of aggressiveness are transformed into cooperative processes. The reproductive process is a cooperative one, and in addition, development as one of a litter or group of siblings represents another early experience in the development of cooperation; development within a family represents a still further experience in the learning and practice of cooperation; but this is to anticipate.

Innate tendencies toward some sort of social life are present in even the lowest organisms, and such a thing as a completely asocial variety of animal probably does not exist. This seems to be the first point to grasp in arriving at any understanding of the nature of the social. The social behavior may be limited to the short mating association or to the period of *care* of the eggs, as in many insects,[36] or extended to the complexities of the social behavior characterizing human communities. A second point is that social life confers distinct biological advantages upon the organisms participating in it. Allee and Emerson, indeed, regard as at least partially social any group in which the organisms confer distinct survival benefits upon each other. Implying the same thing, but rather more ascetically, Tinbergen would regard as social the keeping together of organisms on the basis of their interaction, and he would even call much of the behavior in a pair of organisms social. Third, and most important, the dominant principle of social life is not competition or the struggle for existence in the competitive sense, but is cooperation—the process of interactive behavior between organisms in consequence of which they confer survival benefits upon each other.

Fourth, some form of social life, of aggregate existence or association, is probably coeval with life itself, otherwise life could not have become established and evolved, and finally, the organic basis of social behavior is to be found in the nature of the reproductive relationship between parent organism and offspring. Nothing would seem more appropriate than that the reproductive process, which is concerned with the creation of life, should constitute the fundamental social relationship, and that in the evolution of living organisms, from the simple to the complex, mutually beneficial mass physiological interactions continue to form the organic basis of social life. Man is no exception to this rule, but he is the one animal most capable of modifying it by means of his cultural devices.

Some Definitions

Society. We are now, perhaps, ready for a tentative definition of society. *Society denotes that complex of fundamentally cooperative interactions or interrelations which exist between and among the members of a group.*

A Society. *A society, as distinct from society, is a group the members of which consciously or unconsciously cooperate to maintain a common life.*

The Social. *By social we mean all those interactive relations between individuals or groups in which needs are satisfied.* The social is essentially a continuous relational reticulum in which the indispensable condition is interaction, the establishment or process of reciprocal relations and influences between and among the members of a group. The fundamental quality of social life is cooperation—the process of interaction between organisms during which they confer survival benefits upon each other.

These definitions apply to the whole animal kingdom including man. There is, however, one aspect of society which is by many students either held or implied to be peculiar to man, and that is *culture.*

Culture. *A culture is the particular form which characterizes the social activities of a group.* Society is the generic term and culture is a species of society; the cultural is the particular form of the social. Cooperative interaction between and among the members of a group is social behavior, and such behavior is more or less common to all animal groups. What is not common to such groups is the form which that behavior takes. This distinctive form constitutes the culture of a group. As Linton has written of human behavior: "the actual behavior observed will rarely if ever be identical for any two individuals or even for the same individual on two occasions. The variations will tend, however, to cluster about certain norms. The sum total of these norms together with their interactions, is taken to constitute the culture of the society."[37]

Is Culture Unique to Man?

Warden, in an interesting book on this subject,[38] has attempted to show that animals do not have a cultural but are characterized by a social life. He has suggested a threefold criterion of culture, namely, invention, communication, and social habituation. Culture necessitates the development of some new form of behavior which is communicated to other members of the species so that it becomes the normal form of behavior to a large number of them. This type of behavior, Warden claims, is not found in any animal other than man. What appears to be cultural among lower animals is, according to Warden, "biosocial" behavior which is determined phylogenetically or by heredity, whereas culture in man is ontogenetic, developing during the lifetime of individuals as a result of the action upon them of more purely social conditions.

Culture in Nonhuman Animals

Let us examine the facts. Are new forms of behavior ever invented or developed by animals and communicated by them to other members of the species so that the greater part of such a group will normally come to exhibit such behavior? There is some evidence that such modifications of behavior do occur among lower animals.

In the first place, it is known to most experienced field naturalists that separated local groups of the same species of animals will exhibit clearly recognizable differences in behavior, and in several such groups the development and establishment of a novel form of behavior within the group has actually been witnessed. Several instances of this may be given. All African lions belong to the same species. Throughout the greater part of Africa they customarily hunt alone or in pairs accompanied by their young. Occasionally several lions will combine to attack a wounded water-buffalo which would be more than a match for them singly. In Kenya Colony, however, lions have developed the habit of hunting in packs with a regular division of function. The pack spreads out in a surrounding movement and closes in, roaring; in this way driving the game within the surround to a place where one lion lies quietly in ambush. Old hunters, according to Linton, say that within the memory of persons now living Kenya lions used to hunt in the manner common to lions elsewhere in Africa. They suggest that the change in the lions' method of hunting is due to the diminishing supply of game. Whether this is the real reason or not, it would appear that a new pattern of behavior has been developed and established in this local group of lions as the normal form. Such behavior is transmitted to the young from generation to generation.[39]

If these lions have altered their mode of hunting, then culture as the social transmission of socially modified forms of behavior, by

Warden's threefold criterion or any other criterion, is certainly exhibited in the behavior of these Kenya lions.

The question arises whether the possession of culture would have been denied to all lions had they all exhibited the kind of behavior which is apparently peculiar to the Kenya lions. Such behavior, it would have been said by most students, is instinctive, "biosocial," being too uniform and invariant to represent anything other than the expression of a genetically determined pattern of behavior. This is the customary argument applied to the description of all animal behavior as noncultural. Behavior such as the rat-catching activities of cats has traditionally been discussed as clearly instinctive because of the regularity with which it is exhibited by cats. No one, until fairly recently, was inclined to ask how much of this behavior was due to hereditary predisposition and how much to learning and to cultural acquisition. The now classical experiments carried out by Kuo are in this connection illuminating.[40]

Kuo's Cats and Rats

Kuo reared three groups of kittens under the following conditions: (1) kittens reared with mothers who killed rats in their presence, (2) kittens reared without any contact with rats until they were several months old, and (3) kittens reared with rats as companions. In the first group 85 per cent of the kittens killed rats before they were four months old. In the second group only 45 per cent became rat killers. In the third group the cats lived amicably together with their rat companions, never molesting any one of them. What is more, they never molested any strange rat of the same variety, although 16 per cent of these cats did kill rats of other varieties.

Clearly, the process of conditioning plays a much more important role in determining the behavior of cats in relation to small animals than has been customarily allowed. A great deal of what has passed for the instinctive behavior of cats is proven to be due to enculturation or culturalization. Under wild conditions it may be necessary for cats to kill small animals if they are to survive, and they apparently inherit a disposition to do something of the kind, but even this disposition does not appear to be strong since only 16 per cent of the unconditioned cats in this experiment became rat killers—rather, killers of other varieties of rats. What seems clear is that the kind of development its behavioral potentialities shall undergo largely depends upon the kind of experience to which the animal is exposed. These potentialities can be developed, directed, or more or less completely inhibited by early conditioning. In this process the behavior of the parent in the presence of the offspring plays a significant role. The behavior potentials of the offspring become organized in terms of the pattern of behavior originally offered to them by the parent. When the kittens observed their parents killing rats 85 per cent of them became rat killers. In the finally established behavior of the individual, it is evident, early conditioning plays almost as large a part as predisposition and individual learning combined.

Indeed, as Kuo says: "Our behavior researches in the past have been in the wrong direction, because *instead of finding how we could build nature into the animal, we have tried to find nature in the animal.* Nothing is more natural than for the cat to 'love' the rat. And if one insists that the cat has an instinct to kill the rat, I must add that it has an instinct to love the rat too. In behavior nature is what can be built in and not what is supposed to unfold from within."[41]

Few more important words have ever been written in social psychology than are contained in that last sentence of Kuo: "In behavior nature is what can be built in and not what is supposed to unfold from within."

Cooperation in Cats and Rats

Much light has been thrown on the "love" of cats for rats by means of several studies conducted by Professor Loh Seng Tsai of Tulane University. In a first series of studies three domestic kittens about one month old and four alley cats about two months of age learned to live peacefully together with laboratory white rats. In a second series of experiments Tsai tried to discover whether a confirmed rat-killing cat could be taught to live amicably with a hooded or colored rat. For this purpose a special apparatus was used. This apparatus consisted of three sections, each separated by an electrically controlled screen. The first section was the entrance, where cat and rat met for each test. When the gate was opened the animals entered the second section—the reaction chamber. To enter the third section, where a dish of food awaited them—the goal chamber—cat and rat had to step on a floor button simultaneously. When they did this together the gate went down and they were free to enter the goal chamber and eat the food.

First both animals had to learn that the buttons were the keys to the food. They had to learn that neither would be rewarded when only one stepped on the button at any one time. They had to learn to cooperate, to step on the button at the same time, if they were to obtain satisfaction.

In his first experiment Tsai placed three domestic kittens and three young rats together in a cage where they learned to live together as they grew. From the first they exhibited no signs of aggression or fear. For two years they lived peacefully together in the same cage without a single "misunderstanding." They lived together, ate together, slept together, and played together. A movie record was taken of a cat with a rat riding on her back.

Tsai put the three kittens and rats in the apparatus described above. One of the cats began to play with his partner's tail and accidentally both pressed the two buttons simultaneously, in this way opening the gate. So the cat would continue to play with the rat's tail, imagining, apparently, that this tail playing would open the gate for him. But one of the rats was much more ingenious. He would attract the cat's attention with his tail, and, when the cat's paw was on the cat's button, he would scurry over to press his own.

In a short time all pairs were working together. In the beginning they averaged two or three successful trials a day, then five, then ten, then fifteen within half an hour. In a few weeks they finally took only two seconds from the time they left the entrance to the time they reached the goal. Their cooperation, at first accidental, became more and more deliberately cooperative.

But Tsai was not satisfied. Thus far his experiments had been made with animals that had lived together from shortly after birth. What could he do with alley cats?

In his second experiment Tsai employed four alley cats, born, he tells us, in New Orleans' French Quarter. These cats were already weaned and were more than two months old. Tsai writes:

> Being alley-born and alley-raised, they should have had the experience of chasing after and killing alley rats. However, to my surprise, these alley cats also lived peacefully and cooperated with their rat-partners at least just as well as their domestic cat predecessors. They became friendly to the rats without much experience of living together with them in the same cage. One of the rats even sought protection from a cat and often stood right under the cat's belly, eating with him out of the same dish.

Alley-cats and rats learned to cooperate very satisfactorily in the experimental apparatus.

In his third experiment Tsai installed an extra key in the reaction chamber in front of the entrance gate. One member of the pair was put in the reaction chamber while the other was kept in the entrance compartment. Observing that his partner was confined and that he would be unable to open the gate alone, the released cat would refuse to go to the old buttons but instead would press the new key at once in order to release his partner. The rat, because of poorer vision, would tend to go forward to the old buttons. Failing to find his partner there, he would return to press the new key before the entrance door, thus releasing the cat. As soon as the cat was free the rat would run back to the old buttons to cooperate with him. Tsai points out that such behavior indicates that stereotyped position habits are not involved, but the responses are appropriately made to their partners as social simuli.

Tsai was still not satisfied, for although the alley cats were already weaned and assumed to have chased and killed alley rats, no authentic information could be obtained with respect to their actual rat-killing activities. The question was also raised whether these alley cats could cooperate with rats of another strain or color. Tsai therefore set out to discover whether a confirmed rat-killing cat could be taught to cooperate with a hooded or colored rat.

A ferocious rat-killing cat was obtained who, Tsai stated, "had enjoyed a long and glorious record of rat-killing." This female was eight months of age when she was brought to the laboratory.

In the course of training the apparatus was divided longitudinally into two sides along the midline by three pieces of glass, which were changed later into wire mesh partitions, thus separating the cat and rat all the way from the entrance through the reaction chamber to the goal. This was a safety device to prevent the cat from killing the rat, which past experience showed she would have done at the first opportunity.

> After about 700 trials of training in 28 days distributed over three and one-half months, the cat finally cooperated with the hooded rat without any act of aggression. It took about 550 trials before the partition, first of glass, and later of wire mesh, was removed from the goal. From then on, the once ferocious rat-killing cat would be peacefully eating with the hooded rat face to face out of the same dish. Another 150 trials were taken before the last partition in the reaction chamber was completely removed. The cat was also trained to release the rat confined in the entrance compartment by pressing with his paw a tiny electric key of one inch in diameter, located on the right hand side of the reaction chamber mid-way between the two screen doors. This was to make him realize that he could not solve the problem without first bringing in the rat-partner. In other words, the rat has become a necessary instrument as well as an invariable sign of food to the cat.[42]

Tsai believes that his observations throw "overboard the traditional dogma in psychology that in animal nature there is an ineradicable instinct of pugnacity which makes fighting or wars inevitable. . . . My experimental results give the death blow to any such fighting instinct theory."

Quite obviously when the conditions of life are changed predators change their ways of life toward their prey, particularly when their own existence is dependent upon that change.

Evidence of Cultural Behavior in Birds

What appears to constitute a good example of the invention, transmission, and perpetuation of behavior is presented by the case of certain species of birds known as "tits" (*Parus*). In 1921 tits were first reported as opening the tops of milk bottles left on doorsteps and drinking the milk. This first report came from Swaythning, near Stoneham, Southampton, England. Since 1921 this practice on the part of tits has been reported from many parts of England and some parts of Wales, Scotland, and Ireland. To date eleven species of the genus *Parus* have been reported as engaging in this bottle-opening practice.[43] There are over four hundred records of bottle opening by tits, and observations to a lesser extent are also available on house-sparrows, blackbirds, starlings, robins, chaffinches, and hedge-sparrows.

Most British tits are resident, not normally migrating from their usual territory even in winter; they may move a few miles from their breeding place, but usually not more. This fact would support the suggestion that when the bottle-opening habit is observed in tits more than fifteen miles distant from any place where the habit has been previously recorded the discovery or invention of bottle opening has been independently made by individual birds. The distribution of the records is consistent with the view that the new source of food was discovered originally only by a small proportion of a local tit population and then passed on to other individuals. As Hawkins states: "In England and Wales, it seems likely that the habit has arisen *de novo* at least once per vice-county and may have arisen more often than this. . . . The evidence that the area in which the habit occurred, as well as the actual number of records, increased more rapidly each year, is enough to support the view that when the habit has been acquired by one tit it can then be spread through the population by some form of imitation or learning."

The tits usually attack the bottles within a few minutes after they have been left at the door. There are several reports of parties of tits following the milkman's wagon and removing the bottle caps while he is delivering milk to the houses. A great variety of bottle-opening methods have been reported. When the milk bottle is capped with a metal foil the bird usually first punctures the cap with its beak and then tears off the foil in strips. Sometimes the whole cap is removed and sometimes only a small hole is made in it. Cardboard tops receive a much wider variety of treatments. The whole top may be removed, or only the press-in center, or the cardboard may be torn off layer by layer until it is thin enough for a small hole to be made in it; the milk may be taken through the hole, or the bird may insert its beak through the hole and flick the whole top off. The records show that several different methods may be used in the same district, and that individual birds may employ more than one method.

Since 1949 opening of milk bottles by tits has been reported from Sweden, Denmark, Switzerland, and Holland. In Holland milk bottles disappeared in 1947–1948. It is unlikely that many of the tits which had learnt the habit of opening milk bottles in pre-war years still survived in 1948, the habit must, therefore, have originated in all recorded localities since 1948. Since Great Tits are relatively sedentary birds, it seems certain that the habit must have started in many different places, and that it was initiated by many different individuals.[44]

That birds are capable, within limits, of learning and communicating new forms of behavior has long been known.[45] Clear-cut cases of invention and transmission, perpetuation and individual capacity for variation in behavior have not, however, hitherto been available as they are for these European tits.

Scott's classical experiments on the song of young orioles, carried out in 1901, are of interest. Scott separated the young orioles from their parents before they had an opportunity to learn the usual oriole song from them. The orioles thus deprived developed a song of their own. When other young orioles were placed among these, they, too, learned this song.[46]

Conradi has shown that when sparrows are placed among canaries they imitate the song of the latter.[47] It is a well-known fact that these and many other varieties of birds will improve their song when afforded the advantage of listening to a "virtuoso" in their particular field, and that such accomplished songsters are kept by bird fanciers for this very purpose. Evidently, within certain limits, birds are capable of developing and communicating new forms of behavior, and clearly their behavior combines ontogenetic as well as phylogenetic elements; it contains cultural as well as innate predispositional elements.[48]

Lorenz has shown in convincing detail that jackdaws teach their young to recognize the enemy "by actual tradition by handing-down of personal experience from one generation to the next."[49]

The mothers of innumerable animal groups teach their young to perform a variety of acts. Birds teach their young to fly and also which enemies to avoid; dogs teach their young under domestication to open and close doors, ring bells, and so on; apes teach their young to walk. With reference to apes, Yerkes, our foremost student of their behavior, has given an excellent account of the acquisition, establishment, and transmission of new behavior in chimpanzees.[50] Years ago pushbutton water fountains were installed in each of the chimpanzee living cages at the Orange Park, Florida, laboratory. This was done with some misgiving since it was felt that the animals might never learn to use the device or that they might have to be taught individually. Except at the outset, tuition has proved unnecessary, and it is years since any individual has required other than the stimulus of seeing its companions obtain water by pushing the button. Social tradition carries the lesson.

Three generations of association with man in the Orange Park laboratories has produced many opportunities for these chimpanzees to observe and to develop forms of behavior such as spitting through the teeth, squirting water, clapping the hands, using such objects as balls, keys, and hammers. Any or all of these activities, Yerkes suggests, may become behavioral traditions in a chimpanzee group.

The use of these chimpanzees in experimental situations and their intimate and continuous association with man has resulted in the development of very definite cultural acts which are both persistent and cumulative, since they are passed along from individual to individual by imitation and from one generation to the next by social tradition. To the experimenters it is a boon to work with animals that increase in usefulness year by year by reason of their capacity for individual adaptation, and to have successive generations regularly outstrip one another as a result of social tradition. These chimpanzees are clearly exhibiting cultural behavior.

Behavior and the "Social Field"

At this point the fact perhaps requires to be emphasized that the discussion as to whether or not nonhuman animals are capable of culture is not simply an academic one. It is not merely a matter of understanding our relations to each other as human beings which may be illuminated by such a discussion, but what is in its way no less important, our relations to the so-called lower animals. The great importance of St. Francis of Assisi in the western world is that he was among the first to grasp something of the significance of this, although in the East this relationship has been well understood for several millennia.[51]

We have assumed, in our culture, that animals have a nature which is unalterably fixed by their heredity, that their behavior is predestined by heredity. To some extent this is, of course, true, but we appear to have overemphasized the extent to which this is true and permitted the lower animals hardly any potentialities for plasticity or educability. Hence, we speak of hereditary enemies among animals, "the nature of the beast," while the contrary examples which accumulate in increasing numbers tend to be dismissed as quaint aberrations, even though the example of domestic animals living together is constantly before us.

When we ask what the nature of the beast really is, we are likely to obtain an answer structured in terms of the question. That is to say, we go out into the field and observe, and return with a description of the behavior of the beast, and the description serves as an account of its behavior. But that is not a sound way of inquiring into what we really want to know, namely, what it is that has been built (and by what means) into the animal that has become its nature. This way of asking the question leads us to regard the animal as a function of its total environment, the environment within it, which may be called the *in*vironment, and the environment without it, of which the organism is quite as much a part as of its invironment. We know that when we alter the invironment we can often produce behavioral changes. May it not be that when we alter the environment similar changes might be produced—changes in what we call "the nature of the beast"? The fact is that the organism is but a part of a total field of energies which affect it. Change any part of the field and the change will be reflected in the organism.

It was, for example, for many years taken for granted that bass reared in breeding ponds of Departments of Fisheries in this country were instinctively cannibal, until it was noticed by Dr. T. H. Langlois in 1931 that the few successful ponds in which cannibalism did not exist were wide, shallow ponds with little or no vegetation. It was found that when bass are put into weedy ponds they tend to become separated by the vegetation and fail to form large social groups. Some of the fish take up lodgings in secluded spots and begin to prey on the smaller bass. Any small outsider unlucky enough to stray into these restricted territories gets eaten. The cannibalism does not stop when other food is thrown into the pond. The predators are unable to see the food owing to the vegetation. Langlois' solution was simply to remove the vegetation from the ponds before stocking them with young bass. Now when food was thrown to them they all ate together. With everybody well fed and everybody acquainted with everybody else, nobody tried to eat anybody. In some ponds it has been possible to bring about the cessation of cannibalism by introducing bass from other ponds who had learned to be dependent upon the food introduced by the fisheries men. These bass continued to be dependent upon the external food supply and appeared to influence the other bass to do likewise. But in some cases the introduced bass appeared to adopt the habits of the other bass in the pond and quit taking the offered external food.[52] In other cases it has been possible to induce individual bass that have claimed holdings to give them up, by causing a school of fish that have learned to follow the person who feeds them to swim repeatedly over the area which the individual bass is attempting to protect. In these cases the individuals have given up their holdings and joined the aggregation, but in some other cases this has not been possible.

We perceive, then, how slight changes in the environment are sufficient to change the behavior of creatures from a cannibalism that was erroneously thought to be instinctive to social behavior that is cooperative. When animals cannot see where their next meal is coming from they are likely to get it where they can. In this all animals are alike, and it seems now quite clear that under natural conditions some animals prey upon others simply because they would starve if they did not. Were such animals to develop under socially satisfying conditions in which an adequate amount of food were at their disposal it is doubtful whether more than a few of them would prey upon any other animal. Wanton killing is limited to a small number of animals, conspicuous among the latter being man.

Competition for Food

The competitiveness which animals exhibit over food is almost certainly influenced by the sparsity factor as well as by their conditioning. At least, such experimental data as we have bear out this suggestion. For example, Fredericson set out to test the hypothesis that a limited period of hunger-motivated competition for food during the infancy of mice will cause them in adulthood to show increased competition for food even when not motivated by hunger. Hungry infant mice were therefore trained to compete for food for a few days shortly after weaning. They were then permitted to grow into adulthood without having to compete. This experience in competition during infancy turned out to cause them to fight over food on a retest many weeks later when they were sexually mature; they were not hungry at this time. The littermates of the experimental subjects were raised without competitive experience during infancy. This control group did not compete for food when adult and not hungry.[53]

Calhoun has pointed out that as soon as animals begin to modify their environment through the elaboration of relatively permanent artifacts such as trails, nests, burrows, and the like, their biological conditioning assumes something of a cultural aspect. While it is true that such artifacts satisfy basic organic needs—dens and nests being places of retreat where the young are safe, trails leading to food or harborage, and food caches serving to make food more accessible—it is also true that in addition to their physical properties these arrangements serve as the physical molds in which the social matrix takes its form.

It is in relation to the construction and utilization of these physical artifacts that many patterns of behavioral relationships become established. Animals using the same trails order their behavior in relation to other familiar animals. Young animals in the artificially modified environment find life easier than the original colonizers. They not only find places of retreat, harborages, food sources, trails, and so on, already established for them, but they also experience a stabilized social structure within which their integration and development is facilitated.

"This alteration," Calhoun correctly states, "of the habits and social behavior of one generation by the activities of generations which precede it represents a cultural process, when culture is considered from a broad biological viewpoint."[54]

To the question, then, as to whether nonhuman creatures are capable of cultural behavior or not, the answer is that insofar as nonhuman creatures have been studied in any context relevant to our question they have been found to exhibit behavior which is indisputably cultural, satisfying the criteria of invention, transmission, and perpetuation of new behavior, and that this has been found in fish, in birds, and in mammals.

While the subject of animal culture has been far from adequately explored, sufficient has been said to show that at least some lower animals do possess cultural potentialities which under varying conditions can be, and often are, adaptively utilized to meet the requirements of particular conditions. It is probable that to a greater or lesser degree such cultural potentialities are possessed by a large proportion, if not by all, vertebrates; furthermore, that *to some extent* such social behavior as we observe many of them to exhibit constitutes, in reality, their adaptive cultural behavior, the *manner* of their social interaction, the expression of their acquired social heritage in interaction with their biological heritage.

Animal and Human Culture

There is some ground for believing that there is really no sharp dividing line between animal and human cultural behavior. There *is* a difference, but this would appear to be one of degree rather than of kind. The degree or quality of difference is, however, great. The difference between the rudiments of culture characterizing some lower animals and the complexity and variety of human cultures is enormous.[55] What, then, are the limiting factors responsible for the rudimentary nature of animal as compared with human cultural behavior?

These limiting factors are unquestionably represented by a difference in genetic potentials for the development of cultural behavior. The system of genes which has permitted the development of the specifically human mental capacities enables man to adapt himself to his environment by calling upon the inventiveness which those genes make possible. Other animals adapt themselves to their environment by responses which are genetically both more limited and more fixed. So far as his psychological responses to the world are concerned man is almost wholly emancipated from dependence upon inherited biological dispositions, uniquely improving upon the latter by his ability to learn that which his social heredity (culture) makes available to him. Man possesses the genetic equipment which renders possible a much more efficient achievement of immediate or long-term adaptation than that possessed by any other species of animal—adaptation through learned responses or improvements upon these responses in the form of inventions and improvisations.

Two Types of Biological Adaptation

In general, two types of biological adaptation in evolution can be distinguished. One is genetic specialization and genetically controlled fixity of traits. The second is genetic plasticity, and consists in the ability to respond to a given range of environmental situations by evolving traits favorable in these particular situations. It is known, for example, that the composition of the blood which is most favorable for life at high altitudes is somewhat different from that which suffices at sea level. A species which ranges from sea level to high altitudes on a mountain range may become differentiated into several altitudinal races, each having a fixed blood composition favored by natural selection at the particular altitude at which it lives; or a genotype may be selected which permits an individual to respond to changes in the atmospheric pressure by alterations in composition of the blood. Heredity determines in its possessor not the presence or absence of certain traits but, rather, the responses of the organism to its changing environment. The responses may be more or less rigidly fixed, so that approximately the same traits develop in all environments in which life is possible. On the other hand, the responses may differ in different environments. Fixity or plasticity of a trait is, therefore, genetically controlled.

Whether the evolutionary adaptation in a given phyletic line will occur chiefly by way of genetic fixity or by way of genetic plasticity will depend on circumstances. In the first place, evolutionary changes are compounded of biochemical changes in genes, of mutational steps, and consequently the kind of change that takes place is always determined by the composition of the store of mutational variability which happens to be available in the species populations. Secondly, fixity or plasticity of traits is controlled by natural selection. Having a trait fixed by heredity, and hence appearing in the development of an individual regardless of environmental variations is, in general, of benefit to organisms whose milieu remains uniform and static except for rare and freakish deviations. Conversely, organisms which inhabit changeable environments are benefited by having their traits plastic and modified by each recurrent configuration of environmental agents in a way most favorable for the survival of the carrier of the trait in question.

Comparative anatomy and embryology show that a fairly general trend in organic evolution seems to be from environmental dependence toward fixation of the basic features of the bodily structure and function. The appearance of these structures in embryonic development of higher organisms is, in general, more nearly autonomous and independent of the environment than in lower forms. The development becomes "buffered" against environmental and genetic shocks. If, however, the mode of life of a species happens to be such that it is, of necessity, exposed to a wide range of environments, it becomes desirable to vary some structures and functions in accordance with the circumstances that confront an individual or a strain at a given time and place. Genetic structures which permit adaptive plasticity of traits become, then, obviously advantageous for survival and so are fostered by natural selection.

Educability as a Species Character of Man

The possession of the gene system which conditions educability rather than behavioral fixity is a common property of all living mankind. In other words, educability is truly a species character of man, *Homo sapiens,* a genotype which is capable of a very wide range of phenotypes. It is this quality of educability or plasticity of his behavioral or mental traits which confers upon man the unique position which he holds in the animal kingdom. Its acquisition freed him from the constraint of a limited range of biologically predetermined responses. He became capable of acting in a more or less regulative manner upon his physical environment instead of being largely regulated by it. The genetically controlled plasticity of mental traits is, biologically speaking, the most typical and uniquely human characteristic. Man's suppleness, plasticity, and, most important of all, ability to profit from experience and education are unique. No other species is comparable to man in its capacity to acquire new behavior patterns and discard old ones in consequence of training.

Considered biologically as well as socially the limiting factor which prevents nonhuman animals from functioning at a level equivalent to that at which human beings function is the comparative genetic fixity of their behavioral potentialities, their comparative lack of behavioral plasticity or educability.[56]

Instead of having his responses genetically fixed as in other animal species, man is a species that invents its own responses, and it is out of this unique ability to invent and to improvise his responses that his cultures are born.

Educability and the Use of Symbols

The most important vehicle through which educability is effected and expresses itself is speech or language. Again, man is unique in the degree to which he possesses this faculty.

Animals do communicate with one another by sounds, movements of the body of a meaningful sort, by gestures, facial and bodily expression, and various visible attitudes. Their communication appears to be limited mainly to matters of immediate import largely without reference to the past or future, and has principally if not exclusively to do with response to stimuli in the external environment.[57] Communication and language must be distinguished. Communication is a general term and refers to the behavior of an individual or of a group that influences others. Language is a specific term and refers to the utilization of a specific system of symbolic activities which is calculated to influence the behavior of others in a specific way. A symbol may be defined as a meaning or value conferred by those who use it upon anything, tangible or intangible. A sign, on the other hand, belongs to the physical world; it is, as White says, "a physical thing or event whose function is to indicate some other thing or event.[58] Or, as Cassirer says, "a symbol is part of the human world of meaning. Signals are 'operators'; symbols are 'designators.'"[59] Language is a species of communication.[60] Lower animals do not habitually make use of symbols. The chimpanzee has formed the subject of detailed study with regard to its ability to utilize symbols. Yerkes and Nissen concluded that the chimpanzee is occasionally capable of symbolic processes, but that those processes are relatively rudimentary and ineffective, and finally that there does not seem to be any increase in frequency and functional value of symbolic response with increase in experience and age.[61]

These findings are of the greatest interest, the more so in view of the fact that in the whole living kingdom the chimpanzee is probably the animal most nearly related to and most like man. It is quite unlikely that any other nonhuman creature (with the possible exception of the orang and gorilla) even approximates the chimpanzee in its very rare attempt at the use of a symbolic process. Rats under conditions of repeated training do show some evidence of a primitive symbolic capacity,[62] but this is extremely rudimentary. However this may be, the degree of symbol usage among chimpanzees and the kind of sociocultural behavior they exhibit, or are known to be capable of exhibiting, give us the clue to the essential difference both in the character of their communication and thought as compared with those of man, and in their lack of a developed culture. These differences are almost certainly due to the limited coefficient of educability of these animals and their consequent inability to make anything like an extended use of symbols. Here we perceive that we are, indeed, dealing with a difference in degree rather than of kind, a relative difference rather than an absolute one. It is, therefore, not correct to say as Dr. Leslie White has, that man alone uses symbols, and that there are no intermediate stages between a creature that does and one that does not use symbols.[63] Upon comparatively rare occasions chimpanzees are able to make rudimentary and inefficient use of symbolic processes, hence the rudiments of symbolic thought can be said to be present in at least one group of nonhuman primates. What distinguishes man from the ape is not that the one is able to use symbols and the other is not, but that man is capable of thinking and communicating with others almost exclusively by the use of symbols, by sounds and devices which stand for the thing represented. Such referred meanings and values man utilizes with great ability and increasing improvability both in the individual and in the group. In the chimpanzee not only are symbolic processes of thought rarely used, but when on occasion they are used it is with the greatest difficulty and most inefficiently, and, what is equally important, there seems to be no improvement in the use of such symbols through childhood to maturity.[64] In man, on the other hand, the growth and development of symbolic thought from childhood to maturity is considerable. It is these fundamental differences which explain the great gap between the cultural behavior of an ape and that of a man.

Symbolic Thought the Basis of Language

Without the ability to make free use of symbolic thought neither language nor culture can develop above the level which characterizes these activities in animals. Indeed, language is nothing but a system of symbols for producing action in specific ways. The meaning of a word is the action it produces. Language is the vehicle of human culture. There could be no human culture without language, and language is the inevitable correlate of symbolic thought. It is the tie that binds human society together.[65]

Given the structural vocal equipment with which man is endowed, organs of voice which, from the anatomical point of view, are far superior to anything of the kind possessed even by such animals as the apes,[66] articulate speech simply becomes a matter of finding sounds denoting symbols wherewith to express feelings, desires, and thoughts. The systematic use of such sound symbols constitutes spoken language, speech. No human being can ever develop the ability to use language or to become a cooperative member of a culture without the power of symbolic thought. The human child commences to speak meaningfully only when it has begun to master this power, and it is mainly through the use of symbols that it develops the ability to use more and more complicated relational systems of symbols. Human learning consists principally of the process of building up new systems of symbol relations and integrating them with already existing ones. Thought is essentially the process of educing relations from symbol correlates. In this symbolic type of learning and thinking lies man's uniqueness, and his ability to acquire and develop complex behavior of a cultural kind. Mind arises through the communication of such symbol-meanings in a social process or context of experience.[67]

Man has been described as the reasoning animal, *animal rationale.* But other animals can reason, too. As Oliver Goldsmith put it:

> Logicians have but ill defin'd
> As rational the human kind;
> Reason, they say, belongs to man,
> But let them prove it if they can.
> —from *The Logicians Refuted*

Reason is not peculiar to man, but the extended ability to learn to use symbols is, for all practical purposes, confined to man. It is this ability rather than the faculty of reason which distinguishes man from all other animals. Man should therefore be defined, as Cassirer has suggested,[68] as the *animal symbolicum,* the symbol-using animal. Becker has suggested *Homo loquens,* man the talker.[69] This suggestion has some merit, for the ability to utilize symbols is largely dependent upon language usage. The higher animals communicate through signals, by "mood convection," through the transmission and reception of sign stimuli which convey moods. Such signs are in no way comparable to spoken language, but are more akin to such expressions as yawning, wrinkling the brow, and smiling.[70] There is some evidence that human infants retain this capacity for interpreting sign stimuli, although in adults it seems to degenerate for want of practice. The more adept one becomes at symbol usage the poorer one becomes at sign reading.

Without symbol usage the objectification of subjective processes is limited to a narrow range of emotional cries, and the designation or description of objects is impossible.[71] Emotional "language," but not propositional language, is possible. Without propositional language and imagery the development of anything resembling human culture is beyond reach. Though language must be developed by every individual it is an error to regard language as something secondary. Language represents the development of a potentiality, it is something more than a mere acquisition. The potentiality is, of course, inherited in man, though what he shall say and how he shall use that potentiality is determined by the particular culture or segment of culture in which he lives. As a potentiality human speech is a matter of heredity, as a systematic performance it is a matter of culture. These are key points to remember. Just as the child has to learn to walk so he has to learn to talk, except that complex as the process of learning to walk is, learning to talk is vastly more complex. Whatever language man learns to speak, and however well or poorly he learns it, the process of learning involves an enormous number of organic changes necessitating the most delicate types of neuromuscular coordination and adjustment, as well as the establishment of innumerable complex interrelations within the body the character of which we have scarcely begun to know.

The so-called speech center of man is known as Broca's area. This is situated in the third frontal convolution. Injury to this region results in motor speech aphasia, that is, in an inability to express language vocally or to think linguistically. Since Broca's day several other areas of the brain have been recognized as being intimately concerned with the language functions. The roughly posterior three fourths of the superior and middle temporal convolutions are associated with the ability to recognize spoken words; injury to this area results in word deafness, a sensory auditory aphasia leading to disturbance of the ability to understand the meaning of words and language as heard. Both macro- and micro-scopically the structure of these areas of the brain is not known to differ in the apes and man. There is, however, a region at the posterior part of the second temporal convolution in man, adjoining the area for the reception of impulses from the organ of hearing, the development and great expansion of which is not approached by any other creature. This is the area of the brain which is associated with the ability to understand vocal symbols. Situated immediately above Broca's area is the region associated with the ability to write language, injury to which results in agraphia, an inability to write. In the paraoccipital region behind the auditory area is the region associated with the recognition of the printed word, injury to which results in word blindness or visual aphasia (alexia) or in disturbances of perception of the meaning of language as read.

We know today, from the study of thousands of brain-injured persons, that the process of learning language is the process of structurally organizing the nervous system in certain functional conceptual relations. Much more than structure is involved in language. Injury to the area of acoustic symbolism will reduce a human being practically to the level of an ape. Such a person loses his ability for understanding and using propositional language—the language of definite objects or actions, as well as relations between them, imagined by the speaker and guiding his understanding and speech. All that he will retain is the capacity for reactive or emotive language of the ejaculatory or automatic type. Examples of this are "Oh! dear me," "Yes," and "Hello."[72] To an unusual degree the behavior and thought of such an aphasic patient is centered about his own personality, and its relation to the world. He acts rather than thinks or speaks about the world.[73] On the other hand, as Markey has suggested, when symbolic thinking is well established and becomes automatic it appears that self-reference has greatly diminished or has reached a minimum.[74]

Words for the aphasic patient have lost all symbolic value; the same word can no longer be used for totally different objects, it can only be used in a concrete way and not in a general or categoric sense. Words have simply lost their character as useable abstractions, and the patient is unable to construct any sort of abstraction. Had he been born with such a potential deficiency the patient could never have become a functioning member of human culture. The ability to isolate relations, to consider them in their abstract meaning, independent of concrete sense data—visual, auditory, tactile, and kinesthetic—is the intellectual process beyond all others which characterizes man. "Language," as Wilhelm von Humboldt said, "never represents objects themselves but the concepts which the mind has formed of them in the autonomous activity by which it creates language." Without this autonomous activity, to which there seems no limit, man's life would be restricted to his immediate biological needs and interests, and he would be forever shut out from any experience of the "ideal world" which is opened to him by his culture.

From the brief reference to the evidence of the language disturbances exhibited by brain-injured persons it is clear that language develops as an integral part of the body–mind complex, and that a person is much more profoundly what he thinks than is customarily supposed. Thought is to a large extent subvocal language. Speech is thought made explicit. We need not go so far as Watson[75] and identify language with thought, nor align ourselves with those others who have attempted to reduce language to a system of conditioned reflexes.[76] There can, however, be not the least doubt that without human language there can be no human thought, and that language is the basis of thought whether vocalized or unvocalized. No more convincing proof of this relation can be had than that which is obtained from the study of the languages together with the cultures of nonliterate (so-called "primitive") peoples. Such studies reveal the amazing fidelity with which the culture is mirrored in the language. There is, indeed, no better nor more revealing way of commencing the study of philosophy and of scientific method, not to mention the study of culture, than submitting oneself to a good course in (comparative) linguistics. The great variety of ways in which different peoples view the world is very closely reflected in the categories of their language and the formal rules, the grammar, which govern their use. Therefore the study of the structure and functions of such language can be a very illuminating tool not only in the study of the cultures in which they function but of our own.[77] "Wer fremde Sprachen nicht kennt, weiss nichts von seiner eigenen,"[78] said Goethe.

But language is not merely an instrument or parallel process of thought or, as Malinowski put it, a duplicate of the mental reality of man in a secondary flow of verbal equivalents. It is also a very active ingredient of human behavior, one of the chief cultural forces and an adjunct to bodily activities,[79] a complex set of bodily habits.[80] Man learns much of his language in action situations where all sorts of personal physical as well as mental experiences are involved. This is, of course, particularly true of the periods of infancy and childhood. Malinowski is certainly largely right when he suggests that it is the pragmatic use of speech within the context of action which has shaped its structure and determined its vocabulary.[81] Ultimately, Malinowski suggests, the meaning of all words is derived from bodily experiences, from such experiences in the infant as hunger, dampness, painful position, and so on. The meaning of the cries or sounds emitted by the infant under such conditions may be variously understood by adults, but it produces action on the part of those adults which ministers in some way to the child, and it is this action which constitutes the meaning of the sounds it makes. The meaning of a sound is the response it produces. The child's sounds, its vocalizations, are a means of mobilizing its environment, and to a large extent this is the pattern which his language maintains throughout his subsequent life. The relation between the person and the environment in this respect is, of course, a reciprocal one; just as he mobilizes the environment by means of language, by the same means he, too, is mobilized.

We perceive, then, that in the integration of the self, the symbolic process through the use of language is basic. If the essential feature of thought is symbolism,[82] language, vocal or subvocal, is the vehicle or matrix of symbolism. Symbols represent stimuli not present to sense. As Deese says: "Symbols are stimuli which stand for or lead to other stimuli. The relation of symbols to the stimuli for which they stand is an artificial one that comes about through learning. Symbols have meaning as a result of learning. Thus, learning is of fundamental importance to symbolic behavior."[83]

It is clearly because man's learning capacity, his educability, is so much greater than that of any other creature that his capacity for symbol usage is so large. Man learns almost all his symbols through language, and by symbols he increases and deepens his language and develops additional and more profoundly operative symbols.

The Representative Function of Symbols

Through the use of symbols man is able within himself to bridge a gap in the absence of external stimulation. This type of representational symbol usage enables him to make the appropriate responses long after the external stimulus has been removed. The rat is limited to brief delays of little more than several minutes; higher animals do better. Man can bridge the delays over long periods of years.

By means of representational symbols man can solve complicated problems.

By means of linguistic or verbal symbols, by the use of words, the tools of language, man can control his environment symbolically, and practice the most highly developed form of *vicarious* trial-and-error behavior.

By means of verbal symbols the history of the person's experience, actual and vicarious, may be built up as a huge repository that can be brought to bear upon present and future problems. This function of symbols is largely limited to human beings. As Deese puts it: "Animals can 'remember,' but almost entirely only when they are faced with the appropriate conditioned stimuli. Humans, however, can draw upon a large number of linguistic symbols, which, in the last analysis, are the most important things that contribute to their high ability to solve problems."[84]

Human culture cannot be comprehended unless the parts which symbolic thinking and language play in its development are fully understood. The significant relationships between symbol, language, and culture must, indeed, be understood as interdependent and reciprocal.

Symbols necessarily arise in the context of the social situation, and in addition to integrating the self (of the person) within that context, symbols serve to integrate all the complex interrelations of the group. The significance of these facts cannot be overestimated for the past, present, and future development of man. Their full appreciation is basic for any sound analysis of the nature of culture.

There exist several fundamental differences between animal and human potentialities for cultural development. The first of these is the great plasticity or educability of man as compared with all other animals, and the second is man's great potential ability to make use of symbols and language, whereas the lower animals and even the higher nonhuman animals are unable to make more than an occasional and inefficient use of either. In these relative differences in potentialities lies the chief difference between the nonhuman animals and human.

Having arrived at these fundamental differences in educability and potentiality for cultural development between human and nonhuman animals, it will be in order to turn in the next chapter to an examination of the nervous system through which that education or socialization is largely secured. We shall then go on to consider the nature of those basic organic needs of the organism which through the instrumentality of culture become culturalized. Meanwhile, we may conclude that Warden's threefold criterion of culture: invention, communication, and social habituation, is applicable to many nonhuman groups, but that what distinguishes human beings from nonhuman animals is the marked degree to which human beings are capable of realizing the elements involved in this concept of culture.

The qualities of culture are: (1) It is transmitted and continued not by the mechanism of genetic heredity but by that of social heredity, through the interaction of educable organisms. (2) However it may come about in and through individuals, culture quickly tends to become suprapersonal and anonymous. (3) It falls into patterns or regularities of form and style and significance. (4) It embodies values.[85]

Culture Defined

Culture consists of patterns or regularities of and for behavior, overt (as mores) or felt (as folkways),[86] acquired and transmitted by symbols through the interactions of human beings, constituting the traditional (historically derived and selected) ideas and especially their associated values.[87]

In short, culture is whatever man learns as a member of society.[88] Culture is what remains of men's past working on their present, to shape their future.[89]

3 THE MEANING OF MAN'S NERVOUS SYSTEM

. . . an enchanted loom where millions of flashing shuttles weave a dissolving pattern, always a meaningful pattern though never an abiding one. —SIR CHARLES SHERRINGTON*

THE INTEGRATIVE ACTION OF THE NERVOUS SYSTEM

In view of its fundamental importance for the development of human behavior and for the understanding of the role it plays in relation to the basic needs or drives of man, a brief discussion of the nervous system is in order here.

The nervous system is not an anatomically or physiologically distinct part of the body. When for the purposes of study we select, that is, abstract, a certain part of the body from a complex interrelated functional system, we sometimes forget that it is an integral part of a complex relational whole, and we tend to speak of it as a separate part of the body. The mind-body dichotomy is a good example of this unwarranted separation and distinction. There is no such thing as a mind *and* a body, there is only a living body, an organism, and mind represents but one aspect of its functioning. Similarly the separation between "structure" and "function" is arbitrary. Structure and function are interdependent processes, the organism forming itself structurally by function, and functioning through its form.[1] As Monné says, "Structure and function of protoplasm are intimately correlated with each other. Any function is accompanied by regular changes of the structure of protoplasm on the microscopical, submicroscopical and stereochemical levels."[2]

* Charles Sherrington, quoted by Grev Walter in *The Living Brain,* New York, Norton, p. 36.

The whole body is a system of differentiated interacting tissues directly or indirectly integrated with the nervous system. It is impossible to dissociate any functioning organ or part of the body from its nervous connections. When the organism acts it acts as a whole, and that it is able to do so is principally due to the fact that that body is, in a real sense, a nervous system. No act is ever performed without the integrative action of the nervous system.

The Nervous System

The nervous system is functionally the stimulus-responding system of the organism. The cells and nerve fibers which comprise it form an interconnecting network which links every part of the organism together. The fact of living implies stimulation and response, and it is the function of the nervous system to coordinate the activities of the body in the stimulus-response relations, that is, in response to internal and external environmental conditions. The harmonious response which the person is as a whole able to make to his environment is due to those innumerable fine adjustments which the coordinating or integrative action of the nervous system is able to produce. Many of these adjustments may be made through the agency of the lymph and blood, the vascular system, and the internal secretions circulating in the blood. The physiological nature of the reactivity of the nervous system at any given time can be altered by the action of substances circulating in the vascular system, such as metabolites (by-products of metabolism), internal secretions, gases, and toxins. Vascular and glandular activities are, however, essentially regulated by the nervous system. The principal function of the nervous system is the adjustment of the organism to its environment. This is achieved through (1) the coordination of the sustaining systems, (2) learning or habit formation, and (3) making possible reflective thought and planned adaptation.

Functional Divisions of the Nervous System

The functional divisions of man's, or of any other vertebrate's nervous system which are customarily distinguished are the following:

The central nervous system, consisting of the brain and spinal cord.

The peripheral nervous system, comprising the cranial and spinal nerves or cerebrospinal nerves with their respective ganglia.

The autonomic nervous system, consisting of the parasympathetic and sympathetic components.

The Central Nervous System

Twelve pairs of nerves arise from the brain or cerebrum, and thirty-one pairs from the spinal cord. The cerebrospinal nerves reach most parts of the body. They are composed of afferent and efferent fibers. Afferent fibers are those which receive stimuli and carry sensory impulses to the central nervous system. Efferent fibers convey outgoing or motor impulses from the central nervous system to the organs of response. The proper adjustment and coordination of the afferent and efferent impulses is the function of the central nervous system. The performance of this function requires the presence of billions of central or association neurons, and it is of these that the central nervous system, the brain and spinal cord, is principally composed. Donaldson has estimated that there are about 12,000,000,000 neurons in the human brain, of which 9,200,000,000 are in the cerebral cortex;[3] Eccles gives the number in round figures for the cortex as 10,000,000,000.[4] Each neuron is composed of perhaps a million billion molecules and ions.[5]

The Neuron

The neuron is the basic functional unit of the nervous system and consists of a nerve cell and its processes, the dendrites and axon. The neuron is itself in constant process of chemical change.[6] The conduction paths of the nervous system are formed by chains of neurons. The length of some of these neurons may be such that they reach from the top of the head to the lumbar region, and from the nape of the neck to one of the toes. Since nerve impulses are conducted at rates varying up to 100 meters (approximately 328 feet) per second it will readily be understood with what speed the stimulus-response reaction can occur. Neurons are so arranged that the axon of one always establishes functional relations with the cell body or dendrites of many other neurons. The place at which such a relation is established is known as a *synapse.* There is no continuity of nerve substance between neurons; the relationship is one of contiguity, each neuron being separated from every other by a distinct plasma membrane. Something in the nature of the synaptic interval determines the propagation of the impulse in one direction only. This unidirectional transmission of the nerve impulse is resumed in the *law of dynamic polarity,* although under experimental conditions a nerve fiber may be made to conduct impulses equally well in either direction.

The manner of propagation of an impulse across a synapse is not fully understood. But as the result of Dale's and Loewi's work it is now fairly certain that such conduction will not occur in the absence of an excitor substance liberated by the axon terminals of the first neuron. This substance is believed to excite the second neuron and to initiate a nerve impulse in it. The electrical theory, in contrast to this chemical theory, suggests that the second neuron is excited by the action current potentials which have been generated in the axon terminals of the first neuron. The nerve impulse is not transmitted as such across the synapse.

Nerve fibers are axons with or without covering membranes. Axons which are covered with a fatty substance, myelin, supported by a reticulum, are known as *myelinated fibers* and are found in the spinal cord and brain. Myelin gives the nerve fiber a whitish color.

Naked axons or unmyelinated fibers are especially numerous in the central and peripheral nervous system, and, indeed, give that matter its gray color. The autonomic system is largely composed of unmyelinated fibers.

Myelinated axons which also possess a nucleated sheath, the *neurilemma sheath,* abound in the peripheral nervous system.

In myelinated fibers the conduction rate is rapid, in unmyelinated fibers it is by comparison slow. For example, one tenth of a second may elapse from initiation to completion in the myelinated fibers of the saphenous nerve (in the hind limb) of the cat, while it may take almost a minute in the unmyelinated fibers of the same nerve.[7] However, the usual rate in myelinated fibers is 100 meters a second as compared with 2 meters a second in unmyelinated fibers.

Conduction Rates in Myelinated and Unmyelinated Nerve Fibers

The fact that the cortex of the brain and the central associative system of the brain and spinal cord are made up chiefly of unmyelinated fibers is of great interest in the light of these differences in conduction rates. The central nervous system is the great integrating system of the organism; it is, therefore, advantageous in such a system that impulses shall travel at the rate which will assist the necessary coordinating changes to occur without the production, as it were, of a traffic-jam. In the peripheral nervous system, on the other hand, speed is desirable. Because of this the central nervous system is constructed of chains of neurons and their synapses, whereas in the peripheral nervous system single axons in large numbers, bound together and uninterrupted by synapses, are (with the exception of the autonomic components) the rule. Similarly, that part of the nervous system which is principally concerned with the processes of homeostasis or organismal stability, the autonomic, is constructed of nerve fibers which are often unmyelinated, and therefore have a slower rate of conduction than myelinated fibers.

With respect to myelinization there prevails a certain amount of erroneous and confusing opinion in much of the current literature, the "adhesion" of an earlier age. This consists in the belief that unmyelinated fibers are normally incapable of conducting impulses, or that a nerve fiber or tract of nerve fibers is not a "neurological pathway" until it is myelinated. Thus, in a well-known and deservedly popular book—to name but one—by two well-known psychiatrists we find the right advice against commencing early toilet training being given for the wrong reason: "because . . . the tracts of the spinal cord are not completely myelinated until the end of the first year. . . . it is rather futile . . . to ask the child to exercise a control over his organs for which he does not have the neurological pathways completely laid down."[8]

There are more recent works which make similar statements. But the work of Angulo y Gonzalez has demonstrated beyond any question that myelinization is not necessary for function and that the so-called "myelinogenetic law" is false.[9] It has already been stated that Gasser found that unmyelinated nerve fibers conducted impulses, the only difference being that they conducted them at a slower rate than myelinated fibers. Furthermore, there is some evidence which suggests, though it does not prove, that activity in a nerve stimulates, if it does not give rise to, the development of myelinization. Held, for example, found that if he opened one eye in kittens or puppies several days prematurely the optic nerve of that eye myelinized more rapidly than that of the opposite eye.[10]

Myelinization is accelerated at birth, whether full-term or premature. The fact that myelinization is prematurely induced in premature babies is good evidence of the importance of environmental influences upon the process of myelinization. The relationship would seem to be a reciprocal one between myelinization and behavior, rather than of dependence of either one upon the other.

The Autonomic Nervous System

Those aggregations of neurons (ganglia) that lie outside the central nervous system and cerebrospinal ganglia, and that include the cells connecting such neurons with the central nervous system, are together distinguished as the *autonomic system*. There also exist certain centers in the brain stem itself which are autonomic in nature.

Functionally the autonomic system may be distinguished as comprising those parts of the neuron system which are primarily concerned with the regulation of visceral activities. In the execution of these functions both the central and peripheral nervous systems are involved. While the autonomic system possesses a certain anatomical and physiological autonomy from the cerebrospinal or somatic nervous system, nevertheless, the two systems are to be regarded as two aspects of the functioning of an integrated whole.

The autonomic system is the efferent (motor) system innervating smooth muscle and glands which are not under the voluntary control of the cerebral cortex. It is the motor system of the iris of the eye, the lachrymal, sweat, and digestive glands, the heart and blood vessels, as well as the bronchi, the gastrointestinal, and genitourinary tracts.

The nerve fibers of the autonomic system are separable on the basis of their origin into three streams or outflows:

1. *The cranial stream or outflow,* whose fibers pass through the third (oculomotor), seventh (facial), ninth (glossopharyngeal), and tenth (vagus) cranial nerves.

2. *The thoracolumbar stream or outflow,* whose fibers pass through the twelve thoracic and upper two lumbar nerves.

3. *The sacral stream or outflow,* whose fibers run in the visceral rami of the second, third, and fourth sacral nerves.

The Ganglia of the Autonomic System

Vertebral (paravertebral) or sympathetic ganglia, comprised of two ganglionated cords on each side of the vertebral column, extend from the level of the second cervical vertebra to the coccyx. There are three cervical, eleven thoracic, four lumbar, and four sacral ganglia, united together by nerve fibers.

Collateral (prevertebral) ganglia or sympathetic plexuses consist of three great ganglionated plexuses situated in front of the vertebral column in the thoracic, abdominal, and pelvic regions. These are, respectively, the *cardiac, coeliac,* and *hypogastric* plexuses. They are made up of nerves and ganglia, the nerves being derived from the sympathetic trunks and from the cerebrospinal nerves. The plexuses distribute branches to the viscera.

Terminal ganglia or visceral ganglia lie near, on, or within the walls of the organs with which they are associated. Little is known about them, and they may contain a mechanism for purely local reflex action. Cannon has described the sacral outflow of the parasympathetic as a mechanism for emptying, *i.e.,* it is motor to such hollow organs as the bladder and rectum and is concerned in the erection of the penis.

Both the vertebral and collateral ganglia are related to many smaller plexuses, and in each of these plexuses sympathetic and parasympathetic fibers are present.

The vertebral ganglia are associated with the cephalic (head) plexuses, cervical (neck) plexuses, and the collateral ganglia are associated with those of the thorax (chest), abdomen, and pelvis.

The fibers of the thoracolumbar outflow, the trunk of lateral ganglia which lie on either side of the vertebral column, join the sympathetic trunk, while the fibers of the cranial and sacral outflows do not, but run directly to the sympathetic plexuses. Furthermore, while the primary fibers of the thoracolumbar outflow end in the trunk or collateral ganglia (grouped around the aorta and some of its large branches), those of the cranial and sacral outflow end in the terminal ganglia, the latter lying close to the structures they innervate. Functionally as well as anatomically the cranial and visceral outflows belong together, being antagonistic in their action to the thoracolumbar outflow. When one is excited the other is inhibited. Hence, for these reasons the cranial and sacral outflows are grouped together as the craniosacral outflow or *parasympathetic system,* the thoracicolumbar outflow being distingushed as the *sympathetic system*. Since most of the structures innervated by the autonomic system receive their nerve supply from both divisions it will be readily understood how by the balanced opposition of their functions the organism is able to maintain the state of coordinated activity which is essential to its proper functioning. Thus, dilation of the pupil is brought about through the action of the sympathetic, contraction by the parasympathetic, balanced dilation by the action of both. The parasympathetic vagus (tenth) nerve slows the activity of the heart when it is stimulated, but the sympathetic cardiac nerve has exactly the opposite effect.

The autonomic is the system which performs for us the unconscious, involuntary, vegetative adjustments between our varying internal and external environments. The balanced coordination thus produced has been called by Cannon *homeostasis*.[11] Homeostasis frees the individual from the task of paying routine attention to the management of the details of bare existence.

In general the parasympathetic system may be said to be concerned with the functions of hunger, sex, and bodily elimination; while the sympathetic is concerned with those functions which express themselves in the form of the emotions. An emotion may be described as the set of internal physiological changes which assist the organism to return to normal equilibrium. The "epistemic correlates of emotions are neuronal events in circuits."[12] It is here important to observe that there is probably no behavior of which emotion does not constitute a part.[13] Myers finds that the sole objective distinctions between "emotional" and "intellectual" activities are those expressing the relative discreteness or diffuseness of segmental activity evoked in a given situation. Where the somatic and visceral activity of the organism is limited to relatively few neuromuscular segments, we may speak of it as relatively "intellectual" irrespective of whether it proves adaptive or not; and where wide participation of neuromuscular segments is apparent, we may speak of the activity as relatively emotional.[14] Obviously, from this point of view no activity of the organism can be considered as either purely emotional or purely intellectual, the distinction being quantitative only.

While the actual perception of emotion is largely cortical, consciousness of the functioning of the parasympathetic is, if anything, associated with a pleasant feeling of organic tone. On the other hand awareness of the operation of the sympathetic system is associated with an unpleasant feeling of organic tone. The sympathetic is roughly described as the preparer for emergencies, the parasympathetic the protector or supervisor.

The autonomic system is, therefore, closely associated with the satisfaction of the basic organic needs of human beings. The feeling tone of the organism as a whole of well-being or otherwise is produced through the action of this system, but awareness of that feeling tone is largely if not entirely cortical. The dominant component in such feeling as loss of appetite after tasting a bad egg or following the reception of bad news is due to cortical reflexes mediated through connections with the lower autonomic centers of the hypothalamus. Severe disturbance of the whole autonomic system may be produced by the consumption of spoiled food.[15]

The cortical representation of the autonomic is in the motor and pre-motor areas; parasympathetic and sympathetic being represented together and not separately, thus simultaneous adjustments in the activities of the autonomic together with other cortically integrated reactions become possible.

The Hypothalamus

The great shunting and coordinating center of the autonomic system is the hypothalamus. The hypothalamus is, however, always under the domination of the cortex. Removal of the cerebral cortex in animals removes all cortical inhibition, with the result that such decorticized animals exhibit, on the slightest provocation, all the signs of rage, including struggling, erection of the hair, dilation of the pupil, increased respiration, and heightened arterial blood pressure. Stimulation of the hypothalamus experimentally produces specific autonomic reactions of the same kind. These are, however, simply the motor accompaniments of emotion, not the emotion itself. Feeling is cortical. The hypothalamus is the center in which emotional expression is integrated into behavior patterns on its way to the muscles and glands.[16] As an information center the hypothalamus translates messages from other parts of the brain into visceromotor endocrine impulses. Direct stimulation of the hypothalamus in the human subject under local anesthesia jumps the basal pulse rate from 55 to 145 beats per minute, with an accompanying increase in systolic blood pressure (the blood pressure due to the rhythmical contraction of the heart). Operative manipulation of the anterior part of the hypothalamus produced loud gastric peristalsis, nausea, and in one instance vomiting, and in 4 out of 8 patients abrupt loss of consciousness. Tumors of the hypothalamus in human subjects invariably produce disturbances in the autonomic system, and in particularly severe cases almost every function of that system may be involved.

In brief, the autonomic system is that system through which the emotions are *expressed,* while it is through the thalamocortical system that they are *perceived*. The central nervous system mediates the responses of the organism through the skeletal muscles; the autonomic through the visceral and vascular systems.

The experimental and pathological evidence also indicates that the hypothalamus is intimately associated with the regulation of the sleep-waking rhythm, of body temperature, and of the whole delicate involuntary adjustment to the external environment. "In addition, through its nervous connections with the cerebral cortex and the thalamus, it is the recipient of those vague and indefinable stimuli which arise in association with all sorts of visceral activities and metabolic processes. In this way it mediates the integration of visceral and psychic impulses, and plays an essential part in the control of the internal milieu of the organism."[17]

The Neurohumoral System

There is good evidence that the hypothalamus, through its hormonal secretions, initiates the activities of the pituitary gland and through the latter exercises a regulative effect on the endocrine system, and thus, in turn, upon the whole organism. Marked endocrine and other changes may be produced in the organism as a result, conscious or unconscious, of cortical activities, by thoughts or by dreams. Normally, such changes are of an adaptive nature, as in flight or fear reactions. Under abnormal conditions, such as prolonged emotionally disturbing states, states of anxiety, or repeatedly occurring stress,[18] the organism may exhibit a wide range of somatic disorders—a result of the overactivity of the *neurohumoral system*. The function of the neurohumoral system is to maintain the balanced physiological functions of the organism to produce general adaptation. The neurohumoral system may be described as that system which is constituted by the interaction of the nervous with the endocrine system through the fluid medium of the blood and its gaseous content. It is by inducing abnormal activity of this system that the pregnant mother's emotional states, for example, may affect the fetus.[19] It is through this system that severe physiological damage may be done to the depressed or unloved infant,[20] and it is through this system that the mechanism of shock works its effect, and similarly it is through the activities of this system that the exhaustion of the organism is produced as a result of prolonged or repeated stress and strain.

Attention has been paid to the autonomic system for two reasons: first, because it happens to be that part of the nervous system which operates below the level of consciousness and there is therefore a tendency to overlook it altogether; and second, because it is closely identified with the functioning of the sustaining systems of the body and therefore with the basic organic needs. Indeed, the socialization of the organism is so intimately bound up with the functioning of this part of the nervous system that understanding of an individual's behavior is assisted by a knowledge of the interaction that occurs between the socializing process and the autonomic system. To a significant extent the functioning of the autonomic is related to the functioning of the hypothalamus and that part of the nervous system which is situated immediately above the hypothalamus and beneath the end-brain. These and the immediately adjacent areas of the brain (gyrus cinguli, and the hippocampus) may be regarded as associated with the elaboration of central emotion and as participating in emotional expression.

Fundamentally, life consists in seeking experiences which will maintain the emotional tone of the organism at a satisfactory functional level. The thalamic and hypothalamic functions are organized at a high level of affectivity or feeling tone. Thus affectivity is not visceral but is induced by experience of the external environment and mediated chiefly by the central nervous system. It is believed that the thalamus and hypothalamus play a large part in the functioning of consciousness, and in some of the simpler affective processes such, for example, as protopathic sensibility, *i.e.,* the ability to discriminate generalized sensations, and the discrimination of forms requiring synthesis of visual and tactile impressions.

Functioning under the control of the cerebral cortex through an extensive system of thalamocortical pathways, the thalamus serves as the center of integration for all those processes which cooperate in the development and functioning of the great variety of enduring attitudes and forms of reaction which give to the individual his peculiar character and personality and perhaps his feeling of identity. As Herrick says, "There is . . . a more closely knit assembling of all those internal processes, both inborn and acquired, which give the organism its sense of well being or malaise, its awareness of personal identity, and its distinctive disposition and character."[21]

Some evidence is available which vaguely suggests that there exist autonomic, cerebral, and thalamic types of personality. I say "vaguely" because it seems, in fact, that every part of the nervous system is involved in the responses of the organism, and at best one may perhaps attribute a dominance in the functioning of one part of the nervous system as compared with another, depending, probably on genetic and experiential factors. To identify the cortex with intellect and discrimination and the thalamus with emotion is no longer possible since both qualities represent a function of the activities of both structures.[22] However, the "vaguely" recognizable autonomic types tend to "internalize" showing their tensions in visceral types of upset, and they also incline to be free of more overt behavior difficulties. The cerebral types show their tensions in more overt behavioral disturbances, and tend to be less affected by visceral disorders;[23] while the thalamic types seem to live to a large extent on their affective or emotional capital. In this connection H. E. Jones has shown that in young babies a mildly disturbing stimulus will in some produce striped muscle responses, in others visceral responses; the one response tending to preclude the other.[24] The evidence for the existence of the thalamic type is now quite old and plentiful. This whole field, however, is largely unexplored, and awaits its Ptolemy before a Copernicus will be able to do anything with it. The brain functions as a whole and not in separate parts, but it may be that in functioning as a whole some parts of the brain play more important roles than others.

Something of a beginning in this field has been made by contemporary experimental psychologists. Mowrer, for example, has cogently suggested that by virtue of their different structural organization and functions the central (voluntary) and autonomic (involuntary) nervous systems are subject to very different learning processes. Mowrer points out that under ordinary conditions the autonomic responses occur in an autonomic manner, serving the "equilibrium-restoring" or "homeostatic" function. However, such responses can be made to occur not only to physiological needs but to conditioned stimuli or signals of many kinds. When the autonomic responses occur on the latter basis as *anticipatory states* they produce rather than eliminate physiological disequilibrium and are consciously experienced as *emotion*. The learning of such responses is quite distinct from the learning whereby ordinary habits are acquired—the latter being principally acquired through the central nervous system, the former through the autonomic by conditioning.

Autonomic learning is basic for the healthy development and survival of the organism, and hence it should be clear why such learning should become established in the form of automatic emotional responses. The emotional response puts the organism into a state of disequilibrium, being to some extent basically painful and constituting, as it were, a challenge to the organism which it must meet with the problem-solving, drive-reducing part of its nervous system (the central nervous system).

Trial-and-error or effect learning parallels the pleasure principle, conditioning more closely parallels the reality principle. Conditioned responses or emotions are acquired not because it is pleasant to do so, but because it is realistic. It is not pleasant to be afraid, but it is helpful for the purposes of survival. It is also biologically helpful to learn those responses which reduce drives. And as Mowrer points out, "it is apparently quite necessary that the neural mechanism which mediates this kind of learning be different from the mechanism whereby emotional, or attitudinal learning comes about."[25]

The Cerebral Cortex

The cortex is essentially the organ of inhibition, of delayed reactions, and of learning. It is not, on the whole, directly actuated by incoming nervous impulses from either the internal or external environments, but comes into play principally through activities going on in the lower correlation centers and in situations which those centers cannot adequately meet. Nervous impulses, therefore, which reach the cortex are to a large extent the overflows, as it were, from subcortical centers whose simpler reflex outlets are inadequate. The effect of cortical activity is the inhibition, the regulation, of lower nonadaptive reactions. A man "stops to think," an insect reacts at once. Where there is no interval between stimulus and response there can be no psychologic process.[26] The inhibitory potentialities of man's cerebral cortex are unique, and it is through the secondary functioning of these that all his characteristic qualities of self-control, poise, and deliberation are made possible. It is largely through the inadequately understood capacities of the cortex for inhibition that man can get outside himself and take a "second look" as it were. No other animal can do that. The cortex is, of course, much more than an organ of inhibition for among its principal functions is that of recombining every possible kind of stimulus, including lower reflex units, into patterns determined not only by the stimulus-complex acting at the moment, but also by the relevant, personally acquired mnemonic vestiges of previous allied reactions. This mnemonic capacity of the cortex is that highly developed faculty which enables the human being to accumulate experience and to act in the light of that experience—that is, to predict the consequences of action.

Experimental and clinical evidence indicates that specific functions are not located in any particular part of the cortex, that habits and memories are not stored in any limited area, but rather that there exists a multiple representation of every function, operating through some sort of reduplicated network of equivalent functional reverberatory circuits, constantly active. The excitatory effects of this multiplicity of interacting circuits are transmissible around various types of cortical interruption.[27] It is quite possible that the elaboration of cerebral functions may 'depend largely not so much upon the number of cerebral units as upon the richness of their interconnections.[28]

From the physiological point of view the mind may be regarded as a pool of reverberating electrical circuits which are built up in patterns to a large extent influenced or determined by exposure to certain configurations of experience. Learning may actually represent the process of establishing new relations between neuronal electrical circuits.

The Physiology of Learning

Precisely what the mechanism of learning is we do not know, "but the assumption which best fits the observed facts," Herrick suggests, "is that every cortical association pattern when once actuated leaves the synaptic thresholds (or whatever may be the apparatus of facilitation of path by use) in a different structural arrangement or 'set' which makes the reactivation of these neurons in this particular pattern easier than it was before. The thing which is preserved is static, a changed structural arrangement of parts."[29] A more microscopic and complementary explanation has been offered by Monné, who points out that synthesis of new proteins within the cytoplasm of various cells is induced either by internal or external agents. During development of the embryo synthesis of new proteins is brought about under the influence of internal agents, the nuclear genes. "Nevertheless, the cells are also able to 'learn' to synthesize new proteins under the influence of external agents. . . . By synthesizing new enzymes the cells are able to 'learn' to induce new chemical reactions. It may be," says Monné, "that neurones are particularly 'intelligent' and consequently able to 'learn' with particular ease, to synthesize new proteins within their cytoplasmic fibrils. Only the amazing variability of proteins can explain the fact that all that we experience during our life is stored in our memory."[30]

Within the nerve cell there are certain macromolecules or Nissl bodies known as chromidia. These chromidia contain proteins, ribonucleic acid, lipoids, calcium, magnesium, and also certain respiratory and hydrolizing enzymes. The chromidia may be the sites of cytoplasmic genes (plasmagenes). Monné suggests that the cytoplasmic proteins are synthesized by the chromidia, and that at any moment when new perceptions and concepts arise in the mind chromidial mutations causing synthesis of new proteins within neurons may occur.

> It is known [writes Monné] that mental functions are intimately associated with physiological functions of the neurones of the cerebral cortex. For this reason our mental functions must also be accompanied by regular structural alterations of the cytoplasm of the neurones at the microscopical, submicroscopical and chemical levels. It is obvious that memory must be associated with some permanent structural changes of the cytoplasm (cytoplasmic fibrils) of neurones. These postulated alterations are called engrams. Chromidial mutations, synthesis of new specific proteins and new connexions between various chromidia and between various neurones may be the structural changes of the brain associated with all intellectual activities. Some alterations of this mechanism may be associated with clever and others with pathological thinking. It may be that a high mutation rate of the chromidia is characteristic of clever thinking. Instincts are inherited because the specific mode of protein synthesis and structure formation within the nervous system are also inherited. Inherited behaviour seems to be determined by protein synthesis within the nervous system under the influence of nuclear genes, and acquired behaviour is determined by protein synthesis within the nervous system under the influence of exterior agents. Feeling is possibly associated with changes in the colloidal properties of the lipoid-protein compounds of the cytoplasm.[31]

Learning, according to Monné's hypothesis, may be a matter of protein synthesis within neurons and in relation to other neurons. This view is independently supported by Halstead, who, in discussing protein organization and mental function, points out that the nucleoprotein gene acts as a template on which replica molecules are formed. If instead of the biologically inherited templates of the genes we postulate the formation of templates as a result of individual experience we have a mechanism for memory. It is suggested that the template molecule organizes the available neural proteins into protein lattices which register the particular memory trace.[32] According to Hydén and Hartelius the protein-producing system is poorly developed in mentally disordered persons.[33]

The cortical system of neurons, it is necessary to point out, is not constructed like an automatic telephone exchange, one which is constructed to give identical responses to repeated stimuli. It resembles rather an extensive electrical network or lattice of neuronal chains and circuits in a state of fluctuating equilibrium. What response will be made to a particular stimulus depends upon the system's state of equilibrium at the moment an impulse enters it. The system is therefore eminently one which makes for great plasticity.[34]

An outstanding characteristic of the human cortex is this great plasticity, a plasticity which enables a human being to make free and multiple associations of innumerable kinds without necessarily ever repeating them, and potentially allowing the maximum of freedom and originality in thought and behavior. In short, the human cortex is so educable as to be the single phenomenon in the animal kingdom of which it seems uniquely possible to be able to say that it can develop (increase in complexity) almost without limit. It is, of course, true, as Lawrence Kubie points out, that "Unfortunately these same human beings who have inherited this adaptive plasticity also limit their own freedom through certain rigid psychologic mechanisms, which confine closely their instinctual patterns." But, as he goes on to add, "it is reasonable to expect that in the course of time it will be within our power to alter our limiting compulsions and phobias by processes of emotional education."[35]

The cortex, more than any other part of the brain, is a forecasting mechanism. It forecasts its own efferent messages for its own use, and this the cortex is able to do by converting a spatial into a temporal sequence. There is a continuous process of correcting and improving while the forecasted messages pour forth. When talking, for example, we have a dimly grasped or vague outline of what we are about to say in our head, but the precise formulation of our words and sentences proceeds as we talk.[36] The function of the cortex is to oppose and make order out of randomness, to organize the unorganized. This is to say that the function of the cortex, among other things, is to provide the organism with an analogue of the external environment or situation, and thus to enable the organism to adjust its behavior accordingly. In this respect it operates very much—though, with much more complexity—like an analogue computer fed by sensory clues.[37]

Any further discussion of the human mind beyond what has thus far been attempted would scarcely be fruitful until we examine the materials presented in the pages which follow. At this stage it will possibly suffice to say that the human mind represents the social organization and patterning of the potencies of the neuronal net. Unless the potencies of that neuronal net undergo such social organization and patterning, mind cannot develop.

Mind as we know it phenomenally, as a process of behavior, is knit into the whole network of living as a natural event. Organically the nervous system is the adjusting system of the body as a whole, the fundamental equipment for the adjustment and control of behavior. It is the system which serves to adjust the parts of the body to one another and the body as a whole to the pressures of the internal and external environments. It is in this process of adjustment that, as Murphy suggests, the clue to personality lies.[38] Intelligence, reason, abstraction, idealization are also part of man's equipment for the adjustment and control of behavior, but on a new and qualitatively higher plane, a plane regulated and determined by the interaction of man's organically determined potentialities and the cultural processes in which they undergo development.

4 HEREDITY AND ENVIRONMENT

Heredity determines what we can do and environment what we do do.
—J. McKeen Cattell

Heredity provides the possibilities and environment determines which of them shall be realized.
—C. M. Child*

The Heredity–Environment Fallacy

Among the concepts concerning which it is necessary to be clear in studying the process of socialization is that of heredity, especially in its customarily dichotomized form, heredity *and* environment. It has sometimes been asserted that many, if not all, cultures assume the particular form they do as a consequence of the differences in the hereditary biological composition of the groups giving rise to them. Since it has also been claimed that the genetic composition of the individual constitutes a definite limiting factor so far as his achievements as a personality are concerned, it becomes necessary to clarify our thinking on this subject before proceeding further.

There are few ideas concerning which more widespread misunderstanding exists than the generally held idea of heredity. This misunderstanding or fallacy is the bogus distinction between heredity and environment. Here again we see the danger which is associated with all abstract reasoning. When for the purposes of analysis and experiment we abstract the ordinates from some interacting coordinate system, the procedure is a perfectly legitimate one, but one falls into grievous error when one then begins to speak of those ordinates as if they were self-sustaining autonomous variables. This

* C. M. Child, in E. Dummer (editor), *The Unconscious,* New York, Knopf, 1927.

is what has been done in the case of the concepts of heredity and environment, both of which are complex variables which are always part of the same functioning coordinate system determined by the mutual interaction of their physicochemical properties.

Some biologists still think like preformationists: as if they believed that the ultimate character is unalterably determined at conception. The quanta of heredity, as they may be called, the "genes" or "determiners" of the organism, so say such thinkers, are present in the sexual cells of the parents, and when these combine they do so in a definite pattern, this pattern developing part by part, organ by organ, into the predetermined individual. The environment is spoken of as if it were merely superimposed upon the genetically predetermined characters, not as a condition of their development.

Such a view of the nature of heredity is widespread, and it is false.

The primary agents of organic development are the genes. In the fruit-fly *Drosophila melanogaster,* in which there are four pairs of chromosomes, it has been estimated that there are between 5000 and 10,000 genes. Man has 23 pairs of chromosomes, so if we tentatively award him the same number of genes as *Drosophila* is believed to have on at least one chromosome—1250—then man has at least 28,750 (1250 × 23) genes in the chromosomes of his sex cells[1] and trillions throughout his body. In a single mating the possible combinations between the 23 chromosomes of the male and those of the female are 16,177,216, or 2 raised to the twenty-third power, and the chance of any one such combination being repeated more than once is 1 in 300,000,000,000,000 (three hundred thousand billion). The different combinations which a 28,750 gene system can assume reach a stupendous figure. This is on a purely quantitative basis. When the physicochemical factors and those of the environment are introduced as modifying agencies the possible differences in human development become practically infinite.

The Nature of Genes

Genes are enzyme proteins or giant self-duplicating protein molecules or catalysts (estimates of size vary between 4 or 50 millimicrons in diameter—a millimicron is one-millionth of a millimeter, estimated gene size is therefore between one 250,000th and one 20,000th of a millimeter). Each of these protein molecules is susceptible to chemical change under varying conditions. The development of the body occurs under the influence of these enzyme proteins, *in interaction with one another*. Enzymes, and therefore genes, are organic catalysts that accelerate essential chemical reactions of living systems.[2] The genes do not represent unit characters—as even the most distinguished of biologists may still believe[3]—that is, chemical packages which control the appearance of specifically determined characters in the offspring. There is no gene for eye color, tallness, shortness, or hair color. The belief that each gene is a specific unitary determiner for some particular character came into being as a result of inadequate observation and its natural associate, invalid inference.

Heredity and Development

In the early stages of genetic experimentation it was observed that certain characters were transmitted as if they were regulated by single units or representative particles. These representative particles were conceived to be the genes, and it was thought that each one represented such unit characters as head shape, eye color, and so on. Later research showed that except in the case of two parents who differ in but a single pair of genes affecting the character in question, there is no such thing as unit character inheritance. On the other hand, the interaction of many genes enters into the development of any character, and every gene affects many characteristics. The development of the individual is determined by the manner of interaction of the genes and what they produce will depend upon the conditions under which they interact, their environment. This is the critically important point to grasp. A genetic type per se, which has developed in the absence of an environment, or of an environment that has affected that type, does not exist. The organism always develops in an environment. The environment varies to some extent for every individual, and apparently affects various genes differently, some genes being less affected by the environment than others. Such, for example, are the blood-group genes which under all known environments appear to remain unaffected and express themselves in the same way. On the other hand the genes involved in the development of skin color, height, and weight, are much subject to the influence of the environment, which may modify their expression considerably.

Interaction Between Genes and Environment

The cumulative effect of environmental changes may produce changes in the structure of a gene, known as mutations. Mutations can be produced by radiation, and some scientists believe that the accumulated effects of solar or cosmic radiation may produce mutational changes in genes. However, the changes in the expression of genes we are here considering are those of a developmental nature brought about by the interaction of the gene system with the environment. The environment influences the process of interaction between genes in all sorts of ways, so that the final expression of that interaction, depending upon the requirements prevailing in any given environment, may be judged as either more or less advantageous or disadvantageous. The character or trait which is the final expression of that interaction is rarely in itself either advantageous or disadvantageous, but only in relation to a particular environment. It is of the utmost importance to understand that this truth applies no matter whether the environment be a socially accepted norm or a purely physical condition. Thus, a tall member of a pygmy group would be at a positive disadvantage in some situations and at a definite advantage in others. The same would apply to a dwarf living among ordinarily tall men. He would be at a distinct disadvantage in many ways, but there are certain environments—in airplane factories, for example—in which the advantages, for certain types of work, would be all with him. A negroid skin under certain conditions is considered desirable, and under tropical conditions of sunlight is certainly an advantageous trait; but under certain other entirely social conditions, a negroid skin may have a high negative social value. It thus becomes associated with an environment which is capable of exerting a tremendously depressing influence upon the hereditary development of the person. Under different conditions the same organism will develop differently. In one environment a plant will grow tall and narrow, in another the same plant will grow short and wide. In sunlight a plant will grow green leaves; in the absence of sunlight the same plant will grow etiolated (pale or white) leaves. Similarly, a sailor exposed to sunlight will develop a highly tanned skin; the same sailor in solitary confinement will tend to lose most of the pigment from his skin. Plants raised in the mountains and others of the same generic stock raised in the valleys are so different in appearance that they would be classed as belonging to different genera by those unacquainted with their history. Alpine plants transferred to the rich soil of the valleys have undergone the most spectacular transformation, so that they would not have been recognized as belonging to the same species by those who had not witnessed the transformation. When, after thirteen generations, these plants were removed to poor and stony soil they reverted to the characters of their Alpine ancestors of thirteen generations earlier. The same alterations occurred when the seeds of plants grown in the rich soil of the valleys were transplanted to the poor Alpine soil.[4]

Whether the expression of the interaction of the genes in some particular form of a character is due to a change in the structure of the gene itself (mutation), or to the modifying influence exerted by the environment (modification), it should be clear that we can never speak of the purely genetic development of any organism, for every organism develops in and is influenced by an environment. The genes make adjustive responses to the environmental factors acting upon them. Hence, the organism, or any part of it, is best regarded as the *physiological* form of a particular genotype. Latent gene potentialities express themselves differently in different environments.

Characters, then, are the product of the interaction between a particular genetic composition and a specific group of environmental conditions, and what precisely may be due to the one and what to the other can, in the final analysis, only be decided by experiment.

Heredity is not a disjunctive but a conjunctive process, not a process in which the inherited factors operate independently of environmental ones or to the mutual exclusion of the one by the other, but one in which both factors are more or less continually interacting.

Potentialities and Heredity

It would be more helpful to everyone, and a more correct picture of the nature of heredity would emerge if instead of using the word "heredity" we were to use the word "potentialities." The newborn organism, so far as its heredity is concerned, is best regarded as a complex of specific potentialities that have a controlling and directive influence on the vital synthetic process.[5] These potentialities are developed and assume their functioning form under the regulative influence of the environment. The expression of heredity, therefore, is a function of two interacting variables, the organic potentialities and the environment. The heredity of an individual is constituted by the interactive effects of the organic potentialities for development with which he is born, and of the environment in which those potentialities have undergone development.

Those who would object to including the environment after birth as a part of heredity, would logically find themselves in the position of having to object to its inclusion at any time after conception.[6] The reason why neither of these positions can be maintained is that the facts show, beyond any question, that the expression of the elementary particles of the organic potentialities is always a function of both their nature and the environment in which they interact. In other words, the expression of genes is both a function of their nature and their nurture. *The organic potentialities do not develop at all in the absence of environmental influences.* This is true of physical potentialities; it is even more true of mental ones. The development of the mental potentialities presents virtually infinite possibilities under the action of varying environments. We can, of course, say that no two persons are ever born with quite the same potentialities, and that at birth those potentialities may be said to exist apart from any significantly influencing environmental factors, and thus recognize that on the one hand there exists a complex of potentialities which may be called the heredity of the individual, and on the other a complex of environments which must be distinguished from heredity. For the purposes of abstraction and analysis this is often done and is a perfectly allowable procedure, but the fact is that we know and can only know the potentialities of any human being in their environmentally influenced expression. A physical or mental character is the expression of a potentiality or group of potentialities under the influence of an environment or group of environments. The environmental influence may be small or it may be large. In the environments in which human beings live differences in many features of the organism are mainly due to the action of the genes, in other features the differences are mainly due to the influence of the environment upon the expression of the potentialities determined by the genes, but whether little or much, the environment—internal or external or both—is always involved.

Physical and Mental Characters

The basic physical characters of human beings are to a large extent determined while the child is being carried by the mother. Basic physical characters are color and form of the eyes, the color of the skin and hair, and the form of the body. The differences between individuals in these respects are principally the result of differences in genic structure. Monozygous (one-egg) twins, having the same genes, are usually closely alike in their physical characters, while heterozygous (different-egg) twins, having different genes, are very much more diverse in their physical characters. On the other hand, the development of man's behavior, his psychical or mental potentialities, is to a considerable extent influenced by environmental factors. In fact, the mental potentialities of human beings remain undeveloped in the absence of the necessary environmental factors, the stimulation which the interaction with other human beings makes possible.[7] Mind, indeed, represents the cultural organization of those potentialities. And the hereditary background of a person's mind must be considered to be as much the environmental factors which have influenced his potentialities as the quality or properties of the potentialities themselves. As Dobzhansky has cogently pointed out:

> . . . A Negro, or for that matter anybody having a slightly pigmented skin, may be different or aggressive in a social environment in which his pigmentation subjects him to discrimination and handicaps. This "psychology" may correctly be called inherited, just as the skin color is called inherited, although in some people the skin color is greatly changed by exposure to sunlight. Heredity which causes the skin to be black and behavior self-conscious may result in a quite different behavior in an environment in which discrimination is absent.
>
> Non-geneticists may feel disinclined to regard as hereditary a trait so plastic that it appears in some environments but not in others. Yet all degrees of environmental plasticity occur. . . . Behavior is influenced so much by environmental variables, particularly training, social conditions and accumulated experience, that the genetic variable is frequently masked. The designation "hereditary" can not be restricted to traits which show a certain degree of constancy of expression. The degree of constancy is itself inconstant. . . . Theoretically, the action of any gene may be controlled. To say that man's psychology is inherited does not, by any stretch of the imagination, mean that it is fixed and unalterable. We cannot change our heredity directly, but heredity is not implacable destiny to which one must submit in resignation. We should seek for ourselves, and contrive for others, environments in which our heredities respond most favorably.[8]

The Control of Heredity Through Environment

Where we control environment, we to some extent control heredity. Heredity determines what we can do, and environment what we do do. Genes do not make a mind, but the environmental, the cultural, organization of the potentialities which they determine, do. We know that in their gene potentialities all men differ, and are equal only in that they possess such potentialities for mental development. We know that differences in the possibilities for development of those potentialities are already present in the infant at birth. But however variable those potentialities are in any human group, they do exist, and they constitute the material out of which society weaves mind—the social development of the person. Society reaches those potentialities through the responses it makes to the basic needs of the infant and subsequently by the responses it induces in the person through its institutional controls. Hence, from the point of view of socialization it may be said that heredity represents the social organization of the potentialities of the individual according to the patterns of organization prevailing in the culture into which he is born. Heredity is not something static or immutable; on the contrary, it is a dynamic process in which the limited predetermined capacities for performance, the potentialities, are made to undergo development in relation to the conditions with which they interact.

The process of learning the traditional cultural patterns is called *socialization,* and is essentially cultural in character. We may, then, call the natural endowment of human potentialities *primary human nature,* and the socialized development of those potentialities *secondary human nature.* Human nature, therefore, consists of both primary and secondary elements, the innate and the acquired. Where most errors are committed is in the identification of the latter with the former.[9] What is customary should not be mistaken for what is natural, for custom is man's own extension of what is natural.[10]

The Genetic Unity of Humanity

All the evidence we possess indicates that there are no really discontinuous differences in the variability of the genic potentialities to be found in any group of mankind. No two individuals are ever alike in the genic potentialities which they inherit, nor—within the range of the normal—are they ever so unlike as to exhibit the absence of any potentiality. From the point of view of the capacity for social development every individual possesses all the necessary potentialities, and this is true for human beings in every ethnic group and has certainly been true of our species for many hundreds of thousands of years. In their capacity for social development, within the range of the normal, all men fall within the range of equality at birth. This is our basic assumption, while at the same time it is recognized that appreciable individual differences in this and in other respects exist in every case.

Scott has pointed out that because of man's greater learning powers organic heredity as such has smaller effects upon his behavior than it does in lower animals.[11] This is perhaps equally significantly stated the other way round: because organic heredity plays so small a role in man's social development, what he learns through the socialization process plays a vastly more important part in his development than it does in nonhuman animals.

In man, the evidence indicates, there does not seem to have been any significant differential selection for mental characters. There is no good evidence that any human group differs from any other in the nature of its gene potentials for mental or social development.[12] Hence, until evidence to the contrary is forthcoming, we may rule out any effect of a genetic factor in differentially determining any of the cultures in the great range of human society known to us. It is not genes which determine culture, but the organization of the genic potentialities through the medium of the basic and derived needs, by the particular conditions of the social environment in which man lives. These conditions condition the character of the person's social development, and they arise not from any genic differences between groups but from the difference in the history of their experience.

5 LIFE IN THE WOMB AND THE TRAUMA OF BIRTH

Yes,—the history of man for the nine months preceding his birth, would, probably, be far more interesting, and contain events of greater moment, than all the threescore and ten years that follow it.

—SAMUEL TAYLOR COLERIDGE*

The question may be asked—is it important that we should concern ourselves with the details of birth or earlier pre-natal experience? If we are interested in tracing the early patterns of consciousness we must needs turn our attention to the phenomena occurring in that pre-natal period which, through their very presence, would seem to influence and color the child's emotional and personality patterns after birth.

—M. E. KENWORTHY**

THE PERIODS OF DEVELOPMENT

The developmental history of the individual is separated by the act of birth into two distinct periods: the one preceding birth, *the prenatal period,* and the other following birth, *the postnatal period.* On physiological grounds these two periods are again customarily subdivided into the following periods:

Prenatal Life

PERIOD OF THE OVUM: From fertilization to the close of the second week of prenatal life.

PERIOD OF THE EMBRYO: From the end of the second week to the end of the eighth week.

* Samuel Taylor Coleridge, *Miscellanies, Aesthetic and Literary* (collected and arranged by Thomas Ashe), London, Bohn Standard Library, 1885, p. 301.

** M. E. Kenworthy, "The pre-natal and early post-natal phenomena of consciousness," in E. Dummer (editor), *The Unconscious,* New York, Knopf, 1927, p. 181.

Period of the Fetus: From the end of the eighth week to birth at the tenth lunar month.

Postnatal Life

Birth: The period during which the organism passes from its uterine shelter into the external world.

Neonatal Period (or period of the Newborn): From birth to the close of the first month.

Period of Infancy: From the beginning of the second month to the close of the first year, or until the habitual assumption of the erect posture (during, on the average, the sixteenth month).

Period of Childhood: (1) *Early childhood*: From the end of the period of infancy to the end of the fifth year. (2) *Middle childhood*: From the commencement of the sixth year to the end of the ninth year. (3) *Later childhood or pre-pubertal period*: From the commencement of the tenth year to about the middle of the fourteenth year in females, and toward the end of the fifteenth year in males.

Period of Puberty: The middle of the fourteenth year in females, and toward the end of the fifteenth year in males.

Period of Adolescence: From puberty to about the twenty-first year in females, and about the twenty-fourth year in males.

Early Maturity: From the end of the adolescent period to about the thirty-fifth year.

Later Maturity: From about the thirty-fifth year to 55 or 60 years of age.

Terminal Age: From about 55 or 60 years of age to death.

Psychological Phases of Development

The psychological phases of development of infancy, the dependency period, do not correspond to the physiological developmental periods, except very roughly. The following psychological postnatal phases may be recognized:

Psychological Phases of Infancy

Birth: The period during which the organism passes from its uterine shelter into the external world.

Period of Infancy: From birth to the end of the sixth year. This period has three phases: (1) From birth to the commencement of the sixth month; (2) From six months to the third birthday; (3) From the third birthday to the end of the sixth year.

Prenatal Life

From the point of view of the total social development of the person the prenatal life of the organism is not without some relevance. There is no direct connection between the nervous system of the mother and that of the fetus. Hence there can be no direct mediation of the mother's experiences to the fetus through the nervous system. There exists no avenue through which the mother's mental states can, as such, be transmitted to the fetus. On these grounds the belief in "maternal impressions," for example, is generally held to be nothing but a myth. So far as the blood stream is concerned we know that no blood normally passes from mother to fetus. The placental barrier, in fact, normally regulates the passage of various materials through it. The placenta will not usually pass substances that are completely soluble in the blood plasma if their molecules are larger than .0004 of an inch. Such protein molecules must be broken up chemically into components of smaller molecular size, either simpler proteins, proteoses, or still smaller amino acids.[1]

It is, however, well known that maternal hormones are capable of reaching the fetus, and it is highly probable that the physicochemical changes accompanying certain mental states in the mother may reach and act upon the fetus. Indeed, the "common endocrine pool" of mother and fetus forms a neurohumoral bond between them. Even such physical changes as occur in the mother as a result of cigarette smoking, or the inhalation of a small quantity of amyl nitride, are reflected in the fetus by an increase, or less frequently a decrease, in heart rate.[2] The gases absorbed by the mother must clearly pass through the placenta to the fetus. It is now also well established that from the end of the eighth uterine week the fetus becomes progressively more capable of responding to tactile stimuli,[3] and that within the last three months of intrauterine life it is capable of responding to sounds outside the mother's body. For example, striking the side of a bathtub in which a pregnant woman was lying induced a sudden jump on the part of the fetus 31 days before it was born. Concerts attended by another woman toward the end of pregnancy resulted in vigorous movements of the fetus.[4] Sontag and Wallace found marked increase in fetal movements from the thirteenth week onward when a doorbell-buzzer was held opposite the fetal head.[5] The responses, according to these observers, were somewhat convulsive in nature. Subsequent work has shown that the human fetus in utero is capable of being stimulated by, and responding to, a wide range of tones.[6]

Sontag and his co-workers have found that emotional disturbance or fatigue of the mother produces a marked increase in the activity of the fetus.[7] Several mothers reported that the vibration of a washing machine and also concerts of piano music during the last two months of pregnancy resulted in marked increase of fetal activity. Fetuses that were very active during the last two prenatal months tended to be light in weight in relation to length; such fetuses also tended to have a more advanced motor development. Sontag has also observed an association between prenatal stimulation of the fetus and postnatal feeding difficulties. The drugs used by the pregnant woman, her nutrition, endocrine status, emotional life, and activity level may very likely contribute, Sontag concludes, to the shaping of the physical status, the behavior patterns, and the postnatal progress of the child.[8]

The Fels Institute workers have found that if the pregnant mother undergoes severe emotional stresses, especially during the latter part of her pregnancy, her child is likely to be born and develop as a hyperactive, irritable, squirming, crying infant who cries for his feeding every two or three hours instead of sleeping through the four-hour interval between feedings. The irritability of such infants involves the control of the gastrointestinal tract, causing emptying of the bowel at frequent intervals, as well as regurgitation of food. As Sontag puts it, "He is to all intents and purposes a neurotic infant when he is born—the result of an unsatisfactory fetal environment. In this instance he has not had to wait until childhood for a bad home situation or other cause to make him neurotic. It has been done for him before he has even seen the light of day."[9]

In this connection Halliday mentions the clinical impression that "patients who develop recurring depressive states in adult life frequently provide a history . . . showing that the mother was grievously emotionally disturbed during the intrauterine phase of the patient."[10]

Phyllis Greenacre suggests that the evidence indicates the possible existence of pre-anxiety reactions in fetal life without, necessarily, any psychic content.[11] She suggests that traumatic stimuli such as sudden sounds, vibrations, umbilical cord entanglements, and the like, including the "trip through the birth canal" may produce a predisposition to anxiety which, combined or not with constitutional and traumatizing birth experiences, might be an important determinant in producing the severity of any neurosis.

Converging evidences at the present time would tend to lend strong support to Greenacre's suggestions. Much further research, however, is required. Meanwhile, it would seem quite likely that Samuel Taylor Coleridge was not far off the mark when, more than a hundred years ago he wrote: "Yes,—the history of man for the nine months preceding his birth, would, probably, be far more interesting, and contain events of greater moment, than all the threescore and ten years that follow it."[12]

The Psychoanalytic View of Uterine Life

Freud originally, and many psychoanalysts since, have claimed that their psychoanalytic experience convinces them that prenatal existence is normally supremely pleasurable. The satisfactions and security of intrauterine life, according to Otto Rank, the principal proponent of this theory,[13] constitute a blissful state which is rudely destroyed by the experience of birth. That experience is, according to this theory, a tremendous psychic shock, and constitutes the trauma or injury of birth, from which the person is all his life endeavoring to recover by a symbolic effort to return to the paradisial bliss of the womb. Birth is the primal separation and the cause of the primal anxiety. Anxiety is the apprehension of separation. With birth there is not only a cataclysmic change both in environment and modes of functioning but also a loss of the intrauterine state of security and freedom from effort. The experience produces feelings of helplessness and anxiety. The severance of the physical and psychical attachment to the warming, nourishing, protecting mother is something which the deepest levels of the person never accept. The whole of later existence is, in fact, a reaction to extrauterine suffering and loneliness, an attempt to make the whole world a substitution for the womb—a womb with a view.

According to Rank, all later pleasure-seeking impulses have as their final goal the re-establishment of the prenatal pleasure state. The resentment of the child during sphincter training represents the child's expression of its claim to intrauterine freedom. Thumb-sucking is an attempt to replace the mother's body by the child's own. Toe-sucking re-establishes the intrauterine position of the body.

Freud, while agreeing that "the act of parturition appears to be the first individual anxiety experienced to give the characteristic traits of the expression of an anxiety affect" (through the motor innervations of the respiratory organs and the heart), objects to the notion that every anxiety reproduces the original birth situation. He can see no justification for such an idea.[14] Freud, however, accepts intrauterine security and pleasure as a fact, but Rank's development of the concept of the trauma of birth he can accept only in a much modified form. The experience of birth he regards as producing a sense of physical and psychic helplessness rather than of severe shock.

In criticism of the psychoanalytic view of the uterine state it has been said: (1) that no real evidence has ever been produced which would even suggest that such a state of bliss exists; (2) if such a state does exist then it can at most be a thalamic state, it can have no cortical content, since—it is alleged—the evidence at present indicates that cortical activity of any really functional kind does not begin till almost three months after birth. Furthermore, there is some evidence that the quality of an affective state is to some extent dependent upon the existence of a functioning cortex and the development of pathways between it and the thalamus.[15] Any discriminative act of feeling or affective awareness by the fetus must be assumed to be dependent upon the existence of corticothalamic pathways the very existence of which at this early stage of development is questioned. It has therefore been argued that on neuroanatomical grounds the state of uterine bliss of which the organism is said to be aware or to recall during the allegedly cataclysmic process of birth must be doubted.

To such objections the reply may be made that it is far from established that corticothalamic pathways do not exist in the late fetus, but that on the contrary there is every reason to believe that they do. Furthermore, there are now some grounds for believing that the thalamic reticular system, connected with the cortex through ascending sensory (afferent) and efferent connections, "may be actually the primary physical basis of the background of conscious awareness."[16] However, the thalamic reticular system has not been investigated in the newborn. We do know that the organism is capable of experiencing and functioning in the absence of a cortex. Such an organism is capable of exhibiting fear, rage, and other emotional forms of behavior. This is one of the most firmly established facts of neurophysiology. The fact that a six-week-old baby is able to recognize whether a person is hostile or friendly by responding to lip-sucking or klucking sounds with sustained laughter, strongly suggests that cortical activity with psychic content is possible at this early age. Furthermore, as we shall see, conditioning of the newborn to respond to the sign of an original stimulus would suggest neurological activity through the intermediation of the cortex. It has long been known that in the three-month-old fetus the cortex is already laid down in its essentially permanent form. Whether the fetal cortex is capable of registering its experiences must, however, remain an open question until the unequivocal researches have been carried out that alone will enable us to return an answer to that question.

Birth Trauma

Not all psychoanalysts agree that the process of birth is as shocking an experience as some have claimed. Ferenczi, for example, an early and particularly sensitive psychoanalyst, denies the existence of such a phenomenon altogether. "The more I observe," he wrote, "the more I realize that none of the development and changes which life brings finds the individual so well prepared as for birth." Physiological preparation, reflexes, and the intuition of the parents, he believed, go to make the transition from the womb to the external world as smooth as possible. On the other hand Fodor, who has made a long-time clinical study of this subject, states that "The change-over from pre-natal to post-natal life involves an ordeal as severe as dying. Hence the fear of death begins at birth and is based on a maelstrom of bewildering experiences that are covered by infantile amnesia but break through in nightmares or become converted into symptoms."[17]

The child's cry is not, as it has often been taken to mean, a cry of distress, but purely a reflex activity, a necessary one, following immediately upon the filling of its lungs with atmospheric air. Physiologically the first cry is an emergency form of breathing, a bellows-like action of the diaphragm which serves alternately to expel fluids from the lungs and suck in oxygen. "The sound element at this time is largely incidental and is in all probability due to a wavelike action of the vocal cords as the air passes in and out."[18] With its first cry the newborn announces the functioning, the primitive functioning, of his first and enduring basic need, oxygen hunger. He does not "cry" because he suddenly realizes what a vale of tears he has entered, but rather because he is satisfying a want. The newborn usually has no tears, and his "crying" is not what at a more mature level it is often subjectively misinterpreted to mean. Far from constituting one of the evidences of the traumatic nature of birth, the newborn's crying is but a proof of the fact that the primary basic need of the newborn is being satisfied, that the organism is receiving what it wants.

An important piece of evidence for the theory of birth trauma insofar as the trip through the birth canal is concerned, would be what Kenworthy has claimed as having been noted, that "the Caesarian sectioned child is prone to be less sensitized—he cries less, is markedly less irritated by the contacts of handling, etc.—than the first-born child delivered through the birth canal."[19] Such data would, however, not have any bearing on the effects of the separation of the fetus from the womb. An interesting and important piece of research is indicated here. Mothers who have had Cesarean babies with whom I have discussed this matter are very positive about the following two facts: First, that the head shape of the child is noticeably roundheaded as compared with the molded head of the normally born child, and second that the skin appears to be much less wrinkled than that of normally born children. These facts would lend support to the notion that the birth process is at the very least physiologically hard on the infant. Opinions seem to be divided as to whether Cesarean delivered children are more or less sensitive than normally delivered children.

Kenworthy has suggested that the birth trauma is apt to be more excessive with the first-born child; as we shall see there seems to be some evidence for this suggestion.

Prematurely Born Children

Of interest here are Shirley's findings that premature children exhibit a significantly higher sensory acuity than term children, and in comparison are somewhat retarded in lingual and motor manual control, as well as in postural and locomotor control. Control of bowel and bladder sphincters is achieved later and with difficulty. The attention span is short, such children being highly emotional, jumpy, anxious, and usually shy. In interpreting this prematurity-syndrome Shirley points out that "Premature births often are cataclysmic; unduly prolonged or precipitant, both of which conditions subject the baby to birth trauma." At birth the premature suffers a more prolonged weight loss, and an arrest in development that writes its permanent record in the growth of bones; may it not also write a permanent record in that much more impressionable material, the nervous system? "Thus," Shirley adds, "it seems possible that, through a less favorable prenatal environment, or through the too early loss of intra-uterine media, or through the lack of adequate time for the birth preparatory responses, or through birth injuries that sometimes are so slight as to be unrecognized or through a combination of these factors, the premature may be predisposed toward the development of a higher degree of nervous irritability than the term child."[20]

In England, Drillien, studying English prematures, has fully confirmed Shirley's findings on American prematures. In addition, Drillien found that the prematures showed a significantly higher incidence of nasopharyngeal and respiratory infections, especially during the first year. Behavior disorders, particularly with regard to feeding, were more frequent among premature infants.[21]

These observations have been confirmed by American investigators who have found a higher incidence of behavior problems of various sorts and a variety of affections of the nervous systems in children at school age and in later life who had been prematurely born.[22]

Birth Trauma, Dependency, Neurosis, and Culture

Freud maintained that it was through its sense of physical and mental helplessness that the dangers of the outer world become of greater importance to the newborn, "and the value of the object which can alone protect from these dangers and replace the lost intra-uterine life is greatly enhanced." The need for love is created which, Freud says, "will nevermore leave the individual." Birth, since it is the first dangerous situation through which the infant must pass, establishes a physiological anxiety pattern which the ego (the organized personality) makes use of in later danger situations to give the "pain signal" to the id (the aggregate of basic drives or urges).[23]

It should be reasonably clear that it is the birth process which produces the major reinforcement of the dependency needs; the infant is mortally afraid and desires to return to the womb; thus death, fear, womb, and birth remain closely related in the infant mind. Rank suggests that from the point of view of the average healthy adult one can designate the person's childhood as his normal neurosis. In neurosis this infantile condition may continue into adult life.[24] The neuroses, according to Rank, represent futile attempts to overcome the birth trauma, whereas man's cultural adjustment represents man's largely successful attempt to overcome the birth trauma.[25]

Evidence as to the Reality of the Birth Trauma

The nature of many fantasies and dreams, upon analysis, lends strong support to the views of both Freud and Rank with respect to the psychic consequences of the birth trauma. Fodor, who for many years has investigated the fantasies and dreams of his patients from the psychoanalytic point of view, finds evidence not only for the reality of the trauma of birth but also for the existence of a state of positive "uterine bliss." Patients whose dreams and fantasies indicate that their illnesses stem from the experience of birth and the subsequent exacerbation of that experience, have been cured by what Fodor calls "birth therapy." Demonstration of the prenatal character of an abnormal urge "cancels the patient's resistance to the therapeutic effort and permits a speedy integration of personality."

Fodor claims to have traced a genetic connection between the experiences of the fetus *in utero,* between the trauma of birth, and various forms of behavior which he interprets as a desire to return to the state of fetal bliss, and also certain anxiety states such as nightmares of suffocation, claustrophobia, insomnia, nightmares of falling, of water, fire, and so on.[26]

Fodor's study is the first intensive clinical investigation of the trauma of birth to be published. But while it is suggestive it cannot be said to have proved anything. However, additional support for Fodor's views has come from independent investigators in England and in the Netherlands. Kelsey has reported upon a number of patients who, under hypnoanalytic treatment, were regressed to what could only be interpreted as uterine stages of development. One of these patients even regressed to the period of conception! Here is an extract from a case report of an unmarried woman of 44 years of age:

She says "I am very tiny. I seem to be lying on something very soft and white. I am very comfortable but somehow it is not right. I used to be a part of a 'oneness,' and now I am separated." At this I [Kelsey] told her that at "ten" she would find herself again part of the "oneness." As I reached "ten" she said quite calmly and quietly and positively, "This is the womb." She went on: "There is something beating in me and through me—my mother's heart. I can't see—and it feels as if I've got no mouth." I asked her in what position she found herself. She replied, "Curled up," and immediately assumed the foetal position.

After some time I told her that at the count of "ten" she would start to leave this place. At "ten" she arched her back, put one hand on her head, and an expression of severe suffering appeared on her features. She was portraying in fact exactly what one can imagine that the foetus feels when the first contraction of the uterus clamps down upon it. In a moment or two this attitude was relaxed, only to be repeated a few moments later. At length I told her that at "ten" she really would leave this place. At "ten" she began to moan from the pain in her head, and then, just as one felt that the head must soon emerge, she suddenly gasped, "I can't breathe," and she appeared to be fighting for air. Then came a short period of gasping and gulping, interspersed with cries that she could smell blood. It was distressing to witness. Then she suddenly gave a great sigh of relief—"That's better"—and appeared to fall asleep. She retained the foetal position. . . . At a subsequent session I regressed the patient back to the "oneness" and then asked her to go back where she was before she reached the "oneness." There followed half an hour of extraordinary material. She appeared to find herself in a place which she described in incompatible superlatives. It was dark, yet filled with heavenly music; it was still, yet everything was quivering. And so on. . . . This patient had had opportunities in her life of acquiring obstetrical knowledge.[27]

However, other patients were, at least on the conscious level, utterly ignorant of such knowledge. Of course, such knowledge may have been repressed and then recovered under hypnosis. Kelsey describes many other extraordinary cases in his remarkable report, and in the Netherlands Peerbolte has published an account of similar findings.[28] Quite clearly further investigation in this field will be necessary. Meanwhile, it will be desirable to keep an open mind. One cannot help but be impressed by the recurring theme in the dreams of children which takes the form of finding themselves in a dark narrow chimney, through which they are struggling to descend, often accompanied by a terrifying feeling of imminent suffocation.

Suggestive evidence for the reality of the birth trauma has been provided by Sontag and his co-workers. This evidence indicates that the severity of the "trip through the birth canal," the shock of such birth itself, is even capable of affecting the growth of the infant's skeleton. These workers have shown that certain fine white striae which develop in the tarsal bones of some neonates are highly correlated with the severity of the birth process which such children have undergone. Severity is measured by length and difficulty of labor, forceps delivery, primiparity, and the influences of such factors as might enable the infant to withstand the shock of birth, such as nutrition, persistent vomiting or nausea during pregnancy, and economic status insofar as this may reflect the action of nutritional and similar factors. The facts are set out in Table 1.

TABLE 1. COMPARISON OF FACTORS OF GESTATION AND BIRTH FOR MOTHERS OF INFANTS WITH STRIAE AND THOSE OF INFANTS WITHOUT STRIAE

Factor	Incidence in Mothers of Infants with Striae (*per cent*)	Incidence in Mothers of Infants without Striae (*per cent*)
Forceps delivery	31	6
Precipitate delivery	31	15
Primiparity	39	19
Long labor	8	9
Basal metabolic rate below 0%	26	19
Persistent nausea and vomiting	25	8
Poor health	6	0
Hemoglobin control below 70%	42	36
Inadequate economic status	10	0

SOURCE: L. W. Sontag and L. M. Harris, "Evidence of disturbed prenatal and neonatal growth in bones of infants aged one month," *American Journal of Diseases of Children,* vol. 56, 1938.

The authors' conclusions, in their own words are as follows:

Our findings lead us to believe that the tarsal striae frequently found in the roentgenograms of 1 month old children are the result of disturbances in growth produced by the process of birth itself and influenced by such factors as maternal health and nutrition. We believe that the shock of birth is an important factor and that it is determined by the severity of the birth process plus the physical condition of the infant. We consider the mechanism comparable to that involved when striae are laid down in the long bones of growing children as a result of a surgical procedure or of severe illness.[29]

If the severity of birth is capable of producing such marked effects upon skeletal growth, it will not be unreasonable to conclude that normal birth is to some extent shocking to the child.

Wile and Davis have investigated the relation of manner and order of birth to behavior. They studied children who were instrumentally delivered and compared these with children who were spontaneously born.

Every nonspontaneous birth involves some trauma and physical compression regardless of birth order. Nonspontaneously born children were found to be more frequently hyperactive and distractable than the spontaneously born. First-born children have, in general, a harder time getting born, as measured by duration and complications of labor, than later born children. Such children are more frequently behavior problems than the later born. This is a fact of some importance, but whether the behavior problems of many first-borns are due to birth trauma or to subsequent experiences is an open question. The percentage frequencies of the types of behavior problems presented by the two groups are set out in Table 2.

"The children with instrumental birth" write Wile and Davis "appeared to show a general reduction of personality energy rather than a mere increase in sensitivity and irritability, although the physical element was generally noted as a restless, distractible, irritable hyperactivity. We may conclude, therefore, that behavior reactions are not to be interpreted as shocks of birth, with a per-

TABLE 2. PROBLEMS PRESENTED—TOTAL: 380 SPONTANEOUSLY BORN (A), 120 INSTRUMENTALLY DELIVERED (B)

	A (*per cent*)	B (*per cent*)
Aggressive types of behavior (rages, tantrums, pugnacity)	65	33.3
General hyperactivity (restlessness, irritability, distractibility)	25	50
Submissive types of behavior (fears, unhappiness, fantasy life, no friends)	40	25
Tics, nail-biting, food fads	70	33.3
Peculation	12	6.7
Infantile home relationships	55	20
School difficulties	45	22.3
Intersibling conflicts	30	15
Physical ills	10	3.3

sistence of fear and pain and an anxiety state that later might become a source of neurotic behavior." These investigators point out that "the process of birth offers environmental factors whose impact upon personality may modify structure and possibly may shift and even alter some of the genetic bases of accomplishment by limiting their growth." Birth trauma in the Rankian sense they believe has comparatively little meaning in the light of the behavior exhibited by their two groups.[30]

It would seem, however, that this investigation does throw some light upon the crucial problem of the relation of the trauma of spontaneous birth or nonspontaneous birth to anxiety. Greenacre has pointed out that "the forerunner of anxiety exists in a condition of irritable responsiveness of the organism."

> [What is] important in the development of anxiety potentials in any human being, is the degree of tension existent, dependent on the sensory-motor balance, i.e., the ratio between the sensory stimulation and the capacity (development and opportunity) to effect some sort of motor discharge. Where there has been considerable disproportion between an increased sensory stimulation and a limited motor discharge over a period of time such tension may conceivably be incorporated into the working balance of the individual, and becomes temporarily or permanently a characteristic of his makeup. Where this is true a sudden in-

crease or decrease in the established tension level of the individual contributes to symptoms of anxiety. There is, however, in each individual a unique primary organization and level of tension that is determined, in some measure, by the birth experience, furnishing an important element in the patterning of the drive and energy distribution of that individual.[31]

Irritability and reduction in personality energy are two among the cluster of traits characterizing the anxiety state. These were the traits which Wile and Davis found more frequently in the nonspontaneously born children. It is a likely suggestion that these traits are significantly correlated with the greater traumatization which these children are known to have suffered at birth.

Schroeder found that distractibility and hyperactivity were characteristic personality traits of children who had been instrumentally delivered,[32] and Despert found that out of 35 "anxious" children of nursery school age 19, that is 54 per cent, were instrumentally delivered.[33] Finally, Boland has found a significantly greater number of instrumental births among a group of 209 stutterers than occurred among other large samples of the general population born in hospitals.[34]

Summarizing the best available evidence we may conclude that it appears to be reasonably certain that the prenatal experiences of the fetus are to an important extent capable of affecting the subsequent psychic development of the organism. The evidence indicates that the organism constantly seeks the state of relative stability which is enjoyed in the womb, a state which was so rudely interrupted by the separation and experience of birth. Birth, the evidence suggests, constitutes the first major anxiety-producing experience.

Whether such statements be regarded as facts, theories, hypotheses or opinions, it must be conceded that the prenatal life of the organism can no longer be disregarded if the development of the person as a whole is to be understood.

The Trauma of Birth and the Fear of Separation

We have already observed that birth may be regarded as the first separation which the organism experiences, a separation which is productive of the first anxiety. Any separation which the organism experiences thereafter, whether it be at weaning, or physically from the mother, or from an accustomed environment or state, tends to re-evoke the anxiety of the original separation. Anxiety could be defined as the expression of the repressed fear of separation. Separation is here understood to include the idea of separation in any part from oneself, as in threats to the integrity of one's ego, challenges to one's belief or security, the fear of falling either psychologically or physically, and the like. Love, conversely, could be described—in this respect—as the maintenance of the organism in a manner such that all anxiety-producing situations are kept at a minimum, principally by ministering to the dependency needs of the organism in a satisfactory manner, but distinctly *not* by helping to cover up existing fears. To resolve conflicts by facing fears and critical situations is the road to maturity and character.[35]

It may well be that the suffering and psychic disordering of the separated child (see pp. 200–243) is ontogenetically related to the suffering and disordering of the newborn. The function, it may be suggested, of the disordering produced at birth in this previously highly organized creature is to enable its re-ordering to proceed upon a higher level of organization than that which it vegetatively underwent during the prenatal phase of its existence. The vegetative process gives way to an increasingly active participating role on the part of the organism in its own development. This is precisely what is believed to occur in shock treatment delivered to mentally disturbed patients. It is in this sense that from complete dependency the organism develops postnatally to increasingly larger degrees of freedom in self-actualization.

6 THE BASIC AND ACQUIRED NEEDS

Man, like the generous vine, supported lives:
The strength he gains is from the embrace he gives.
—ALEXANDER POPE, *Essay on Man*

MAN BORN A SOCIALLY UNDIFFERENTIATED ANIMAL?

Like all other mammals man appears to be born a socially undifferentiated animal. The experience of the developing fetus in the womb may be regarded as a prenatal protosocial preparation of the developing organism for the experience of postnatal socializing life. The many months of "comfortable" dependence of the fetus upon its intrauterine environment reinforces the conditioning of the unborn fetus to the habit of dependence and the maintenance of an optimum state of comfort. As we have seen, it is believed by some students of the subject that the process of birth constitutes the first major discomfort suffered by the fetus, the first real disturbance of its intrauterine security. Hence, the re-establishment of the newborn infant in its extrauterine environment in some sort of security, in which the expression of its needs receives more or less satisfactory attention, constitutes a social process which may be linked with the newborn's generalized consciousness of the immediately antecedent conditions of intrauterine life and birth.

Man Born a Culturally Undifferentiated Animal

With respect to the question whether man is born a socially undifferentiated animal, it is possible to argue that the elements of a social process exist under intrauterine conditions in the cooperative interaction of the fetus with its environment. For our immediate purposes, then, it is strictly more accurate to say that man is born a *culturally* undifferentiated creature. We are not for the moment concerned with returning an answer to the question: How is this culturally indifferent animal differentiated as a sociocultural being? The answer to that question is reserved for a later section of this book. Here we are concerned with the answer to the more fundamental question: What are the basic needs of man the satisfaction of which constitutes the end to which culture is the means?

The Basic Needs

Malinowski has cogently argued that if we are ever to develop a sound scientific theory of culture which will yield efficient general laws, that theory must start from the organic needs of man and attempt to relate to them the more complex, indirect needs of the spiritual, economic, or social type. All behavior that relates to human nutrition, to sex, and to the cycle of life, including birth, growth, maturation, and death, is fundamentally and invariably associated with physiological changes in the body, in the nervous system of the person, and in that of his fellows. The problems and complexities of cultural behavior are, then, best approached, as Malinowski says, by attempting "to relate them to organic processes in the human body and to those concomitant phases of behavior which we call desire or drive, emotion or physiological disturbance, and which, for one reason or another, have to be regulated and coordinated by the apparatus of culture."[1]

This is essentially the view adopted in the present volume. Man as an animal must breathe, eat, excrete, sleep, maintain adequate health, and procreate. These basic needs constitute the minimum biological conditions which must be satisfied by any human group if its members are to survive. These physiological or biogenic needs and their functioning interrelations constitute the innate nature of man. As will have been concluded from an earlier chapter, these needs cannot be exercised without the integrative action of the nervous system, and it should be evident that it is through the agency of the nervous system that those needs can be controlled, socialized, and culturalized. In the socializing process the nervous system itself becomes organized into the controlling mechanism of an interrelated system of bodily habits of which symbolic thinking and language are perhaps the two most important.

A basic or biogenic need may be defined as any urge or need of the organism which must be satisfied if the organism or the group is to survive.

Malinowski has defined the concept of basic needs as "the environmental and biological conditions which must be fulfilled for the survival of the individual and the group."[2]

Reduced to the form of elementary impulses these needs and the behavior which they determine are set out by Malinowski in a table representing the permanent vital sequences which are invariably incorporated in every culture.

TABLE 3. PERMANENT VITAL SEQUENCES INCORPORATED IN ALL CULTURES

(A) Impulse	(B) Act	(C) Satisfaction
Drive to breathe: gasping for air	Intake of oxygen	Elimination of CO_2 in tissues
Hunger	Ingestion of food	Satiation
Thirst	Absorption of liquid	Quenching
Sex appetite	Conjugation	Detumescence
Fatigue	Rest	Restoration of muscular and nervous energy
Restlessness	Activity	Satisfaction of fatigue
Somnolence	Sleep	Awakening with restored energy
Bladder pressure	Micturition	Removal of tension
Colon pressure	Defecation	Abdominal relaxation
Fright	Escape from danger	Relaxation
Pain	Avoidance by effective act	Return to normal state

SOURCE: Bronislaw Malinowski; *A Scientific Theory of Culture and Other Essays*, Chapel Hill, University of North Carolina Press, 1944.

The Sustaining Systems

The vital sequences listed in Table 3 constitute forms of behavior that together form a complex of conditions constituting the irreducible minimum of vital functioning necessary for the survival of the individual and of the group. Intimately associated with the functioning of these vital activities are the sustaining systems of the body. These sustaining systems are the *respiratory* sytem, which controls the intake of oxygen as well as the utilization and elimination of carbon dioxide; the *circulatory* system, which conveys the oxygen through the blood vessels to the capillaries to supply the cells, and, in turn, to take up the gaseous waste products and return them to the lungs; the *digestive* system, which is concerned with the ingestion and chemical breakdown of solid foods and liquids; the *eliminative* systems, which carry the waste products from the alimentary tract, from the urinary tract, and from the skin through the sweat glands; the *reproductive* system, essential for the propagation of the group; the *nervous* system, which enables the organism to make the proper responses to the stimuli it receives through that system; and the *endocrine* system, which, in addition to the important part it plays in growth and development and in behavior,[3] assists in the functioning of all these systems. The *neurohumoral* system is constituted by the interacting nervous and endocrine systems acting through the fluid medium of the blood and circulatory system.

The harmonious operation of these sustaining systems is dependent upon the ability of the organism to perform the acts leading to the satisfaction of the impulses to which functioning of the sustaining systems partly give rise. The acts, listed in the second column, which lead to the satisfaction of the basic impulses are organically determined in the sense that they are performed principally as the result of certain organic conditions and that they are acts *which do not require to be learned*. In other words, the original impulses arise in consequence of the existence of certain states representing a disturbance of physiological equilibrium which is expressed in a certain state of tension. The acts leading to the restoration of physiological equilibrium, that is to say the reduction of tension by the satisfaction of the needs (which are the basic impulses), follow more or less automatically from the presence of such physiological states.

The Criteria of Dependability

Klineberg has suggested a threefold criterion of dependability which must be satisfied by any form of behavior if it is to be regarded as a fundamental tendency of the organism.[4] The first requirement in man is the existence of continuity between a particular form of behavior and that found in other animals, particularly the anthropoid apes. The second is a biochemical or physiological basis for such behavior. The third requirement is the universality of such behavior. Malinowski's list of permanent vital sequences fully satisfies these criteria, and may be accepted as the minimum complex of basic urges or needs necessary for the survival of the individual and the group.

Needs and Satisfactions

These vital sequences of behavior must further be reduced to the states which condition them. "Impulse," "act," and "satisfaction" inadequately define the conditions. While the conditions described by Malinowski as impulses can quite properly be described by such a term in the sense of an influence or force acting upon the body, it would be less confusing and more accurate to describe the basic states of disequilibrium in their functional relation. The states called "impulses" by Malinowski are all characterized by a certain tension or, better, urgency. Their conditioning factors may therefore be said to give rise to a state of urgency, and these states may therefore best be described as *urges*. It will clarify our thinking to realize that Malinowski's impulse is an urge or drive, and that the urge or drive is the need. Fatigue is an urge to rest, somnolence an urge to sleep, thirst an urge to drink, and so on. The acts of resting, sleeping, and drinking are the actual processes of satisfaction of the urges, while Malinowski's "satisfactions" really describe the end effects of those processes or acts. Thus, the terms *urge* and *need* may be used interchangeably. It is not that the physiochemical or physiological states give rise to an urge that produces a need, that is then followed by an act that produces satisfaction, but rather that the urge *is* the need, while the activity that satisfies the need is the process or act of satisfaction, the end result of which is the restoration of the disturbed part of the organism to a normal state of balance. From the point of view of the end results the urge-needs can be described, and often are described, as desires. We shall adhere to the terms *urge* and *need,* and we shall use them as synonyms.[5]

The *impulse* of hunger, then, may be better described as a positive physiological tension that is expressed in the form of an urge or need to ingest food. The physiological tension of hunger leads to satisfaction by the appropriate activity, in this case the ingestion of food. According to Malinowski, satisfaction consists in the restoration of the organism to a state of equilibrium or homeostasis, through the process of food ingestion and its end effect satiation.

What Malinowski has failed to note is that the acts which lead to satisfaction are in themselves tension-reducing, satisfying, pleasurable, and may be indulged for their own sake. That satisfaction consists of a process comprised of (1) the satisfying acts, and (2) the restoration to equilibrium. In a schematic form this may be represented as follows:

			Satisfaction	
Physiological tension	=	*Urge or need to* ⟶	*Which leads to the act of* ⟶	*Homeostasis*
Hunger (tension)	=	ingest food (imperative need) ⟶	ingesting food (act of satisfaction)⟶	satiation (restoration to equilibrium)

This diagram may be read as follows: The *physiological tension* of hunger represents the *urge or need to* ingest food. It is an imperative need, one which must be satisfied if the organism is to survive. This need usually *leads to the act of* ingesting food, a satisfying act in itself, and this usually results in satiation, a replenishment of energy and a restoration to equilibrium, *homeostasis*. It is to be noted that the act of ingesting food is part of the process of satisfaction, and that satiation is the end effect.

These physiological tensions which are experienced (by the organism) as urges or needs can be described in terms of anatomy, physiology, biochemistry, and physics. From these points of view the cultural reference is for all practical purposes taken as absent. Culture plays no part in the original basic structure of such physiological tensions. Nor does it play any part in the performance of the basic physiological acts calculated to bring about the appropriate adjustments. But culture does, to a varying extent, play a part in bringing about modifications in the character of those physiological tensions, and in the performance of the physiological acts. The point is that theoretically a cultureless individual would exhibit all the basic vital sequences of behavior in their primary states, and would do so under cultural conditions, but that ultimately culture would serve to influence and modify the character of some or all of those sequences of behavior. Normally, the physiological tensions or needs begin to be culturally influenced from the moment of birth, and even before; however, before continuing with the discussion of this aspect of the subject it will be necessary to inquire into the nature of physiological tensions or basic needs.

The Nature of Basic Needs*

Three components probably enter into the structure of every basic need. These are (1) a biochemical, (2) an inherited but modifiable network of nerve cells (neuronal net), and (3) the complex of cultural psychic experience which Kubie describes as "a complex psychic superstructure of fantasies and of obligatory and phobic patterns which together shape the derivative instinctual drives."[6] The degree to which the latter will enter into the structure and functioning of any basic need will vary in different cultures, in different persons, and in different needs.

* This section owes much to the work of Lawrence S. Kubie and G. L. Freeman.

Basically, any tissue deprivation musters the organism as a whole to secure its restoration. The tissues are so organized that any deficiency (or excess) in them will give rise to states of internal excitation or physiological need within the body as a whole. This excitation affects the neuromuscular system in such a way as to induce overt behavior calculated to produce alleviation of the basic tissue disturbance.[7] This is the process of *homeostasis* which may be defined as consisting in the coordinated and cooperative physiological processes which maintain most of the steady states in the organism.[8] The degree of psychological craving associated with the internal excitation or physiologic need will vary under different conditions, but it will always be present whether the organism has been culturalized or not. In short, a basic need is at once a biochemical, neuromuscular, and psychological state, and these three interwoven components of the need can be dissociated arbitrarily only for the purposes of investigation and analysis. The relative importance of any one of these components may vary in the constitution of each basic need. By constitution is meant the expression of the interaction between what is inherited and what is acquired—hence the possibility of normal and pathological development within the area of any basic need.

Homeostasis

Homeostasis means "steady state." Every organism possesses systems of physiological mechanisms each of which function to return to a steady state any part of the organism which has become unbalanced or disturbed. Many enduring and apparently constant or static states of the organism are the product of a processual interaction of forces, an interchange of substances, a constant building up and reducing. The living organism is in a constant state of inconstancy in innumerable respects. It is the function of each organ system, alone or in interaction with others, when there has been any departure from the balance of interacting forces to restore that balance.[9]

Homeostasis is not a cause but an effect of the functioning of various qualitative processes in the organism. The balance restored in the organism is not most illuminatingly described as "equilibrium," but rather, as Maze states, by "some specific amount or concentration or intensity of a particular property." Thus, it is the *kind* of change that we must recognize as significant—for example, electrolytic activity of the kidney in relation to the heart and vascular system, the carbon-dioxide content of the blood in relation to the respiratory rate, the water-sodium balance, the *p*H of the blood, and the like.

As both Maze and Mace[10] have independently pointed out, homeostasis is not properly a descriptive term applied to the functioning of the organism as a whole, but to the functioning principally of parts of the organism. The concept of homeostasis is most useful when it is applied to the case, as Mace says, in which (1) the norm is defined in terms of some internal condition of the organism, (2) this norm is merely maintained or restored, and (3) it relates to some specific need as contrasted with the general welfare of the organism or the personality as a whole.

A need is a tension, resulting from an alteration in some state of the system and expressing itself in activity which continues until that state is restored. The expressed activity may be said to be *goal-directed,* and the state the activity seeks to secure—freedom from tension—is its end or goal or satisfaction.

The Interval Between Stimulus and Response

Kubie has pointed out that the generalization that there can be no psychologic process without a time interval between stimulus and response applies to a tissue need and its alleviation.

> In unicellular organisms the absence of such intervals makes impossible any psychologic development; because in such organisms under favorable circumstances all processes of exchange go on continuously at the surface membrane; and only unfavorable circumstances which interpose some barrier to this exchange can cause a delay between tissue requirements and their satisfaction. In differentiated multicellular organisms, however, even under optimal conditions such a delay must always occur; since it takes time to gather in the essential substances from the environment and distribute them through the body; and since it takes additional time to gather up tissue waste, to transport it, and get

rid of it. Thus the higher organism's structural complexity interposes unavoidable delays which make possible the entire superstructure of psychologic evolution.[11]

Kubie points out that in each primary or vital process there is a time-consuming series of overlapping component steps, as follows:

1. Intake of raw material
2. Assimilation and temporary storage of material
3. Release of new material from body reservoir
4. Transport of raw material throughout body
5. Neutralization and destruction of metabolites; and/or the production of specialized tissue products
6. Transport of waste
7. Storage of waste
8. Evacuation of waste

Kubie uses the phrase "primary or vital instincts." If we substitute for this, in our own terminology, "basic needs or drives," then we may agree with him that basic needs or drives are patterns of behavior which are built upon the intake and/or output ends of the above series, "since only the first two steps and the last two can give rise to behavior which is goal-directed towards the external world. Consequently only these initial and terminal steps are subject to psychologic representation and elaboration, the intermediate phases being wholly internal."[12]

Warning Mechanisms

Lashley has shown that every instinct is associated with a warning mechanism,[13] and Kubie has pointed out that man's basic needs are similarly associated with warning mechanisms.[14] It would seem clear that the warning mechanism has a direct relation to the mechanism of anxiety,[15] and comes into play before there is any actual tissue depletion.

In respiration, for instance, we do not normally experience air-hunger. Nor is there a state of oxygen-want in the tissues at the onset of each normal respiratory cycle. This occurs only in states of acute or chronic interference with the exchange of gasses in the body. Therefore oxygen-lack is not the immediate stimulus which sets off the normal respiratory mechanism. This is done rather by the accumulation of carbon dioxide and the attendant tick-tock oscillations of the acid-base equilibrium, which set the threshold of the respiratory center for its response to proprioceptive impulses from vagus endings in the lungs (the Hering-Breuer reflex). Consequently it is not strictly accurate to say that we breathe because we need oxygen; but only that we breathe because if we did not breathe then we would very soon begin to need oxygen, whereupon we would have to breathe or else die.

Actually in normal life we breathe for psychologic reasons before we have to breathe out of physiologic necessity. There is a faint phobic stir underlying every breath we take, as the breath-holding Yogis well know.[16]

The same holds true for all other basic needs. We are warned long before there is any actual tissue depletion or experience of excess. The intervals between the warning activity and biochemical depletion or excess vary, the margin of safety varying from a few seconds in respiration to hours in water balance. The longer this interval the greater are the psychological complications which can be developed. The extent to which psychological processes can influence the various warning mechanisms varies widely.

The warning mechanism, then, is a minimum physiological change which provides the organism with cues which enable it to anticipate the high pressor effects of depletion or excess. Thus, we generally drink before we become conscious of intense thirst, or indulge in activity long before we feel any intense need for it, and we breathe long before we are aware of the "faint phobic stir" which precedes every breath. The warning mechanism or minimum physiological cue enables the organism to anticipate its needs before the latter become too disturbing. Forestalling behavior therefore becomes possible.[17]

Since the warning mechanisms operate through a phobic-like anxiety, failure to obtain the necessary satisfaction of the need which develops serves to increase anxiety. And as Kubie remarks, "every instinct [basic need] functions between the pressure of normal phobic and normal compulsive psychologic processes which are the anlage of all pathologic distortions."[18]

Under certain conditions the warning mechanism and the basic need may become detached from each other. So that the warning mechanism in the form, for example, of a sense of dryness, may continue to operate even though the tissues are thoroughly hydrated. Or vice versa, there may be a considerable degree of dehydration without any sense of dryness or thirst. Such dissociations are usually pathological. Anorexia or chronic lack of appetite is a well-known example.

It will now be readily understood how differences in conditioning and learning may affect the character of the basic needs and therefore, to some extent, the person's patterns of adjustment to the environment. This may be seen to be a matter of the interaction of excitations or physiological tensions in the organism and the varying degrees of frustration or conditioning imposed upon their expression by the environment. This process is further complicated by the warning mechanism interval, which in relation to the need is also subject to cultural conditioning. The phobic aspect of the warning mechanism has a genuine physiological substrate in the biochemical changes of which it is constituted.

The warning mechanism itself arises out of afferent impulses which are set up by a series of biochemical changes in the tissues with respect to such processes as carbohydrate metabolism, hydrogen ion concentration, hydration, salt balance, oxidation, and so on. Both by local action and reflex paths these produce local vascular, glandular, secretory, and neurohumoral changes, and eventually smooth and skeletal muscle adjustments. So long as adjustment is not made to these changes the phobic excitation remains. Inadequate satisfaction of basic needs or satisfaction of such needs when the margin of safety has been exceeded may therefore produce a paradoxical condition in which anxiety is experienced whenever a particular need is satisfied. This is, of course, a pathological condition, but it occurs with great frequency.

The Basic Vital Sequences

We may, then, reschematize the basic vital sequences as follows:

TABLE 4. THE BASIC VITAL SEQUENCES

Warning Mechanism →	*Physiological Tension* =	*Urge or Need to* →	*Which Leads to the Act of* → (*Satisfaction*)	*Homeostasis* (*Satisfaction*)
Accumulation of CO_2 →	Oxygen hunger	= intake air →	breathing →	oxygenation of tissues
Periodic gastric waves →	Hunger	= ingest food →	ingesting food →	satiation
Dryness of mucous membranes →	Thirst	= intake liquid →	intaking liquid →	quenching
Tumescence →	Sex	= conjugate →	conjugation →	detumescence
Reduced organization →	Fatigue	= rest →	resting →	restoration of muscular & nervous organization
Excess energy →	Restlessness	= action →	activity →	reduction of energy to equilibrium
? →	Somnolence	= sleep →	sleeping →	awaking with restored energy
Tonic disturbance →	Bladder pressure	= micturate →	micturition →	tension removal
Peristalsis →	Colon pressure	= defecate →	defecation →	tension removal
Autonomic activity →	Fright	= escape →	escaping from danger →	relaxation
? →	Pain	= avoid →	avoidance →	return to normal state
Activator →	Internal Excitation	= Craving →	Neuromuscular Act →	Equilibrium

Nonvital Basic Needs

In addition to the vital basic needs the satisfaction of which is necessary if the individual and the group are to survive, there are also several nonvital basic needs which must be satisfied if the organism is to develop and maintain adequate mental health. These nonvital basic needs have their origin in the same kinds of physiological states as do the vital basic needs. Two of these nonvital basic needs may be schematized as follows:

		Satisfaction	
Physiological tension =	*Urge or need to* ⟶	*Which leads to the act of* ⟶	*Homeostasis*
Feeling of non-dependency or aloneness =	be with others→	physical contact→ or association	feeling of security or interdependency
General need or tension =	expression ⟶	communication→	social recognition

The tension of nondependency or aloneness is doubtless phylogenetically connected with the genitor-offspring relationship which is in one way or another characteristic of all living things, and ontogenetically in man is associated with his prolonged intrauterine existence. During these phases of its existence, that is, *in utero* and during infancy, the organism is *dependent* upon the maternal organism for the satisfaction of its needs, a fact which in man establishes a pattern which requires the maintenance and satisfaction of those dependency needs throughout life. Social life, as we shall see, further reinforces the strength of these dependency needs.

Dependency

Dependency may be defined as the state of reliance of an organism upon objects outside itself for the satisfaction of its needs.

In other words, dependency is the state of striving to obtain support from sources external to the ego. The directiveness of drives is, therefore, outward in order to obtain gratification of needs from objects stimulated by the appropriate acts.

All needs are dependent, even such needs as bowel and bladder tensions, fatigue, and restlessness. These are obviously dependent upon the proper functioning of the sustaining systems of the body, which are external to the ego, in much the same sense as are air, food, and such socially emergent objects as have become need-satisfiers. Bowel and bladder tensions are dependent for their satisfaction upon the proper functioning of the eliminative system; fatigue, upon the functioning of the neurohumoral system; and restlessness upon the proper functioning of the respiratory, circulatory, and nervous systems. It is the business of the ego, as Freud says, to discover "the most favorable and least perilous method of obtaining satisfaction, taking the external world into account."[19]

Expression

Every tension constitutes a need which requires to be satisfied. From the earliest age all needs are made known by some expressive act. Within the limits set by the organism's capacities such acts may take any form. Vocal expression is one of the earliest and most consistent forms which such acts take. It is through this form of expression that the infant learns of his ability to make an impression upon the world outside him, to stimulate others to recognize his needs. The development of speech comes about as rapidly as it does because it is so highly rewarded. Speech becomes the most expressive of the acts of which any human being is capable. It is the principal agency through which needs are made known. Muscular acts which produce pleasure-giving vocalizations, or sounds which are identified with pleasure-giving objects, are associated with pleasure and come to be repeated under similar either existing or desired conditions.[20] Speech, at all age levels, is perhaps the greatest of all tension-reducers. In speaking of the physiological tension of general need or general tension giving rise to the urge to expression, it should be obvious that any form of expressive act which leads to "contact" with another object may be experienced by the organism as a communicative act. Infants almost certainly establish such "contacts" with their clothes, the parts of their cribs which they can either touch or see, and their toys. The animistic approach of the child to his world enables him to communicate with inanimate objects of every sort not only by speech, but by touch, and in imagination.

Clearly, if the physiological tensions of nondependency and general need are not the same things they are very closely related. The urge to expression is an urge to be with others, and physical contact or association is but a form of communication. Recognition and the feeling of security or interdependency obviously have the most intimate genetic kinship.

Ian Suttie has pointed out that expression is not merely an outpouring for its own sake, but an overture demanding response from others. It is the absence of this response, he believes, that is the source of all anxiety and rage, whose expression is therefore wholly purposive.[21] Linton has stated that perhaps the most continuously operative of man's psychic (nonvital basic) needs is the need for emotional response from others—not simply behavioral response, but response with positive emotional quality.[22]

The reason for supposing that nondependency and general tension are not the same things is that while it is possible, at least as an adult, to survive without physical contact or association with other human beings, it is doubtful whether it would be possible to survive without being able to express oneself, however elementarily, in some communicative manner. Deaf-mutes as well as isolated children are endowed with such communicative potentialities, and even though they may never be subjected to culturalization, they nevertheless perform communicative acts, however rudimentary. Touching, for example, may be such a rudimentary communicative act, or even hearing the sound of one's own voice. The suggestion is that any act which is conceived by the actor to establish contact with an object (whether that object be oneself or another object) is a communicative act.

Cutaneous Stimulation

The mention of "touching" brings us to the consideration of yet another extremely important nonvital basic need. For all we know it may be a vital basic need, but until that is established one way or another it had best be considered as nonvital. I refer to tactile or cutaneous stimulation.

Whether touch or cutaneous sensibility is the earliest sense to develop we do not know. We do know, however, that in the human fetus as early as the 8-week stage, when the crown–rump length is no more than 25 mm., reflex movements are easily elicited by tactile stimulation with a hair bristle.[23]

It will have been noted that the mothers of many mammals spend a good deal of time after the birth of their young licking or nuzzling them. This is always seen in such domesticated animals as the horse, cow, cat, and dog. The act is popularly described as "washing." The young seem to enjoy being "washed" greatly.[24] However, the universality and invariability of this act in these animals, as well as other considerations, would suggest that a much deeper biological significance is to be attached to this act of licking than simple washing. The evidence indicates that such licking acts as a stimulus to development of the nervous system and thus to the organism as a whole. There is good evidence which indicates that when young nonhuman mammals are removed from the mother before they have been licked they tend to die from what appears to be a functional failure of the gastrointestinal and genitourinary tracts. The suggestion is that the newborn must receive a certain adequate amount of cutaneous stimulation if the proper reflexes are to be mediated to the autonomic nervous system. Failure of such stimulation appears to result in a failure of the autonomic to be properly activated. The manner in which the young of all mammals snuggle and cuddle against the body of the mother and against the bodies of their siblings or any other introduced animal strongly suggests that cutaneous stimulation is an important biological need of the organism.[25]

Since this is a subject which up to the present time has received very little attention we may devote some space to it here.

When one makes inquiries among animal breeders, husbandrymen, veterinarians, and any other persons who have been much associated with lower animals, those who have any positive observations to offer reveal a significant unanimity in the kind of effects they report. The substance of their observations is that if the newborn animal is for some reason unlicked,[26] particularly in the perineal region, it is likely to die of a failure to function of the gastrointestinal and/or the genitourinary system.

Here, then, we have a hint concerning some of the possible functions of cutaneous stimulation. The indication is that such cutaneous stimulation serves in the activation of the gastrointestinal and genitourinary tracts. It would seem that peripheral stimulation of the sensory nerves of the skin constitutes a necessary part of the process of activating the gastrointestinal tract through the connection of the peripheral and sensory nervous systems with the autonomic. It would appear that when cutaneous stimulation is inadequate the autonomic is inadequately stimulated and there is a failure of activation of the gastrointestinal tract.

So far as the genitourinary system is concerned the evidence indicates that this will simply not function in the absence of cutaneous stimulation. The most interesting evidence I have on this point I owe to the kindness of Professor James A. Reyniers of the Laboratories of Bacteriology of the University of Notre Dame. At the Lobund Laboratories at Notre Dame Professor Reyniers and his colleagues have been interested in raising germ-free animals.[27] In the early days of their experiments it was found that the experimental animals apparently died from a functional failure of the genitourinary and gastrointestinal systems. Fortunately, an ex-worker in a zoological garden brought her own experience to bear upon the solution of this problem, advising the Notre Dame group to stroke the genitals of the young animals after each feeding until urination and defecation occurred.[28]

Professor Reyniers writes:

With respect to the constipation problem in hand-reared newborn mammals the following may be of some interest: Rats, mice, rabbits, and those mammals depending upon the mother for sustenance in the early days of life apparently have to be taught to defecate and urinate. In the early period of this work we did not know this and consequently lost our animals. The unstimulated handfed young die with an occlusion of the ureter and a distended bladder. Although we had for years seen mothers licking their young about the genitals I thought that this was a matter largely of cleanliness. On closer observation, however, it appeared that during such stimulation, the young defecated and urinated. Consequently, about twelve years ago, we started to stroke the genitals of the young after each hourly feeding with a wisp of cotton and were able to elicit elimination. From this point on we have had no trouble with this problem.[29]

Motherless kittens, and I doubt not other animals, have been successfully raised by similar means.[30]

The human fetus is capable of urination and defecation *in utero,*[31] and apparently its external genitalia require no external cutaneous stimulation in order to function properly, but whether this is also the case in all other members of the Order Primates, the order of mammals to which man belongs, we do not know.

In 1925 Hammet quite inadvertently found, in the course of a series of surgical experiments, that "gentled" rats—rats which had been stroked and gently handled—were far better operative risks than those which had not been so "gentled." In the ungentled rats he found the picture as a whole to be one of constant high irritability and neuromuscular tension in contrast with the rather friendly behavior of the "gentled" rats. In the "ungentled" series 79 per cent died in parathyroid tetany within 48 hours of thyroparathyroidectomy, whereas only 13 per cent of the "gentled" rats died after the same operation within the same period. The same ratios were maintained when the rats were parathyroidectomized alone. "Ungentled" rats when "gentled" underwent a reduction in mortality rate to zero in the relatively small series studied.[32]

Subsequent experience and observations at the Wistar Institute (where Hammet did his work) have shown that the more rats are handled and petted the better do they seem to thrive in the laboratory situation.[33] More recently Weininger found that rats which had been gentled for 3 weeks for 10 minutes a day following weaning showed a significantly greater mean weight, more activity and less fearful behavior in an open field situation, and sustained, as adults, less physiological damage to the endocrine, cardiovascular, and gastrointestinal systems under prolonged emotional stress than did a comparable group of ungentled controls. Weininger suggests that the physiological damage seen in the heart and vascular system, as well as in the gastrointestinal system, may be considered an end product of the action of the adrenocorticotrophic hormones (ACTH) from the pituitary in releasing hormones from the adrenal cortex. "The relative immunity to stress damage on the part of the gentled animals may, therefore, have resulted from a decreased ACTH output from the pituitary in response to the same alarming situation that also faced the nongentled animals. If this were the case, it could be expected that a comparison of adrenals from gentled and nongentled rats following stress would show the latter to be heavier, after being stimulated by more ACTH output. Such was indeed the case."[34]

Hammet's and Weininger's independent observations indicate something of the possible importance of "gentling" or cutaneous stimulation for the viability of the organism under conditions of stress. The effects recorded are produced through the activities of the neurohumoral system. We may recall here Osler's aphorism: "Taking a lady's hand gives her confidence in her physician."[35] We may also recall the fact that taking almost anyone's hand under conditions of stress is likely to give both the taken and the taker a feeling of greater security by reducing anxiety. Contact has a soothing effect.

The relation between cutaneous stimulation and breathing has received insufficient attention.[36] For several thousand years, at least, it has been known that if the newborn fails to breathe a hearty slap or two on the buttocks or massage or dipping it alternately into warm and cold water will often be sufficient to initiate breathing. It has long been known that a shower of cold water over the nude body causes one to "catch one's breath." Throwing water in the face of a person who has fainted is often sufficient to restore him to consciousness. Cold water stimulates to activity, warm water to relaxation. Similarly with the cutaneous stimulation of cold air and warm air. Most human beings like to have their backs scratched, and most human beings enjoy the soothing effect of having their skin stroked. To stroke a child on the cheek or head is a common act of affection. We stroke people the right way, and rub them the wrong way, we pat them or hit them on the back, and sometimes we get under their skin.

It is probable that the proper development of the respiratory function is to some extent dependent upon the amount and kind of cutaneous stimulation which the infant receives. It is not unlikely that persons who have received inadequate cutaneous stimulation in infancy develop as shallow breathers, and become more susceptible to upper respiratory tract and pulmonary disorders than those who have received adequate cutaneous stimulation. There is some reason to believe that certain types of asthma are, at least in part, due to a lack of early tactile stimulation. There is a high incidence of asthma among persons who as children were early separated from their mothers. Putting one's arm around an asthmatic while he is having an attack may interrupt or alleviate it.

May it not be that the contractions of the uterus during labor represent, in addition to their other vital functions, a series of massive cutaneous stimulations calculated to activate such vital systems as the respiratory, gastrointestinal, and genitourinary? This is a question which can to some extent be answered. Cesarean-delivered and some prematurely born infants ought to throw some light on this. If there have been no or few contractions of the uterus or delivery has been precipitate, the amount of uterine cutaneous stimulation the infant will have undergone will be minimal. According to the present theory such infants should exhibit a higher frequency of respiratory and gastrointestinal difficulties than normally born children. And, indeed, a considerable amount of evidence now exists which tends to support these expectations. The evidence for cesarean-delivered babies, however, remains doubtful, owing to the fact that so few studies have been made on their subsequent development. Meier found that the behavior of infant monkeys delivered by cesarean section was depressed in comparison to normally delivered monkeys, they were less lively, vocalized less, and were less adept at learning an avoidance response (G. W. Meier, "Behavior of Infant Monkeys: Differences Attributable to Mode of Birth," *Science,* vol. 143, 1964, pp. 968-969; see also J. M. Joffe, *Prenatal Determinants of Behavior* [New York: Pergamon Press, 1969], and Ashley Montagu, *Prenatal Influences* [Springfield, Ill.: Charles C. Thomas, 1962]).

Dr. Mary Drillien, we have already seen, found that prematurely born children showed a significantly higher incidence of nasopharyngeal and respiratory troubles than normally born children, and that this difference was especially marked in the first year.[37]

Dr. Mary Shirley found that, among other things, prematurely born children achieve bowel and bladder sphincter control later and with greater difficulty than do children born at term.[38] Both Shirley and Drillien observed that prematures as children presented more frequent and greater feeding problems than children born at term.

These observations suggest the possibility of inadequate cutaneous stimulation playing a role here and, in some cases at least, resulting in a greater susceptibility to infection and disorder of the respiratory and gastrointestinal systems. Margaret Ribble has pointed out that the tactile experiences of the infant may be registered in improved breathing.

> Respiration which is characteristically shallow, unstable and inadequate in the first weeks after birth is definitely stimulated reflexly through sucking and through physical contact with the mother. Infants who do not suck vigorously do not breathe deeply and those who are not held in the arms sufficiently, particularly if they are bottle fed babies, in addition to breathing disturbances often develop gastro-intestinal disorders. They become air-swallowers and develop what is popularly known as colic. They have trouble with elimination or they may vomit. It seems that the tone of the gastro-intestinal tract in this early period depends in some special way on reflex stimulation from the periphery. Thus, the touch of the mother has a definite, biological implication in the regulation of the breathing and nutritive functions of the child.[39]

Love has been defined as the harmony of two souls and the contact of two epidermes. A truth spoken in jest, it hits off at least one fact which is too often overlooked, the contact of epidermes. Cutaneous contact between infant and mother is obviously of some organismic value to the infant. I say "obviously" because it is obvious to anyone who has ever observed an infant snuggling up to its mother's body that it derives pleasurable sensations from that contact. Cutaneous contact between infant and mother usually constitutes the first act of communication between them, and cutaneous contact would seem to be the language which for some time the infant best understands. It may, perhaps, be recalled here not altogether without relevance that it was through the skin that Helen Keller and Laura Bridgman were first reached and through which they learned to communicate with the rest of the world. Perhaps it should also be noted here that the skin and the nervous system are derived from the same embryological blastocystic ectodermal layer. The skin would appear to be the largest and least understood sensory apparatus which the nervous system presents to the external world.

The application of the baby's lips to the mother's nipple and breast is undoubtedly one of the most pleasurable of such early experiences, and much of the cutaneous stimulation which the individual subsequently experiences is largely associated with stimulation of the lips. The lips are, of course, eversions of the oral mucous membranes and are not strictly speaking cutaneous at all—the relationship is, however, close. As is well known, the representation of the lips in the cerebral cortex is simply enormous as compared with other parts of the body. In fear, shock, worry, or weeping, the hand is frequently applied to the lips, as if to secure succor and support, and under conditions of stress persons often go into labored breathing reminiscent of breathing at birth. Stroking, caressing of the skin under such conditions will often serve to restore the sufferer to equilibrium. It is of great interest to observe that paranoics suffering from asthma when in the non-asthmatic paranoid state dislike being touched, but when in the asthmatic state are anxious to be touched.

When a baby is put to nurse at the mother's breast shortly after birth, the involution of the uterus is accelerated, and there is a resulting significant reduction in bleeding.[40]

Lóránd and Asbót have shown that slight stimulation of the nipples in pregnant, parturient, and nursing women results in a marked increase in the contractions of the uterus. Near term the usual slight spontaneous contractions double in intensity, last longer, and continue for some time after the stimulus has been discontinued. In most of the parturients the contractions are only moderately increased. In the nursing woman the contractions are strong, often as painful as during labor.[41]

The benefits which the nursing infant receives from both the sucking and perioral stimulation are seen in the comparative rarity of gastrointestinal disorders in the breast-fed baby as compared with the bottle-fed baby. Further investigation will probably reveal that the breast-fed baby is respiratorily more efficient than the bottle-fed baby.

Human beings do not lick their young, but in all cultures a certain amount of caressing is normally given the infant by the mother. Breast feeding brings the infant into close physical contact with the mother, resulting in much labial and facial tactile stimulation in cultures where infant and mother wear clothes,[42] or total body stimulation where infant and mother habitually remain nude. It is possible that such cultural differences in raiment or nudity in the nursing situation, apart from other incidental nursing practices, have some effect upon the subsequent development of the infant. This is a subject which has thus far received no adequate study. However this may be, the fact is that in all human cultures physical contact between persons plays an important role in their interpersonal relations. Hand-shaking, nose-rubbing, kissing, putting one's arm round another person, holding hands, walking arm-in-arm, nuzzling, and the like, are evidences of affection or friendliness. Avoidance of such acts indicates the withholding of affection or social nonrecognition. In western cultures it is still the practice of well-bred persons to apologize to a stranger whom they may accidentally have touched, and to do so even to a friend or close relative. To establish contact with another constitutes an act of communication, of social recognition. If there has been no formal or other occasion for such social recognition the act is considered out of place. "Touch," Bain has said, "is both the alpha and omega of affection."

Children want to touch everything. It is only gradually that they learn what and when they may or may not touch. There is a strong tendency on the part of human beings to take nothing for certain unless they can touch it. We want "tangible," "palpable" evidence. What we perceive through our other senses as reality we at best take to be nothing more than a good hypothesis subject to confirmation by touch. We believe nothing that we cannot "grasp."

Spurgeon English has stated that love and touch are inseparable and indivisible, that love cannot arise in the human being without touch and sensuous arousal, and that the cooperation necessary for social conformity is not possible without affection and tactile stimulation. What we love we want to touch. The supreme act of touching is the sexual act with its physiological relief of tension through orgasm.[43] Physical proximity insofar as it approximates tactile association tends towards social homeostasis. Separation tends to produce disequilibrium.[44] As English says: "Misunderstandings which arise through wide separation are cleared up on close contact."[45] When people "get together," "into touch," or "contact," they "stroke" each other the right way, when they remain apart they are more likely to "rub" each other the wrong way.

Charlotte Wolff points out that "In protective affection tenderness has a 'tactile' quality, expressed chiefly by cautious and subtle gestures of the hands which satisfy both the pleasure of contact and an unconscious physical curiosity. By touching the object of affection the child gains his first emotional and sensuous knowledge of others."[46]

Tactile stimulation during infancy, and especially during the first months of nursing, is extremely important for the subsequent development of the person. Inadequate stimulation may retard and mar the development of the person in a variety of ways which, though not yet investigated or demonstrated, nevertheless can be conjectured. On the physical level persons who have received insufficient tactile stimulation in infancy are frequently shallow breathers and are more susceptible to disorders of the gastrointestinal and respiratory tracts and possibly the genitourinary tract than those who have received an adequate amount of cutaneous stimulation. Behaviorally it may be that such persons are abnormally preoccupied with securing cutaneous stimulation in all sorts of ways. These are but conjectures about possible relationships which remain to be investigated. Schematically the need for cutaneous stimulation may be analyzed as follows:

			Satisfaction	
Physiological tension	=	*Urge or need to* →	*Which leads to the act of* →	*Homeostasis*
General tension	=	be caressed ⟶	contact ⟶	soothing effect

It is possible that we need to caress, to massage, infants rather more than we have recognized as necessary in the past. If it is true that cutaneous stimulation is a way of communicating with the infant, should not the infant receive more assurance through his skin than he has customarily been given? May it not be that if we massage the skin in infancy it may in many cases later be unnecessary for a physician to massage his psyche?[47]

7 NEEDS, CULTURE, AND VALUES

If there is any harmony between our instinctive preferences as living things and any standards of value established in nature, its basis lies in the organized stuff of life. —EDMUND W. SINNOTT*

THE INTERRELATION OF NEEDS

The primary basic needs and the secondary or nonvital basic needs together form a fully integrated system of the whole functioning organism. Each need represents but an aspect of the functioning of the whole organism. Together these needs represent the drive system of the organism as a whole. Each of the basic needs is, therefore, closely interrelated with every other. It will have been gathered, for example, from the last chapter, that the need to be with others, the need for expression, the need for tactile stimulation, and restlessness, are very closely related to and dovetail with, as it were, one another.

NEEDS AND CULTURE

The basic needs determine sequences of behavior which must be incorporated into every human culture. Given man's peculiar potentialities it may, indeed, be said that the response which he makes to these needs is the basis of all culture. It is the organization of such responses to his basic needs which constitutes the basic structure of every human culture. The organic needs of man set up a sequence of imperative demands which must be met. The manner in which these demands are met constitutes the culture of the group. Man gives a particular, and in different groups a variable, form to his basic responses, and in so doing creates a novel, secondary, or

* Edmund W. Sinnott, *Cell and Psyche, Chapel Hill,* University of North Carolina Press, 1950, p. 85.

artificial environment. That secondary, artificial, or man-made part of the environment is culture. What men do, what they think, and what they make is a broad description of culture. It is novel because it is an environment which is peculiarly human, it is secondary because the biological environment is prior to it, and it is artificial because it is essentially made by man. It is not, however, something separate from man but grows out of the satisfaction of his basic biological needs. The biological responses made to those needs in the process of their satisfaction are cultureless in their basic character. But since cultural factors begin to operate on the human infant from birth with respect to the satisfaction of (responses to) most of his basic needs, it is not for long that those responses remain without cultural content. Nor do the basic needs those responses are calculated to satisfy go altogether unmodified. Specific associations are established between these physiological tensions and the mode of their satisfaction, and these modifications and associations are as much the effects of the process of socialization as is any other form of socially conditioned or canalized behavior.

The Perpetuation of Culture

The cultural environment has to be reproduced and maintained. Its reproduction and maintenance depend upon two primary factors, the physical reproduction of the group and the organized transmission of specific forms of behavior. These processes immediately give rise to other conditions which become necessary forms of behavior if a culture is to maintain itself. Methods of socialization must exist in every culture, and these must exist by mutual agreement. All this at once implies *organization,* arrangements of various sorts for the sanctioning of various forms of behavior.

Before all else man has to live. He must have organized forms of behavior at his disposal which enable him to satisfy all the needs of his organism. Feeding, heating, housing, clothing, and protection from cold, wind, weather, and noxious animals are activities which are dependent upon some form of organized social service or economic organization,[1] as is the maintenance of the culture as a whole.

These primary problems are solved for the individual by organization into cooperative groups, by artifacts, by the development of knowledge, of a sense of value, and of ethics. From all that we know of prehistoric and living man it can safely be said that these are the means by which human beings have always met the demands of their basic needs and those which are derived from them.

Derived Needs and Institutions

The responses which human beings make to their needs, basic and derived, are to a greater or lesser extent cooperative, and it seems fairly clear that the responses in a cooperative group to the basic needs give rise to the derived or socially emergent needs, and these in turn to the responses calculated to satisfy them. In all human societies the form of such responses is determined by the accepted traditional values, the institutions of the group. An institution, then, is an organized circumscribed system of purposeful values, an organized type of activity. In order to achieve any purpose, reach any goal, human beings have to organize. Those segments of experience which they have organized as the system of values or norms by which their behavior shall be regulated constitute their institutions.

Man's institutions are based fundamentally on the satisfaction of his basic needs, though the structure of his institutions is made up of those derived needs which arise out of the cooperative process of satisfying the basic needs. These derived needs have been called, by Malinowski, *instrumental imperatives*—arising out of such types of activity as economic, normative (setting up a norm or standard), educational and political—and *integrative imperatives*—knowledge, religion, and magic.[2] As Malinowski points out, the self-sufficiency of each culture is brought about by the satisfaction of its basic, instrumental, and integrative needs.

The conditions arising from the satisfaction of man's basic needs form the basis of the development of his institutions. It is obvious that the whole sequence of vital functions (function = the satisfaction of an organic need) always operates in a cultural setting, and that the integrative interaction between man and his institutions is what constitutes culture. Those institutions always act through human beings and, as we have said, ultimately arise out of the satisfaction of their basic needs. Thus, the family, courtship regulations, marriage, kinship, and so on, are ultimately traceable to the satisfaction of the sex urge or need. The clan and tribe, age-grades, and systems of classificatory relationship are some of the institutions which arise out of the derived needs which come about in the satisfaction of the basic needs. The satisfaction of hunger gives rise to such institutions as food gathering, hunting, agriculture, food preparation, production, and distribution. Fatigue—to bodily comforts and all that implies by way of clothing, housing, and furniture. Right—to safeguarding protective activities. Pain—to health and hygienic activities. Restlessness—to movement and activity of various sorts. Visceral pressures—to toilet arrangements and stylized forms of behavior commensal with them.

The Plasticity of Needs

Each need is, of course, to some extent modified by culture. Such a statement implies the fact that the basic needs are plastic, that human nature is plastic. And this is the observed fact, for the members of different human groups can learn to make the same responses to their basic needs in a large variety of ways. Such apparently organically based processes as laughter, weeping, sneezing, walking, sleeping, and love-making assume a different character in different cultures. Each culture teaches the satisfaction of needs by different culturally specific forms of activity, so that the *forms* of the responses determined by canalization and conditioning come to vary as between different cultures, and to a lesser extent even between the members of the same culture. This being so, an indispensable approach to the study of personality must consist in the analysis of the specific ways in which the child learns to become a socially integrated being in a particular culture. This will involve not only the study of his culture, but of his family, and the subgroup or subgroups within the culture which have participated in his culturalization. Learning theory, therefore, should constitute a significant area of interest for the student of socialization and personality. Unfortunately, learning theory is in no condition at the present time to be very helpful to the student of socialization and personality, so that what there is to be said on this subject has been relegated to an appendix in this book.

To repeat a statement from Linton, already quoted: "the actual behavior observed will rarely if ever be identical for any two individuals or even for the same individual on two occasions. The variations will tend, however, to cluster about certain norms. The sum total of those norms, together with their interrelations, is taken to constitute the culture of the society."[3] It should be remembered that culture is originally something outside the organism, a processual continuum *into* which the organism is born. Because culture is originally outside the organism it is something which must be learned. By learning the norms of the culture into which it is born the organism becomes a person, and personality, therefore, means the internalization of cultural process in terms of the organization of the unique potentials of the organism for being human. The logic of a culture consists in the sequence of necessary responses which the group has devised to meet its needs, the needs of the parts (its members) and of the whole (the group).

The Cultural Modification of Needs

Under cultural conditions no basic need can ever function as a purely physiological state. Needs function in a culture and culture modifies them. It is evident, therefore, that the vital sequences of behavior, while constituting a very necessary point of departure in the analysis of man as a cultural being, cannot alone, however well analyzed, tell us much about man unless we analyze them in their cultural setting. Each vital sequence has to be considered with reference to the individual, the organized group, the traditional values, norms, and beliefs, and also to the artificial environment in which most of the urges are satisfied. Each sequence, then, is part of a total configuration of events in relation to which it must be considered. Thus, the concept of *need* in its cultural setting becomes the state of the human organism in which culturally and environmentally modified basic physiological urges (which must be satisfied if the organism or the group is to survive) express themselves.

Let us briefly consider something of the variety of ways in which a few selected basic needs are handled in different cultures.

Breathing

Immediately following upon exposure to atmospheric air the newborn's previously unexpanded lungs fill with air and the various changes in pressure which occur at the moment of birth help to initiate the postnatal type of respiratory movements which continue throughout the life of the person. The urge to breathe is so compelling that a three-minute denial of it is often sufficient to cause death. It is the most imperative of all man's basic urges, and the most automatic. The process of learning to breathe is an anxious one. As we have already seen (p. 124), with every breath we take even as adults there is a faint phobic stir. Under conditions of stress many persons go into labored breathing reminiscent of breathing at birth. Under such conditions the person often regresses to fetalized activities and assumes fetal positions. In fear or anxiety one of the first functions to be affected is breathing. Yet in spite of its automaticity breathing or respiration is under voluntary control and under conscious control for short periods of time, as any person who has ever taken singing lessons knows, and for very durable periods of time as every Yogi well knows. This control is actually exerted during the ordinary activities of daily life, such as speaking, swallowing, laughing, blowing, coughing, and sucking. Breathing, indeed, is not simply a physiological process but part of the way in which an organism behaves.

Stertorous breathing probably occurs more frequently among members of the lower classes than it does among those of the upper, just as sipping or rather inspissating one's coffee or soup with an "accent" does. Differences in the rate of breathing and oxygen-combining capacity of the lungs, as Dill has shown, are closely correlated with occupational status.[4] Insofar as breathing serves the function of speech it is utilized in an enormous variety of different ways. Even in the same culture the "tone" of the "voice," the "accent," may be very distinctive of class, rank, caste, and locality. Depth of breathing may be altered by differences in occupational activity, and activities resulting from differences in social status. In such cases the influence of culture is indirect. On the other hand, the modifying action of culture is direct where the various forms and aspects of speech are concerned. The adjustment of deep breathing to performances in oratory, debate, whispering, the utterance of formal statements, the recital of magical formulas, and singing all represent forms of cultural breathing which significantly differ from one another. Malinowski points out that the interaction between magical and religious beliefs and those connected with etiquette and breathing, would supply another co-determinant of behavior to that of physiology in cultures in which the exhalation of breath, especially at close quarters, is regarded as dangerous, impolite, or noxious, while the deep, noisy intake of breath is regarded as a sign of respect or submission.[5]

In the process of developing the power of vocal communication the child learns to control its breathing by conscious effort. Anyone who has ever observed the infinite patience with which the American Indian parent repeats the correct pronunciation of a word, in teaching the child to put the glottal stop in just the right place and to pronounce the vowels clearly, will not need to be told with what effort in the control of breathing man's speech is acquired.

Much earlier than this in many cultures it is highly probable, as Rosenzweig has pointed out, that in addition to its natural tendency to react to unpleasant situations by crying, the infant learns to cry in other, not necessarily unpleasant, situations as a means of commanding attention when its other signals go unheeded.

The common belief that it is natural for a baby to cry when it wants something leads parents to disregard the many other ways in which babies attempt to make their wants known, such as brief lip-licking or lip-sucking, and to *expect* the baby to cry. This practice soon causes the baby to learn that he must cry in order to be understood. The learning process, as Rosenzweig puts it, is as follows:

> In situations of real distress at the beginning of life, the infant cries or screams as an unconditioned response to pain. Ordinarily he then experiences relief, since the attending adult hurries to his aid. In other situations requiring the attention of an adult, the child may emit various *other* unconditioned responses closely related to the need in question. For example, he may smack his lips or protrude his tongue as a signal that food is desired. If, however, the parent fails to respond to this type of signal, the baby soon finds himself in a situation of distress in which crying becomes a natural mode of expression. He yelps and the parent comes. In this way the child learns to substitute for the more direct smacking of the lips—or other comparable response—the response of crying.
>
> Since the parent takes it for granted that the child *has* to cry in order to make his wants known, there is ordinarily no effort on the part of the parent to look for other cues. After a short time the various responses alternative to crying as a means of communication tend to drop out and are superseded by crying as the preferred mode of communication left to the baby.[6]

Hunger

Hunger is satisfied by eating. But *how* one eats, and *what* one eats, and *when* one eats is to a large extent determined by the traditional ways in which these things are done in the group. Among the Australian aborigines anything that is edible is food. Cooking with the use of hot water is unknown. There are no cooking or eating utensils. In France and England certain land snails are regarded as a great delicacy. In America the stomach is outraged at the thought. In the lands bordering the Mediterranean Sea octopus is a common food. In England and America it is only the occasional gourmet who eats it. Though availability and nonavailability has much to do with the food habits of people, it is tradition—the heritage of ideas and practices, and the canalization to which these lead—which is the determining factor.[7] Milk-giving animals are abundant in mongoloid Asia but innumerable Asiatic Mongoloids regard milk as disgusting. Sheep's eyes are regarded as a great delicacy by many Arabs; practically all other sheep-raising peoples discard them. What one may eat is determined according to what the culture holds is palatable, admissible, and ethical. In the satisfaction of his hunger the person is governed by tastes which have largely been influenced by culture, by magical, religious, and hygienic rules relating to the nature and preparation of food. Even the amount of food, the order in which and the times at which the person eats it, and the times when he experiences the need to eat are culturally determined.

The Sex Drive

Sex, in the form of sexual intercourse, is the one basic need the satisfaction of which is not essential for the survival of a particular organism, though it is obviously necessary for the reproduction of the group. Because sex is not necessary for the survival of the organism it would appear to have been endowed with a high pressor effect in all animals, and especially males. The high pressor effect assures the impregnation of a sufficient number of females to ensure the survival of the group. The male is capable of fertilizing a large number of females, the female is capable of being fertilized by only one male; thus, while the female can have only one pregnancy at a time the male can during that period produce a large number of pregnancies. The human male is sexually more easily aroused than the female, and sex plays a more dominant role in his life than it does in that of the female.[8] As Tinbergen puts it, "Since the female carries the eggs for some time, often even after fertilization, and since in so many species the female takes a larger share than the male in feeding and protecting the young, she is the more valuable part of the species' capital. Also, one male can fertilize more than one female, an additional reason why individual males are biologically less valuable than females . . . and this may be the main reason why courtship is so often the concern of the male."[9]

Because of the great importance of the sexual drive it would seem strange that when the organism becomes seriously disordered the first system to break down functionally should be the sexual. It were as if nature protects the living from the burden of offspring for which they would be incapable of caring properly, and protects the offspring from the effects of inadequate care.

Culturally the expression of the sex drives varies from the greatest freedom to the most rigid and puritanical controls.[10] Virtually every possible expression of the sex drive has been culturally influenced by human beings, from variations in the understanding of the meaning of sex, so that in some cultures, and not infrequently in the most "enlightened," some persons have had produced in them a virtual ignorance of the very existence of sex or its significance,[11] while the techniques of lovemaking, under the influence of the sex drive, may differ as the poles apart in different cultures. The techniques of intercourse, for example, customary among some peoples may be completely unknown to others, while what may be taken to be the most obvious and universal forms of sex behavior in some cultures may, in fact be strictly limited to that culture.

Sex is hedged around by some prohibitions in all societies, as in laws concerning incest, abstinences at various times, vows of chastity, celibacy, and so on, but the manner of the expression of these forms of behavior, as in lovemaking, wooing, sexual attraction, and conjugation, differs greatly in different cultures. Similarly, the responses made to fatigue, somnolence, thirst, and restlessness, bladder and colon pressure, and the states of pain and fear are all culturally modified.

Culture, Life, and Death

The basic physiological urges become culturally and environmentally modified; and it is the satisfaction of these modified urges —not the purely physiological urges—upon which the survival of the organism and of the group depends. The importance of this formulation of the facts cannot be too strongly emphasized. The purely physiological urges may be satisfied and yet if the culturally conditioned aspects of one or another of those urges is not satisfied both the individual and eventually the group may break down and even perish. Culture is man's device for increasing the ease and rendering more gratifying the means of satisfying his basic needs. When, for any reason, this particular form of gratification is lost the organism is, as it were, shocked, and presents the appearance of a depression of vital energy which, falling below a certain minimal level, may result in death. The depopulation of many parts of Melanesia[12] and of aboriginal Australia,[13] following the advent of the white man is believed to be due to such a cause. Indeed, there now exists good evidence which indicates that the fertility of populations as of persons can be much influenced by their psychic state.[14]

The phenomenon of "voodoo" death in a healthy adult who believes himself to have been the victim of fatal black magic or of the doom which results from the breaking of some taboo, is a good example of the effect of a fatal depression of vital energy following upon the loss of the sense of gratification in the responses made to the psychic states. Such cases have been examined by Cannon, and his suggestion is that in such instances death is due to shocking emotional stress—to obvious or repressed terror and its depressing effects upon the body as a whole, through excessive activity of the sympatheticoadrenal system. This latter system breaks down, the circulation is affected, the red blood corpuscles separate from the serum and begin to clump, semipermeable membranes become permeable and the serum passes through them to drown the tissues which have already been depleted in their oxygen supply owing to the clumping of the red blood corpuscles. There is thus a failure of the circulation with a consequent failure of vital organs to receive a sufficient supply of oxygen to maintain their functions.[15] The actual physiological changes in the organs of animals exposed to anxiety and alarm-producing conditions have been independently described by Selye, by Weininger, and by Wolff.[16]

Needs and Neurosis

The evidence suggests that a neurosis, in any culture, is a result of the failure of the ego to receive adequate satisfaction of the psychic components of its needs, whether basic or derived. When the child suffers need-deprivation, a disturbance in the state of dynamic equilibrium which exists between his needs is produced. Disharmony is generated. Tensions are maintained which should have been reduced and the organism's steady states are thrown out of balance.[17]

Since the motive forces of the organism's behavior draw their energy from this reservoir of needs, should a blocking of energy intake occur the organism will suffer from disturbed tension or need states. Anxiety will increase, and satisfaction will be sought in some other way. Since, furthermore, it is during childhood[18] that the person usually suffers his severest privations, it is probable that most, even all, neuroses have their origins in the privations and disordered responses made to them by the child during the first six years of his life. The child does not know that it is physiologically relaxing to react to frustration as directly as the situation will allow.[19] Indeed, adults in our culture very rarely learn this.

Man is an open energy system constantly receiving, exchanging, and transforming energy within the larger whole, society, of which he is a part. The social or cultural process is an energy system and social man is an interacting part of that system. In such a system man derives the greater part of his zest for living from his life in society. When he feels that there is no longer any place for him in society, when everyone "cuts him dead," and acts as if he were non-existent, an apathy, a depression is likely to overtake him which will result in some pathological state. As Murray has pointed out, zest is highly correlated with pleasure and activity, apathy with unpleasure and inactivity.[20] These are simply two different states of energy. Society supplies the energy by means of which the person maintains his psychophysical equilibrium, and the form in which this energy is made available and secured is culturally determined. In the course of culturalization the person becomes habituated to receiving his energy in certain forms and his satisfactions consist in the transformation of those energies to his own uses, to the uses of his organism, the satisfaction of his needs. Any substantial variation in the form in which that energy is supplied may render it no longer acceptable to the person, and though he may attempt to utilize it, it will be in an apathetic manner which may cumulatively have a seriously shocking or depressing effect upon him. Hence, it is obvious that satisfaction of physiological urges is not enough; the *form* which those urges have assumed through cultural conditioning must be satisfied if the healthy functioning of the person in his society is to be maintained.

The Culturalization of Needs

Persons who are made to eat food to which they are unaccustomed and which they would not voluntarily eat not only feel unsatisfied after such meals but may even experience a greater or lesser degree of nausea following them. Under such conditions the response to the hunger need is not their own, not that to which they have become habituated; no satisfaction follows and there is no restoration of the organism to equilibrium. Materials for the production of energy have been taken in, but under such unfavorable conditions they may never even get a chance to be partially transformed into energy—they may be vomited. If they do pass through the gastrointestinal tract they may be only partially digested and the amount of energy thus made available will, to varying degrees, be less than usual. Physicochemically some of this energy may be utilized to meet the demands of the physiological urge, but those demands cannot be fully met because the energy has not been properly channeled to it. The deprivation thus suffered and the presence of some energy which has not been properly canalized is a situation which readily leads to more or less serious maladjustment. The surplus energy must find some outlet, and this it may do in a variety of ways. It is in such conditions of disequilibrium that psychosomatic and psychoneurotic disorders frequently have their origin.[21]

Precisely similar states of disequilibrium may result from the inadequacy of the responses made to any of the other needs. Unless, for example, the received canons of sexual attractiveness are satisfied, the partners to a sexual act may obtain little or no gratification from it. In such persons the sex need will not have been satisfied, and among married people may lead not infrequently to a functional sterility with actual failure of ejaculation or even to impotence on the part of the male. The standards of sexual attractiveness are for the most part culturally determined. Lack of sexual attractiveness generally fails to evoke any sexual response. It is not the sexual object but the sexually *attractive* object which evokes the proper response.

This point is fundamental, that it is not the condition but the *culturally* transmuted condition which must do the satisfying: the cultural condition or type of condition to which one has become habituated. Culture has conditioned the form of the urges and the proper responses to them, and the satisfactions are secured in terms of cultural values. But culture is not a response to a specific need but to the integral satisfaction of a series of needs, and no institution can be functionally related to one basic or cultural need alone. Culture is not a molecular, but a molar phenomenon.

Derived Needs

Our next task will be to trace in some detail how these basic needs become socialized. We have now briefly to consider those secondary or more purely cultural needs which arise out of the integral processes of cultural response to the satisfaction of the basic needs. Since these needs are derived from this process they may be called *socially emergent needs* or, following Malinowski, the *derived needs,* cultural needs or cultural imperatives. It is possible that all derived needs are ultimately based on the satisfaction of the basic needs.

Man must cooperate with other men in an economic relation; he must care for and educate the young; and he must implement the means of enforcement in all such activities.

These cultural imperatives and their responses have been synoptically formulated by Malinowski as shown in Table 5.

It is easy to see how these imperatives and responses grow out of the satisfaction of such a basic need, for example, as sex.

The sexual act leads eventually to the birth of a child. The help-

TABLE 5. DERIVED NEEDS

Imperatives	Responses
1. The cultural apparatus of implements and consumers' goods must be produced, used, maintained, and replaced by new production.	1. Economics
2. Human behavior, as regards its technical, customary, legal, or moral prescription must be codified, regulated in action and sanction.	2. Social Control
3. The human material by which every institution is maintained must be renewed, formed, drilled, and provided with full knowledge of tribal tradition.	3. Education
4. Authority within each institution must be defined, equipped with powers, and endowed with means of forceful execution of its orders.	4. Political Organization

lessness of the child necessitates the expenditure of a great deal of time and energy devoted solely to its care. The men and women who have organized in a permanent sexual relationship will have to organize further to provide the infant with special comforts and protection. Domestic activities will have to be put on a new basis, the infant will have to be fed, cleaned, his wants attended to, and he will have to be trained. In this process specialized tasks fall to the lot of each parent, and they share somewhat different kinds of authority. The arrival of the child entails the development of a new relationship with the members of neighboring families and the social (legal) recognition of the new bonds which have been established between the parents and the child. In turn, recognition must be established of the new bonds which have been created by the parents with the group, for the parents now have become responsible to the group for the proper education of the child.

These new obligatory relationships will inevitably arise in all human societies and will, of course, involve the whole series of basic and derived needs.

The economic, social control, educational, and political responses, the responses arising out of the satisfaction of the basic and derived needs, in turn give rise to all or almost all of those cultural responses which we know.

Again, following Malinowski, some of these cultural responses may be stated in the following scheme:

1. Patterns of communication: gestures, language, writing, etc.
2. Material traits:
   a. Food habits and food getting;
   b. Personal care and dress;
   c. Shelter;
   d. Utensils, tools, etc.;
   e. Weapons;
   f. Occupations and industries;
   g. Transportation and travel.
3. Exchange of goods and services: barter, trade, commerce.
4. Forms of property: real and personal.
5. Sex and family patterns:
   a. Marriage and divorce;
   b. Methods of reckoning relationship;
   c. Guardianship;
   d. Inheritance.
6. Societal controls:
   a. Mores;
   b. Public opinion.
7. Government:
   a. Political forms;
   b. Judicial and legal procedures.
8. Religious and magical practices.
9. Mythology and philosophy.
10. Science.
11. Art: carving, painting, drawing, dancing, music, literature, etc.
12. Recreational interests: sports, games, etc.

In the process of socialization the person acquires a knowledge, sufficient for his purposes, of most of these cultural responses. No person, however, with the possible exception of some who live in the simplest societies, ever acquires a knowledge of the whole of his culture. The individual is fitted for participation in his culture as a person and not simply designed to become a mere repository of it. The member of a culture is so equipped that he can, under favorable conditions, become an innovator and thus a modifier of his culture.[22]

If culture enlarges the scope of man's potentialities, it also limits or constrains their development. As Bidney points out, man's self-consciousness "enables him, individually and collectively, to reverse himself and to attempt to reform his ways in accordance with rational requirements. Since culture is the gift of human freedom, man is able to determine, within limits, the direction which the cultural process should take in the light of his experience and aspirations."[23]

Acquired Needs

Any want, any object abstract or concrete, upon which the person sets value can become a need. Anything to which a person becomes habituated can become a need—bridge, tennis, tobacco, alcohol, philosophizing, poetry, a faith in the substance of things to come, reading, writing, in short, almost anything of which one can think. Some of these needs may have an indirect connection with the satisfaction of basic needs, some may not. It may be that most, if not all, needs, no matter how artificial their form, could be shown to have some relationship to the satisfaction of basic needs. Bridge, to take a crass example, like all games is an activity which satisfies the tension of restlessness, a basic need. So far as emotional nonvital basic needs are concerned the game brings the player into association with other persons, it affords him an opportunity to satisfy his need for expression and the desire to obtain social recognition. In such games the desire to excel in competition with others may become the dominant motivation of a person. He may play to satisfy his need to win or excel. He may not even be interested in the normal rivalry of the game or in the persons with whom he plays. Analysis of such a person's behavior, however, will usually reveal the fact that his competitive drive rests upon something much more profound than the simple desire to win. The re-creation of an infantile general state of tension and its relief may be the underlying motivation of which he is unconscious, as is the case with many gamblers.[24] Dostoyevsky's gambling, for example, affords a good illustration of this.[25]

The element of tension in competition may or may not be itself satisfying. Relief or the promise of relief from that tension certainly is.

Needs and Tension Reduction or Increase

Thus far the satisfaction of needs has been discussed in terms of tension-reduction or a return to equilibrium. Such tension-reduction is, indeed, necessary for the survival of the organism. But the organism may obtain satisfaction from the maintenance or increase of tension. The tensions of sex, bowel, and bladder are among the commonest examples of this fact. The tensions of dangerous sports, circus-thrills and the like, of creative work, and speculation constitute further examples of the satisfaction derived from tension. But in all these instances it should be quite obvious that were the tension to be greatly prolonged it would become decidedly unpleasant, adequate or complete satisfaction being possible only when relief from tension is the end effect.

Competition as tension has its satisfying effects, and in the sense of outdoing others is rewarding in terms both of socially approved achievement and the security of one's ego. Competition is an acquired, not an inborn, drive. It will to a large extent depend upon whether the values of his culture are oriented toward cooperation or competition whether the person will develop competitive traits or not.[26] As an ego-value or means of maximizing one's ego competition is to some extent seen in all human cultures, whether men compete to cooperate or conflict with one another. Competition is, however, certainly not a basic need of any kind. Those who claim that competition in man is an inborn drive have not thus far produced any evidence in the least adequate to support their claim.

But to return to the consideration of wants—any wants—as needs.

Whether or not such acquired needs are traceable to the indirect satisfaction of basic needs, it seems clear that such needs are not necessary, in the sense of being necessary for the survival of the person or necessary to the maintenance of his mental health. In this sense, for example, tobacco may be a need, and it may be felt as a necessity, but it never becomes a necessary necessity. It becomes, as Jowett put it years ago, an unnecessary necessity. Survival and mental health are in no way dependent upon the need for tobacco. The satisfaction of such a need may be completely and abruptly terminated with, on the whole, nothing but benefit accruing to the person. In point of fact, smoking in the cultures of the West is a rather complex form of behavior which is largely indulged because it psychically serves the function of specific tension reduction. "Be nonchalant—light a Murad," was an advertising slogan of some years ago which gave explicit recognition to the function of the cigarette as a tension disguiser in certain social situations. Physiologically tobacco increases tension. It is the behavior associated with smoking which reduces tension. In most situations the person who is smoking is no longer at an advantage over the person who is not, for he is now the acknowledgedly weaker character.

Alcohol, on the other hand, is both physiologically and psychically a tension reducer—in fact, the best sedative known to medicine. Poetry and philosophizing are capable of performing the same function for persons who have acquired such needs, just as religion or TV may for others.

As everyone knows, acquired needs, unnecessary necessities, may become drives as strongly motivated as the most pressing of the basic drives, even though from the standpoint of biological survival they are quite unnecessary.

The number of man's acquired or psychic needs is very great, and varies in different cultures. It would be impossible to list those needs here.

Linton names three of what he considers to be man's most outstanding psychic needs. These are: (1) the need for emotional response from other individuals; (2) the need for security; and (3) the need for novelty of experience.[27] It is probable that the need for emotional response and the need for security are really one and the same thing, and that both spring from the dependency need for love. With respect to novelty of experience a doubt may be expressed as to the universality or strength of this need. Somehow there always seems to be a plentiful supply of conservatively minded (psycho-sclerotic) persons who object to novelty in any shape or form. Novelty undoubtedly constitutes a need for many persons, but how frequently it is distributed in any population is a question.

The use of the term "psychic" to describe acquired or emotional nonvital basic needs as distinguished from vital basic needs may, perhaps, be questioned on the ground that the basic needs are themselves largely psychic, even though in their elementary forms they rest on physiological foundations. It has already been pointed out that the basic needs are largely experienced as psychic or culturalized needs, and it is clear that as the person grows the psychic content and ramifications of his basic needs become progressively more complex. The derived needs, as we have already seen, emerge out of the social satisfaction of the basic needs.

Needs Defined

Since all needs possess a high psychic content it would be less confusing to use distinct terms or phrases to distinguish the various large classes of needs from one another. The following definitions are, therefore, suggested.

Vital Basic Need: *Any biological urge or need of the organism which must be satisfied if the individual or the group is to survive.* Examples are the need for oxygen, food, liquid, activity, rest, sleep, bowel and bladder emptying, escape from danger, avoidance of pain, and conjugation.

Emotional (Nonvital) Basic Need: *Any biological urge or need which is not necessary for the physical survival of the organism, but which must be satisfied if the organism is to develop and maintain adequate mental health.* A satisfactory short definition of mental health is the ability to love and the ability to work (Freud). Examples are the need to be loved, the need to love, the need to be with others, communication, and tactile and kinesthetic stimulation.

Derived or Socially Emergent Need: *Any need which arises out of the process of satisfying basic needs, which is not necessary for the physical survival of the organism, and which is not biologically, though it may under certain conditions become socially, necessary for the maintenance of mental health.* Examples are the need for proper clothes, grooming, shelter, the development of skills or the acquisition of knowledge, creative work, etiquette, and religion.

Acquired Need: *Any need which does not arise directly out of the process of satisfying basic needs, which is not necessary for the physical survival of the organism, but which grows out of the person's relation to the derived or socially emergent needs, and is not usually necessary for the maintenance of mental health.*

The acquired needs are, as it were, superimpositions upon the derived needs. The need for shelter, for example, is a derived need, but the desire to decorate one's house in a particular style is an acquired need. The desire to live in a hut, an apartment, or a house is a derived need, but wanting to put a piano in it is an acquired need. The desire to play the piano or listen to someone playing it may indirectly satisfy some basic need, vital or emotional, but it is not a necessary satisfaction. The desire is posterior to a certain kind of organization of derived needs.

Acquired needs are individual, personal, idiosyncratic needs—idiosyncratic in that acquired needs may differ from person to person within the same culture, whereas the derived needs are usually the same for all persons in all cultures, no matter how their form may differ. In the same culture some persons need tobacco, others do not; and so it is for all acquired needs.

Satisfaction of needs makes for health and cooperativeness; frustration of needs for dis-order or dis-ease and hostility, whether the needs be basic, derived, or acquired.[28]

Maslow has distinguished between "lower" and "higher" needs, and has pointed out that the organism itself dictates hierarchies of values. He points out that the basic needs arrange themselves in a fairly definite hierarchy on the basis of the principle of relative potency. For example, the need for safety is stronger than the need for love, because the former dominates the organism when both needs are frustrated. The physiological needs are stronger than the safety needs which are stronger than the love needs, which are stronger than the esteem needs, which are stronger than the idiosyncratic needs for self-actualization.[29] Higher needs are of later evolutionary and ontogenetic development, but they are no less natural than the lower needs. They are, however, less imperative for sheer survival, less urgent subjectively, their gratification produces more desirable subjective results; a higher value is placed upon them than upon "lower" needs, and their gratification has more desirable health, civic, and social consequences, leading to stronger and truer individualism—that is, the individualism which goes with loving mankind most and being most developed indiosyncratically. As Hadley Cantril puts it, our independence increases with our interdependence.[30]

Lower needs are more localized, more tangible, and more limited than higher needs. As Maslow puts it, "Hunger and thirst are much more obviously bodily than is love, which in turn is more so than respect. In addition, lower need satisfiers are much more tangible or observable than are higher need satisfactions. Furthermore, they are more limited in the sense that a smaller quantity of gratifiers is needed to still the need. Only so much food can be eaten, but love, respect, and cognitive satisfactions are almost unlimited."[31] It is essentially because of their development of higher needs that human beings are human. No creature wanting these needs is human. Through their needs human beings create cultures. As Maslow says, culture is not only created for human needs but by them. The difficulty is, however, that the more complex culture becomes the more removed do our cultural responses become from the understanding of the needs they were originally designed to satisfy. In these respects human beings have culturally often achieved the ultimate limits of confusion—as, for example, in the meeting of aggression with aggression, the removal of babies from their mothers after birth, training in competitiveness, and the like. The higher needs, being as weakly expressive as they are, call for a much more sensitive understanding than most cultures, especially of the western world, have yet bestowed upon them.

Needs and Values

Organismal Values

Whatever we experience as a need is valued by us; therefore needs provide the origins of our first values, whether the needs be basic, derived, or acquired, whether they have a strong or a weak pressor effect. Thus it comes about that certain values are biologically based, founded on the basic needs, and it is the organism's conscious experience and judgment of these needs which constitutes their value. As far as the organism is concerned no value is attached to anything unless the organism experiences it as a need and places a value on that need by striving to satisfy it and being satisfied as a consequence of an adequate response. Value does not exist without choice. The basic needs constitute the organism's biologically determined system of choices concerning the nature of the satisfactions it must secure if it is to survive and develop in health. It is more than doubtful whether there is at first any cognitive evaluation of the need; but certainly the organism exhibits, from the first, great interest in the satisfaction of its needs. The organism behaves in striving to attain satisfaction of its needs as if it "considered" such satisfaction desirable. But it is perhaps the unconscious autonomic responses—the "wisdom of the body"—that produce the appearance of evaluation or consideration, without there being, in fact, any active thinking involved.

Needs exist in order to accomplish the purposes of the organism, and the purposes of the organism may be briefly described as the actualization of its potentialities. The organism performs the valuing of responses to its needs in terms of the requirements of those needs. Responses or experiences in relation to the organism's needs are not needed because they are valued, but valued because they are needed. It is only when we develop acquired needs that we begin to need things because we value them.

The human organism at birth is equipped with a biologically determined value system which, on the whole, automatically enables it to choose and to demand what is good for it and to reject what is bad. Needs are biologically incorporated *organismal values* which cause the organism to discriminate and choose certain types of satisfaction in preference to others. It is when the organism is able to think about and evaluate the types and forms of satisfaction of its needs that one may speak of *personal values* as contrasted with organismal values.

It is the orientation and directiveness of the biological needs of the human organism, that is to say, its organismal values, which determine the tendency of the personal values of the person in society, and hence, the tendency of the fundamental social values. In many human societies these tendencies have been greatly obscured by the distortion and overlaying, as it were, of social institutions which run counter to these tendencies.

The basic needs are the primary biological values, and our thinking about those needs are but secondary valuations which may or may not add sharper definition and understanding to our conceptions of them. If the basic needs constitute our primary biological values then the latter are as natural events as are the former. In this way value is brought into the realm of fact. The intrinsic requirements of the organism are its basic needs, and these are its basic psychophysical biological values. Whatever the organism values is a value for it. If some philosophers have distinguished the process of attaching value to an object as distinct from the intrinsic value of the object itself, we may readily agree, but we need not fall into the error of thinking that while the latter is a fact the former is not. Value judgments may differ in the specific materials with which they have to do, but as Dewey points out, one must deny "that as judgments, or in respect to methods of inquiry, test, and verification, value-judgments have any peculiar or unique features."[32] And as Julian Huxley has put it, "It is not true that the nature of things is irrelevant to the interests of man, for the interests of man turn out to be part of the nature of things. Nor is it true that science cannot be concerned with values. Science is a method of inquiry which can be applied in all kinds of fields. In any particular field, it has to deal with the subject matter it finds there. In biology it can do something toward explaining the origins of conscious evolution. But as soon as it is applied to man, it finds values among its data; you cannot either understand or control human affairs without taking them into account. For a science of man, the problem is not whether or not to have anything to do with values, but how to devise satisfactory methods of studying them and discovering how they work."[33]

Basic needs are physiologically given or innate "judgments," as it were, statements of the intrinsic requirednesses or necessities of the organism.[34] These are the organismic values. Many of the person's social values will be built upon and developed out of the organismic values under the stimulation of the social environment. This is not to say that all social values are based on organismic values—they may well be, however indirectly—but this is a matter upon which more research is required.[35] Since the basic needs or organismic values minister to the health and survival of the organism, they can *never* be "wrong," whereas the social needs or values can be and often are wrong because they are so frequently based on erroneous interpretations as to what is "good" and what is "evil" for man. The organismic values are innate givens, the social values are derived or emergent evaluations or socially created needs. There are biogenic and social values.

The Basic Test of Value

The basic test of a value is the extent to which it contributes to the survival of the organism as a healthy and harmonically functioning interdependent whole. Health is the state of being organismically sound: that is, sound according to the requirements of the organism. Health is *the* organismic value, the summation of all the organism's values.[36] A soundly functioning organism is something which has a real existence and whose critical requirements can be investigated. When we can state these criteria of health we shall be describing the organismic values. Insofar as organismic health is concerned—bodily "and" mental health—we can determine by experience, by scientific techniques, what conditions make for health and what make for illness. And we can then say that the conditions which make for health are desirable while those which make for illness or malfunctioning are undesirable. The fact is that by so doing we are simply recognizing the intrinsic requirements, that is, the organismic values, of the organism. In science the test of a value which is not arbitrary is its truth. The criteria of organismic health provide such a test.

An organismic value is a property of the organism which has an existence altogether apart from the process of being valued. This being so it becomes possible to identify and describe values as natural events. It has been said that "what is right is what is right for man's nature." The "rights" of man's nature are the "rights" demanded by his basic needs. The rights demanded by man's basic needs are certain kinds of organismal states which can be produced and developed only by certain kinds of satisfactions, for needs exist not simply to be satisfied but also to provide the bases for the growth and development of the organism. The process of satisfaction is the means by which the organism is stimulated to develop; so that the "rights" of man's nature are the satisfactions which his needs require. A need is a term for the particular requirements of the organism. It is of the utmost importance to note that the need determines the nature of the satisfaction it demands. It is the need, so to speak, which sets the value, the criteria of requiredness, and does the valuing. For such basic needs only certain kinds of experiences, within certain limits, can act as satisfactions. Experience is evaluated by the needs as either satisfying or unsatisfying, with all the gradations between. As Maslow states it, "The requiredness of basic needs differentiates them from all other need gratifiers. The organism itself, out of its own nature, points to an intrinsic range of satisfiers for which no substitute is possible as is the case, for instance, with habitual needs."[37]

If we could know what the criteria of requiredness of the basic needs were, we should be able to say how human beings should be satisfied if they are to develop in full organismic health. It has been said that biological facts have nothing to do with human values, with what *ought* to be. The answer to that assertion is: if it can be shown that there exist certain biological facts, biological functions of the organism, which are constant, and which if treated in one way lead to malfunctioning of the organism, to sickness, and to disoperative behavior, and treated in another way lead to well-being, mental health (the ability to love and the ability to work), and to cooperative behavior, then it could be stated that the biological functions of the organism determine the nature of the values of the world in which it must live, for the words *should* and *must* are here equivalent if the organism is to survive creatively as such. Insofar as we fail to recognize this fact we are in danger of overlooking the only scientific means by which we can discover how we should live.

Professor L. O. Kattsoff, who has independently arrived at similar conclusions, puts it this way:

> If a value is that toward which the individual directs his behavior, and positive values are those goals which are conducive to the health of the individual, then we have a meaningful and effective basis for the "ought." A positive value is one which ought to be encouraged or aimed at, its authority deriving from its relation to the health of the individual. The sanction for violating such a value is ill health—a punishment guaranteed in the sense that it will inevitably follow. So we can declare that an individual *ought* to strive for that which is conducive to his health, though he may or may not do so. If he does not, we then can say that he is doing what he ought not to do.
>
> The concept of the "ought," like the concept of value . . . has its basis in the very structure of the organism. It is, therefore, an absolute basis for any ethics or for any theory of values.[38]

The Context of Value

The context of functioning of our most fundamental values is to be looked for in the structure of the organism's basic needs. Here is to be found the natural calculus of biological values, the values by which men must live if they are to develop in health and survive in creative harmony. The objectivity of these values must be recognized, and they must be studied, for the biological values are the natural systems which indicate the direction in which the organism should travel. At a higher level, the level of socially derived values, values constitute the compasses by which men attempt to steer their course in the world of experience. The organism recognizes certain ends as desirable, and because this is the case we can successfully inquire into the objective constituents of its value system. Its preferences are not arbitrary but are conditioned by its organic requirements. When we examine the objective constituents of value we discover that the need determines the character of the satisfaction, and that satisfactions are satisfactory only to the extent to which they meet the requirements of the need. Furthermore, we find that these biological values are universal, that is to say, all men are born with them, with definite needs for definite satisfactions, which are biologically much the same for all men everywhere. When we speak of needs we imply also satisfactions of a particular need-determined kind; for this reason we should, perhaps, speak of need-satisfactions rather than simply of needs.

Basic Needs as Evaluators

Hart writes, "No thing or event has value as a whole, with all its qualities. It has value only partially. To evaluate an object means to reflect upon its properties in terms of the sustenance and enhancement of our life. What an event does, what consequences follow from its occurrence, these comprise our knowledge of its value. Neither motives nor deeds are good or bad in isolation. Their value depends upon the whole context of events, antecedent and subsequent."[39] Biologically the basic needs may be regarded as evaluators, evaluators which are capable of telling us what the organism requires vastly more efficiently than anything else can do. We must therefore study the consequences to the organism which follow upon certain types of satisfactions offered to it, and upon the basis of the consequences to it determine what constitutes the best satisfactions for the particular need and for the organism as a whole. These needs and their specific satisfactions are biological organismic "goods" and therefore must be considered to be social goods. The healthy society must be so constituted as to make readily available the specific satisfactions which the organism requires in order to develop its potentialities to the full. When fully understood recognition of the "goodness" of human basic needs is inevitable, as is the inevitable abandonment of such erroneous notions as "instinctual drives" which are directed toward destructiveness, hostility, and death. As Maslow points out, from the "bad animal" interpretation of man's "instincts" the misconception followed that civilization and all its institutions are but so many bad-animality-restraining forces.[40] In addition to bearing the physical stigmata of his physiological origins within him, it is often said that man also bears the stigmata of his psychological origins within him, and that these are represented by his "instinctual drives." The only way in which such assertions can be answered is by a thorough study of the nature of human drives under different environmental conditions. Such studies have yet to be conducted, but such evidence as we have at the present time unequivocally and unexceptionally points in the opposite direction, namely, that man's innate drives are all oriented in the direction of goodness, and that "badness" is largely the effect of "bad" environmental conditions. The evidence of psychiatry suggests that what the psychiatrist does for the person whose basic drives have been frustrated and disordered, whose neurosis is an expression in part at least of that disorder, is to relieve him of the factors of deformation and frustration, and to restore him to the ability to act in terms of his undeformed and unfrustrated drives more in keeping with their original nature. When, in the ordinary course of living, we have learned to pay attention to the basic needs of the organism in terms of its requirements the labors of psychiatrists will be reduced to a minimum.

As Braatøy has pointed out, "the most basic rule in personal psychotherapy [is] to detect as best one can the essential needs of the patient and let those needs set the rules."[41]

A psychiatrist, Sol W. Ginsburg, has written that "Values represent our orientation to society and our attitude to human welfare. *In the last analysis, adjustment is a name for the process of living up to a set of values.*"[42] The orientation of the *biological* organism *Homo sapiens* to life is as a reinforcer of satisfactions in terms of love.

In the concept of love we have the scientific criterion by which we can measure the satisfaction or nonsatisfaction of human needs—or what is the same thing, human values.

It has been said that "In an age in which science and rationality are all important, many people are unwilling to accept values simply on the basis of faith or precedent. The lack of any other accepted basis for value judgments may thus result in personal disorientation or social disorganization. This has been one of the major effects of an increasing use of the scientific method."[43] It is to be hoped that such an analysis as we have here attempted may contribute toward the more satisfactory evaluation of values in a scientific manner. The view may be expressed, contrary to Margenau, that ethical codes *can* be extracted from the facts revealed by science. "There is a lack of continuity somewhere as one passes from science, which is a descriptive, explanatory description, to ethics, which is normative. Something else must be introduced."[44]

What must be introduced, of course, is the process of extraction. The scientific facts never speak for themselves, but when we ask them the right questions they are likely to give us the right answers. The question we have to ask of the world of fact in order to secure an answer for the world of value of human beings is: What is it that contributes toward human health and welfare? We must always remember that we have become human because we are the valuing creatures of this earth, because of our ability to transmute facts into values and values into facts. "Goodness" and "right" are constituted by whatever contributes to human welfare, and human welfare consists in the capacity to love others and to be loved by them. As we shall see in the following pages, this is but a short way of saying that goodness consists in realizing one's potentialities for behaving in such a manner as always to confer survival benefits in a creatively enlarging manner upon all our fellow human beings, born and unborn.

8 DEPENDENCY, INTERDEPENDENCY, AND LOVE

Nothing in the world is single,
All things by a law divine
In one another's being mingle—
Why not I with thine?

—PERCY BYSSHE SHELLEY

THE NATURE AND MEANING OF DEPENDENCY

The fundamentally social nature of all living things has its origin in the physiological relationship between parent and offspring which is embraced in the reproductive relationship. In the mammals the maternal and uterine (unborn) organisms are for a time bound together in an interacting association, the uterine organism being entirely *dependent* upon the maternal organism for its sustenance, for the satisfaction of its needs. This process of dependency, as far as we can tell, proceeds largely but by no means entirely, upon a vegetative level.[1] At birth the dependent relationship simply becomes a more externally active process on the part both of the newborn and the maternal organism or its substitute. The dependency of the newborn is a continuation of the dependency of the fetus, a dependency which has its origin in the once inseparable connection between the organism and that other organism out of which it grew.

It is unnecessary to resort to explanations which go beyond what the evidence at present allows, to account for the feeling of dependency and the need for love. Whether a newborn has a feeling of dependency which is sharp and clear-cut, we do not know. It has hungers, needs, and these give rise to or are the states of disturbance or tension in the organism. Such unsteady states, together with the more or less generalized awareness on the part of the organism that it will, following certain motor acts, be restored to a steady state, constitute the conditions necessary for a feeling of dependency. It may legitimately be doubted whether the newborn experiences feelings in terms of anything more than urges, satisfaction, and dissatisfaction. It may also be doubted whether there exists any *distinct* feeling of dependency. It is possible, however, that there exists a generalized, diffused tonal state of the organism which is described most nearly by the word *dependency*. But it must be some time before this diffuse tonal state assumes a more definite form. There is some evidence that this diffuse state never assumes a definite form in the absence of stimulations received from socializing agents. To be dependent means to rely upon some other person or persons for the satisfaction of one's needs. The consciousness of a distinct feeling of dependence cannot be developed in the absence of factors which produce a growing awareness in the infant that practically all his satisfactions are obtained through the responses made to his basic needs by other persons. Such an awareness is, as it were, a precipitate of recurring experiences of cravings which have eventually been satisfied by others, save for whose intervention those cravings would never have been satisfied.

The child is born in dependency, and it also learns that it is dependent. The whole of its social training, however anarchic it may be, teaches it to maintain something of that dependency. Interdependency is the social state. Nondependent individuality is the nonsocial state.

There is good reason to believe that the feeling of helplessness which the child is supposed to experience after birth is a reality, even though it may not be experienced as such, with any sharp definition, for some weeks or even months after birth, just as its feelings of dependency may, during this early period, be of a diffuse and generalized nature. It would seem that the increasing need for love represents the growth and development of a condition originating in the stimulation of the impulses of the diffuse dependency state, impulses which are developed by those who help to give more articulated form to the dependent state by satisfying the child's needs. To have one's needs satisfied is to be loved and at one and the same time to learn to love.

The newborn's appreciation of the stimuli of the external world is already at a significantly developed level. While it has been argued that for the first two weeks or so of his life the newborn is not truly awake, except possibly for brief intervals, in the sense of having a percipient consciousness (a consciousness capable of endowing sensations with meanings, of turning sensations into perceptions), the evidence is now clear that neonates can be conditioned within the first week of life,[2] and there is good evidence of learning in relation to the feeding situation within the first month.[3] There is also good evidence that the fetus is capable of being conditioned *in utero*.[4] In brief, it may be true that the periods of overt activity of the neonate are but blurred half-conscious states, a fuzzy primordium of what will later develop as consciousness; nevertheless it is quite clear that the newborn is capable of learning and registering what it has learned, even though what it has learned may not appear to be overtly enduring or stable. The fact is that an experience has been registered within the dimensions of the mind.

The Registry of Experience

In the responses of the fetus to stimuli of various kinds, and in the peculiar behavioral syndrome of premature babies, we have fair evidence of the registry of experience within the organism. The prematurity syndrome furnishes proof of the fact that the environment is capable of exercising a substantial and constant influence upon the character of the developing personality, when the organism is exposed to that environment at an early developmental age. Whether or not the influence is constant, the point is that the organism is seriously affected by the environment at a premature age, so far as its future behavioral development is concerned. Is it not, therefore, likely that the stimuli to which the fetus responds *in utero* also write their permanent record, which subsequently influences the development of behavior, into the nervous system? And may not such experiences, as Greenacre and Shirley have independently suggested, contribute toward a predisposition to anxiety?[5]

It has, however, been argued that the incomplete development of the central nervous system and its connections with the sense organs, together with the insufficient amount of oxygen circulating in the brain, serve to maintain the fetus during birth in a state which effectively protects it against such shocks as some psychoanalysts postulate. During the birth process the amount of oxygen which reaches the brain is negligible, so that even were the brain well developed it would fail to record, it is urged, even if it could appreciate, the experience of birth.

To these objections reply may be made that the organism is certainly capable of registering the experience of birth if, as we know it to be, it is capable of responding to the stimuli of the birth process. The registry may have no sharply delimited conscious psychic content, although such evidence as we today possess indicates that the physiological changes induced by birth leave their impress upon the nervous system. But whether these changes may be regarded as traumatic cannot with any certainty be said at this time. The indications are that they can.[6]

The so-called "pleasures" and feeling of "security" of intrauterine existence, the relation of these to the security-seeking patterns of later life, the "anxiety" state originally produced by the "birth trauma," and the relation of the latter to various phobias are no longer in the category of bright speculations to be relegated to the department of unsubstantiated hypotheses. These concepts now occupy the status of good hypotheses which have received appreciable support from different sources, but which require further investigation and verification before they can be accepted as facts.

The reference to phobias recalls the fact that Freud has himself criticized Rank's explanation of child phobias (e.g., fear of small animals as they vanish into or emerge from holes), as based on a birth impression on the ground "that it rests on a presupposition that the infant has definite sense impressions, especially those of a visual nature" at birth, adding "it is not credible that the child at birth has anything beyond tactile and general sensibility." The newborn, it would seem, has a great deal more than that, but however that may be it is seriously to be doubted whether more than a small fraction of children have the least fear of small animals entering or emerging from holes. Infantile anxiety typically "occurs when the child is left alone *in a dark room* (usually the bedroom at bed-time)." According to Rank, "This situation reminds the child, who still is close to the experience of the primal trauma, of the womb situation—with the important difference that the child is now consciously separated from the mother, whose womb is only 'symbolically' replaced by the dark room or warm bed."[7] Freud pointed out, and Rank agreed, that the anxiety disappears as soon as the child becomes conscious of the existence (nearness) of the loved person (contact, voice, etc.).[8] "Every pleasure," Rank asserts, "has as its final aim the re-establishment of the intrauterine primal pleasure."[9] In other words, the person seeks to re-establish the state of pleasure which was his *before he was* separated from the mother. Freud, we think, missed the point when he objected that most children feared the dark. Of course they did, during the nineteenth century. Modern children are much less frequently affected by such fears. With the development of more enlightened means of handling children's bedtime, and the elimination of the horrifying bedtime stories which so often turned the dark into a nightmare, modern children tend to find the dark objectionable only because it puts a period to their day. When children fear the dark it is highly probably the case that they have been taught to fear it.

The fact is that all healthy children enjoy a certain amount of solitude and of darkness, and certainly every healthy person requires some of both. However, to many persons darkness means separation, loss of contact, insecurity, and privation of love; solitude usually having the same meaning for them. Such persons do not enjoy being alone in the dark for any length of time. To them solitude is rarely welcome, while darkness is welcome only as a condition of sleep. To the insecure darkness is anxiety-producing, while light is safe.

On the other hand, to the secure darkness is relaxing while light is adventuresome and stimulating.

In discussing the transition between prenatal and postnatal life several matters of much interest and importance have been touched upon which would bear further discussion here. The first of these is the concept of dependency, its relation to the development of love and the social development of the person. While these matters might be more properly dealt with later, it will be profitable to say a few words at this point. It will in a sense provide a summary of our discussion and direction for the road along which we are yet to travel.

Dependency, Love, and the Development of the Person

Dependency may be defined as the relation of the organism to the conditions which support it. The state of dependency during intrauterine life is largely physiological. There is some evidence that the fetus probably has a sort of generalized awareness of that dependency. With birth the state of dependency is continued in a physiologically altered form for some two or three weeks, and there is an increasing growth in awareness during this period. During the neonatal period the organism is dominantly engaged in the process of adjusting itself to a new environment. Before the fourth week of life is over the infant makes its first personal-social responses in the form of tactually perceptible postural adjustment when taken up, and of a selective regard for the face. It pays attention to sound and to moving objects, and it has differential cries for discomfort, pain, and hunger. Its subsequent development is one of differentiation, enlargement of consciousness and the development in it of a greater specificity of its potentialities.[10] In all this it is assisted by the maturation of its nervous system and the stimulation it receives from those who care for it.

The Cooperative Benefits of Interdependency and Dependency at Birth

The interdependency and dependency naturally implicit in the cooperative relationship between infant and mother at birth are profoundly more significant than has hitherto been realized. During the last few years it has been discovered that immediately after birth the greatest physiological and psychological benefits are conferred upon the mother by the infant and by the mother upon the infant *if the cooperative relationship is permitted to follow its natural course*. In our trained incapacity we have become accustomed to handling the childbirth situation by separating mother and infant, thus deliberately interrupting the biological benefits which they would otherwise normally confer upon one another.[11] Throughout the whole mammalian group there is not a single example to be found in which the young are separated from the mother at birth, and yet this is what we as civilized members of the western world have been doing for a long time. Things were a great deal better before women started going to hospitals to have their babies. Today almost all American women have their babies in hospitals. Today, also, there is good reason to believe that the advantages of having the baby at home far exceed any to be gained, except in the relatively few abnormal cases, from having the baby in the hospital. The belief that it is more dangerous to have the baby at home than it is in the hospital is contrary to the truth. For example, during the period from January 1952 to July 1954 the records of the Chicago Maternity Center show that home deliveries amounted to more than 8,339 without the death of a single mother. Of some 300 pathological cases requiring hospitalization, three proved fatal. This is a far better record than the average hospital can show.[12] In America we are inclined to forget that in the rest of the civilized world most deliveries are performed by midwives and take place in the home. The advent of "rooming-in," where the maternity arrangements in the hospital are such as to keep mother and baby in the same room, constitutes the beginning recognition of the importance of not separating mother and child. Under less "civilized" conditions the baby's first cry seems to act as a signal to the mother that the child needs to be nursed at the breast. As already stated, immediate nursing at the breast results in changes in the mother which have the most beneficial effects upon her. In the first place, within a few minutes of the commencement of nursing the uterus begins to contract and to return to its normal size and state, while without immediate nursing the uterus practically never returns to normal size. In the second place the hemorrhage which is associated with delivery of the baby is reduced to a minimum as a consequence of the contracted uterus induced by the nursing and probably by accompanying psychological factors.[13] Third, afterpains are either reduced to a minimum or entirely unfelt. The baby, in turn, receives stimulations through contact with the mother's body which serve the important function of further activating its gastrointestinal and genitourinary tracts. Such nursing babies, unlike bottle-fed babies, rarely develop diarrhea or other gastrointestinal disturbances (unless the mother's diet has been high in carbohydrates). Through its sucking the baby receives much needed nourishment and stimulations in the oral and perioral regions, which together with those which it receives from the mother's body activate every sustaining system of the body: the alimentary, the endocrine, nervous, the genitourinary, and particularly the respiratory system. It is important, therefore, here as elsewhere, to remember that what Nature hath brought together no one should ever take it upon themselves to put asunder—unless there exist good reasons for doing so.

The care of the child should begin with caring for the child. The relations between mother and infant during the first few days following birth are of the utmost importance for each of them. The newborn needs the presence of a loving, solicitous voice, the warmth and softness of touch of its mother's body. Bevan-Brown considers the infant's experiences at the breast of fundamental importance for its subsequent healthy mental development. The sucking, tactile, oral, esophageal, and gastric sensations which it experiences are highly significant for its development of a feeling of security. "The infant must be in close association with the mother for the first hours, days, weeks of life, so that whenever he wakes he has the feeling that she is near. Such an association makes the closest possible approximation to his intrauterine security and placental attachment, which has just been broken."[14] If birth is in any way a traumatic experience, then surely what the newborn requires is something a little more calculated to inspire a feeling of being wanted than what it at present so frequently receives. In short, everything possible should be done to reassure the infant that it is among friends, and that although the journey into this world may have been a rough one, it has entered into a secure haven which gives promise of better things to come.

The Importance of the Mother

The first fulfillment of the infant's drive to receive love from the mother constitutes a fundamental cooperative act. As Alfred Adler has pointed out, "the first act of a new-born child—drinking from the mother's breast—is co-operation, and is as pleasant for the mother as for the child."[15] There is the tactile stimulation about the lips and face, the tongue, the oral cavity, and the liquid and associated stimulations of the gastrointestinal tract. Here, in this act, is the first step in the development of the sense of contact with another person—a pleasure-giving person. Adler comments:

> The child's inclination to co-operation is challenged from the very first day. The immense importance of the mother in this respect can be clearly recognized. She stands on the threshold of the development of social feeling. The biological heritage of social feeling is entrusted to her charge. She can strengthen or hinder contact by the help she gives the child in little things, in bathing him, in providing all that a helpless infant is in need of. Her relations with the child, her knowledge, and her aptitude are decisive factors. . . . It may readily be accepted that contact with the mother is of the highest importance for the development of human social feeling. . . . *We probably owe to the maternal sense of contact the largest part of human social feeling, and along with it the essential continuance of human civilization.*[16]

One of Adler's students, M. Bevan-Brown, has written a valuable book the main theme of which is the importance of breast-feeding for subsequent mental—and physical—health.[17] "It is obvious," writes Bevan-Brown, "that a child's mother is, or should be, the first person in the world with whom he associates. She represents the first *personal* relationship, the first *social* relationship, the first *sensuous* relationship . . . it would be reasonable to assume that this relationship, being the first, sets the pattern of all subsequent relationships."[18]

Inadequate Mothering and Dis-ease

Frustration of the drives to receive love from the mother (not necessarily the biological mother, a mother-surrogate will do) at this period not only produces anxiety in the infant, rage and despair, but also a retention of unexpressed hunger for maternal mother love which may then find an outlet through any one of a number of *dis*-eases and especially through gastrointestinal *dis*-ease.[19] Similarly, if the infant's cries for attention remain unanswered the unsatisfied tensions may express themselves through the bronchial tree in the form of asthma or other respiratory disorders.[20] Kezur and his co-workers, in a study of twenty-five women with peptic ulcers, found that all of them exhibited profound and overt personality disorders. The majority had been rejected by the mother and had turned to the father for support. Ulcer symptoms were precipitated when the supporting figure failed them.[21] Such responses may be regarded as constituting involuntary emergency discharges through the organ-systems involved in the frustration of the need. The energies which should have been discharged outward are now discharged inward.[22] The affection of the organ or organ-systems becomes an affect-equivalent for the original gratification sought by the organism. A large proportion of, if not all, neuroses and psychosomatic disorders may be so explained—their foundations being laid within the first six years of life. In the infant, as in the human being at any age, good health depends upon the adequate satisfaction of basic needs and upon the ability to discharge anger externally when the needs are not satisfied.[23]

"The somatization of tension" is, apparently, a frequent occurrence in children who have undergone severe emotional deprivations. Bettelheim and Sylvester, who have described many such "somatizations" in children, have pointed out that such symptoms may disappear in the course of psychotherapy "without ever having become the specific object of the analytic process. They become unnecessary when the patient grows less anxious with his increasing ability to communicate and therefore acquires more adequate forms of expression."[24] Interestingly enough, as such children undergo reintegration the appearance of new symptoms and their eventual disappearance are seen to represent characteristic steps in the integrative process of their readjustment.

There can be little doubt that the physiological components of the emotional needs of the child must receive the proper stimulations if adequate somatic development is to occur. The subtle alchemy by which love is transmuted in the child into what it most requires for somatic as well as psychic development may, at the moment, be obscure, but that that "alchemical" process occurs there can no longer be the least doubt.

Social Binding and the Fallacy of Individuality

The process of caring for the infant consists principally in satisfying its needs. This process represents the commencement of the socialization of the person, the preparation of the person for participation in the social group. To telescope much into a few words, as the child matures and the socializing process continues, with its frustrations as well as its satisfactions, the child becomes more and more firmly bound to the socializing agent, more and more dependent rather than more free, and this social binding continues throughout life. This view of the development of the person cannot be too strongly emphasized. Its implications are of the first order of importance. The conventional view of the person in the socializing process as developing to greater and greater individuality is a seriously misleading one. Of course, every person has a unique personality in the sense that it is never identically like that of any other person, and the differences between personalities are important and tend to become more distinct with age. This is something to be thankful for. But it must be realized that every one of these differences has developed under the influence of socializing factors, and that were it not for the creative action of those socializing factors, those functional-structural differences which characterize each person would not exist.

Every person is socially bound to the group in which he has been socialized. In this sense the "individual" is a myth. From the point of view of the social situation there are no individuals, except as abstracted biological entities or for the quantitative purposes of a census. Even physically and physiologically it is doubtful whether the "individual" has a separate existence in any but an arbitrary sense. Have we not in the term "individual" created separateness where separateness does not exist—where, in fact, relatedness is the true condition? Certainly individualization in man exceeds that which is ever attained by any other animal, but it is an individualization which integratively takes place more fully in relation to the group than in any other living creature. A creature apart from a social group is nothing but an organic being. The member of a human social group is a person, a personality developed under the molding influence of social interstimulation. The person is a set of social interrelationships. As Bogardus has put it, "As a result of intersocial stimulation he moves up from the biological level. The interstimulation that occurs between him and members of the group, not as mere individuals but as persons, explains him more than any other method of approach can do."[25] "It makes no sense," writes Sullivan, "to think of ourselves as 'individual,' 'separate,' capable of anything like definitive description in isolation . . . the notion is just beside the point."[26]

Says Whitehead, "The individual thing is necessarily a modification of its environment, and cannot be understood in disjunction."[27] Both the fallacy of absolute individuals and the excess of individualism, writes Whitehead, are vicious. And as Gutkind puts it, "To think in terms of absolute individuals—absolute individuals are but things—is the outgrowth of our obsession with acquisitive urges. To think in terms of relations is human and paves the way toward the solidarity of mankind."[28] Child writes as follows: "The individual represents primarily a reaction pattern in a protoplasm of a certain constitution and the kind of individual that develops in a particular case depends not only upon the gradient pattern but upon the constitution of the protoplasm in which it occurs. In one kind of protoplasm, for example, the most active region gives rise to a circle of tentacles and a mouth, in another it develops a head, in still another into a growing tip."[29] So, too, the kind of person that develops in a particular case depends not only upon the gradient pattern of his particular inherent potentialities but upon the constitution of the social groups in which his development occurs. The responses which his socializers cause him to make to the stimuli they offer become the habits which form the particular person. The important point to recognize is that the "individual" represents primarily a reaction pattern which makes him a *part* of a whole of which he always remains a part. It is the unhealthy person who regards himself as the whole and everyone and everything else as the part. A person is the product of a field of interactive biological and social forces, and every person constitutes a part of that field all his life.

The so-called "individualist" is no more an individualist than is the soldier under command. Whatever each does he does because he has been subordinated to imperatives which, in each case, are functions of his cultural conditioning. Each acts as he does because he is the end product of certain historically conditioned processes. Each acts as he does not because he is an independent individual, but because he is a dependent person, bound to his social group by ties which cause him to desire to maintain his relationships according to the requirements, in each case, sanctioned and demanded by the group. This does not mean that the person is without free will. Free will the person most certainly has in the sense of being able to achieve ends or purposes. But it is a will that functions largely within the limits and conditions determined by his own past experience within the culture of his own social group. The "spontaneous" conduct of the person is seldom *de novo,* for however seemingly new and original it may appear to be it is usually conduct based on and influenced by models which have been learned in a particular social group. In brief, the person constitutes an interdependent system of social relationships, and it is by abstraction alone that this system may be recognized as a unit.

There is no suggestion intended that the group is superior to the person. The obligation of the group towards the person is to do everything in its power to maximize his potentialities and preserve his integrity as a person. The obligation of the person to the group is to contribute to this development of himself and to that of other persons. In the ultimate analysis the person is not to be conceived as living for the group, or the group solely for the person; each serves the needs of the other. When this has been said it is necessary to add that this reciprocity is best served by the service of the group—and the group consists of socially related persons—to the person. In this way service to the person leads to service to the group. In the profoundest sense of the word, greatness, both for the group and for the person, consists in service.

The Soldier and The Group

The recognition of the importance of this dependence, this precarious dependence, of one person upon another has recently, perhaps, been best illustrated in the findings concerning what used to be called "shell shock" and is today known as combat exhaustion. It has been known to military observers for some time that some combat units suffer fewer psychiatric casualties than others, and this in spite of an equal or a greater degree of battle stress. In the battle situation there is an omnipresent conscious or unconscious fear of death. This fear, it has been discovered, exists in direct proportion to the confidence which the soldier has in his platoon or company, the confidence that his comrades are "all in there together" with him and will support him in his need. During the training period the soldier gains this confidence in the protective functioning of his unit, his group. Colonel Albert J. Glass of the United States Army Medical Corps who reports these findings, writes, "Even the timid soldier comes to feel secure by being in a powerful group and often assumes the aggressive attitude of the organization. . . ."[30] "In brief, the group offers protection against fear to the soldier and provides for his emotional needs, but demands that he give up personal desires and selfish considerations. In its simplest form, group identification is a matter of 'united we stand, divided we fall.' "[31]

Glass points out that "When men fight together and share common tribulations, they become bound by the closest of emotional ties. This affection, which is akin to love, serves to lessen concern for one's own life, thereby decreasing the crippling subjective sensation of fear." The commonness of such an emotional bond has been demonstrated by numerous instances in which soldiers have unhesitatingly performed dangerous and heroic deeds to save their friends, while the close kinship of men forged in battle is responsible for instances in which soldiers prematurely leave the hospital or a rear assignment to rejoin their comrades. Glass concludes, "A member of an adequately led combat unit has an increased resistance to mental breakdown because of the emotional and actual support provided by the group. The failure of such an environmental support is the major cause of combat exhaustion."

To put it plainly: what the soldier must have is the knowledge that he is supported, loved, that he is a recognized and valued part of the group. By virtue of his position the soldier is more precariously dependent upon his fellows than most men are in the normal situations of life. His situation is reminiscent of the maternal-infant dependent relationship, for he is dependent upon his comrades for his very life. What his experience as a soldier so forcefully underscores is that life and love are closely interknit.[32]

Love Described Rather Than Defined

We have spoken much of love but have not yet defined it. This is so because, as has already been pointed out, definitions are meaningful only at the end of an inquiry. However, at this juncture we may not altogether inappropriately tentatively offer a general description of love.

Love may be described as the process of communicating to another that you are "all for" them, that you will support them, not merely that you will accept them, but that you are actively for them. By being "all for" is meant, first, that one is *actively interested* in the well-being of the other, that one is willing to do whatever one can to support him in his needs and further his interests and development *as a human being,* that one is actively interested in him this way not only for his sake but for ours. To love, one must be emotionally involved with the loved one—unemotional love is *not* love, whatever else it may be—and this emotional involvement must be conveyed to the loved one. To love is to be, and to convey the feeling of being, absorbed in another. To love is to confer developmental and survival benefits upon another. Since human beings are so perilously involved with life, love is the assurance, the reassurance, that we convey to them that we are positively for them and that they need have no fear, that they can *depend* upon us, that we will not fail them, and that we are there not only standing by ready to serve, but always will be. The greatest treason that one human being can commit against another is to fail him when he most needs you, and human beings need their fellow men, not merely some of the time but all of the time.

Foote has defined love as "that relationship between one person and another which is most conducive to the optimal development of both. The optimal development is to be measured in the growth in competence in interpersonal relations."[33]

Sullivan writes, "When the satisfaction or the security of another person becomes as significant to one as is one's own satisfaction or security, then the state of love exists."[34] Fromm writes, "the essence of love is to 'labor' for something and 'to make something grow.' . . . To love a person productively implies to care and to feel responsible for his life, not only for his physical existence but for the growth and development of all his powers."[35] Love, writes Suttie, seeks *"any state of responsiveness* with others as its goal. Sociability I consider as a need for love. . . ."[36]

The Person, Cooperation, and Freedom

Leo Loeb has remarked, "In consequence of the more and more intricate interaction between environment and psychical-social individuality, a separation between individuality and environment, especially the social environment, becomes impossible."[37] And that is the truth which must for ever shatter what may be called the biologistic fallacy, the pathetic fallacy which maintains that man is essentially a function of his genes. The biologically exclusive sacredness of the individual is a chimera not only for man but for all other animal groups. The biology of an earlier day may have cried "the individual for itself." To this the twentieth century's greatest physiologist, the late Sir Charles Sherrington, has made the proper reply in one of the outstanding books of our time.

> The individual? What are the most successful individuals which Life has to show? The multi-cellular. And what has gone to their making? The multi-cellular organism is in itself a variant from the perennial antagonism of cell and cell. Instead of that eternal antagonism it is a making use of relatedness to bind cell to cell for co-operation. The multi-cellular organism stood for a change, in so far, from conflict between cell and cell to harmony between cell and cell. Its coming was, we know now, pregnant with an immense advance for the whole future of life upon the globe. It was potential of the present success of living forms upon the planet. Implicit in it was for one thing the emergence of recognizable mind. It was among the many-celled organisms that recognizable mind first appeared. It is surely more than mere analogy to liken to those small beginnings of multi-cellular life of millions of years ago the slender beginnings of altruism today. Evolution has constantly dealt with the relation between physical and mental as more than mere analogy. The bond of cohesion now arising instead of being as then one of material contact and interchange between related cell-lives is in its nature mental. It is a projection of the self by sympathy with other life into organismal situations besides its immediate own. It is altruism as passion. It marks, we may think, at the present time the climax of mind.[38]

To bind cell to cell for cooperation by projection of the self in sympathy with other organisms, that is the essence of social life. But no cell is more intricately bound to another than is man to his fellows, to his social group. The binding of the person to his group represents, in fact, a loss of *individual* freedom and a gain in *personal* freedom through increasing identification with the social group—an identification in which the wholeness of the person is increased and preserved only because it is a functioning interactive part of a greater whole, society. In this process the consciousness of self may actually become intensified, the sense of personal identity may become even more vivid, and one's bondage to one's society more firmly established than ever. "Individuation," as the development of personal identity, is neither the contrary nor the contradictory of social identification; it *is* social identification.

As Robert Frost has said:

> "Men work together," I told him from the heart,
> "Whether they work together or apart."

This view of the relationship of man to his fellow men in society does not mean that the social process turns men into automata. Even in the most totalitarian of states, Nazi Germany and Soviet Russia, men have not been turned into machines, and however much like automata they may have appeared and appear, they have been far from being so, they have still remained human beings, misguided human beings. And that is the point. It is possible to misguide human beings, and human beings are constantly in danger of being so misguided. The danger is such that it would, in fact, be possible to make at least reasonable facsimiles of automata out of human beings.[39] In virtue of the fact that man is behaviorally so malleable a creature, he can be molded, within the limits of being human, to almost any possible behavioral form. Because this is so, because of the danger of the "insectification" of mankind, as someone has termed it, we must make quite certain that there is nothing in our actions or in our ideas which might lead to the debasement of man. More positively, we must recognize what it is that requires to be done. To recognize that men are inextricably bound to each other, and that the will which they have as persons functions strictly within the limits determined by the pattern of the social group, constitutes reason for alarm as well as for hope. Alarm, because man is capable of extreme and fatal confusions, and must therefore be constantly on guard against these, and hope because he is actually capable of discovering truths which can teach him to live in fruitful and creative harmony with himself and his fellow men. This alarm may be recognized as vigilance, but is more accurately described by the term anxiety. A certain amount of anxiety accompanies the expression of all needs, and when these needs are perceived as the total functioning of the organism,[40] they are seen to constitute the one great need: the need to be loved *and* the need to love.

It is necessary to be anxious, to be vigilant concerning one's needs and the manner in which they are to be satisfied. But this does not mean that one has to be constantly worrying about them, any more than one needs to worry about being dry in order to satisfy one's need for water. It does, however, mean that one must be alert to all possible changes in the environment, for the environment is part of ourselves, as we are part of it. Finally, it means that it is imperatively necessary for man to discover the requirements which must be fulfilled if he is to live in harmony with himself and his fellow men—with his total environment. It should always be remembered that separation between the organism and its environment is, again, an arbitrary act.[41]

Culture and Neurosis

The individual—the set of interrelated physical and physiological functions—becomes a person with a distinctive identity only through the process of socialization—the process of becoming identified with a social group. Dissociations such as are implied in the phrases "the self in conflict with society," "man against society," imply a false separation of conditions. Society is made up of interacting selves, of men; it is human beings in interaction. The conditions of conflict which arise in human beings do not normally originate from within them, from their organic states, but from those social conditions which fail to satisfy their needs, and exercise a distorting effect upon them. In this sense a neurosis may be produced which is a result of a disorder of some part of his social experience to which the person has been unable to adjust himself.[42] In our society, for example, there are conflicting and mutually irreconcilable institutions which put too great a strain upon the adaptive capacities of most persons—the Christian ethic of love and the business ethic of competition or "free enterprise," for example.[43]

The importance of institutions in determining the content and structure of neuroses is clearly seen in those cases in which the structure of the culture is such as to omit any institutionalization of certain forms of behavior. In such cultures neuroses of certain kinds never occur, whereas in cultures presenting such institutions neurotic forms of behavior with specific reference to these institutions do occur. For example, shamanism and possession are forms of behavior which occur wherever beliefs in the supernatural and the ability of supernatural powers to take possession of certain persons are strongly held. Where such beliefs do not exist or are weakly developed, shamanism does not occur. In medieval Europe when such beliefs were the rule witchcraft and possession were common phenomena. With the decline in the belief in the supernatural, witches and possession have all but disappeared in Europe. In other lands such beliefs have been replaced by counterparts which fit more satisfactorily into the existing cultural structure—such, for example, as the hunting of "communists," anti-semitism, and racism.

The relation between culture and neurosis is significant. On Okinawa, for example, Moloney found out of a population of 450,000 souls that only two persons had become psychiatric casualties after four months of siege and heavy bombardment. He found mental health to be the rule, and was able to determine that the probabilities were high that the extraordinary care and affection which the Okinawans bestow upon their children is related to their mental health as adults.[44] The remarkable mental health of such nonliterate peoples as the Australian aborigines, the Eskimo, the peoples of many coral Pacific atolls, and many American Indian peoples appears to be highly correlated with their permissive child-rearing practices.[45]

Persons, that is to say socialized organisms of the species *Homo sapiens,* come into being only through social interactions. "They are differentiations within the social field of relations. The group, therefore, is genetically prior to personality."[46]

In short, the physiological dependency of the fetus and the newborn becomes, in society, a socially organized dependency, a social dependency in which the interacting person finds the meaning of his life in his relations with other persons and their thoughts and activities. He becomes, as Rank says, a collective being.[47] Unheeded, the socially dependent adult falls into an apathy which may lead to death. As Erich Fromm has put it, "Unless [the person feels that he belongs] somewhere, unless his life has some meaning and direction, he would feel like a particle of dust and be overcome by his individual insignificance. He would not be able to relate himself to any system which would give meaning and direction to his life, he would be filled with doubt and this doubt eventually would paralyze his ability to act—that is, to live."[48]

Dependency and Culture

John Fiske originally, and many others since, have pointed out that the long period of dependency which is characteristic of the human infant generates social conditions which lead to the peculiar developments of human culture. The importance of this lengthy period of dependence cannot be overemphasized, but the emphasis can and often has been put on the wrong places.[49] Were the anthropoid apes characterized by a period of dependent infancy which was ten times as long as that of man's, they would still not develop anything resembling human culture, since they do not possess the necessary neuropsychic potentialities.[50] The length of the infancy dependency period in the absence of such potentialities has a limited significance for the development of culture. But once granted those potentialities, what we know as human society is inevitable.

This is not to say that if the human infant were so constructed as to be able to learn to walk, think, talk, and care for itself within a few weeks after birth, human culture would not have developed. It would most certainly have done so, and it is equally certain that the human personality would be an appreciably different thing from what it is today in all human beings. But by virtue of such an elimination of the socialization process it is also likely that societies would assume a somewhat atomistic form. However this conjecture may be, the fact is that the prolonged period of infant dependency produces interactive behavior of a kind which within the first two years or so of the child's life determines the primary pattern of his subsequent social development. It is within this period that he learns to love others: the mother who has so consistently, intimately, and lovingly attended to his needs; the father, his brothers and sisters, and whoever else has participated in the process of satisfying his needs. Certain persons become to him the symbols of satisfaction, for they are always the objects which provide him with the means of satisfaction, and the first conditioning which the child undergoes is this: that persons who have fairly consistently been the objects which have provided the infant with the means of satisfying its needs now become satisfying objects in themselves.

The satisfaction of its basic needs becomes indissolubly associated in the infant's mind with persons who have become linked with those satisfactions. The mother is, of course, normally the principal producer of satisfactions and she becomes the first love-object of the child. In this sequence of events, from prenatal to postnatal life, can be seen the determinants, as it were in high relief, of the pattern of life which every person everywhere seeks to secure, namely, a state of dependency in which one's needs are satisfied by persons whom one (therefore) loves. What human beings desire most of all is to have their needs satisfied, security. They also want to feel dependent, either upon some mother-ideal, a deity, other persons, or narcissistically—that is to say, pathologically—upon themselves, but dependent they must feel. Man does not want to be independent, to be free in the sense of functioning independently of the interests of his fellows, freely and detached. This kind of negative independence leads to lonesomeness, isolation, and fear.[51] What human beings want is that positive freedom which follows the pattern of his life as an infant within the family: dependent security, the feeling that one is part of a group, accepted, wanted, loved, and loving; the positive freedom which makes the development of the person emphatically a matter of personal realization; self-actualization, in terms of his membership in the social group in the mutual interest, more or less, of the person and of society; and finally, the opportunity to develop interdependently, not as an "individual" but as a person. As André Gide so well put it, "Man! The most complex of creatures, and for this reason the most dependent of creatures. On everything that has formed you you depend. Do not balk at this apparent slavery . . . a debtor to many, you pay for your advantages by the same number of dependencies. Understand that independence is a form of poverty; that many things claim you, that many also claim kinship with you."[52]

The directiveness and creativeness of the human organism at birth is toward realization in terms of dependency upon other organisms. Everything we know points to this fact.

John Donne (1572-1631) beautifully expressed these ideas in his seventeenth *Devotion,* written in 1624:

> No man is an *Island,* entire of itself; every man is a piece of the *Continent,* a part of the *main;* if a *Clod* be washed away by the *Sea, Europe* is the less, as well as if a *Promontory* were, as well as if a *Manor* of thy *friends* or of *thine own* were; any man's *death* diminishes *me,* because I am involved in Mankind; And therefore never send to know for whom the *bell* tolls; it tolls for thee.[53]

Transference and Dependency

The phenomenon of "transference" as observed in the psychoanalytic therapeutic situation, constitutes, as Freud has pointed out, a proof that adults do not overcome their childhood dependency.[54] In the "transference" situation the patient develops emotional relations toward the analyst that are clearly derived from emotions which were originally directed toward the parents. The feelings of dependency upon the parents are transferred to the analyst. The patient becomes deeply attached to his analyst, he falls in love with him, and does everything in his power to maintain the dependent relationship. What he is doing, in fact, is either to continue or to reproduce the early dependency situation of his infancy. It is by making this clear to the patient that the transference is eventually overcome and converted into an instrument for the exploration of the patient's psyche. The reason psychoanalysis can make so little headway with the person who has been unloved is that such a person is often incapable of transference.

Personality and Dependency

A person is not an object in itself, except for census purposes, but a function of activities which he exhibits in interaction with other persons, that is to say, the constituent interacting element of culture. As Harry Stack Sullivan has suggested, personality "is the hypothetical entity that one postulates to account for the doings of people, one with another, and with more or less personified objects."[55] Personality is, in fact, an abstraction, the segmentation of a process at a particular time involving the behavior of a person in relation to others. Whether it is Ego who is doing the segmenting or judging or other persons, the personality is always a function of relations with other persons. The person is a set of interpersonal relationships, and it is during infancy that the pattern which these relationships shall take is largely determined.

Love and Dependency

From the earliest period, during which the infant is primarily concerned with being loved, it learns to love those who love it. This is not the same as to say that the infant is primarily concerned with the satisfaction of its needs, with self-love; the infant does not become aware of its needs unless it is not loved—what it wants is to be maintained in the state of security, stability, or equilibrium in which there is a minimum of need-pressure. Self-love, or as Freud misconceived this stage of development, "Narcissism," is a pathological development resulting from inadequate love by others.[56] When others do not love it the organism attempts to love itself.

The infant inevitably, and to varying degrees where various needs are concerned, becomes aware of its needs, and in this way, perhaps more than in any other, it gradually learns to love those who provide the means of its satisfaction. Without the state of infant dependency human love would not be what it is, and without those affective bonds which tie one human being to another it is more than doubtful whether there could ever have been any future for the human species.

Love is an active *process* with which the infant is born and upon which it improves by learning; it is a process which is developed in dependency, and it is the dependent pattern of love which is maintained throughout the life of the person. We love only those things upon which we are dependent; not, however all things upon which we are dependent. Those which are associated with frustration we hate or dislike, but those which are associated with pleasure, either present, recollected, or anticipated, we love.

It is when human beings begin to think, erroneously, that they can be independent of one another, "social isolationists," that they begin to frustrate and hate each other, that they do violence to all that they are and create much psychological and social havoc. When men learn to understand how dependent they are upon one another, that they are interdependent beings in a great cooperative enterprise, that it is in their nature to be affectionate, cooperative persons, when they understand that being anything else is to be in conflict with themselves and to create divisiveness within society, mankind will be a great deal happier and healthier than it is today. A dynamic science of anthropology, of sociology, of psychiatry, of psychosocial medicine, which is interested in social diagnosis and social planning must become fully cognizant of such facts as these and make use of them.

Relatedness

Man is related to himself only insofar as he is related to others. To love is to relate oneself to others. The infant is born with drives whose urgency is directed toward relating himself to others and having others relate themselves to him. Life is social and man is born to be social, that is, cooperative—an interdependent part of a whole, a working interacting part of a community. Again, I should like to quote Alfred Adler's mature judgment here.

> The individual's proper development can only progress if he lives and strives as a part of the whole. The shallow objection of individualistic systems has no meaning as against this view. I could go still further and show how all our functions are calculated to bind the single individual

to the community, and not to destroy the fellowship of man with man. The act of seeing means to receive and make fruitful all that falls on the retina. This is not simply a physiological process; it shows that man is part of a whole that gives and takes. In seeing, hearing, and speaking we bind ourselves to one another. Man only sees, hears, and speaks rightly when he is linked to others by his interest in the external world. His reason, his common sense, forms the basis of his control of co-operation, of absolute truth, and aims at eternal rightness. Our aesthetic sense and views—perhaps the strongest powers that impel to great achievements—have an eternal value only when they lead to the well-being of humanity in the direction of the evolutionary stream. All our bodily and mental functions are rightly, normally, and healthily developed in so far as they are imbued with sufficient social feeling and are fitted for co-operation.

When we speak of virtue we mean that a person plays his part; when we speak of vice we mean that he interferes with co-operation. I can, moreover, point out that all that constitutes a failure is so because it obstructs social feeling, whether children, neurotics, criminals, or suicides are in question. In every case it can be seen that a contribution is lacking. No isolated persons are to be found in the whole history of humanity. The evolution of humanity was only possible because mankind was a community. . . .

If the person understood how in evading the demands of evolution he had gone astray, then he would give up his present course and join the general mass of humanity.

All the problems of human life . . . demand capacity for co-operation and preparation for it—the visible sign of social feeling. In this disposition courage and happiness are included, and they are to be found nowhere else.[57]

As Galt has pointed out, the fundamental unit of social motivation and behavior is not the person but the group. The person no more represents the unit of social behavior than the discrete reflex represents the unit of physiological behavior.[58]

The Self

In spite of assertions to the contrary it seems indisputably clear that the infant is not born with an ego, with a "self," but that the infant acquires its "self" from other selves, long before it is aware of its own "self." The "self" is learned from other selves, and therefore the type of its own self depends largely, if not entirely, upon the kinds of selves to which the child has been exposed. If it is true that one learns to become a "self," then it is evident that children may learn to become selves in good, bad, and indifferent ways, to name but a few categories. That, indeed, is why children so often resemble their parents, and why the self of the child is a good clue to the covert self of the parent. The overt self worn by the parent may conceal the real covert self. From infancy onwards people can be seen trying on selves likely to be more successful than their own, and sometimes continuing to wear obvious misfits. This is a further evidence of the manner in which the self is acquired.[59]

Beata Rank points out that a fragmented ego is usually acquired from a mother with such an ego. She writes, "When the mother herself is a poorly organized personality, narcissistic and immature, though not infrequently extremely conscientious and eager to become a mother, the child's ego has a very precarious existence. It remains largely undeveloped and hence is not capable of organizing and controlling (libidinal and aggressive) drives. . . ." The ego is fragmented.[60]

Many other investigators have similarly shown that when the mother's ego organization is defective this is almost certainly likely to be reflected in the ego organization of the child. Thus, for example, Spitz found that children whose mothers were characterized by an infantile personality, exhibiting constant rapid shifts in their attitudes, showing hostility alternating with overprotectiveness towards their children literally within minutes, there was severe failure of ego organization. "There was a definite and significant retardation in the social responses and in manipulative ability. Such a retardation is the expression of a diminished capacity of these children to relate themselves to human beings or to manipulate inanimate objects. The resulting clinical picture was a specific one: objectless bodily activity became the children's outstanding occupation."[61]

Similarly Beres and Obers, reporting on a group of adolescents and young adults who had suffered extreme deprivation of maternal love in infancy, state that their findings in every way "confirm the basic concept of the early mother-child relationship in the development of the ego and superego."

> Children who have been deprived of the most important factor essential for normal development—that is, continuous and satisfactory contact with a person who can offer the opportunity for satisfactory identification—suffer a distortion of psychic structure. Our cases can be understood in terms of the functioning of an immature ego along with deficient superego development. Normally the ego functions increasingly in accord with the reality principle and less in accord with the pleasure principle. This development requires the ability to tolerate frustrations and postpone gratifications. Our cases, especially in the group of character disorders, manifested a striking weakness of this function. Disturbances of learning, also an ego function, are to be expected and occur with great regularity in these cases. The importance of identification in the learning process is well known. In our patients, difficulty in establishing satisfactory relationships went hand in hand with difficulty in learning. Object relationships, too, are disturbed and consist for the most part of identifications which are transient, superficial and narcissistic in nature.[62]

These investigators found that the damage thus done to ego and superego development was not irreversible, that many of their patients had made some sort of social adjustment.

That the self or ego is not an inborn structure but is created after birth during what has been called "the undifferentiated phase of development" is now coming to be a generally accepted idea.[63]

The awareness of self develops from the merging of the earliest bodily sensations with sensations derived from others. There must be identification with others. Spitz states that the first attempts at identification become visible in the first quarter of the first year, and that these attempts are the same as what has been called "identification with gesture."[64] It seems, however, improbable that identification occurs at so late a stage of development.

According to Jacobson:

> The nuclei of the early infantile self-images are our first body-images and sensations. Like the primitive object-images, our concept of the self is at first not a firm unit. It is fused and confused with the object-images and is composed of a constantly changing series of self-images,

which reflect mainly the incessant fluctuations of our mental state. With advancing psychosexual and ego development and the maturation of reality testing, a more stable, uniform, and realistic concept of the self and a lasting, firm cathexis of the self-representations will normally be established.[65]

The infant's ego, its self, develops only as the organism comes to recognize and adjust to reality. The infant is clearly not egocentric to begin with. The infant is conditioned to become egocentric by processes of culturalization which produce egocentricity. While the process of socialization, particularly in cultures of the western world, has the effect of binding the person to his social group, that process often has the effect also of rendering the person functionally asocial. The child is trained in what is expected of him and what he may expect of others. But his training, as Galt points out:

> . . . is subsequent and parallel to a process in which there is a weaning of the child from the sense of biological continuity and solidarity with his kind, and the establishment within him of a sense of personal identity, motivation and authority which of its nature must be in conflict with the identity and motivation of others of his social group. Expressed differently, the total social behavioral pattern which is the biological heritage of the human infant, as it is of other animal species, is disrupted, and an undue individuation takes place. The individuation, which in the course of time sets up an autonomous individual with private hopes, desires, wishes, gains and losses, of necessity brings about severe conflict when the desires of two or more elements or individuals happen to interfere with one another. The incentives to behavior have inadvertently become tied up with the individual as an arbitrary center of action and motivation rather than with the social group as such a center.[66]

"I" Versus "You"

The workers at the Lifwynn Foundation, under the leadership of the late Trigant Burrow, state, after many years of investigating and analyzing the so-called normal behavior of men in so-called normal communities, that "The normal individual, like the neurotic, was found to be constantly thinking and acting in terms of his individualized self. He has established an image of himself as an isolated unit of behavior with private values, wishes and motivations, and this same image dominates his social interrelations."[67] As Burrow says:

> In a word, the individual neurosis is but an exaggeration of "normality." It is but an expression, in miniature, of the social neurosis. Man is suffering from an organismic dislocation from the environment, from an "I"-complex or "I"-persona. The partitive sovereignty of the separate self. The result is a divisiveness of function, in which dissociation and conflict assume supremacy over the organism's unity and centralization of function. Man's relation to man becomes disordered through the subordination of the human organism to the conditioned artificial affects and prejudices of the "I"-persona. This social mood is divisive to its core, inciting each person to compete with others in the interest of the self. The principle upon which this divisive socially conditioned mood operates is "I"-versus-"You."[68]

In such persons the central principle of creative motivation, the drive to realize the social feeling that is within them, becomes if not blocked then seriously disordered. The personality develops divisively and may become seriously fragmented. At any rate, it largely loses the power to coordinate, to unify, and to operate as a whole. As Adler says, "It is always the want of social feeling, whatever be the name one gives it—living in fellowship, co-operation, humanity, or even the ideal-ego—which causes an insufficient preparation for all the problems of life. In the presence of a problem this imperfect preparation gives rise to the thousandfold forms that express physical and mental inferiority and insecurity."[69]

The muted voices of our inner consciousness strive to tell us what we ought to be, of the life we have failed to live, but could have lived had not something, we know not quite what, skewed the course of our lives. That something is the history of our earliest childhood, the conditioning, the socialization process to which we had been exposed as infants and children. It is that which has made so many of us, in the western world, the partitive, split, disordered, hostile, aggressive, egocentric creatures we have become. We have become slaves of our own egos instead of masters of them. We are out of line with our evolutionary destiny, which is integration and cooperation, *not* disintegration and antagonism. On the personal, communal, national, and international planes, the effects are those of an "I"-persona conditioning: disorder, disease, and disoperation. Burrow says:

> It is useless to essay a policy of social and economic cooperation on a non-cooperative basis of motivation. We will achieve a pattern of social cooperation and harmony among individuals and nations only when we have accepted the pattern of internal balance and coordination within the organism of man as a species. As things stand today in this world of division and conflict, the war we have fought will have been fought in vain. It will have been no less vain than the many political and economic wars that have preceded it. Vain too must be the unilateral program of peace that will issue out of it. All our international covenants, all our external diplomatic treaties, all the peace programs yet to be devised must forever remain unavailing if our behaviour dichotomies and antagonisms are ultimately traceable to a functional brain-twist that is internal to the organism of man as a race.[70]

The functional brain-twist is the "I"-persona conditioning of the mind which opposes itself to man's innate drives toward his natural function, which is cooperation.

Education and Social Feeling

We may agree with Adler when he writes as follows:

> A careful consideration of individual and collective existence, both past and present, shows us the struggle of mankind for a stronger social feeling. One can scarcely fail to see that humanity is conscious of this problem and is impressed by it. Our present-day burdens are the result of the lack of a thorough social education. It is the pent-up social feeling in us that urges us to reach a higher stage and to rid ourselves of the errors that mark our public life and our own personality. This social feeling exists within us and endeavours to carry out its purpose; it does not seem strong enough to hold its own against all opposing forces. The justified expectation persists that in a far-off age, if mankind is given enough time, the power of social feeling will triumph over all that opposes it. Then it will be as natural to man as breathing. For the present the only alternative is to understand and to teach that this will inevitably happen.[71]

The one point upon which there might be disagreement with Adler is that social feeling will inevitably triumph. On the other hand, if western man continues as disoperatively as he has been doing during the recent past the chances are not inconsiderable that he may destroy himself. It has become *vitally* necessary to learn and teach the facts as we have come to know them, and what it is that requires to be *done;* for to secure the developing "inevitability" of social feeling knowledge of the facts is not enough, they must be implemented by wisdom and the proper action.

Another point Adler seems to have overlooked is that the harmonious cooperative life, in which social feeling does appear to be almost as natural as breathing, has been achieved by several human groups—human beings whom we used to call "savage," "primitive," and now, thanks to the increased understanding of such peoples given us by the anthropologist, "nonliterate peoples."[72] The best known examples of such groups are to be found among the Australian aborigines and the Eskimos.

Aggressiveness

We of the western world are the inheritors of a trifold tradition concerning the inborn nature of man. This tradition is religious, secular, and scientific. The origins of the religious tradition are buried in the mists of antiquity, but as we know it it has been transmitted to us through the Old and New Testaments, namely, that man is born a rather wild, disorganized, evil, sinful creature. The secular tradition of the last two millennia has in every way confirmed the religious tradition, for the conduct of most human beings during the last two thousand years has in no way challenged that tradition. Finally the scientific teachings of the nineteenth century concerning the nature of nature and the nature of human nature, as influenced by Darwinian theory and subsequently by Freudian theory, has largely served to confirm that tradition.

However, the view that the child is born egocentric, evil, and aggressive, in "sin," though widely held, represents nothing more than the projection upon the child of our own conditioning in egocentricity, in aggression, in evil, and in "sin." The view that the child is born egocentric is not supported by the facts. In the first place, as has already been pointed out, the infant is not born with an ego, it acquires an ego only as a result of the stimulation of other egos. What its own ego will become depends very largely upon the kind of egos which condition it. The fact is that the human infant is born an actively cooperating organism. Charlotte Buhler has pointed out that cooperative behavior among children is more basic than competitive response, finding that the latter type of response in her group of observed children did not make its appearance till about the third year.[73] All observers have found that aggressive responses to the child tend to increase as it grows older.[74] From her great experience Bender finds that far from being inborn, hostility or aggression in the child "is a symptom complex resulting from deprivations which are caused by developmental discrepancies in the total personality structure such that the constructive patterned drives for action in the child find inadequate means of satisfaction and result in amplification or disorganization of the drives into hostile or destructive aggression." "The child" she writes "acts as though there were an inherent awareness of his needs and there is thus the expectation of having them met. A failure in this regard is a deprivation and leads to frustration and a reactive aggressive response."[75]

Indeed, the creativeness of the organism is directed toward maturation in terms of cooperation. Bender calls it "the inherent capacity or drive for normality." And as she says "The emphasis on the inborn or instinctive features of hostility, aggression, death wishes, and the negative emotional experiences represents a one-sided approach which has led our students of child psychology astray."

Maslow writes "I find children, up to the time they are spoiled and flattened out by the culture, nicer, better, more attractive human beings than their elders, even though they are of course more 'primitive' than their elders. The 'taming and transforming' that they undergo seem to hurt rather than help. It was not for nothing that a famous psychologist once defined adults as 'deteriorated children.' " "Could it be possible," Maslow inquires, "that what we need is a little *more* primitiveness and a little *less* taming?"[76]

Similarly, Banham, who during the course of twenty years has studied over 900 children from four weeks to four years of age, concludes that children are born with outgoing affectionate drives, and that "they only become preoccupied with themselves, withdrawn or hostile as a secondary reaction, when rebuffed, smothered with unwanted ministrations, ignored or neglected."[77]

Beata Rank finds that aggression is not correctly conceived of as an unmodifiable innate force of destruction. Aggression she considers to be the human being's adaptation to the surrounding reality, and hence a part of ego-organization. The manner in which the responses are expressed to inner or outer frustration depends primarily upon the structure of the ego—and that is something which is acquired.[78]

With the notion that the child is born to be "disciplined" goes hand in hand the idea that culture exists in order to control and suppress the evil that is within him. Religion, education, penology, psychology, and even psychiatry have been dominated by this point of view. Consider, for example, this typical expression by a psychiatrist of the Jungian school, Dr. M. E. Harding:

> Beneath the decent facade of consciousness with its disciplined, moral order and its good intentions, lurk the crude instinctive forces of life, like monsters of the deep—devouring, begetting, warring endlessly.[79] They are for the most part unseen, yet on their urge and energy life itself depends: without them living beings would be as inert as stones. But were they left to function unchecked, life would lose its meaning, being reduced once more to mere birth and death, as in the teeming world of the primordial swamps. In creating civilization man sought, however unconsciously, to curb these natural forces and to channel some part at least of their energy into forms that would serve a different purpose. For with the coming of consciousness, cultural and psychological values began to compete with the purely biological aims of unconscious functioning.[80]

This is not, it is to be feared, pure phantasy, because Dr. Harding has, in common with many others, inherited these ideas as part of the common tradition of western thought. This tradition is a myth, but we of the western world believe in it as if it were a universally established truth. This myth is part of our traditional but erroneous way of thinking about "Nature" and the animal world. "Nature," according to this tradition, is a jungle pullulating with animals instinctively dedicated to the task of devouring each other. Beasts are brutal murderous creatures who can, only occasionally, be tamed for domestic purposes, and we human beings are animals who have inherited a bestial nature which it is the task of culture to overcome and eradicate.[81] Our nearest relatives, the chimpanzee and the gorilla, so the myth goes, are among the most fierce and bestial of the animals. Is not primitive or prehistoric man closely related to the beast, *Pithecanthropus erectus,* and Neanderthal man, for example?

The Myth of the Beast

In a significant sense the tradition of the western world has inverted the true course of man's social evolution. We suffer from the belief that man originated as an aggressive, hostile, belligerent cannibal, a savage monster who dragged his womenfolk about by the hair. As typical of this, the following is an extract from a recent popularly written book on prehistoric man.

> One never knew on retiring whether one would actually be there when morning broke. . . . The facts show now that a bitter struggle for supremacy had been going on ever since our old world was created. . . . Man had constructive ideas. He *wanted* things, and if his neighbors had a specially comfortable shelter in which to hide at night, envious thoughts arose and at times he was able to drive them out of the coveted retreat and occupy it himself. . . . How easy it was to sneak up on an enemy in a neighboring clan in the dense jungle and tap him none too gently on his thick skull with a heavy club or a piece of sharp stone.[82]

This is the characteristic popular picture which many writers and some scientists (who should know better) have aided and abetted in building up in the popular imagination. According to our cultural myth progress or social evolution has taken something like the following course: Commencing with bestial savage prehistoric ancestors who were in a more or less continuous state of warfare with one another, we have gradually, slowly, and painfully developed toward civilization and greater and greater cooperation and peacefulness.

Contrary to this view the evidence indicates that prehistoric man was, on the whole, a more peaceful, cooperative, unwarlike, unaggressive creature than we are, and that we of the civilized world have gradually become more and more disoperative, more aggressive and hostile, and less and less cooperative where it most matters, that is, in human relations. The meaning we have put into the term "savage" is more correctly applicable to ourselves than to the people to whom we have customarily applied it.[83] They trusted and cooperated with us, we savaged, ravaged, and did our best to exterminate them.[84] They trusted and cooperated with us, but we failed them. They had never heard of Christianity or democracy before we descended upon them, but most of them practiced the Sermon on the Mount and the principles of democracy far more successfully than we of the western world have ever done.[85] Just as we have projected our own bestiality upon the "beasts" we have projected our own savagery upon primitive peoples. Thanks to the labors of anthropologists we now know that primitive peoples are not primitive, except insofar as their technological development may be concerned; we know that they are not savages in the commonly misunderstood meaning of that term, and furthermore, we know that they function in a substantially more cooperative manner, for the most part, than we do.

Neither the "beasts," the chimpanzee and gorilla, prehistoric man, nor "primitive" man are the aggressive bestial creatures we have been traditionally taught to believe. In the cultures of the western world we seem to have forgotten not only the ties which link us to our fellow human beings but those also which link us to our fellow creatures of the nonhuman animal world. As Maurice has remarked, "Mankind is in desperate need of learning and understanding the truths of Life itself, and these he can only learn in and from the ecology to which he belongs. . . . It is but rarely, if at all, that one finds in the life of the wild, avarice, mean jealousy, treachery, and the other deadly sins with which mankind is obsessed. One reason at least for attempting to save the innocent creatures of the wild is that they present a greatly needed example of mutual tolerance."[86]

Chimpanzees and gorillas are among the most peaceful of creatures. They never attack any living creature, are completely vegetarian, and in the "wild" when they encounter a man, they usually exhibit a natural curiosity which having at a distance satisfied they take their departure in peace.[87] Maslow, who has had considerable experience with young chimpanzees and gorillas writes, "I can certainly say that these young animals are friendly, cooperative, mutually helpful, affectionate and even altruistic, as contrasted with lower animals."[88] It is perhaps not altogether an accident that our best and most sympathetic accounts of apes should have been written by women who have brought up these creatures and long been associated with them. From these accounts we can learn how really docile, retiring, and unaggressive these creatures are.[89] Capturing, mistreating, and isolating "wild" animals, then judging them to be ferocious is a common practice, but that does not make such animals necessarily ferocious by nature. We have projected something of our own "ferocity" upon these creatures, not being able to face it in ourselves as easily as we can in the "wild" animals upon whom we have visited it. Certainly, many wild animals *are* ferocious to the animals they prey upon, but not all animals are predators, and the line of animals which led to man does not appear to have been guilty of the sins which have been visited upon it by civilized writers. Our nearest relatives, the great apes, are peaceful unaggressive creatures. Prehistoric man, up to the Late Neolithic, some 10,000 years ago, seems to have been so. From the Neolithic the progress of man seems to have been modified in the opposite direction, mostly in those societies which were affected by the development of the techniques which enabled men to live increasingly more urbanized lives.[90] With the increasing brutalization of the lives of so many human beings in such societies, with its increasing competitiveness, the development of a point of view which despairs of man and asserts his essential evil is not difficult to understand. To many it would appear that a creature capable of so much evil as man must be born evil. And hence, babies are alleged to be born evil. Such inversions and twists of thought are peculiarly numerous among human beings, and this particular one has already proven well-nigh catastrophic for man. Instead of seeing that it is an evil society which makes men evil, we have inverted the process and said that it is evil men who make an evil society.

It is not evil babies who grow up into evil human beings, but an evil society which turns good babies into disordered adults, and it does so on a regimen of frustration. Babies are born good and desirous of continuing to be good. More than a hundred years ago the woman who later became John Stuart Mill's wife and coadjutor, Harriet Taylor, clearly saw and stated these facts in an essay which was not published till 1951.

> We believe [she wrote] that a child of good physical organization who were never to hear of evil, would not know from its own nature that evil existed in the mental and moral world. We would place before the minds of children no examples but of good and beautiful, and our strongest effort should be to prevent emulation. The spirit of Emulation in childhood and of competition in manhood are the fruitful sources of selfishness and misery. They are a part of the conformity plan, making each person's idea of goodness a thing of comparison with some received mode of being good and happy.[91]

Now, more than a hundred years later, we can only regret that Harriet Taylor was not spared long enough to persuade Mill to present this point of view at length to the public.

The belief in the inherent naughtiness of the human infant is a myth, the projection of what we have ourselves, in part, become, and with the warp of our accidie, and with imperfect means resulting from a confused conception of our goals we have produced a progressive deterioration of our children—of humanity.

9 LOVE AND THE PRIVATION OF LOVE

I on my part have come to regard the desire to love, to give, and "to be good" or "co-operative" as influencing the appetites from their very first thwartings. —IAN D. SUTTIE*

All men are born good. He who loses his goodness and yet lives is lucky to escape. —CONFUCIUS

LOVE IS RECIPROCAL

The infant soon learns that in order to be satisfied, in order to be loved, he too must love, he must satisfy the requirements of others, he must cooperate. He learns that he must gracefully give up or postpone the satisfaction of certain desires if he is to achieve satisfaction in others, and if he is to retain the love of those whose love he needs. This, too, is at cnce a recognizable adult pattern of behavior which takes its origin in these early experiences. From the beginning this pattern of behavior provides the most important means by which the socialization of the organism is achieved—first, through love as a feeling of belongingness (security), and second, through love as authority, the authority of the affectionate tie. "I belong to this family, and it is because these people love me that I belong. I like to 'belong,' therefore I must obey them and retain their love so that I may continue to belong." This is what the child resolves for himself though he may never give conscious expression to the thought. The relationships of his family life condition his personal relationships throughout his life. "They are loaded with affection

* Ian D. Suttie, *The Origins of Love and Hate,* New York, Julian Press, 1953, p. 42.

and carry the burden of giving to each a *place*—a sense of belonging, a meaning to the process of arriving and being."[1]

Outside the family, as a "grown-up," the approval (love) of one's fellows is secured by conforming to the standards of the group. This is the family pattern repeated on a less intensive but more extensive scale. To conform means the willingness to forego certain satisfactions in order to obtain others, to suffer a certain amount of deprivation and thwarting of satisfactions as a discipline which may ultimately lead to what are socially esteemed as greater rewards. Conflict, repression, and aggressiveness are the consequences of those experiences both in the family and in the group.

The Privation of Love

The importance of love in the early social development of the infant cannot be overemphasized. Its significance can best be understood when we consider a disease from which, at the beginning of this century, more than half the children in their first year of life regularly died.[2] This disease was known as *marasmus,* from the Greek word meaning "wasting away." The disease was also known as infantile atrophy or debility. When studies were undertaken to track down its cause, it was discovered that it was generally babies in the "best" homes and hospitals who were most often its victims, babies who were apparently receiving the best and most careful physical attention, while babies in the poorest homes, with a good mother, despite the lack of hygienic physical conditions, often overcame the physical handicaps and flourished. What was wanting in the sterilized environment of the babies of the first class and was generously supplied in babies of the second class was mother love. This discovery is responsible for the fact that hospitals today endeavor to keep the infant for as short a period as possible. The best place for the infant is with its mother, and if its own mother is not available, with a warm foster mother, for what the infant must have is love. Drs. Ruth and Harry Bakwin, pediatricians of great experience, make the following point:

The effect of residence in a hospital manifests itself by a fairly well-defined clinical picture. A striking feature is the failure to gain properly, despite the ingestion of diets which are entirely adequate for growth in the home. Infants in hospitals sleep less than others and they rarely smile or babble spontaneously. They are listless and apathetic and look unhappy. The appetite is indifferent and food is accepted without enthusiasm. The stools tend to be frequent and, in sharp contrast with infants cared for in the home, it is unusual for 24 hours to pass without an evacuation. Respiratory infections which last only a day or two in the home are prolonged and may persist for weeks and months. Return to the home results in defervescence [disappearance of fever] within a few days and a prompt and striking gain in weight.[3]

Mother-Love

The emotional deprivation suffered by infants in hospitals may do vastly more damage than the physical condition which brought them there. The infant can suffer no greater loss than the privation of its mother's love, for it would seem that the satisfaction of the generalized feeling of dependency, in itself a basic need, is best accomplished through mother-love. An old Egyptian proverb says that since God could not be everywhere He created mothers. The fact seems to have been more than glimpsed long ago that because the mother is the person usually most profoundly interested in the welfare of her infant it is from her that the infant is most likely to receive the supports and reassurances which love bestows. This is not to say that some other person could not do as much for it. There is every reason to believe that devoted foster mothers or nurses have often successfully taken the place of the actual mother in giving the infant all the love that it required. Normally, however, the infant receives its love from the person best qualified to give it, the mother.

Let us observe what is likely to happen to the infant who is separated from his mother shortly after birth. A typical and early case is one described by Dr. Margaret Ribble.

Little Bob was born in the maternity hospital where the writer was making studies of infants at the time. He was a full-term child and weighed six pounds three ounces at birth. During the two weeks stay in the hospital the baby was breast fed and there was no apparent difficulty with his body functions. The mother, a professional woman, had been reluctant about breast feeding because she wished to take up her work as soon as possible after the baby was born, but she yielded to the kindly encouragement of the hospital nurses, and the feeding was successful. Both mother and child were thriving when they left the hospital.

On returning home the mother found that her husband had suddenly deserted her—the climax of an unhappy and maladjusted marriage relationship. She discovered soon after that her milk did not agree with the baby. As is frequently the case, the deep emotional reaction had affected her milk secretion. The infant refused the breast and began to vomit. Later he was taken to the hospital and the mother did not call to see him. At the end of a month she wrote that she had been seriously ill and asked the hospital to keep the child until further notice.

In spite of medical attention and skillful feeding, this baby remained for two months at practically the same weight. He was in a crowded ward and received very little personal attention. The busy nurses had no time to take him up and work with him as a mother would, by changing his position and making him comfortable at frequent intervals. The habit of finger sucking developed, and gradually the child became what is known as a ruminator, his food coming up and going down with equal ease. At the age of two months he weighed five pounds. The baby at this time was transferred to a small children's hospital, with the idea that this institution might be able to give him more individual care. It became apparent that the mother had abandoned the child altogether.

When seen by the writer, this baby actually looked like a seven months' foetus yet he had also a strange appearance of oldness. His arms and legs were wrinkled and wasted, his head large in proportion to the rest of his body, his chest round and flaring widely at the base over an enormous liver. His breathing was shallow, he was generally inactive, and his skin was cold and flabby. He took large quantities of milk but did not gain weight since most of it went through him with very little assimilation and with copious discharges of mucus from his intestines. The baby showed at this time the pallor which in our study we have found typical of infants who are not mothered, although careful examination of his blood did not indicate a serious degree of anemia. He was subject to severe sweating, particularly during sleep. A thorough study showed no indication of tuberculosis. The child's abdomen was large and protruding, but this proved to be due to lax intestinal muscles and consequent distention with gas and to a greatly enlarged and distended liver, which was actually in proportion to that of the foetus. There was no evidence of organic disease, but growth and development were definitely at a standstill, and it appeared that the child was gradually slipping backward to lower and lower levels of body economy and function.

The routine treatment of this hospital for babies who are not gaining weight is to give them concentrated nursing care. They are held in the nurses' laps for feeding and allowed at least half an hour to take the bottle. From time to time their position in the crib is changed and when possible the nurse carries them about the ward for a few minutes before or after each feeding. This is the closest possible approach to mothering in a busy infants' ward. Medical treatment consists of frequent injections of salt solution under the skin to support the weakened circulation in the surface of the body.

With this treatment the child began to improve slowly. As his physical condition became better, it was possible for our research group to introduce the services of a volunteer "mother" who came to the hospital twice daily in order to give him some of the attention he so greatly needed. What she actually did was to hold him in her lap for a short period before his 10 A.M. and 6 P.M. feedings. She was told that he needed love more than he needed medicine, and she was instructed to stroke the child's head gently and speak or sing softly to him and walk him about. Her daily visits were gradually prolonged until she was spending an hour twice a day, giving the baby this artificial mothering. The result was good. The child remained in the hospital until he was five months of age, at which time he weighed nine pounds. All rumination and diarrhea had stopped, and he had become an alert baby with vigorous muscular activity. His motor coordinations were of course retarded. Although he held up his head well and looked about, focusing his eyes and smiling in response to his familiar nurses, he could not yet grasp his own bottle or turn himself over, as is customary at this age. The finger sucking continued, as is usually the case with babies who have suffered early privation.

In accordance with the new hospital procedure, as soon as the child's life was no longer in danger, he was transferred to a good, supervised foster home in order that he might have still more individual attention. Under this regime, his development proceeded well and gradually he mastered such functions as sitting, creeping, and standing. His speech was slow in developing, however, and he did not walk until after the second year. The general health of this child is now excellent at the end of his third year; also his "I.Q." is high on standard tests, but his emotional life is deeply damaged. With any change in his routine or with a prolonged absence of the foster mother, he goes into a state which is quite similar to a depression. He becomes inactive, eats very little, becomes constipated and extremely pale. When his foster mother goes away, he usually reacts with a loss of body tone and alertness, rather than with a definite protest. His emotional relationship to the foster mother is receptive, like that of a young infant, but he makes little response to her mothering activities except to function better when she is there. He has little capacity to express affection, displays no initiative in seeking it, yet fails to thrive without it. This lack of response makes it difficult for the foster mother to show him the affection which he so deeply needs. Without the constant friendly explanations of the situation from the visiting nurse, she would probably have given up the care of the child.[4]

The Institution Child

Contemporary research indicates that to a greater or less extent the history of the emotional development of Little Bob represents the pattern of the history of most mother-separated infants. The history of this unmothered child is by no means extreme, but it does illustrate, rather strikingly, the effects upon the newborn and infant of the absence of those stimulations which are provided by the mother's love. Without those stimulations the psychosomatic effects upon the child are often disastrous. Such a child may be emotionally crippled for life. As adults such children remain fixated at their early dependent infantile level, they demand affection but cannot return it. In this particular field the research findings are now abundant.[5] What is required are studies which will not only inquire into the personality development of unmothered children, though this is indispensable, but it is also highly desirable to discover the variation in mothering which different mothers have given their children, and to inquire into exactly the amount and quality of mothering the person has received from the mother and how much from nurses and other persons.

Studies are also required on the variations in the kind of mothering the same mother gives her child over the course of the years. A mother may be good for her child for the first year but not for the second, or she may be good for the first two years but not for the next few years, and so on in all possible combinations and permutations. This is a problem which has thus far received no attention. (See Sylvia Brody, *Patterns of Mothering* [New York: International Universities Press, 1956].)

Studies carried out on children who have spent their infancy in institutions lead to the following conclusion, in the words of one of the earliest investigators in this field:

> [Such infants] undergo an isolation type of experience with resulting isolation type of personality, characterized by unsocial behavior, hostile aggression, lack of patterns for giving and receiving affection, inability to understand and accept limitations, much insecurity in adapting to environment. These children present delays in development and intensification as well as prolongation of behavior manifestations at these levels. At the time of the transfer [to a foster home], the children are at a stage when they can form only partial love attachments; hostility and aggression are at a peak; egocentricity is marked, and they do not recognize the individuality and needs of others. They are unprepared for and unequal to the demands and limitations of a family setting. They are exposed to attention and affection far in excess of anything they have previously known, and react excessively either by extravagant behavior, negativism or both.[6]

The work of Goldfarb originally, as well as that of others since, has demonstrated conclusively that the institutionally reared child is characterized by a personality which is strikingly less differentiated than that of the home-reared child. Such children are markedly more passive and apathetic, as a consequence, presumably, of their highly routinized experience. Motivation and ambition are lacking. Language retardation is severe and persists well into adolescence. Aggressive behavior and instability of emotional response are usual, and deficiencies of inhibition the rule. Such children are restless, aimless in their behavior, unreflective, and lacking in persistence. The impoverished social environment of the institution, the lack of a dynamic and varied social experience, is reflected in the inability of the institutionalized child to develop meaningful reciprocal human relationships. The absence of the loving attention, affection, and stimulation of the family with its human protecting and supporting ties in the experience of such children, leads to a marked insecurity with a resulting hunger for attention and affection. In the younger children attention-seeking behavior is particularly marked, and this is usually combined with hostile, overtly aggressive acts. Eventually, the conflict between the hunger for affection and the inability to respond to normal human relationships is resolved by a more consistent defense of emotional isolation, resulting in apathetic social responses and a pattern of withdrawal from life's tasks.[7]

Such children, while they may improve following adoption into a family, never fully recover from the effects of their early deprivations. It is not difficult to recognize such persons as adults. The basic personality defects are congealed at a level of extreme immaturity. By the age of three years the damage has usually been so effectively done as to affect the institution child for the rest of his life. This does not mean that all institution children are so affected or those that have been cannot substantially recover.[8]

As Goldfarb points out, "Under normal circumstances, early dependency becomes the constructive basis for the development of a growing and secure sense of independence. In other words, independence is a positive and mature adaptation based on a secure grasp of the self in relation to other people. This is to be differentiated from the isolation reaction of the institution group, for the latter reaction represents defensive adaptation to a confused, hazy, and thus fearful grasp of one's relationship to the world of people and things as well as to inadequate methods for meeting reality."[9]

The dependency needs normally satisfied by the mother are in institution children *inadequately* satisfied, and the result is a more or less serious failure of development of the affective life of the person. Such children suffer conspicuously from what David Levy has called "primary affect hunger," which he defines as "a state of privation due primarily to a lack of maternal affection, with a resulting need, as of food in a state of starvation."[10]

It is important to note that *inadequate* satisfaction of the dependency needs, *not* complete deprivation, is sufficient to produce this failure of affective development. It appears that the damage done is related to the degree of privation suffered by the infant. For example, rejected children will show very similar symptoms to institution children. The differences, however, are significant, depending on variables that have been operative or not upon such children.

The deprivation situation is characterized by a marked poverty of affective and social stimulation. In the institution child this is further reinforced by the handicapping barrenness and narrowness of the institution environment. The world of things and of people, of experience, as something lived or undergone is flattened out, and severely limited. The interstimulation of family relationships in all their manifold aspects is lost. And as Goldfarb so well puts it, "The institution child thus establishes no specific identifications and engages in no meaningful reciprocal relationships with the people. The basic motivations to normal maturation and differentiation of personality are absent. Paucity in content and organization of both intellect and feeling follow. The ego structure is primitive and undeveloped . . . Both the 'I' of the inner life, and the 'It' of the outer life, are crippled."[11]

On the other hand, while the rejected child may suffer from a greater or less degree of affective deprivation, the horizon of its experience is usually not nearly as limited as that of the institution child. It is perhaps for this reason that the rejected child does not usually exhibit any defects in abstract thinking as does the institution child. He is more anxious than the latter, more ambitiously purposeful, and possesses a much greater capacity for insight. He therefore usually responds to treatment, whereas the institution child rarely and with much greater difficulty effectively responds.

It is possible that there are some homes in which the rejection of a child has been so extreme as to produce symptoms in it of deprivation identical with those of the institution child. This is an area of social pathology which requires further investigation.

René Spitz has paid particular attention to the child which has been confined to an institution during its first year of life. Infants in two different institutions were simultaneously studied. These institutions were well organized in all physical respects: in housing, asepsis, food, and hygiene. Infants were admitted to both shortly after birth.

The institutions differed in but one factor: in the amount of emotional interchange offered. In the first institution, called "Nursery," the infants were looked after by their own mothers. In the second institution, called "Foundlinghome," the children were raised from the third month by overworked nursing personnel, one nurse caring for from eight to twelve children. The absence or presence of emotional interchange between mother and child formed the one independent variable in the comparison of the two groups.

The response to this variable showed up in many ways, but perhaps most comprehensively in the developmental quotient, which represents a measure of the total development of six sectors of the personality: mastery of perception, of bodily functions, of social relations, of memory and imitation, of manipulative ability, and of intelligence. Toward the end of the first year though the "Foundling home" infants had a developmental quotient of 124 to start with, whereas "Nursery" had a developmental quotient of 101.5, the deprived "Foundlinghome" infants sink to a D.Q. of 72, while the "Nursery" infants rise to 105. By the end of the second year the D.Q. had fallen in the "Foundlinghome" group to the amazing low of 45, corresponding to a mental age of about 10 months. As Spitz remarks:

> We have here an impressive example of how the absence of one psychosocial factor, that of emotional interchange with the mother, results in a complete reversal of a developmental trend. . . .
>
> It should be realized that the factor which was present in the first case, but eliminated in the second, is the pivot of all development in the first year. It is the mother-child relation. By choosing this factor as our independent variable we were able to observe its vital importance. While the children in "Nursery" developed into normal healthy toddlers, a two-year observation of "Foundlinghome" showed that the emotionally starved children never learned to speak, to walk, to feed themselves. With one or two exceptions in a total of 91 children, those who survived were human wrecks who behaved either in the manner of agitated or of apathetic idiots.[12]

The mortality rates in the two institutions were striking and significant. During five years of observation involving 239 children who had been institutionalized for one year or more, "Nursery" did not lose a single child through death, whereas in "Foundlinghome" 37 per cent of children died during a two-years observation period. Death, Spitz remarks, is but an extreme consequence of the general physical and psychological decline, which affects children completely starved of emotional interchange.

A large proportion of the children deprived of mother-love show various degrees of depression, in which the main presenting system is a great increase in the exhibition of the emotions of displeasure. Spitz has called this condition "anaclitic depression." In this condition anxiety reactions to the point of panic will occur upon the appearance of a strange person or some ordinary toy. Such children will scream by the hour, often with accompaniments of tears, heavy salivation, severe perspiration, convulsive trembling, dilation of the pupils, and so on.

In 19 children exhibiting the clear-cut symptoms of anaclitic depression the mother had in each case been removed from the child somewhere between the sixth and eighth month for a practically unbroken period of three months, during which the child did not see its mother at all, or saw her at most once a week. The separation had been unavoidable, and before it the mother had had full charge of the infant, and, indeed, had spent more time with it than is usually the case at home. In the course of four to six weeks following the mother's removal each child developed the symptoms described above. No child whose mother was not removed developed these symptoms. When within a period not more than three months after the removal of the mother she was restored to the child, the recovery of all normal faculties was spectacular. Where, as in the "Foundlinghome" children, the mother was not restored no intervention of any kind was effective in bringing these children out of their depression.[13]

The central importance of the mother or of a mother-substitute for the proper psychosomatic development of the child could not be more dramatically emphasized than by Spitz's findings.[14]

Reference has been made to the important findings of Beres and Obers on a group of young adults and adolescents who had experienced extreme deprivation in infancy. Their findings in every way corroborate those of Spitz and other workers, but more importantly they hold out some hope, if not for the complete recovery of such deprived human beings, then at least for the possibility of considerable rehabilitation.

> When we survey our cases [the authors write], in the attempt to find any correlations that will permit understanding of the causes of modifications of psychic structure that we noted, we are impressed rather by the individual variations. Changes occur with or without psychotherapy; changes occur early and later in life; in some cases changes take the form of continuous improvement, in others of fluctuation in symptomatology. It becomes obvious that available data do not permit any positive correlations at this time. . . .
>
> The implications for therapy are evident. The therapeutic nihilism which has characterized the approach to these cases is not warranted if we limit the aim of therapy to increasing of ego functioning to the level of social adjustment. The most important single therapeutic factor we believe to be the opportunity for the development of a close stable relationship to an adult person, whether in a placement situation, a casework relationship or in psychotherapy. In this sense, we have been working in the tradition of Aichorn[15] who emphasized the importance of the transference relationship in the treatment of his "wayward youth." The treatment of these cases requires a flexible and a patient approach which must utilize the combined skills of caseworker and psychiatrist. To this extent the therapy of such cases would be very difficult to carry out except with the facilities of a social agency.[16]

Complete recovery is far from being claimed as a possibility for such cases, and while our purpose in this section has been to point out the importance of maternal love for the healthy development of the child, and the extremely damaging effects which follow upon the deprivation of such love, it is important not to leave the reader with a sense of the hopelessness of the lot of such emotionally deprived children. As Beres and Obers point out, there are indications that much can be achieved by and for them. Further therapeutic research in this field is urgently needed.[17]

Holman, in a study of 200 children in England, found that separation from the parents had significantly adverse effects upon the development of the child only when that separation was early and permanent. Temporary separation, either before or after the age of four, was not found to be associated with behavior disturbances, nor was permanent separation which began in the fifth year of life or later. Interestingly enough, Holman found that early separation from the father was no less adverse in its effects than permanent early separation from the mother.[18] Incidentally, Holman found that hostility and ill-treatment from parents had a more damaging effect upon the development of the children than ambivalence.

Critical Developmental Periods

Bevan-Brown has pointed out that "The child does not grow uniformly and homogeneously like a crystal or a carrot, but by stages or phases which succeed one another and which differ from one another."[19] For proper growth and development it is necessary that the potentialities for developing human relationships with which the infant is born be exposed to the organizing influences of another human being. Accumulating evidence indicates that there exist critical developmental periods during which the organism is ready for differential development, within which periods it must receive the proper stimulations if it is to develop adequately. These critical developmental periods may be broadly outlined as follows:

1. The period during which the infant is in process of establishing an explicit cooperative relationship with a clearly defined person—the mother; this is normally achieved by five or six months.

2. The period during which the child needs the mother as an ever-present support and companion; this normally continues to about the end of the third year.

3. The period during which the child is in process of becoming able to maintain a relationship with its mother during her absence. During the fourth and fifth years, under favorable conditions, such

a relationship can be maintained for a few days or even a few weeks; after seven or eight years of age such a relationship can be maintained for longer periods, though not without some strain.

The capacity whereby the child simultaneously develops his own ego and super-ego and the capacity to maintain relationships with removed objects is variously described as identification, internalization, or introjection, since it is according to the pattern set by the parents that the functions of the ego and super-ego are incorporated within the self.

The evidence supports the existence of these three critical developmental periods and we find, indeed, that three somewhat different experiences can produce the lack-love syndrome, as follows:

1. Lack of any opportunity to develop attachment to a mother-figure during the first three years.

2. Maternal deprivation for a period varying for days within the first and second years, and weeks or months during the third and fourth years.

3. Changes from one mother-figure to another during the first four or five years.

With respect to the reality of the critical developmental periods, it is, of course, well known that such critical developmental periods exist in the development of the body, with the principle well established that the earlier the interference with their development the more widespread will the disturbance in growth be. Tissues must reach a certain stage of differentiation before they can respond; later such tissues achieve a certain relative fixity, so that they can yield only a more limited type of response.[20] The concept of critical developmental periods for the development of social behavior and susceptibility to environmental changes has been put to experimental test on dogs and other animals, and confirmed.[21]

What the developing child apparently needs is a stable and continuous development in relation to its mother or mother-surrogate. The stability and continuity must be prolonged, and not too much or too often interrupted. Deprivation leads to isolation and asocial behavior, satisfactions interspersed with deprivations lead to ambivalent and antisocial behavior. The "now-I-love-you, now-I-don't" kind of conduct which characterizes the behavior of many mothers towards their small children produces not dissimilar effects. During the development of his ego and super-ego the child needs a firm hand, as it were, at the helm, otherwise his own steering mechanism remains unorganized. It is the mother who guides him when he is helpless and teaches him gradually how to meet the requirements of his environment, and thus helps construct his ego. It is his mother who gradually teaches the child its obligations to others, and thus builds up his super-ego. If the mother or her substitutes fail in this they produce a person who is likely to be crippled both in his ego and super-ego structure.

Unless the child has been firmly grounded in the discipline of love and dependency, it is injured in its capacity to develop clear and definite judgments concerning people and things, and its ability to form such judgments as an adult is seriously handicapped. As adults the judgments of such persons tend to remain blurred and vague. Their decisions about the world, people, and things are characterized by doubt, suspicion, uncertainty, misgiving, and unsureness. They vacillate, in short, they see the world through a mist of unshed tears. They are characterized by an inability to enter into the feelings of others because, when they were young, no one adequately entered into theirs.

The Separated Child

Studies on children from birth to 1 year, from 1 year to 17 months, and from 18 months to 24 months of age, and up to 8 years of age, agree in finding that any separation of the young child from its mother is usually a distressing experience to it. Early attachment to the mother or mother-substitute is an emotional need which must be early satisfied if the organism is to develop in a normal manner. If that need is not satisfied the organism can seldom make deep and lasting attachments to other human beings. The organism's capacity to make continuous cooperative relations with others is impaired, and it is of considerable moment to observe that this is the failure which is characteristic of most persons suffering from mental illness.[22]

Work done at the International Children's Centre in Paris and London has revealed that children who have enjoyed normal healthy relationships with their mothers and not been previously separated from them for more than a few hours, when separated from the mother and cared for in an impersonal environment, commonly progress through three phases of emotional response which may be described as the phases of *protest, despair,* and *denial.* These phases are, of course, not distinctly separated from one another but in reality merge the one into the other, so that a child is often for weeks or days in a state of transition from one phase to another.

Protest

In the protest or initial phase, which may last from a few hours to seven or eight days, the child exhibits a strong conscious need of his mother together with the expectation—based on previous experience—that she will respond to his cries. He is acutely anxious and fears that he has lost her, he is confused and frightened by unfamiliar surroundings, and seeks to recapture her by the full exercise of his limited resources. He has no comprehension of his situation, and is out of mind with fright and urgent desire for satisfactions which only his mother can give. He will cry loudly, shake his crib, throw himself about, and look eagerly towards any sight or sound which might prove to be the missing mother. He may seek to cling to a nurse, perhaps the one who admitted him.[23]

Despair

The despair which gradually succeeds protest is characterized by continuing conscious need of the mother coupled with an increasing hopelessness. The active physical movements have diminished and come to an end, and the crying is now monotonous and intermittent. The child is withdrawn and apathetic, makes no demands on the environment, and is in a state of deep mourning. This quiet stage is often erroneously presumed to indicate a diminution of distress.

Denial

Denial is a phase which gradually succeeds despair. In his great need of loving care, comfort, and physical satisfaction, which he cannot provide himself, the little child may push out of his mind the picture of his mother who has (he feels) so cruelly abandoned him. Because the child cannot tolerate such intensity of distress he makes the best of his situation by repressing his feeling for his mother. In addition to the emotional need of his mother he has urgent physical need of food and comfort, and these he will begin to seek wherever he can find them. In the *denial* phase there are two types of response according to whether a substitute mother is available or not:

1. *Denial of the need for mothering by his own mother.* The child's need of loving care and comfort and of physical satisfactions which he cannot provide himself are so great that he is likely to transfer his attachments to anyone who gives him the necessary attention, and adopt her as a substitute mother. As a first step he will have to deal drastically with his feeling for his own mother who has failed to meet his needs, particularly his need of her as a person to love and to be loved by. In a way roughly comparable to that in which an adult may push out of mind the picture of someone who has caused gross offence, the little child may crush the picture of the mother who has (to his feeling) so heartlessly abandoned him. Then he is free to seek satisfaction of his needs in anyone who offers some degree of substitution.

2. *Denial of all need for mothering.* If the child fails to find a human being who will substitute for his mother, or if he undergoes the disheartening experience of becoming attached to a series of people each of whom leaves him and so repeats for him the pain and sense of rejection of the original loss of the mother, he will develop as one who believes that neither mothering nor any contact with human beings has much significance for him.

He will learn by bitter experience that it is folly to become attached to any one nurse, because nurses move on to other wards; thus, after a series of upsets at losing several nurses to whom in turn he had given his trust and warm affection, he will gradually commit himself less and less to succeeding nurses and in time will stop altogether taking the risk of investing love and dependence in anyone. Instead he will become more and more self-centred, transferring his desires and feelings from people on to material things such as sweets, toys, and food. He will no longer show upset when nurses leave. He will also cease showing feeling when his parents come and go on visiting day, and he will unwittingly cause them pain when they realize that although he has little interest in them as particular people he has an eager interest in the presents they bring—an interest which is no greater than the interest he shows in the diversions which anyone else brings into his restricted life. He will appear cheerful and adapted to his unusual situation (a particularly remarkable fact if he has been confined to his cot for several months or years) and apparently easy and unafraid of anyone. But this sociability is very superficial. If the onlooker, or the person to whom this spectacle is deceptively familiar, will pause long enough to assess the child's human relationships in even the simplest terms it will be apparent that he no longer really cares for anyone—and that, in a way which is highly abnormal for a young child, he denies all need for mothering or intimate care.[24]

As Robertson and Bowlby remark, to the child of under two years his mother is the entire world, she is the omnipotent protector, and if the child loses her by death or separation his whole world is shattered, and he experiences an overwhelming sense of loss and an overpowering anger when his imperative need for his mother is not met. The far-reaching harmful effects of such separation upon later personality development are now fairly clear. "The essential nature of these disturbances appears to be an incapacity to make stable, co-operative relationships with other people."[25]

Something of these essential findings had already been grasped by the great American pediatrician H. D. Chapin as early as 1908,[26] the psychologic care of neglected or institution children being positively recommended by him in 1915.[27] In the early 1930's another American pediatrician, J. Brennemann, established a rule in his hospital that every baby should be picked up, carried around, and "mothered" several times a day.[28]

However, as early as the thirteenth century we find the following being recorded of the extraordinary Frederick II, Emperor of Germany (1194-1250), by the historian Salimbene:

> . . . he wanted to find out what kind of speech and what manner of speech children would have when they grew up if they spoke to no one beforehand. So he bade foster mothers and nurses to suckle the children, to bathe and wash them, but in no way to prattle with them, for he wanted to learn whether they would speak the Hebrew language, which was the oldest, or Greek, or Latin, or Arabic, or perhaps the language of their parents, of whom they had been born. But he laboured in vain because the children all died. For they could not live without the petting and joyful faces and loving words of their foster mothers. And so the songs are called "swaddling songs" which a woman sings while she is rocking the cradle, to put a child to sleep, and without them a child sleeps badly and has no rest.[29]

The Separation of Prematurity

The abnormally early separation from the maternal uterine environment suffered by premature infants should, according to theory, result in some recognizable deprivation effects during early development and in later life. In the effort to reduce the mortality of premature infants very little attention has been paid to their possible emotional needs. Life in an incubator under temperature and humidity control and the more than doubtful benefits of excessive oxygen[30] is no substitute for the close, tender, loving care of a mother. According to theory, then, prematures should in later life show the effects of their lack-love experience during the first months of their lives. The problem in the prematurely born organism is, however, rendered difficult by a large number of complicating factors. First, there is the factor of prematurity itself. The premature infant varies very little, it often fails to run a temperature or even a leucocytosis (increase of white blood corpuscles) in the presence of infection. It is pretty clear that the premature infant is a very different organism from the neonate. It is quite possible that the premature does not require as much love from the mother as does the neonate; on the other hand, it is equally possible that it requires much more. This is a matter for future research to determine. Second, premature children are likely to engender anxious and overprotective mothers, factors which are likely to have very definite effects upon the personality of the developing child. The birth process itself probably constitutes a severe experience for the unready premature. Finally, the rigid schedule upon which premature children are often put adds complication to an already complicated picture.

In a study of 22 prematures in later life Howard and Worrell have attempted to throw some much-needed light upon the psychologic adjustment of the premature. They acknowledge that 22 cases hardly represent a significant sample for statistical purposes, but they offer it for such value as it may have, and in this sense their findings are offered here. With respect to intelligence they found that prematurity as such has neither a beneficial nor a detrimental effect. On the other hand, so far as personality adjustment is concerned it was found that over half their cases were significantly unsatisfactory. "Twelve of the 22 had personalities of the submissive-passive type. Eight of the 22 showed unusual aggressive tendencies. Other aberrations uncovered were nail-biting, two cases of habit spasm and one case of chronic masturbation."[31]

Beskow, in a report of 273 prematures of school age, found that 6.5 per cent of them had suffered cerebral hemorrhage, and later had school difficulty. Fifty per cent presented nervous symptoms.

Hess, in a study of the mental development of 370 prematures, found that 264 were normal, 68 deviated slightly from normal in an expected manner for age, 23 were poor, 6 bad, and 9 were extremely subnormal. Omitting from consideration the 68 prematures who deviated slightly from normal, there remain 38 who were mentally retarded, that is, 10.2 per cent. This is a significant figure.[32]

Privation of Love and Organic Consequences

The student who thinks of mind and body as aspects of the functioning of the organism as a whole will not need to be told that not only are the effects of privation of love in childhood psychological, but that they are also likely to be physical. In addition to the traits of the affectionless character which a lack-love infancy produces, there is some evidence which suggests that social stimulation is closely related to the development of intelligence in infants. Thus,

Gilliland has found in a study carried out on white and Negro infants six to twelve weeks of age, that the infants reared at home were superior in I.Q. by five points to those raised in an institution. Two other unpublished studies by Gilliland's students on white and Negro infants showed that the I.Q. for Negro infants was as high or slightly higher than for white infants. There is no evidence whatever that Negro infants and children are genetically relatively more mature than white infants and children at these ages. Gilliland suggests that "an even more plausible theory is that, in the typical Negro home with more people living in small quarters, the child receives more social contacts. These contacts, like the effects of home vs. institutional care, result in more social-intellectual development and higher test scores."[33] We have already seen that other observers have noted a failure in the capacity for abstract thought in children who have been inadequately loved.[34]

Disturbances in their affective needs cause regressive and retardative physical changes not only in small infants, but also in children and in adults. Binning and others have shown that, as Fried and Mayer put it, "socio-emotional adjustment plays not merely an important but actually a crucial role among all the factors that determine individual health and physical wellbeing . . . it has become clear that socio-emotional disturbance tends to affect physical growth adversely, and that growth failure so caused is much more frequent and more extensive than is generally recognized."[35] Binning, in a remarkable study on the effects of emotional tensions on the development and growth of 800 Saskatoon (Canadian) children, found "that events in the child's life that caused separation from one or both parents—death, divorce, enlistment of a parent—and a mental environment which gave the child a feeling that normal love and affection were lacking did far more damage to growth than did disease," that such an environment, indeed, "was more serious than all other factors combined." Binning shows that where disease has affected growth "in most cases the reason is the emotional tension arising from the disease and its manner of treatment rather than the disease itself."[36]

Using the Wetzel Grid, Binning demonstrates how, in child after child, emotional disturbances in the home environment reflect themselves in disturbances in the growth pattern of body and mind. Referring to one grid which shows the history of a girl who under unfavorable home conditions developed, at critical periods, first pneumonia, then, shortly after the parents had separated, delinquent behavior, and finally, with indifferent care, became a serious behavior problem, Binning concludes as follows:

> [This] grid is by far the most important statistically, whether or not the parents separate. It is also the grid of the child of parents who are "too busy" socially and with business to give the child the time for manifestations of affection the child needs. It is the grid of the child whose parent sloughs his care on to the shoulders of the maid, or the school, or the state. It is the grid of the "spoiled" child. Substitute for delinquency abdominal pain, visual trouble, etc., and it shows too often how medical ailments start. Children need guidance and guidance involves discipline. Not once did we find that discipline administered fairly and with affection harmed growth, even if the family application involved frequent spankings. On the other hand "spoiling" not only seems to *invariably* affect growth but within the growth lag very frequently we see psychosomatic or personality disturbances.[37]

Very similar findings were reported by Durfee and Wolf as long ago as 1933.[38]

Spitz has shown that infants deprived of maternal love suffer severe retardations of growth and development. The physical growth and weight norms are scarcely ever reached in such children, and, says Spitz "It would seem that the developmental imbalance caused by the unfavorable environmental conditions during the children's first year produces a psychosomatic damage that cannot be repaired by normal measures. Whether it can be repaired by therapeutic measures remains to be investigated."[39] Physical development, bodily capacity, as measured by ability to sit, stand, or walk, were all seriously interfered with, as was intellectual capacity, and capacity for social relations.

Talbot and his co-workers, in a study of 51 children who exhibited stunted growth, but in whom no physical abnormalities could be found to account for their dwarfism, found that "the majority were undernourished because of anorexia [loss of appetite] due to either emotional disturbances or mental deficiency or a combination of both, in addition to such factors as parental poverty and ignorance. In the 51 so studied there was a high incidence of rejection by the mother, emotional disturbances and delinquency in mothers, marked poverty at home. Fourteen per cent had severe emotional reactions with chronic grief and anorexia attributable to a broken home brought about by death, divorce and desertion."[40]

Lihn and his co-workers have found that in the infant and childhood histories of adult chronic osteoarthritic patients there was, without exception, the experience, in varying degrees, of being ignored, neglected, or rejected by their overburdened or inconsiderate parents, and often such patients were the victims of early desertion or of the arid emotional conditions of the orphanage.[41]

The Physiology of Privation of Love

The retardation in general growth, in bone growth and the other skeletal disturbances in children and in persons who have been unloved may well be due to the inverse relationship which Selye and others have suggested as existing between the hypersecretion of ACTH (adrenocorticotrophic hormone) and the hypersecretion of STH (somatotrophic or growth hormone) from the pituitary under conditions of stress.[42] The skeletal system is but one of the organ-systems of the body which may be affected as a consequence of emotionally stressful experiences. Selye has shown that under conditions of stress the organism tends to be maintained in adaptive balance through the activities of its neurohumoral system. The integrated syndrome of closely interrelated adaptive reactions is termed the General Adaptation Syndrome (or GAS). The three stages of the General Adaptation Syndrome are, the *alarm reaction, resistance,* and *exhaustion.* Whatever the nature of the stressor (the condition producing the stress), whether it be psychological or physical, these stages of GAS maintain their invariable order.

The alarm reaction (AR) is recognized as exhibiting two phases,

(1) *the phase of shock,* characterized by a fall in temperature and blood pressure, depression of the nervous system, decrease in muscular tone, concentration of red blood corpuscles, deranged capillary and cell-membrane permeability, gastrointestinal erosion, loss of appetite, loss of libido, etc.; and (2) *the phase of counter-shock,* characterized by defense phenomena against shock, with reversal of most of the conditions seen in the shock phase. There is enlargement of the adrenal cortex with increased secretion of cortisone and adrenaline, rise in blood pressure, and so on. If the stress is mild tension and excitement are observed, if the stress is intense depression and shock are characteristic.

Resistance is the second stage characterized by disappearance of most of the symptoms, with increased resistance to the evocative stimulus, but greatly reduced adaptability of the nervous system to other stimuli. Libido remains subnormal.

Exhaustion is the third stage characterized by the reappearance of the conditions which had been present during the AR stage as a result of prolonged over-exposure to stimuli to which adaptation had been developed but which (adaptation) can no longer be maintained. "It was found," writes Selye, "that even a perfectly adapted organism cannot indefinitely maintain itself in the stage of resistance. If exposure to abnormal conditions continues, adaptation wears out and many lesions characteristic of the AR . . . reappear as a stage of exhaustion develops and further resistance becomes impossible."[43]

It may be pointed out here that the first phase of the alarm reaction on the physiological side corresponds on the psychological side to the separated child's response of *protest,* and when the separation is prolonged this moves into despair. Selye's *resistance* roughly corresponds to the stage of *denial.* Spitz has drawn attention to the parallels between the General Adaptation Syndrome of Selye and the Emotional Deprivation Syndrome as observed and studied by himself.[44] The parallels are set out in Table 6.

The general physiology of the Emotional Deprivation Syndrome may be summed up in a few words, as follows: Under prolonged stress impulses originating in the brain stimulate the hypothalamus to activity, and this in turn produces secretion of ACTH in the

TABLE 6

General Adaptation Syndrome (Selye)	Emotional Deprivation Syndrome (Spitz)
Tension Excitement Loss of appetite	Weepiness Demanding attitude Loss of appetite Loss of weight
Resistance to evocative stimulus increases	Social sector increases
Adaptability to other agents diminishes	Arrest and regression of D.Q.
Libido subnormal	Absence of autoerotic activity
Depression of nervous system	Withdrawal. Insomnia. Decreased motility
Adaptation stops	Regression of D.Q. irreversible
Resistance ceases	Infection liability
Arteriosclerosis of brain vessels	Facial rigidity. Atypical finger movements
Breakdown	Morbidity increases
Death	Spectacular mortality

SOURCE: R. A. Spitz, "Infantile depression and the general adaptation syndrome," in *Depression*, Proceedings Forty Second Annual Meeting American Psychopathological Association, 1953, pp. 93-108.

anterior part of the pituitary gland. This stimulates the adrenal glands to secrete cortisone and adrenaline. The posterior portion of the pituitary gland also secretes vasopressin which acts upon the circulatory system to produce the effects already noted. When the stress is long continued the adaptive mechanism becomes exhausted and the system breaks down.

CRITICAL PERIODS AND DEPENDENCY

Stendler has recently postulated two critical developmental periods during which the dependency drives may suffer serious privations, thus affecting the development of the personality. The first critical period occurs toward the end of the first year of life, when the child begins to test out the mother to see whether he can depend upon her. At this period he especially makes demands upon the mother's proximity, to discover whether he can both depend upon and control her.

The second critical period comes during the two- or three-year-old phase. This is the phase of his development when, in western cultures, the child is required to give up his old ways of doing things and to learn new ones. He must give up the attempts to control his mother, and while accepting his dependence upon her he is also required to become independent, to act on his own initiative, for himself and for others in culturally approved ways.

These two periods are anxious ones for the child because they interfere with the goal responses which the child has customarily made. When, during these periods, excessive demands are made upon the child these may produce excessive anxiety and result in a strengthening of the dependency drive with a consequent development of *over*-dependency.

The timing of disturbances which affect the dependency drive [Stendler suggests] will also be a factor in determining how other aspects of personality will be affected. That is, the dependency drive is so related to other aspects of personality that a disturbance during one of the critical periods will affect other aspects of personality and . . . the effects will differ according to the timing of the disturbance. A disturbance during the first critical period will have a different impact upon personality development than will a disturbance during the second critical period. . . .

Overdependent children produced during the first critical period will be children who have experienced helplessness; who have not been able to control the socializing agent at the time when recognition of the importance of that agent for one's own well-being was dawning. Therefore we can expect such children to be low in ego-strength, with resulting low level of aspiration and low frustration tolerance. Also, such children, while they cling to the socializing agent will tend to see that agent as a punishing figure rather than a helpful one. These things may not be true of overdependent children produced during the second critical period. These children are more likely to be affected in the area of conscience.

They will tend to resolve the anxiety generated by the frustration by overdoing the job of building a punishing voice inside. They will be rigid in their ideas of right and wrong, overconforming in behavior, unduly disturbed by the wrongdoings of other children. They will prefer well-defined structured situations to those which allow for more freedom of choice.[45]

In other words, children who have their dependency needs traumatically disturbed during the first critical period are likely to be affected in the ego aspects of personality development, while those who suffer disturbances of the dependency drives in the second critical period are likely to suffer in the super-ego aspects of personality development.

In the first critical period the child suffers when the parent is *absent,* and it wishes that he were *present.* In the second critical period frustration arises from interference and punishment: the parent or parent-person is *present,* and the child wishes he were *absent.*[46] The latter wish produces intolerable conflict in the child, who hates the parent whom he desires to love because he is punishing, and thus, confused and rendered anxious for fear of separation from the beloved figure, he tends to cling to his dependency more than ever.

Mother-Love—Continued

The importance of mother-love for the newborn is slowly being recognized by American pediatricians and a few obstetrical divisions in the hospitals.[47] The practice of spending the period of confinement in a hospital rather than at home is of recent origin. In former years most children were born at home, and the newborn was kept in a cradle—not a crib—by the mother's side, where it could be closely watched and tenderly fondled. But today, in a city like New York, for example, almost all births occur in hospitals, an increase of more than 60 per cent in a very short time. It is the custom in most hospitals to separate the baby from the mother immediately after birth. The infant is placed in a crib in a baby-room where it is too frequently handled with efficient indifference by "baby-hardened" nurses. Except for the assortment of sounds issuing from other babies in similar condition, it is left severely alone. After some twenty-four hours when, at last, the baby is brought to his mother's breast for his first attempt at suckling, he is, indeed, "a little stranger." What should have been for both mother and newborn a warm comforting experience is rendered a cold and arid mechanical meeting, during which the mother is often heard to exclaim, "Oh, I'd almost forgotten about the baby." Or "Are you sure its mine? Sure you've taken it out of the right crib?" In every well-conducted maternity division the wrong baby is occasionally given to nurse to the wrong mother. As the Bakwins point out:

> Separation of mother and baby immediately after birth is unnatural and unphysiologic. Among mammals it is the rule that the young remain close to the mother during early life, snuggling and cuddling against her. The mother and her young constitute a biologic unit and to separate the two in the way commonly practiced in American hospitals finds no analogy in the animal world where so much of our knowledge on nutrition and other aspects of physiology has been obtained. How contact with the mother benefits the newborn is not clear but the universality of this behavior in the animal world suggests that it has biologic value. It may, among other things, be a factor in the ability of the mother to nurse.[48]

The Bakwins might have added that not only is it the rule among all mammals for the young to remain close to the mother during early life, but that this is also the rule among all peoples with the exception of a large proportion of those living in the highly civilized communities of the western world.

The home is still, in most cases, the best place in which to have a child. The birth of a new member into the family is an event and an experience in which the whole family should participate, the children as well as the father. With confinement in the hospital the children are separated from their mother, and they frequently feel that this deprivation is the fault of the new baby, and they resent it. In this way hostility develops towards the new member of the family, and permanent injury may be done to the development of good interpersonal relations within the family. The mother also usually suffers as a consequence of this separation from her children. The birth of the child in the home as an event in which all the members of the immediate family participate is calculated to produce a happy acceptance of the new arrival and to contribute in a positive manner to the greater happiness of all concerned.[49]

The love which the newborn receives is not something abstract, but the concrete activity of the mother or whoever it is who does the mothering. It is all those things which the mother does for her child which makes the transition from the uterine state to extra-uterine life as smooth as possible. Ribble suggests that mothering is really a continuance of the closeness of the prenatal state, and the more nearly it imitates certain of the conditions before birth the more successful it is in the first few weeks. It is believed that frequent periods of contact with the mother are good for the newborn because the warmth and the support give him a feeling of reassurance. Babies tend to stop crying when they are picked up and held. Ribble suggests that contact takes the place of physical connection before birth. In addition to all the routine duties of feeding, bathing, and so on, the important manifestations of love in the form of fondling, caressing, rocking, singing and speaking tenderly to the baby are aspects of mothering which have the profoundest significance for the psychosocial development of the child. This, at least, is what by inference we have come to believe from the effects observed in those cases in which mothering has been absent.

Crippling of the Capacity for Abstract Thought

One of the most serious effects of maternal deprivation, upon which all research workers are agreed, is the crippling of the ability for abstract thought or conceptualization. Why deprivation of love should impair the capacity for abstract thought we can at the present time—in the absence of the necessary researches—only conjecture. It would appear that not only does love provide the incentive and conditions for learning, but that the warmth which it conveys somehow stimulates the development of the capacity for abstraction. Bowlby suggests the possibility that the capacity for abstract thought not only underlies ego functioning, but can develop adequately only if ego functioning itself develops favorably. Bowlby writes:

> The failure of ego development in deprived children is perhaps more easily understood when it is considered that it is the mother who in the child's earliest years fulfils the function of his ego and super-ego. The institution children studied by Goldfarb and by Bender had never had this experience, and so never had the opportunity of completing the first phase of development—that of establishing a relationship with a clearly identified mother-figure. All they had had was a succession of ad hoc agents each helping them in some limited way, but none providing continuity in time, which is of the essence of ego functioning. It may well be that these grossly deprived infants, never having been the continuous objects of care of a single human being, had never had the opportunity to learn the processes of abstraction and of the organization of behaviour in time and space. Certainly their grave psychical deformities are clear examples of the principle that injuries inflicted early produce widespread disturbance of growth.
>
> In the institutional setting, moreover, there is less opportunity for the child who has learnt the processes of abstraction and mental organization to exercise them.[50]

A certain amount of the capacity for abstract thought is recovered by the developing person who has suffered some deprivation of love in childhood. The point, however, is that the undeveloped capacity for abstract thought in childhood would seem to interfere with the child's capacity to pick up even those demonstrations of love which are offered it. Dr. Lauretta Bender goes so far as to say that "once the defect [in the capacity to love] is created it cannot be corrected."[51] Goldfarb has stated that he has never seen "even one example of significantly favorable response to treatment by the traditional means of child psychiatry."[52] However, it seems unlikely that any actual tissue damage has been done. What seems more probable is that certain patterns of relationships have failed to become established in that reverberating pool of electrical circuits which serve human beings for a mind, and that the circuits necessary for a fully functioning human being are simply not there. The necessary circuits with which other electrical circuits can establish the relationships which lead to warm human responses have not been developed.

Upon this view, then, we would be dealing with a failure in development rather than with irretrievable and irreversible damage to brain tissue. Such a view affords hope that with the development of more insight into these cases we may be able to develop methods for restoring such persons to a happier condition.

Effects of Separation at Various Ages

A question often asked is whether there are any critical periods during development in which greater damage is done by privation than during others? We do not yet possess sufficient information to be able to answer this question adequately. What, however, can be said is that it would appear that damage can be done to the child by exposing it to deprivation of maternal love for any appreciable period of time during its first eight years. In general the period of privation which is capable of doing damage of a nature severe enough to be recognized by the investigator is about one to four weeks, but it would seem probable that shorter periods of time are capable of doing damage of a substantial nature even though it may not be recognizable by the investigator—unseen psychic scars are not the less real for being unseen. Indeed, the degree of damage done will depend upon a number of factors, such as age and previous maternal care. Burlingham and Freud, for example, have shown that infants between 1½ and 2½ years of age cannot tolerate separation from the mother for more than a day without showing visible regressive effects.[53]

Vulnerability to privation is still serious between the ages of three and five, though much less so than at an earlier age. It should be understood that separation of a few days or a few weeks appears as a much longer period of time to the small child than it does to the adult. "Social time" is of much greater duration for the child than for the adult, and the younger the child the more extended does time appear to it.[54] Hence, maternal privation lasting a few days may, to a three-months-old infant appear longer than a privation of three weeks to a two-year-old. The rule seems to be the younger the child the more likely is the privation to be harmful.

Children between three and five years of age do not live as much in the present as do those of younger ages, and can therefore conceive of a future when their mother will return. They can also more readily understand explanations, and will more easily take to an understanding substitute for the mother. Children between five and eight years of age who have had a happy relationship with their mothers will tolerate separation much better than those who have not. The anxious child will tend to believe that he has been separated from his mother because he has been naughty. Such a belief will lead to further anxiety and to hatred. This may create serious difficulties with the mother upon reunion, and unless the situation is carefully handled, may lead to profound personality disturbances.[55]

Delinquency, Criminal Behavior, and Separation from the Mother

As a causative factor in delinquency and crime Bowlby has shown that separation from the mother or mother-substitute for long periods or permanently during the first five years of life, plays a highly significant role.

In a study of 44 juvenile thieves Bowlby found that a large proportion exhibited an inability to establish affectionate relationships with other persons, and displayed what he termed the "affectionless character." Fourteen of the 44 delinquents were of this type, and of these, 12 had suffered a prolonged separation from the mother at an early age. These affectionless characters were significantly more delinquent than the other thieves, constituting more than half of the more serious and chronic offenders.

Bowlby points out that strong libidinal and aggressive components were present in the stealing of these juveniles, and that there was a marked failure of super-ego development following the failure in development of the capacity for object-love. He traces this failure primarily to the lack of opportunity for development.[56]

Excessive libidinal and aggressive impulses directed towards the parents are found in one form or another in all cases of functional mental illness. But, Bowlby points out, what characterizes the affectionless character is (1) that he lacks the usual inhibition of these impulses, and (2) that he is unable to establish permanent personal relationships owing to his inability to feel or express love. In other words, while in most neurotics and unstable persons there exists some ability to establish object-relationships, there is an extreme degree of incapacity to do so in affectionless characters. There is a massive inhibition of object-love combined with excessive and relatively uninhibited libidinal and aggressive impulses. Bowlby suggests that the lack of inhibition is the necessary result of a lack of a love-relationship. In short, unless the infant has an opportunity to develop object-love, that is, to recognize and value the mother or mother-substitute as a person from whom love and all its satisfactions are derived, and comes to take pleasure in reciprocating her love, he will never learn to love others. Normally, through the processes of identification,[57] and introjection,[58] there comes to be formed in the child's mind a pattern of feeling and behavior, the super-ego, which is designed to maintain the love-relationship with the object by inhibiting impulses which are inimical to it.

> The super-ego [Bowlby says], although often experienced as a foreign body, an agent of the loved object, is in reality the expression both of the need for the object and of love for it, and this remains so despite its frequent use of aggressive measures to attain its ends. Without some measure of object-love the whole structure of the super-ego, whether it operates by violent inhibition or moderate control, could not exist, since both the purpose which it serves and the needs which it expresses would be nonexistent.[59]

If no opportunity is afforded the infant for the development of object-love it will simply fail to develop that mixture of selfish and altruistic behavior which ensues as a result of the normal mother-infant relationship. The unrequited needs of such an infant lead to attempts on its part to gratify its needs in its own way, libidinously[60] and without inhibition, and at a later stage in phantasy. There is a failure to develop an adequate conception of the meaning of reality because there has been a failure in the organization of the experiences of gratification of needs, the pleasure principle,[61] to realization of the reality principle[62] which usually follows as a consequence of normal object-love development, with its normal educative complements of satisfactions and inhibitions. Hence, such children will often steal, preferably from the mother, in order to secure gratifications which have been denied them.

The adequately loved child will gradually learn by the training which he undergoes how to postpone and even renounce some of his needs. In so doing he adjusts to the cultural reality which his mother constitutes for him; he learns to inhibit,[63] to impose upon his ego the restraints of the super-ego based upon the realities of his disciplining and love experiences.

Inconsistencies in the amount of gratification and frustration which the mother gives to the infant may have much the same effect as inadequate satisfaction of the infant's needs. The same privation may be produced by the presence of too many persons attempting to assume the maternal role, as in the case of many families in which interfering grandparents and uncles and aunts live in the same household. Under such conditions the experience of the infant may prove anarchic. In this connection it is well known that unless a dog is trained at the hands of one person but is ordered about by many persons it is liable to grow up lacking attachment to any person and tend to be wild and intractable. Rheingold has experimentally shown that institutional children will not only develop greater social responsiveness when exposed to one "mother" but will also increase in social responsiveness to other persons (Harriet L. Rheingold, "The Modification of Social Responsiveness in Institutional Babies," *Monographs of the Society for Research in Child Development,* vol. 21, 1956).

The Mechanism of Injury in Privation of Love

The question has been raised as to the nature of the physiological changes which occur in the nervous system of the deprived child. Is the brain of the deprived child in any way affected by its lack-love experiences and its responses to them? Is there any arrest in the growth and development of any part of the neuronal net? Is there, as it were, a "hardening" or consolidation of the type of organization of experience or lack of it, such that it becomes a permanent and unalterable part of the psychophysical nature of the organism?

Bowlby has pointed out that "Children of between 6 months and 3 years who are separated from their mothers often undergo intense emotional experiences of rage and despair and then proceed to organise their social relations on a new pattern; often one in which no particular human being is sought after and loved. It would appear that if this new and psychopathic organisation is permitted to consolidate around the age of three or four years, it tends to become permanent.

"Clearly" Bowlby goes on to say, "this 'setting' of the perceptual and behavioural patterns in the third and fourth years must have as its base important maturational changes in the physiology and anatomy of the brain."[64]

Bowlby's suggestion seems to be that during the critical developmental periods of the first four years unless the organism receives the proper stimulations certain parts of the brain will not grow and develop normally either in structure or in function. There will be maturational changes. "It would be very interesting to know what they are," Bowlby writes. "My own guess would be that the cerebral centres concerned complete their basic patterns of growth at this time, and thenceforward do not change greatly in their general organization. It may be that part of the essential condition for the growth and organization of cerebral centres is the external environment and the sensory stimuli derived from it."

There can be little doubt that every human organism is born with certain potentialities for behavioral development *under the proper stimulation* of certain types of experiencing and responding. Whether these potentialities are localized in "cerebral centres" is, however, open to question. Be that as it may, if we understand Bowlby's "basic patterns of growth" to mean, as he appears to mean, growth within the predetermined inherited potentialities (possibilities) of the organism, then that growth will be completed as a product of those potentialities in interaction with the kind of stimulation those potentialities have received largely from the external environment, and chiefly, if not entirely, from other human beings.

The pattern for growth of these potentialities is a pattern or configuration having a certain general organization and orientation or directiveness. In other words, under the (organismally) normal or expected kinds of stimulations (such as the mother loving the child) the potentialities of the organism will tend to mature in terms of their basic pattern of growth and development. These basic patterns are genotypic, and in interaction with the normal environmental stimuli will develop a normal phenotype; under abnormal or different kinds of stimuli the same genotype is capable of developing a variety of different phenotypes. The genes involved are almost certainly "clocked," that is to say, the rate and time intervals set by the structure of the developing organism itself are factors of quite as great importance for the development of behavior as is "stimulation." These facts hold not only for human beings but also for nonhuman animals. Let us consider some examples from the latter.

Lorenz, Tinbergen, and their co-workers have shown that fish, birds, and the few mammals thus far investigated are born equipped with innate releaser mechanisms (IRM's) which cause the organism to respond to certain simple sign stimuli in a particular manner. Seemingly complex social behavior in these animals is constituted by a relatively few such IRM's. The IRM's do not determine what particular stimuli shall elicit the response, any more than genes determine the characters or traits with which they are connected, but a particular IRM will be activated in a particular manner by a particular class of stimuli. Any object or stimulus within such a class to which the organism is exposed during the appropiate critical developmental period will usually become fixed as the particular stimulus—and no other—which will elicit the particular IRM. This phenomenon is known as *imprinting*. Lorenz has shown that greylag goslings, for example, accept the first living being to whom they are exposed as their mother, and thereafter refuse to accept anyone else as such. Freshly hatched mallards will not respond to the visual stimulus, but will respond to the call-note, and whoever makes the first call-note they will adopt as their mother.[65]

The normal phenotypic expression of the gosling's IRM is toward other geese, but if the "learning" stimuli to which the gosling is exposed during the critical developmental period are derived from other objects of appropiate size, it will thereafter respond only to them. The same is true for mallards with respect to auditory stimuli. The genotype has now become phenotypically conditioned. The object-reaction is now fixed. Such abnormal fixation under ordinary conditions would be extremely rare.

Do IRM's exist in man? At least two IRM's have been attributed to man: the parental response to the baby,[66] and the response by smiling at about the tenth week to anything resembling the human face.[67]

These two responses are social responses in that they are normally elicited by other human beings and require a certain amount of conscious evaluation. It is difficult to see what connection they have with IRM's or imprinting. Walter's criticism is very much to the point here.

> Some investigators also believe that they have found the key to a baby's first smile in these impersonal "innate releaser mechanisms." Spitz found that a mask with two eyes and a nose waved slowly to and fro on the end of a broomstick, was enough to elicit the first smile, between the tenth and the twentieth weeks of life, all smiles before that period being attributable to wind. But it is at least a permissible question whether this is "imprint" or association. It would be strange if, in ten weeks, the appearance of a face had not already become associated with smiling fortune in the baby's mind. For the human brain, even at birth, is so highly organised, the electrical rhythms that sweep it are so suggestive of searching mental activity, that it is difficult amidst so much complexity to tell how soon the ape is left behind. The good fairy's gift of learning by association is found in every cradle.[68]

Indeed, there is a considerable difference between the IRM's of animals and those attributed to man. In animals the IRM becomes permanently fixed in relation to the imprinted stimulus; in human beings no such fixations occur in relation to the alleged IRM's. It would, therefore, seem incorrect to suggest, as Bowlby does, that

IRM's occur in man. Fixation is a process which only superficially resembles imprinting. Fixation is a term which, in Freud's words, refers to "a conjunction of impulses with impressions and with the objects connected with those impressions. This conjunction has to be effected very early, is very hard to resolve, and has the effect of bringing the development of the instincts concerned to a standstill."[69] This could serve beautifully as a definition of imprinting, except that fixation is not necessarily permanent in human beings, whereas in non-human animals imprinting it is.[70]

If there exists anything resembling the phenomenon of imprinting in human beings then it is of a very attenuated nature, and is sufficiently covered by the term *habit*. A child among human beings does not, during any of its critical developmental periods or at any other time, become *fixated* upon any person as its mother, but it does become *habituated* through association to regard a particular person as its mother or mother-substitute. Furthermore, this habituation can be broken and another person can be adopted as the mother. The observations of Burlingham and Anna Freud, among others, abundantly demonstrate this.[71]

Fixation is a pathological process involving an arrest of some part of the libido during the course of its development, with a consequent inhibition of development at an infantile stage. Imprinting is in no way a pathological process, but it is in every respect a normal one.

At the present time it would be best to leave the question open whether the insufficiently analyzed concepts of IRM and imprinting in animals can be applied to man. Further study may reveal that they can, in a modified form, be utilized in the analysis of human nature.

Rate and Frequency of Love

In animals the gears of the developmental clock are set irreversibly. This is also the case in man with respect to physical development, but *not*—and this is the important difference—with respect to behavior.

There are strong grounds for believing that human beings possess a genotype which determines the nature of the respons environmental stimuli will elicit. Not only will the resp vary with the nature of the environmental stimuli, but they also vary according to the *rate* at and the *time* during which th genotype is stimulated.

For example, in embryological development, certain chemical changes must occur between the seventh and ninth weeks if the organism is to develop a normal face. This period is developmentally critical,[72] but the occurrence of the requisite chemical changes is not enough—they must occur at a particular rate.[73] If there is a disturbance in the rate then a cleft palate and harelip may result. Similarly, there is reason to believe that within any period critical for the development of a certain form of behavior the rate at which the proper stimuli are offered to the organism must conform with its genotypic requirements or the responses will fail to develop adequately. For example, during the period in the twenties and thirties when children were being brought up by the pediatrician's clock on a schedule which disregarded the needs of the child, it was possible for a mother to love her child at the scheduled *times*, but in the intervals to give it no love whatever. The damage done to many such children can be explained on the basis of the fact that they did not receive enough love, that is, the *rate* and *frequency* of love which they received was inadequate. Instead of being activated to love by being loved, such children in response to the frustration of their need for love exhibit rage, anxiety, and aggression, and these responses become part of their behavioral organization.

What they do not experience also becomes part of their behavioral organization, and this is at least as important as the rage and despair which these children experience. First, these children undergo a failure of behavioral development owing to the lack of proper social stimuli, and second, the consequent responses of rage and despair take the place of those which would have developed in the form of love and trust.

It is not enough to love children at certain intervals of time; for their proper development during the critical developmental periods they must receive definite quantities of love which must not fall below a certain minimum at any time; this is the *rate* at which love is given. Love must be given at intervals which do not fall below a certain minimum—this is *frequency* (repetition at short intervals). The rate at which love is given is influenced by the frequency with which it is given. If the intervals are too long, then no matter how satisfactory the rate of love may be, the proffered love may fail to produce the proper effects.

An explanation that fits the relevant facts as we know them today, as to what happens in the brain of such children is as follows: Electrical circuits of certain kinds are not established in the neuronal net of deprived children because the necessary charges of energy have not been received. Such a child develops a neuronal net which is wanting in certain patterns of electrical circuits. If a child has not been loved it does not have any developed "love" circuits. Hence, when the critical developmental period for their development has passed, incoming changes resonate or reverberate at most against the inadequately developed "love" circuits, and the responses to them are inadequately made. The "know-how" just is not there because it was never developed. The responses, on the other hand, which such children or persons will frequently make to expressions of love are often in terms of the circuits which have been built up in their brains in terms of aggressiveness, rage, and insecurity.

Cultural and Class Differences

So far as the effects of varying forms of privation upon the personality are concerned the evidence now available for nonliterate and other peoples is extremely suggestive.

In societies of the western world there are great variations in the kind and amount of mothering which infants receive. Class differences here play an important role. Among the upper classes the mother tends to shift the burden of "mothering" the infant to a nurse as soon as possible. In Europe, and in the southern United States until very recently, children were almost always brought up by nurses and governesses. In the middle classes the maternal care of the child varied considerably, in some families the children receiving a good deal of attention from the mother during the newborn and infancy periods, in others this task being delegated to a nurse and later to a governess. Among the lower classes universally the mother is the person who gives the child most attention. Such class differences in "mothering" have undoubtedly exercised an important effect in producing class differences in personality. While there now exist a number of studies on national differences in personality there exist relatively few on class and personality.[74]

The upper class Englishman (and Englishwoman) should prove to be good material for the investigation of this problem. Over and beyond the fact that the early training and inhibitions of the Englishman prevent him from ever exhibiting much emotion, there is detectable a certain lack of warmth which, in common with the members of the upper classes of some other nations, may be found to be due to an early lack of mothering. Not all members of the upper classes exhibit this lack of warmth, and many members of the middle and lower classes may show it. This lack of "warmth" in adults often signifies the inability to love other persons, and in such adults one usually looks in vain for that human sympathy with others which one finds in most human beings. There may be something in the idea that the ability of the upper middle and upper class Englishman to rule and govern conquered peoples and to justify that rule, is to some extent due to such lack of sympathetic understanding for others.[75]

The custom among the upper and upper middle classes in England of sending their children away to boarding schools at an early age, of institutionalizing them as it were, outside the warm ambience of the family, deprives these children of the love and affection which is necessary for the healthy development of the personality. This privation of parental love suffered during the tender years of childhood is probably the principal cause of the "coldness," the apparently unemotional character, of the upper class Englishman. On this aspect of the Englishman's character E. M. Forster has an interesting passage.

> People talk of the mysterious East, but the West also is mysterious. It has depths that do not reveal themselves at the first gaze. We know what the sea looks like from a distance; it is of one color, and level, and obviously cannot contain such creatures as fish. But if we look into the sea over the edge of a boat, we see a dozen colors, and depth below depth, and fish swimming in them. That sea is the English character—apparently imperturbable and even. The depth and the colors are the English romanticism and the English sensitiveness—we do not expect to find such things, but they exist. And—to continue my metaphor—the fish are the English emotions, which are always trying to get up to the surface, but don't quite know how. For the most part we see them moving far below, distorted and obscure. Now and then they succeed and we exclaim, "Why, the Englishman has emotions! He actually can feel!" And occasionally we see that beautiful creature, the flying fish, which rises out of the water altogether into the air and sunlight. English literature is a flying fish. It is a sample of the life that goes on day after day beneath the surface; it is a proof that beauty and emotion exists in the salt, inhospitable sea.[76]

In contrast with the Englishman's alleged emotional anemia and impervious reticence is the emotional warmth and sensitivity of the French or the Italian. It is significant that the French or Italian family is one in which the members are closely bound to one another in a loving, emotional atmosphere which is different from that encountered among English-speaking peoples. In France and Italy it was generally considered something of a tragedy for a girl to entertain the idea of marrying an Englishman—those "cold fish" apparently incapable of all emotion! The French and the Italians still entertain similar views concerning the English.[77] One cannot help recall here the immortal remark of the anonymous American lady who, in 1843, wrote a devastating reply to Charles Dickens' *American Notes,* "An Englishman in love! Was a monumental statue ever in a fever?"[78]

Insofar as one can speak of "national character," it is a legitimate inquiry to seek to discover to what extent such character structure is determined by the influences and pressures of a particular pattern of socialization through the family. But these are matters which we must reserve for later discussion.

The individual who must receive love and respect but is himself almost incapable of any emotion more closely approximating love than respect, has been, we may surmise, in many instances the victim of a lack-love infancy. This suspicion is abundantly borne out by several researches on the "authoritarian personality."[79] Adorno and his co-workers conclude that to produce a warm loving personality "All that is really essential is that children be genuinely loved and treated as human individuals."[80]

Illuminating here is a study by David Levy of 21 anti-Nazi Germans, concerning whom he concludes that "in comparison with typical Germans" the anti-Nazis escaped the conventional and rigid family structure of their nation. The anti-Nazis were brought up with more affection and less restraint. "Their world is a broader one, less limited in terms of religious, social, and intellectual boundaries. They have attained a more critical attitude. They are freer from conventional, stereotyped thinking."[81]

Overauthoritative parents are likely to produce developmental failure of the dependency drives, resulting in a rigidified personality who seeks always to be commanded, and feels safe only when he is commanded.

The Overprotected Child

Yet another cause of developmental failure of normal affective character and of the super-ego is the phenomenon of maternal overprotection. "Smothering" rather than mothering. The over-indulgent mother indulges her child's every wish and protects him from every experience which might deprive him of the pleasure he seeks. He is completely undisciplined. He therefore grows into an egocentric, selfish, demanding, disobedient, impudent, affectively infantilized problem whose social maturation has been seriously impaired. The forms of maternal overprotection and their varying effects upon the child have been thoroughly described by David Levy.[82] Here we may mention the overprotective mother who dominates her child to the point of constricting his development. The dominated, overprotected child becomes shy, withdrawn, submissive, infantile, asocial, and greatly dependent upon the mother.

The *overprotected indulged* children are the victims of an environment rich in love and poor in discipline. The result is an ill-developed super-ego. The *overprotected dominated* children are overdisciplined and therefore not adequately loved. In many of the latter cases the unconscious hostility of the mother to her overprotected child may be very marked, and such children will exhibit all the signs of affect-hunger. But where there is overdiscipline accompanied by some love the super-ego is often developed to the extent of complete submissiveness to and dependence upon the mother. Such a boy is usually described as "too good," a "sissy," very obedient and polite, "ought to have been a girl."

We see, then, how dependent the infant is for its emotional development upon the kind of mothering it has received. And as Spitz and others[83] have shown, this mothering must be given the child especially during the early developmental critical periods of its life if it is to develop as an adequate social being.

The overindulged child looks upon the world as his oyster, and is upset when it doesn't yield to his demands. The overdisciplined child feels that he is inside the shell and is upset at any attempt to extricate him from it. Both wish to keep what they have exactly where it is, for that is how they feel most secure. This form of behavior constitutes an example of a tendency of mental life to maintain at as low a level as possible the quantities of excitation flowing into it or to bring about a minimum of psychic tension. This tendency of mental life has been called the *Nirvana Principle.*

Social Competence

In all the examples of failure of one kind or another in the process of mothering, of satisfaction of basic needs, we perceive as the end effect the failure to develop social competence. These deprived and overprotected children are unprepared to meet the problems of life, and their social incompetence only serves to increase their difficulties.

Life is of its nature a test of social competence, and the penalty of social incompetence is rejection.

The failure to develop social competence is due to the privation of love suffered by the infant during the first six to eight years of life. We are thus led to conclude that in order to be successfully social one must have learned to love by having been loved; that, indeed, society is based on love, in fact, *is* but a developed form of love, which is but another way of saying that society or culture represents the evolution of man's attempts to satisfy his needs. Where hatreds exist in any persons within any society we may be sure that they, too, are due to the involvement with love, for hatred is love frustrated. Aggression is but a technique or mode of seeking love.

Love is in its essence, in its beginning and end, *social.* It arises out of the satisfaction of the self-preservative or basic needs of the organism in the primary dependent relationship to the mother, and it demands always the presence of other persons or their substitutes for it to be able to function adequately.

Man's need for society and his need for love are in essence one and the same thing. Ian Suttie, in one of the great books of our time, has suggested that "play, co-operation, competition and culture-interests generally are substitutes for the mutually caressing relationship of child and mother. *By these substitutes we put the whole social environment in the place once occupied by the mother.*"[84]

Social interaction is the extension of mother-child interaction. The ability of the person to interact socially will depend largely upon the character of his early interaction with his mother or mother-substitute.

The Organism's Innate Need for Love

The organism is born with an innate need for love, with a need to respond to love, to be good and cooperative. Whatever is opposed to love, to goodness, and to cooperation is disharmonic, unviable, unstable, and malfunctional—evil. Were the infant's needs adequately satisfied he could not help but be good, that is, loving. All of man's natural inclinations are toward the development of goodness, toward the continuance of states of goodness, and the discontinuance of unpleasant states. As Ralph Lillie has pointed out:

A property of the *good* (in the universal or Platonic sense) is that conscious effort tends to be directed toward its continuance, since it is the object of desire; while *evil,* the immediately or ultimately painful, is a feature of reality which conscious effort tends to remove or overcome. The former has thus within itself a property or character which favors its continuance and increase; the latter is inherently unstable.

Scientific analysis shows that stability in all highly diversified or composite systems requires harmonious relations—relations of mutual support or equilibrium—between the different components and activities . . . what should be better known and more widely acted upon is that integration *between* different individuals as seen in the mutually helpful relations of the various units in many human and animal communities—or even between different species of animals and plants—is as much a factor in biological survival and evolution as is conflict. The avoidance of useless conflict, and the subordination of individual interests to the interest of the whole reality which includes the individuals, would thus seem to be rational aims for all conscious beings; and these aims have the further sanction of religion when the whole is conceived in its character as ultimate value or deity.[85]

Security

The biological basis of love consists in the organism's drive to satisfy its basic needs in a manner which causes it to feel secure. Love *is* security—but security alone is not love. Mere satisfaction of basic needs is not enough. Needs must be satisfied in a particular manner, in a manner which is emotionally as well as physically satisfying. Babies as well as adults cannot live by bread alone.

It is worth repeating that the biological basis of love lies in the organism's ever-present need to feel secure. The basis of all social life has its roots in this integral of all the basic needs which is expressed as the need for security, and the only way in which this need can be satisfied is by love.

Ethics and Human Nature

It is a discovery of the greatest possible significance for mankind that the ethical concept of love independently arrived at by almost all existing peoples is no mere creation of man but is grounded in his biological structure as a functioning organism. The implications of this discovery are of the greatest importance, for it means that man's organic potentialities are so organized as to demand but one kind of satisfaction, a satisfaction which ministers to man's need for love, which registers love, which is given in terms of love—a satisfaction which is defined by the one word, *security*—secure in the affections of others and secure in one's affection for them. That is what the human being seeks all his life, and society, culture, and man's institutions, however insufficient some of them may be, all exist to secure that one fundamental satisfaction. The emotional need for love is as definite and compelling as the need for food. The basic needs of man must be satisfied in order that he may function on the organic level. But in order that he may function satisfactorily on the social plane the most fundamental of the basic social needs must be satisfied in an emotionally adequate manner for personal security and equilibrium.

When the needs of the developing social organism are inadequately satisfied, that is, where there have been too many frustrations—thwartings of expected satisfactions—where there has been a significant privation of love, the organism becomes disordered, anxious, tense, fearful, and hostile. This, in fact, is the state in which innumerable human beings in the western world live today.

We know from the observation and study of many peoples—such as the Australian aborigines,[86] the Eskimo,[87] some of the peoples of Melanesia,[88] Micronesia,[89] and Indonesia,[90] the Japanese,[91] Chinese,[92] Burmese,[93] American Indians,[94] and also peoples of western civilization[95]—that the well-integrated, cooperative adult personality is largely a product of a childhood which has enjoyed a maximum of satisfactions and a minimum of frustrations. We also know the obverse to be true, that the disintegrated, noncooperative adult personality is largely a product of a childhood which has suffered a maximum of frustrations and a minimum of satisfactions.

The one thing in the world of which one can never receive or give too much is love. One does not spoil children by giving them too much, but by giving them too little.

On the island of Okinawa, the largest of the Ryukuyu chain of islands in the Southwest Pacific, with a population of 450,000 souls, Dr. James Clark Moloney, psychiatrist in the United States Navy, states that he never saw a spoiled, self-centered, fearful child. On the contrary, the children were remarkable for their well-disciplined nature, calm, confidence, and cooperativeness. Dr. Moloney traces these qualities to the excellent mothering which the Okinawan child received.[96] Similar testimony for the children of many other peoples has been given by numerous observers. For example, Mountford, writing of Australian aboriginal children, says:

> The wealth of affection that exists between the adults and the children in an aboriginal tribe has to be seen to be believed. There was one baby boy in camp, perhaps nine months old, who was seldom in his mother's arms except for meals. At all other times some man, woman, boy or girl was either carrying him about or playing with him. The older children seemed to go their own sweet way, without hindrance from anyone.
>
> The little folk sat round our fire at all times of the day, yet, in spite of the apparent lack of discipline by the parents, they were not the slightest trouble, any request that we made being obeyed with perfect good humour. There were sweets, sugar and all sorts of dainties in open cupboards, only a few feet from where they used to sit, yet no child touched them.
>
> We grew very fond of these children, and when the time came, we left them with more than a passing regret.[97]

This has uniformly been the experience of all who have known these remarkable people. The fact is that the Okinawan and the Australian child, by being adequately loved, has developed an ego-structure which is cooperative within itself and with others, which is not in conflict with itself, which has learned to love because it has itself been loved. In short, the aboriginal child has received a fundamental training in being related to itself and to other people. And this is achieved in the mother-child relationship.

The biological basis of cooperation, in short, has its origins in the same sources as social behavior, namely, in the process of reproduction. Social, cooperative behavior is the continuation and development of the maternal-offspring relationship; it is therefore as old as life itself, and in spite of recent appearances to the contrary the movement of evolution has, in man, been increasingly directed toward the fuller development of cooperative behavior.[98] Cooperative behavior has great survival value. When social behavior is not cooperative it is diseased behavior. The dominant principle which informs all behavior which is biologically healthy is love. Love, social behavior, cooperation, and security mean very much the same thing. Without love the other three cannot exist. To love thy neighbor as thyself is not simply good text material for Sunday morning sermons, but perfectly sound biology.

Men who do not love one another are sick—sick not from any disease arising within themselves, but from a disease which has been enculturated within them by the false values of their societies. Belief in false values, in competition instead of cooperation, in narrow selfish interests instead of altruism, in atomism (especially atom- and hydrogen-bombism) instead of universalism, in the value of things and of money instead of the value of life and of man, represents man turning upon all that is innately good in him.

Man's sense of mutuality and cooperativeness may be suppressed, but so long as man continues to exist it cannot be destroyed, for these are traits which are part of his protoplasm.[99] His combativeness and competitiveness arise from the frustration of his need to cooperate. These are important facts to bear in mind at a time when all the surface evidence seems to point in a contrary direction. The word of the moment may be "fission"—whether with respect to physics or human affairs—but "fusion" comes much closer to reflecting man's natural behavior patterns.

Science points the way to survival and happiness for all mankind through love and cooperation. Do what we will our drives toward goodness and good will are, biologically, as basically determined as are our drives toward breathing. Our highly endowed potentialities for social life have been abused to pervert and deny their nature, and this has led us close to the brink of disaster, a disaster which spells doom, unless we realize what we have done and take the proper steps to undo it before it is too late. For we cannot deny the power of the world forces which we share with all life and which have reached their highest development in our potentialities as human beings, without destroying ourselves.

10 EXPERIENCE, CULTURE, AND PERSONALITY

Man is mind, and the situation of man as man is a mental situation.
—KARL JASPERS*

SECURITY AND LOVE

That love constitutes for the infant an assurance of support, of security, is a fact which has been discussed at some length. Love, for the child, *is* security—emotional security. The need for love arises out of the infantile dependency state, and by being loved the child in its turn learns to love. Love is the first stimulus toward social development, and there is good reason to believe that a lack of love in infancy produces an anxiety-ridden personality. Just as aggression always results from frustration, so insecurity always results from a lack of love. Furthermore, this holds true for the person throughout life, no matter what his previous psychical history. The person who, as an adult, finds himself or believes himself to be unloved, no matter how much he may have been loved at an earlier age, feels isolated and insecure. He may attempt to fall back upon his wealth, his prestige, or his power. A good example of this is provided by the hero of Orson Welles' film *Citizen Kane*. Deprived as a young child of the love of his parents, and brought up in the emotionally arid environments provided by sepulchral-looking steel-vaulted trustees, Kane develops as a power-drunk, essentially lonely person. He surrounds himself with people whose services he attempts to buy, with women whose affection he unsuccessfully tries to win, with stupendous quantities of possessions and enormous estates, but the one thing

* Karl Jaspers, *Man In The Modern Age*, London, Routledge, 1933.

which escapes him is love. This he never contrives to secure. Money and power, he finds are no substitutes for love. As he lies upon his bed dying he grasps in his hand a simple toy—a snow-flake globe reminiscent of the day when he was forcibly deprived of his parents' love and protection, and the last word he utters is "Rosebud"—the name of his sled, with which he had been playing on that unforgotten day when he was literally torn from the home to which he was never to return. "Rosebud," the symbol of all he had lost and never been able to recover. Such persons are tragedies to themselves, and when they are in strategic positions, exert a tremendous influence upon their societies, and all too frequently upon the direction of world affairs involving the lives of millions of human beings.[1] This in itself would constitute a good reason for throwing all possible light upon the relationship between love in the socialization of the individual and the functioning personality.

Frustration

Since nonsatisfaction or inadequate satisfaction constitutes thwarting of expected gratification, that is, *frustration,* it would be well to consider here the effects of frustration upon animals under experimental conditions, as well as upon man.

Hunt has shown that the effects of frustration upon the infant albino rat persist into adulthood. The halves of each of two litters of albino rats were submitted to a controlled feeding schedule of fifteen days beginning at the twenty-fourth day of life. Control animals from all litters were allowed free feeding. After a period of five months, during which both experimental and control animals had been allowed only one feeding a day for five days, the results were very illuminating. The infantile frustrates in the 24-day group hoarded more than two and one-half times as many pellets as their litter-mate controls. The infantile frustrates in the 32-day group hoarded approximately the same number of pellets as their litter-mate controls. It is evident that the effects of frustration did endure into adulthood. Hunt has explained these results by assuming that the hunger aroused in the adult feeding frustration served as a conditioned stimulus. This set off hunger-anxiety in those animals that had suffered sufficiently severe hunger in infancy, so that the total excitation aroused by this adult experience was greater than that in the control animals. Hunt argues that the reason traces failed to endure in the 32-day group was because, being older and better developed, the same feeding schedule that was effective for the 24-day group was sufficiently less severe for them so that it failed to fix the traces of the infantile experience.[2]

Fredericson has reported the results of an experiment devised to test the effects of infantile experience upon adult behavior. The problem was to test the hypothesis that a limited period of competition for food during infancy will result in competitive behavior at a later stage in development, despite the absence of hunger. For this purpose three strains of highly inbred mice were used, the 50 animals involved in the experiment being for each strain virtually identical. The sexes were approximately equally represented. The animals were weaned at 21 days of age, and lived in pairs, males with males and females with females.

The techniques which elicited competition over food consisted of presenting a given pair of hungry mice with a single piece of hard laboratory food. The experimental design consisted of two separate experiments, each with its own litter-mate controls.

The first experimental group was given seven one-a-day trials in competition beginning at 29 days of age. Retested at 72 days of age when they were not hungry these mice were found to compete over food. Their litter-mate controls, that had received no experience in food deprivation or competition over food, tested when not hungry at 72 days did not compete or fight over food.

The second experimental group received only a single experience in competition over food at 33 days of age. This group, when retested at 72 days of age, fought and competed over food. The litter-mate controls, that had never been exposed to competition over food, retested at 72 days did not compete over food when not hungry.

Both control groups competed for food as soon as they were deprived of it, but not when they were not deprived of it; whereas the mice that had experience of competition over food in infancy competed as mature animals even when they were not hungry and it was unnecessary for them to do so. The interesting fact is that but a single experience in infancy over food deprivation and competition was sufficient to determine similar behavior in adult life in those mice. Fredericson concludes that the results of his experiments support theories of personality which emphasize the importance of infantile experience.[3]

In another study Fredericson suggests that the food acts like a conditioned stimulus which elicits competition when the animals are not hungry.[4] This would seem so for the animals do not appear to be in any way frustrated, and there is no other obvious reason why they should compete other than that they were conditioned to do so at the sight of the food in infancy.

Kahn has shown that young mice which are attacked and beaten before the age when they would normally fight are, when placed in situations which would usually stimulate them toward fighting, much more inhibited than are animals which are only defeated as adults.[5] Similar observations have been made by Scott and Marston.[6]

Kahn also found suggestive evidence clearly indicating that mice which had early been isolated from their mothers were somewhat more defensive, strikingly more aggressive, and less investigating than those reared to maturity by the mother.[7]

King and Gurney found that male mice (I) that had been isolated from contact with all animals at 20 days were less aggressive as adults than (M) male rats that had been raised exclusively, after their 20th day, with males, and those that had been raised (F) exclusively with females. Groups M and F were almost equally aggressive, and Group I much less so. Group F tended to be slower to enter into combat than Group M animals. The experimenters suggest that mice raised in groups learn to be aggressive through competitive associations, this learning making them more ready to fight than those raised in isolation. Alternatively they suggest that innate tendencies to aggressiveness may be inhibited in direct proportion to the strangeness of the situation. Animals without early associations being more strange to each other than those with early associations, and are therefore more inhibited in a potential fighting situation.[8]

On the assumption that an adequate amount of sucking represents a definite need which must be fulfilled, Levy took two puppies from a litter of six and put them on controlled bottle feeding. All conditions, with the exception of the time devoted to sucking, were kept as constant as possible for 20 days. One pair of puppies did their sucking from nipples in which the holes were small. This pair was also given supplementary opportunities for sucking; these were the "long-time feeders." The other pair, the "short-time feeders," were fed from nipples with large holes. In test situations the short-time feeders showed a tendency to prolonged sucking of all kinds of objects between meals. These observations led Levy to conclude that thumb-sucking in human infants could be similarly explained by their having had inadequate opportunities to satiate the sucking impulse.[9] Ross, confirming these findings, observed that puppies that had early been deprived of their mother tended to exhibit excessive non-nutritional sucking.[10]

In a similar study on chickens Levy, assuming the existence of a pecking need that would require satisfaction, found that chicks raised on wire mesh which restricted the amount of pecking to a minimum were more restless, had a lower average weight, showed more preening behavior and more pecking at droppings and at the wall than did chicks of the same stock which were raised under similar conditions except that the floor of their pen was earth. The restricted chicks were very much more aggressive than the unrestricted chicks, indulged in more feather picking, and virtually denuded their less aggressive pen-mates.[11] Hymovitch has shown that the early perceptual environment to which rats are exposed is influential in determining their later adult learning.[12]

Even more valuable and more to the point than these studies is the totally unpremeditated series of observations made by Hammett in 1921,[13] entirely without reference to and without any prescient knowledge of such problems as are being discussed here. Reference has already been made to these studies.

While making studies of thyroparathyroidectomized albino rats of the genetically homogeneous Wistar stock, Hammett noted that some of the animals did not die. It had been thought by many observers that such an operation must invariably prove fatal, presumably owing to the action of some toxic substance upon the nerve elements.

Hammett found that the operated rats were actually drawn from two separate groups of rats, and that the greater percentage of survivors came from the "Experimental Colony." In this colony the animals had been petted and gentled, whereas the animals exhibiting the higher mortality rate were drawn from the "Standard" stock, a group whose only human contact was that incident to routine feeding and cage-cleaning. These animals were timid, apprehensive, and high-strung. When picked up they were tense and resistant, and frequently exhibited fear and rage by biting. *"The picture as a whole is one of constant high irritability and neuromuscular tension"* (p. 199).

The behavior of the gentled group was in marked contrast to that of the Standard colony animals. The former had been gentled for five generations. When picked up the gentled animals were relaxed and yielding. They were not easily frightened. "They give a uniform picture of placidity. The threshold of the neuromuscular reactions to potentially disturbing stimuli is almost prohibitively high."

So far as their relations to human beings are concerned it is obvious that the group of rats which had been gentled felt secure in the hands not only of those who fondled them but of all human beings. The laboratory attendant had brought them up under conditions during which they were frequently gently handled, stroked, and had kindly sounds uttered to them, and they responded with fearlessness, friendliness, and a complete lack of neuromuscular tension or irritability. The exact opposite was the case with the ungentled rats, the rats which with reference to their relations with human beings had received no attention from them whatever, except that incident to feeding and cage-cleaning. These animals were frightened and bewildered, anxious and tense in the presence of human beings. This constitutes a very interesting confirmation on lower animals of conditions which we know to exist among children brought up under not dissimilar circumstances.

Let us see what happened when thyroid and parathyroid glands were removed in the 304 animals operated from both groups. Within 48 hours of operation 79 per cent of the irritable rats died, while only 13 per cent of the gentled rats died—a difference of 66 per cent of survivals in favor of the gentled rats. When the parathyroids alone were removed, within 48 hours 76 per cent of the irritable rats died and only 13 per cent of the gentled rats died, a difference of 63 per cent.

Standard Stock rats, placed in the Experimental colony at weaning and gentled, became tame, cooperative and relaxed, and resistant to the effects of parathyroidectomy.

In a second series of experiments[14] Hammett investigated the mortality rate in parathyroidectomized untamed wild Norway rats which had been caged for one or two generations. The wild Norway rat is a very excitable creature. A total of 102 rats was used. Of this number 92, or 90 per cent, died within 48 hours, most of the survivors dying within two or three weeks of the operation.

Hammett concluded that the stability of the nervous system induced in rats by gentling and petting produces in them a marked resistance to the loss of the parathyroid secretion which in excitable rats usually results in death from acute parathyroidemia in less than 48 hours. Later researches have given us a more detailed understanding of the mechanisms involved (see pp. 221-223).

The animal studies here briefly discussed suggest that the privations and frustrations suffered by the infant organism not only serve to produce a disharmoniously functioning personality, while the satisfaction of basic needs in an adequate manner serves to produce a more equilibrated personality, but also that, as in the case of Hammett's rats, positive evidence is available to the effect that such privations and frustrations produce substantial functional changes in the neurohumoral system which, through the agency of the autonomic system, express themselves in terms of differential viability under conditions in which the organism is exposed to insult or stresses of various sorts. Clinically this type of relationship between personality and viability under conditions of stress has been well known to physicians and surgeons for many years. The outcome of any disease or operation is always more promising in the well-balanced personality than in the anxious patient. The cheerful patient in general does much better than the cheerless one. All this constitutes good evidence that such differences in resistance, recovery rates, and viability, connected as they are with such differences in personality, represent actual differences in the organization of the nervous system. This suggestion is further corroborated by the evidence of psychosurgery. Persons suffering from depressive involutional neuroses, often leading to attempted suicide, who have either blown out their own frontal lobes or had them partially or wholly removed by operative means, often make remarkable recoveries in which more or less complete relief is obtained from the effects of the neurosis.[15]

When in such persons some part at least of the neurologic structures associated with the patterns of mental functioning of the person are destroyed, that pattern of functioning more or less disappears. The fact, however, scarcely needs to be emphasized that the experiences of the infant become a part of its nervous system and to a very large extent determine the pattern of functioning of that nervous system.

Hunt's work was inspired by Money-Kyrle's hypothesis, based on a comparative survey of primitive societies, that "Free feeding and late weaning would seem to promote generosity and optimism. Oral deprivation and early weaning would seem to promote stinginess and greed."[16]

Hunt's experiments on rats brilliantly confirm this suggestion. The probabilities, as we shall see, are high that Hunt's experimental observations may be legitimately generalized for human beings. Levy's experiments on puppies and chicks agree in almost every particular with the observations made on children under similar conditions.

INFANTS

Margaret Ribble has given an account of her observations on 600 infants with reference to early experience and behavior reactions which might be related to later personality disorders.[17] This work is still in progress, but certain results, which have already been briefly discussed in the light of Ribble's findings, will bear elaboration here. Ribble paid particular attention to the anxiety or tensional states of the infant, its metabolic economy, its circulation, the development of awareness, evidences of security and insecurity, respiratory and skin changes, pleasure getting, and the manner in which the tactile and kinesthetic senses participate in the child's primary orientation and development of its sense of reality. Ribble found that all these processes "are related to an innate need for contact with the mother, and that the mother who supplies this contact unstintingly fosters her child's development."

The infant obtains satisfaction for its physiological needs, the need for oxygen, the need to feel, the need to move, the need to suck—all needs quite as strong as the need for food—from the mere act of contact and being held, carried about, and fondled by the mother. Such acts are indispensably necessary if a well-equilibrated child is to develop. After the first week of postnatal life the human voice begins to exercise a peculiarly soothing effect. It is this satisfying effect of the human voice which gradually succeeds in reducing the infant's innate sensitivity to loud noises, as seen, for example, in the "startle reflex." Holding and fondling similarly serves to reduce the fear of falling which is seen in the Moro reflex. In children who have been inadequately mothered these reflexes tend to persist for an abnormally long period of time.

Proper mothering of the infant is a vitally important factor in bringing about a viable nervous integration of the organism, in conserving energy for mental growth, "and in making possible the sublimation of pleasure-getting, or what Freud has called sexual activities, in the interest of socially approved emotional and later intellectual development."

Ribble found that the reactions to inadequate mothering take one of two general forms in babies. They develop a form of negativistic excitement or a form of regressive quiescence.

Negativism

The negativistic reaction is displayed in a refusal to suck, in a more or less complete loss of appetite and an inability to assimilate food. The body muscles are hypertensed, breathing is shallow, and vomiting as well as periods of violent screaming are common. This corresponds to the phase of protest described on pages 214–216.

Regression

The regressive reaction is even more serious than the negativistic. Such infants when put to the breast or bottle make a few sucking movements in response to the stimulus situation, and then quickly fall into a stuporous sleep. The sucking reflex may altogether disappear, and there is a general loss of muscle and skin tone. The evidence indicates that this type of reaction is the result of frustration from too little peripheral stimulation. The organism simply regresses to a fetal state. Ribble believes that such privation interferes with the blood supply to the higher centers, in this way interrupting the developmental processes through which these centers are brought into action.

Treatment calculated to restore general and cerebral circulation, and to stimulate respiratory development, is generally successful enough to lend support to this interpretation. The regressive reaction is identical or at least similar to the disease of infancy already described and formerly known as infantile debility or marasmus. We have seen that this disorder, resulting from inadequate mothering, may result in serious biological as well as psychological damage to the organism.

Mothering and Love

The child who has been inadequately mothered, who fails to receive a sufficient amount of love, generally fails to learn to love, and such children generally fail to become satisfactorily socialized. Such a child's personality development frequently follows a definite and predictable course. Both as a child and as an adult he continues to exhibit a marked dependency upon others, he is insecure, he is extremely jealous of his siblings, he is excessively dependent upon others for affection, he has an inordinate desire to be loved, and while he is himself *anxious* to return love, to love others, he finds himself quite incapable of doing so. An additional trait generally present in such persons is a state of anxiety which is a dominating and constant motive underlying much of their behavior. Observations which have been made on persons exhibiting many of these forms of behavior strongly point to the same causes: inadequate mothering during childhood. In some instances it is found that the mother died during the early childhood of the subject, in other instances it is found that the child had been left alone for considerable periods of time and given attention only at feeding time. We have already seen that further observations also strongly suggest that similar disturbances may be produced in a child which has been adequately mothered for several years, and then suddenly deprived of such mothering. The clinical literature affords innumerable examples of such cases.[18]

The feeling of helplessness, of hopelessness, and the depressions and depressive states accompanying such feelings, may in most cases be traced back to failure of expected satisfactions especially in the oral phase of development. Unable to satisfy its own nutritional needs, "to get affection, to be loved, to be taken care of, to get 'supplies'" results in a profound feeling of helplessness. As Edward Bibring points out, "Frequent frustrations of the infant's oral needs may mobilize at first anxiety and anger. If frustration is continued, however, in disregard of the 'signals' produced by the infant, the anger will be replaced by feelings of exhaustion, of helplessness and depression. This early self-experience of the infantile ego's helplessness, of its lack of power to provide the vital supplies, is probably the most frequent factor predisposing to depression."[19]

Whenever we meet with a failure to function as an adequate

human being we may be certain that the cause or causes are to be looked for in the love relationships of the person during the first six years of his life. For our purposes we place great emphasis on the importance of love in the socialization of the person because it is through the means of love that the infant first develops a consciousness of himself in relation to another person—the fundamental social relationship. By being loved the child learns to love. By being loved the organization of potentialities receive the only requisite stimulation which encourages their further development, and self-gratification becomes indissolubly associated with the gratification of another object, with gratification directed towards another object—the mother—and this is the beginning of the process of actively learning to love and cooperate with others.

Freudian and Neo-Freudian Concepts

Freud's concept of mental life as an interplay of reciprocally urging and checking forces is most useful in enabling us to understand those processes of mental development which are observable in infant and child. Perhaps we may attempt here a brief and tentative unification of the psychoanalytical parameters of the structure of the mind with some of the concepts which have thus far been developed.

The Id and Basic Needs

The most primitive and unconscious source of all the unregulated urges of the person, in which the desire for gratification reigns supreme, is designated by the psychoanalyst as the *id*. The id may be identified with the source from which the basic needs draw their energies.

The Ego and the Culturally Organized Personality

The id or basic drive supplies the energies, and the organization of the id is brought about by the modifications imposed upon it by the external world. This complex of organized drives is the *ego*. The ego is never entirely differentiated from the id. Part of the ego is unconscious and part conscious. The ego may be identified with the culturally organized personality, the civilization of the person.

The Super-Ego and the Value System of the Person

The *super-ego* is an outgrowth and modification of the ego. Its special function in relation to the ego is to rule it. It is essentially the same as conscience. It is to a great extent unconscious, and largely inaccessible to the ego, though in free communication with the id. The super-ego represents the integrated value system of the person.

According to Freud the unsocialized infant directs its libido mainly along one channel, toward its own body (*autoerotism*). Through the stimulation of the mothering process it learns to direct much of its libido toward external love objects (*alloerotism*), while always diverting a part of the libidinal energy in the direction of the self or ego (*narcissism*). Quite obviously, then, failure to receive adequate gratification from external sources will maintain the person in his autoerotic and narcissistic activities. The development from selfish to altruistic behavior is arrested.

On the other hand, the evidence which has become available since Freud's brilliant speculations in this field indicates that the unsocialized infant directs only a part of its libido toward its own body; that, indeed, most of its libido is directed outward toward securing satisfactions for itself, and not inward, as Freud suggests. The evidence indicates, rather, that the inward direction of libido follows only when the infant's attempts to secure satisfaction from outside, from other objects, have been unsuccessful. It is not then a matter of failure to receive adequate gratification from external sources being responsible for the maintenance of autoerotic and narcissistic activities, but it is rather that in the face of such failures the infant turns its libido inward, toward itself, in order to secure those gratifications from and for itself which it failed to receive from external sources. And it is not that development from selfish to altruistic behavior is arrested, but rather that selfish behavior is produced as a result of the failure to cooperate with the infant, as a result of the failure to stimulate it toward altruistic behavior, by being altruistic toward it.

Banham, on completing her study of over 900 children between four weeks and four years of age, concluded as follows:

> There seems little evidence from the observation of infant behavior that "self-love" comes first in the development of human affections. "Other love" is rather the first to appear, and develops along with the child's differentiating percept, and later with his concept of the human being who cares for him. The child is apparently unaware of, and unconcerned about himself. Certainly, he finds objects of interest to explore and sense. At about three months of age he discovers and watches his fingers, he listens to his own babbling and cooing; but his striving, excited affectionate behavior is directed towards another human being, usually mother.[20]

Mothering, Socialization, and Culture

It cannot be too often repeated that in the dependency relationship of the child to its mother, and later to the father and older persons, is to be seen the primary socializing pattern, a pattern which is variously elaborated throughout one's life. This consists first in the mothering which serves not only to stimulate the development of the infant but also to preserve, by a sympathetic indulgence of its wants, something of the continuity between intrauterine and extrauterine existence. As the infant develops, the indulgence of his wants is gradually changed into a series of regulatory pressures calculated to educate him in the skills and restraints demanded by his social group. This at the same time lays the basis for later attitudes of friendliness, affection, and trust. As Mowrer and Kluckhohn point out, "By withholding the adult cooperation which is so essential to the infant, the parent has constantly at his command a device for increasing the infant's variable, exploratory behavior and for then selectively rewarding (by responding to) those new, more adult-like responses which make their appearance."[21]

In this manner parents make the reward of their love conditional upon the child's making the required response. Such love has been termed *conditional love*.[22] It is because the child is dependent upon others for his satisfactions that he learns to adjust himself to the conditions they set. In studying the processes of socialization we are studying the progressive formation of patterns of behavior in response to social stimuli—the endowing with form of the previously unformed, the organization of the unorganized, the conditioning of certain responses to particular stimuli or patterns of stimuli of social value. Since the stimulus conditions the response, the character of the stimulus must serve as the criterion of the social response. Murphy, Murphy, and Newcomb therefore offer the following definition: "Social responses are those which appear in response to human beings, or to a combination of stimuli in which persons have an important place."[23]

This definition seems unnecessarily to limit the meaning of the social as far as the child is concerned, and also, for that matter, so far as the adult is concerned, particularly in view of the well-known animistic tendencies of the child, that is, the tendency to endow all objects, animate and inanimate, with animate personalized powers, powers which it is possible to commune with and, to some extent, to control. On the other hand, if we take the stimulus as the criterion of the social response, then any stimulus having some social value is capable of evoking a social response. Since the infant shows evidence of regarding almost all things which he experiences in the social situation as objects with which he can interact in a cooperative and mutually satisfying manner, it is not persons alone, in the adult sense of that word, to which he makes social responses, since most objects with which he comes into contact are for the first few years of his life treated as personified objects. The distinction between the animate and the inanimate, between persons and objects, between the absolute value of the immediacy of his own perception and the relativistic value of other people's points of view, are all phenomena of the later childhood socialization process. Furthermore, a vast number of inanimate objects, of artifacts, come to assume more or less considerable social significance, in the sense of eliciting social responses. A crucifix, a flag, a book, a painting, apparel, and a thousand and one other things are all, of themselves, capable of eliciting social behavior principally in terms of socially learned responses to socially significant stimuli. In short, anything which is learned to be a social stimulus to which certain responses must be made is by definition within the energy field of the social, since it is capable of evoking a social or cultural response.

This view of the social has, perhaps, been unduly neglected by many writers on the socialization process, but without a full realization of its significance an important part of that process and its dynamics will be overlooked. The cultural artifacts and the objects of the natural environment in vital association with which the person grows up play a very important role in the socialization of the person. These objects are all endowed with value, and it is necessary to understand that this value originates in basic needs which are culturally satisfied in particular ways according to what is traditionally given in any culture. In that sense the consciousness of the person becomes, as it were, a cultural artifact.[24]

The socialization of the person is largely determined by the operation upon him of cultural processes peculiar to the given society in which the person develops. What a person will think and do socially is a function of the culturalization process to which he has been exposed plus the modifying effects which his own individual constitutional potentialities exert in interaction with that process. We believe, as Frank has put it, that "culture coerces and dominates the individual, through the ideas, conceptions, beliefs and patterns with which he orders and explains his experience, directs his efforts and guides his conduct."[25] This process begins at birth and continues throughout life.

Culture and Genetics

The question is often raised, and in a period which has seen the doctrine take on so insidious and perfidious a form it is a question more frequently asked than ever before: How can we be certain that culture is not something which is to a large extent determined by conditions which are genetically more dominant than cultural factors? May it not be that biological factors peculiar to each group are really the determining ones in giving its character to any particular culture? In the cunningly devised words of a leading Nazi educator, Alfred Baeumler:

> History has shown, and daily shows anew, that man can be trained to be nothing that he is not genuinely, and from the beginning, in the depths of his being; against this law, neither precept, warning, punishment, nor any other environmental influence avails. Realism in the study of man does not lie in attributing evil tendencies to him, but in recognizing that all that man can do emerges in the last resort from himself, from his innate qualities.[26]

This is modestly described as thinking "Copernically" when most others are still thinking "Ptolemaically." Perhaps an unfortunate slip on the part of Herr Baeumler, in view of the fact that Copernicus belonged to an allegedly subhuman "race," for Copernicus was a Pole.

What evidence do we have which significantly bears on such statements? There is, of course, the evidence of America itself where the descendants of immigrants of innumerable nationalities and ethnic groups—English, Scotch, Irish, German, Dutch, French, Italian, Japanese, and others—have become virtually completely identified with American culture.[27] Some groups have not become thoroughly identified with American culture because they have never been permitted to do so, but the influence of the American social environment has been so great that the members of these groups have undergone socialization in a very distinctly more American than foreign manner. The cultural changes which have been wrought in the Japanese and Chinese immigrants into Hawaii have been striking.[28] Culturally, the Hawaiian Japanese and Chinese differ markedly from their Japanese and Chinese ancestors, and this applies to those Hawaiian Japanese and Chinese who have not intermarried.

If any more unequivocally clear cases than this may be called for, they can be readily supplied, thanks to the work of Ackerknecht, who has brought together the data concerning children of white parents abducted by North American Indians during the eighteenth and nineteenth centuries.[29] There are accounts of eight fairly well recorded life histories of such stolen children. All these children were abducted between the ages of four and nine years, with the exception of a girl who was taken in adolescence; all of them forgot their native culture, and even the girl who had been stolen when she was fifteen years of age became "completely" Indianized. In every case these "White Indians" resisted all attempts to persuade them to return to their white relatives and the culture of their birth. As Ackerknecht says, the white Indians seemed to have found "a kind of unity of thought and action and a kind of social cohesion which deeply appealed to them, and which they did not find with the whites, especially not with the pioneers. There is no doubt that this fact largely contributed to their staying with the Indians" (page 34). The remarkable thing about these "White Indians" is that they not only became completely Indianized culturally in the sense of manifesting purely Indian forms of social behavior, but they also developed all the physical powers of resistance said to be peculiar to Indians. Furthermore, most of them lived to be extremely old. Finally, all of them had acquired that facial expression and outward impassability characteristic of the Indians. Concerning four of these "White Indians" it is expressly recorded that having become accustomed to Indian ways they could no longer sleep in a white house or bed.

Such evidence should conclusively disprove the view that culture is something which will express itself in a genetically determined form, emerging from man's "innate qualities," no matter what the environmental influences to which he may be exposed.

11 ISOLATION VERSUS SOCIALIZATION

No man is an Island, entire of itself.
—JOHN DONNE, *Sixteenth Devotion*

IS HUMAN STIMULATION NECESSARY FOR DEVELOPMENT?

What grounds have we for believing that intimate interactive social relations are necessary with another person or persons if the organism is to become socialized? How do we know that a normal individual, left entirely to himself from birth to adult age, would not develop characteristically human forms of behavior?

The answer is that we know with certainty that infants born without the normal sense necessary for the perception of their environments, and without the ability to communicate with others, remain completely unsocialized until some other form of social communication is established with them. The classic cases of the blind deaf-mutes Laura Bridgman and Helen Keller[1] are most illuminating in this connection. Until each of these children had learned the finger alphabet—in other words, communication through the skin—they were virtually completely cut off from interactive social relations with other human beings. They were isolated, and the world in which they lived held little meaning for them; they were almost completely unsocialized. But after the patient efforts of their teachers had succeeded in enabling them to learn the finger alphabet, the world of symbolic communication was opened to them, and development as a social human being proceeded apace. In spite of their blindness and deaf-mutism, the other senses of these children were normal, and from their birth they had been surrounded by other persons, so that it is not true to say that they were completely cut off from all contact with other human beings. The fact is that both children did learn some things from their association with other human beings through the sense of touch, but this was a minimal amount compared to what they learned as soon as they were enabled to communicate efficiently through the symbolic language of the manual alphabet.

Kamala and Amala

Cases more unequivocally clear than these, in spite of a large literature on isolated children, are difficult to cite. The literature has been fully, though not altogether critically, surveyed by Zingg in his book *Wolf-Children and Feral Man*.[2] The occasion for this book was the publication of the diary kept and edited by the late Reverend J. A. L. Singh of the day-by-day history of Kamala and Amala, the so-called "wolf-children" of Midnapore (India). Since this account of the wolf-children in relation to the problem of socialization has been accepted somewhat uncritically by many persons, and has gradually crept into sociology textbooks, it may be useful to examine it here.

Natives and other villagers claimed to have repeatedly seen two children, emerging together with several wolves from an ant-hill which served as the den of these strange companions. According to his own account, while traveling in the company of two Anglo-Indians who witnessed the event, Mr. Singh captured or rescued the two children from the wolves' den at Godamuri, Midnapore, on October 17, 1920. At the time of their rescue it was estimated that the younger child, Amala, was about eighteen months old, while the older one was estimated to be about eight years of age, named Kamala. When taken by the wolves it is assumed that each of the children was about six months of age, and that they had been abducted from different families. Amala died on September 21, 1921. Kamala died on November 14, 1929. Thus, Amala was observed for almost a year, and Kamala for nine years.

When rescued or liberated, it is reported, Kamala and Amala were unable to stand in the erect position, but habitually progressed on all fours. They ate raw meat and entrails in what is alleged to have been wolf fashion, were without sphincter control, howled like wolves, preferred the society of dogs to that of human beings, and so on. They were entirely without speech and all those other attributes which we have come to regard as specifically human.

Unfortunately, Mr. Singh's account of these children rests on the completely unsupported testimony of one person—Mr. Singh. Affidavits testifying to the good character and truthfulness of Mr. Singh have been issued by his Bishop and the local magistrate, to both of whom he was well known. Four well-known scientists contribute forewords to the book testifying to its genuineness. Notwithstanding such testimonials and any impression of genuineness which Mr. Singh's record may make upon us, one cannot, with all the good will in the world, accept such unconfirmed statements as facts. Verification is a cardinal principle of scientific method, and it is not a principle that can ever be suspended. Whether or not children have ever been reared by animals can only be determined by observation, not necessarily premeditated, carried out under conditions which provide the means of verification. Hundreds of stories and legends have as their theme the rearing of children by animals, and the investigation of these stories constitutes a legitimate and significant activity, but most of the time that activity falls into the realm of folklore rather than fact. Our task must be dispassionately to evaluate the worth of such stories.

There are certain statements in Mr. Singh's account which render the whole work suspect.

Mr. Singh states that two Anglo-Indians witnessed the rescue of the children from the wolves' den, but that one is untraceable and the other dead. Why, during all the years that Mr. Singh was making observations on Kamala, did he make no attempt to obtain statements from these and other men who were alleged to have been present at the rescue? Does one keep such records as Mr. Singh kept merely for the sake of the record? Does one not usually keep such records in order to make the information contained in them available to others? Mr. Singh obviously realized the importance of the subject he was presumably seeking to illuminate; why then did it not occur to him to get the facts of the rescue fully corroborated by his witnesses?

Kamala is presumed to have been kept in the wolves' den for seven and a half years. But wolves do not keep their young for anything like so long a period under normal conditions. Is it likely that they would have departed from the universal practice of wolves in the case of Kamala?

Could a six-month-old child be suckled by a wolf? It is possible, but it is difficult to imagine why a wolf would want to do so troublesome a thing.

Even if the statement were fully corroborated that the children were found together with the wolves in their den, that in itself would not constitute evidence that they were brought there by wolves, nor that they had been suckled and reared by them. Mr. Singh states that Kamala and Amala used to howl regularly almost every night at about ten o'clock, and at one and three o'clock in the morning. The idea that wolves howl at regular hours every night is a widespread folk belief that is not borne out by the observations of such trained scientists as have had an opportunity to study their habits. What was obviously intended as an irrefutable indication of the children's lupine nature serves, rather, to arouse further doubts as to the accuracy of the narrative.

The statement that the children were not observed to sweat probably constitutes yet another example of the influence of folkloristic belief upon Mr. Singh's judgment. The widespread notion that dogs do not sweat except through the tongue is untrue. Dogs have numerous sweat glands on every part of the body.[3] But for the purposes of Mr. Singh's narrative, since dogs and wolves are closely related—and since the wolf-children were alleged to have adopted the habits of wolves—it must follow that wolf-children do not sweat.

The eyes of the children are said to have emitted a blue light at night. "Night glare" is a phenomenon not unknown in human beings, but it is a condition of such rarity that the chances against it ever occurring in two individuals living together are so astronomically high that we are forced to give up all attempt at normal explanation. The necessary extreme myopia or hypermetropia may have been present, but there is no evidence of any such conditions in Mr. Singh's account. I have been unable to find any record of children who were brought up in darkness exhibiting a like phenomenon. It is difficult to conceive of the special structure necessary, the tapetum, developing as a special adaptation to the conditions of life of Amala and Kamala. But what is even more difficult to conceive is the emission of "a peculiar blue glare, like that of a cat or a dog, in the dark" without the presence, as far as one can gather, of any external source of light. This, in fact, is quite impossible, for the light must always be of external origin.

As for the "blue" glare itself, this would appear to be impossible in the case of human beings, for the simple reason that the only possible source of such "glaring" is the fundus (the posterior portion of the base of the eye), and this normally reflects either a dark red, or an orange-yellow color. The blue eye glare of cats and dogs and many other animals is due to the reflective action of particles in the tapetum ("bright carpet"), a specialized layer of cells situated either in the choroid immediately behind the retina or in the retina itself, cells similar to those which in the human iris produce the appearance of the normal blue eye, but which in the latter case have no connection with "night glare." In the offspring of Malayan-Negro crosses it is said that the fundus, through the ophthalmoscope, may appear somewhat bluish, depending upon the presence of certain pigment particles, or even gray, but it is doubtful whether in such cases one could obtain a bluish or grayish glare from the eyes. In those rare instances when "night glare" has been recorded in man, the reflection was dark red or, in the case of glioma of the retina, a yellowish reflection.[4]

There are numerous other difficulties[5] which could similarly be discussed. But let us come to the point. Mr. Singh claimed that Amala and Kamala were reared by wolves. What evidence exists in support of this claim? The answer is: *None.*

Were Amala and Kamala abandoned by their parents? No one knows. Were they congenitally defective in any way? Their unsatisfactory portraits tell us nothing. If these children were not congenitally defective then it would be a reasonable inference to draw that their retardation, or rather nondevelopment as human beings, was due to the fact that during the critical period of their development they were practically isolated from the conditioning influences of human interstimulation.

It was during this conditioning period that, the wish apparently being father to the thought, it is assumed they spent their lives with wolves, living the life of wolves, so that behaviorally they became what they were assumed to have been conditioned by—the socializing influence of wolves.

The evidence, it is to be feared, is not good enough, but taking the matter from the general standpoint of the development of behavior, one thing is certain: Given all the necessary normal potentialities, the human organism does not normally become a person simply by virtue of being born into the species *Homo sapiens;* indeed, he cannot become a person unless he is exposed to the socializing influences of other persons. The attributes of personality are a function of human society, of persons in interaction, of human socializing factors acting upon potentialities capable of being personalized.

Since the above was written doctors W. F. Ogborn and N. K. Bose have made a thorough on-the-spot investigation of the story of the wolf-children. The findings of these investigators indicate that although two children named Amala and Kamala lived for a time in the Singh orphanage, there is no evidence whatever to support the account given by Singh and Zingg of these children's "history." Even the village "Godamuri," the alleged situation of the wolves' den, does not exist in Midnapore or anywhere else in India. (W. F. Ogborn and N. K. Bose, "On the Trail of the Wolf Children," *Genetic Psychology Monographs,* vol. 60, 1959, pp. 117-193.)

The Case of Anna

A valuable account of the effects of extreme social isolation upon the development of a child has been given by Kingsley Davis.[6] This is the case of Anna, a girl who from the age of about eight months until her discovery five years later, on February 4, 1938, had been isolated in a storage room situated on the second floor of a farmhouse some seventeen miles from a small Pennsylvania city. The official who first saw the child reported that "the child was dressed in a dirty shirt and napkin. Her hands, arms and legs were just bones, with skin drawn over them, so frail she couldn't use them. She never had enough nourishment. She never grew normally, and the chair on which she lay, half reclining and half sitting, was so small the child had to double her legs partly under her." When removed to the local county home Anna was in a completely apathetic state, she lay limp in a supine condition, immobile, expressionless, and indifferent to everything. She was believed to be deaf and possibly blind, and she exhibited all the symptoms of chronic malnutrition of the non-rachitic kind. No sign of organic disease, however, could be discovered apart from the effects of malnutrition.

Her history up to this time from birth was as follows: Anna was born in a private nurse's home on March 6, 1932. Shortly afterwards she was taken to a children's home, and for a time she was boarded with a practical nurse. She was said to have been a perfectly normal, even beautiful child. Between the age of six and ten months she was taken back to her mother's home because no financial means could be found to support her in an outside home. At home she was confined in one room, where she was fed on a diet consisting solely of milk. Apart from feeding her the milk the mother paid absolutely no attention to her. This was her second illegitimate child. Her own father (the maternal grandfather of the child) wished never to set eyes on it, and so the mother, a high-grade moron or dull normal, took this means of keeping it out of the way. Anna's brother ignored his sister except to mistreat her occasionally.

The bedroom in which Anna was kept reclining on a broken chair contained a double bed on which mother and son slept. Such contacts as Anna had with her mother and brother, except for being fed with milk by the mother, were of a perfunctory or openly antagonistic kind. Toward Anna's fifth birthday her mother began feeding her some thin oatmeal with a spoon, but Anna never learned to eat solid food.

In Anna, then, we would seem to have a child who from about

the age of eight months was the victim of extreme social isolation. Seen over a period of months by Davis, Anna remained virtually completely unsocialized.

Seen three days after she arrived in the county home (which had but one nurse for 324 mostly deficient adult patients!) she had become relatively active, was able to sit up when placed in a sitting position, and to move her hands, arms, head, eyes, and mouth quite freely. She had been given a high vitamin diet, massage, and some attention. She turned her head toward a loud-ticking clock when this was held near her, though other attempts to make her notice sounds, such as clapping hands or speaking to her, failed to elicit any response. All her reflexes were normal. In bed she jounced up and down rhythmically—an activity of which she was very fond. It is of interest to note that she very much liked having her hair combed.

She showed no reaction to toys, which she handled in a distracted manner without any element of play. She would frown and scowl in response to no observable stimulus. When physically restrained she exhibited considerable temper, did not cry and smiled only when coaxed. Her subsequent progress was somewhat slower.

Ten days later she was more alert, with greater ability to fix her attention, with more expression, and she handled herself better. Furthermore—and this is important—she had found her tongue in the physical sense. Whereas it had formerly lain inactive at the back of her mouth, she now stuck it out frequently, and with enjoyment. She showed some taste and visual discrimination, and was able to sit up and dangle her feet from the bed. She had learned one social stunt, rubbing foreheads with the nurse. She had not, however, learned to seek attention, to manifest needs, to chew, or to control her elimination.

A month later there was very little visible change except for a slight physical improvement. She laughed when tickled, and the nurse believed that Anna now recognized her. The doctor believed that she was congenitally deficient.

After another month Anna was more energetic, laughed a good deal, and is credited with having made a sound like "da."

A month later she had scarcely made any improvement, and on

the performance tests given her by Davis she ranked below the one-year-old child.

Two months later she could walk when supported by making deliberate steps. Her interest in other persons had become more obvious, and her responses more definite and discriminating.

Three months later, on November 11, 1938, when she was removed from the county home, there were a few additional changes. She could barely stand while holding on to something. She obviously liked people, but she was still an unsocialized creature who had learned very little.

During the nine months in the county home she had actually received very little social stimulation; everything had been done for her with minimal encouragement to do everything for herself. She had never been disciplined or rewarded, and most of her care was turned over to adult inmates, many of whom were mentally deficient and scarcely able to speak themselves.

When seen again on December 6, 1938, three weeks after her removal to the foster home, Anna presented her visitors with a surprise—she had begun to learn. She could descend the stairs by sitting successively on each one, she could hold a doughnut and munch it like a normal child, she could hold and drink from a glass, and she could feed herself with a spoon. When one beckoned and called her, she would make an effort to come, smiling and going through excited extra motions.

As Davis suggests, this transformation was most probably due to the fact that in the foster home she was the sole object of one woman's assiduous care. "Her new guardian was using the same common-sense methods by which mothers from time immemorial have socialized their infants—unremitting attention, repetitive correction, and countless small rewards and punishments, mixed always with sympathetic interest and hovering physical presence. These Anna was getting for the first time in her life" (p. 561).

Three months later, March 19, 1939, Davis reports her accomplishments as follows (p. 561):

> She was able to walk alone for a few steps without falling; she was responsive to the verbal commands of her foster-mother, seeming to under-

stand in a vague sort of way what the latter wanted her to do; she definitely recognized the social worker who took her weekly to the doctor and who therefore symbolized to her the pleasure of an automobile ride; she expressed by anxious bodily movements her desire to go out for a ride; she seemed unmistakably to seek and to like attention, though she did not sulk when left alone; she was able to push a doll-carriage in front of her and to show some skill in manipulating it. . . . Limitations still remaining, however, were as follows: she said nothing—could not even be taught to say "bye-bye"; she had to be watched to tell when elimination was imminent; she hardly played when alone; she had little curiosity, little initiative; it seemed still impossible to establish any communicative contact with her.

It does not seem accurate to say, as Davis does, that it seemed impossible to establish any communicative contact with Anna. Obviously a number of things had been communicated to her through speech and physical training in the management of various objects and to some extent of herself. She could make more or less adequate responses to certain cues even though she was herself quite unable to speak. Anna herself, after a year of socializing experience maintained a comparatively passive role so far as communication with others was concerned, but that she had participated to a measureable extent in the communicative process can scarcely be doubted.

More than five months later, August 30, 1939—that is to say some eighteen months from the cessation of her period of isolation and the commencement of her exposure to socializing influences—Anna was taken from her foster-home and moved to a small school for defective children. At this time she was a stout girl some twenty pounds overweight for her age, which was seven years and five months. She could walk better and almost run, her toilet habits showed that she understood the whole procedure, and she manifested an obvious comprehension of many verbal instructions.

On November 6, 1930, she is reported as completely unable to speak, simply making gutteral and sucking noises, and wandering aimlessly about, without any ability to concentrate. Examined more than five months later, on April 25, 1940, by the late Professor Francis N. Maxfield, her hearing was found to be entirely normal, vision apparently normal, she was able to climb stairs, her speech was in the "babbling stage," and "promise for developing intelligible speech later seems to be good." On the Merrill-Palmer scale she made a mental score of 19 months. On the Vineland social maturity scale she made a score of 23 months. Professor Maxfield felt that with proper training she would eventually attain a mental level of six or seven years.

On July 1, 1941, the school for retarded children reported that Anna was 46 inches in height and weighed 60 pounds. She could bounce and catch a ball, and conformed to group socialization. Toilet habits were firmly established. Food habits were normal except that she still used a spoon as her sole implement. She could dress herself except for fastening her clothes. Most interesting of all, she had finally begun to develop speech. She was said to be at the two-year level in this respect. She could call attendants by name and could bring one in when asked to do so. She had a few complete sentences to express her wants.

By June 22, 1942, Anna had made slight progress.

> [She] could follow directions, string beads, identify a few colors, build with blocks, and differentiate between attractive and unattractive pictures. She had a good sense of rhythm and loved a doll. She talked mainly in phrases but would repeat words and try to carry on a conversation. She was clean about clothing. She habitually washed her hands and brushed her teeth. She would try to help other children. She walked well and could run fairly well, though clumsily. Although easily excited, she had a pleasant disposition.

Unfortunately Anna died of pneumonia in 1943. The school in which she had been placed was a private school for feebleminded children with little to recommend it as a place of training. Davis strongly feels that Anna never received the attention necessary to overcome the initial social isolating handicaps which she suffered.

The question, of course, arises whether Anna was not in fact congenitally defective, and her slow development due to a significant extent to the limiting action of genetic factors. The mother was subnormal. On the Stanford Revision of the Binet-Simon Scale her performance was equivalent to that of an eight-year-old child, her I.Q. being 50, indicating mental deficiency of "middle grade moron type." Anna's father is believed to have been a 74-year-old man of normal mentality.

Congenital or Acquired Deficiency

The fact is that in the present state of our knowledge it is hardly possible to decide whether in such cases we are dealing with a congenital or an acquired deficiency. The quest for certainty in connection with such cases is highly desirable, for they are capable of throwing a great deal of light upon the nature of the interaction between the organic potentialities of the individual and the socializing influences to which he is exposed; hence it is more than ordinarily necessary that in our endeavor to secure such crucial case histories we should be on our guard against unwarranted assumptions and doubtful examples. We must not go beyond the evidence. Most of the accounts of isolated children which we have are unsatisfactory from many points of view.[7] In general the early history of the child is unknown, the genetic status of both parents insofar as their intelligence is concerned is likewise unknown, and the attempts to socialize such children following their removal from the isolating environment have not been systematic or adequate.

Characteristics of Isolated Children

Without discussing all the cases of isolated children which have been reported, a study reveals that they resemble each other in many particulars. For example, such children are unable to speak, though under special training they can acquire some speech. The senses of sight and hearing are functionally undeveloped; there is poor locomotor development, the child is completely nonsocial, and its capacity to become a normal social being is greatly impaired.

Such children by normal standards would be regarded as exhibiting the most pronounced form of amentia—idiocy, with an I.Q. of less than 20 points or two years. But these isolated children display traits in addition to those normally characteristic of congenital idiots which clearly indicate the effects of isolation and not of genetic limitations. These traits are the extreme deficiency of locomotor functions, the inability to walk and to run, as well as more or less functional blindness and deafness. While defective locomotor coordination and defects of sensation are also seen in idiots, it is rarely of this extreme type. Furthermore, whereas congenital idiots can rarely be trained to toilet habits, most isolated children can be so trained. These are important differences, for they suggest that some, at least, of the isolated children were probably not congenital idiots, and that their deficiently developed senses and locomotor abilities were produced by their peculiar conditions of isolation.

Toilet Control

A seemingly unimportant detail such as the ability to learn control of toilet habits indicates that the potentialities involved were present but that in isolation they were never organized in relation to a definite cultural setting. In most idiots the potentialities necessary are wanting owing to the defects of the nervous system. However, some idiots—the high-grade idiots or low-grade imbeciles of the three-year mental age level—can be trained in such habits. The crucial point here is that while all isolated children have been taught to control their elimination, most idiots cannot be so trained. It would be making too great demands upon the law of chance to assume that all the isolated children of whom we have accounts fell into the selected class of high-grade idiots. It would be more reasonable to conclude that in light of their ability to learn toilet habits they were probably not congenital idiots. Additional evidence in support of this conclusion is provided by their extreme locomotor deficiency, a deficiency which they learn to overcome to a considerable extent. This is not usually the case with congenital idiots.[8] If these children were feeble-minded to begin with, then it should have been possible to train them to do considerably more than they were able to achieve. The failure so to train them must be attributed, at least in part, to the effects of the absence of social stimulation at a critical period in the development of the person.[9]

Growth Potentialities of the Nervous System

The work of Coghill and his school has made it abundantly clear that the potentialities for growth in the nervous system continue throughout the life of the person. Nerve cells spring up and grow according to a definite maturative pattern, and this pattern in the nervous system is established in its main outlines before nervous function, excitation, or exercise begins. The cellular potentialities for specific functions are laid down in the nervous system prior to the functional activities which are subsequently observed as behavior. Under the stimulation of the environment such cells begin to function as a dynamic system, dendrites and axons increase in length, they establish relations with adjacent and more remote neurones, and collaterals appear which link separated groups of cells. Experience does not determine these potentialities, but it does determine when and to what extent the potentialities of behavior shall develop into action. In the absence of the excitation of experience we do not know what happens in the nervous system. It is believed that under the influence of different modes of stimulation new specificities of sensitivity are constantly developing through the growth of dendrite terminals, each in relation to the different modes of stimulation. And Coghill suggests that it is such a progressive differentiation of sensitivity, under the stimulus of experience, that essentially constitutes the conditioning process.[10]

The reaction to the environment of the organism through its inherent potentiality for growth must play a part in the conditioning of its behavior. It is probable "that conditioning processes are registered in structural counterparts in the sense that neural mechanisms acquire functional specificity with reference to the experience. In the counterpart of the form of the pattern . . . the specificity of function is fixed by the relations into which the elements grow. In the counterpart of experience, on the other hand, specificity of function is established by interaction of growth and excitation, that is to say, the excitation fixes upon the growing terminals of neurones its own mode of activation." Thus, it seems very likely that the situations of experience "organize themselves into definite structural counterparts through the interaction of growth and excitation."[11]

The cortical cells of the organism begin their function with the beginning of experience "and grow as experience progresses till all the essential behaviour and conditioning processes are registered in them. Every pyramidal cell as a growing unit may be conceived as blending, so to speak, the experience of the individual from the beginning to the end of stimulation and response."[12]

In brief, the behavior of the organism must be considered the result of the growth potentials which determine its specificity plus the effect of experience which stimulates the growth of those potentials and renders possible the actual functioning of those specificities. In the absence of the stimulus of experience the development of functional behavior simply does not occur. Growth of functionally organized patterns of specificities does not take place. Obviously, upon such a theory man is more than the sum of his reflexes, drives, and reactions of all sorts. As Coghill puts it in the concluding words of his book, "Man is, indeed, a mechanism, but he is a mechanism which, within the limitations of life, sensitivity and growth, is creating and operating himself."[13] When, however, the stimulation necessary to operate himself is wanting, as in extreme cases of isolation from the time of infancy, he simply does not learn to do so, so that his physical development is largely and his mental development is completely arrested. Since there has been a minimum of environmental and absolutely no social stimulation, there is nothing but that minimum of environmental stimulation to organize, to fix upon, the growing terminals of the neurons, a minimal stimulation which maintains the organism at a virtually vegetative level. The absence of social stimulation simply results in a nonsocial being, or in neurological terms, in the failure of organization of neuron potentials into specific functioning morphological patterns.

It is possible for a child who has been deprived of the usual kinds of social stimulation from birth to five years to recover adequate use of its body and sense following intensive training in socialization. Such a case is that of Isabelle. Before turning to the discussion of her case it were well to point out that each case of isolation is itself unique, in that the individual is unique to begin with, the experience of isolation has varied in each case, and there has been considerable variation in the subsequent attempts at socialization. Variability of this kind renders it necessary to proceed with caution when comparing cases. In a well-nourished though thoroughly isolated child, it would be difficult to envisage any real damage to the growth potentialities of the nervous system as the result of an entire absence of social or other environmental stimulation, other than that necessary for the maintenance of life. Nerve cells are not known to atrophy or lose their growth functions with disuse. Assuming, then, for the purpose of argument, that the isolated children of whom we have some knowledge, such as Anna, were normal babies to begin with, how could one account for the apparent damage to their nervous systems, the apparent interference with the growth potentials of the neuronal net?

We have already considered this question with respect to the separated child (see pp. 221–223). Doubtless similar factors are operative in the case of the isolated child, in addition to which chronic malnutrition may so disturb the metabolism of the brain as to do permanent injury to nerve cells and even cause death. The functional blindness of isolated children may have something of a morphological basis in that the nutritional disturbance may reduce the visual purple in the retina of the eyes to a low level.

The Case of Isabelle

Born in Ohio, apparently in April, 1932, Isabelle was discovered in November, 1938. She was then approximately six and a half years old. She was an illegitimate child, and for that reason, she and her mother, a deaf-mute, were secluded from the rest of the mother's family in a dark room where they spent most of their time together. Lack of sunshine and proper nutrition produced extreme rickets. As a result, Isabelle's legs were so bowed that when she stood erect the soles of her shoes came nearly flat together, and she moved about with a skittering gait. When found she resembled a wild animal more than anything else, mute and idiot-like. She was at once diagnosed by a psychologist as genetically inferior. However, a specialist in child speech, Dr. Marie K. Mason, put her through an intensive and systematic training in speech, and in spite of all prognostications to the contrary succeeded not only in teaching her to speak normally, but to achieve with speech all the usual associated abilities. In two years she covered the stages of learning that normally require six. She did very well at school, participating normally in all school activities.[14]

The case of Isabelle conforms to the type picture of the isolated child with malnutrition, idiocy, and muteness, who, nevertheless under intensive training became a thoroughly normal socialized being. Malnutrition did not do any noticeable damage to the nerve cells of her brain, and her development to perfectly normal social adjustment strongly suggests that she probably received a certain amount of love from her mother during their joint confinement. Unfortunately, no data are available upon this point.

We know from cases such as those of Laura Bridgman and Helen Keller, and from our consideration of the basic needs and their satisfaction, that love can be conveyed to the child by many means other than those of speech. We are told that Isabelle communicated with her mother by means of gestures. Isabelle's sensory disabilities and her nonsocialization were due obviously and entirely to her prolonged isolation. Her ability to recover from its effects was almost certainly due to the fact that she had been adequately loved by her deaf-mute mother.

Extreme Organic Helplessness

The great power of love to reach beyond even the most extreme disabilities is illustrated by the following case.

George was born after a prolonged labor of 24 hours, during which he suffered severe cerebral damage. The result was extreme recurring athetosis or fairly complete lack of muscular control, as well as an aimlessness of movements. George could not learn to pronounce more than ten words. He could not stand or walk or balance his head, and could not hold an object even when it was placed in his hands. He was almost postureless and kinesthetically unaware. He did, however, learn to read, to play checkers, to read a clock, and because he received a great amount of loving care he managed to become a cheerful boy with whom other children liked to play. In spite of his handicaps he displayed great morale on many occasions, and before his death from appendicitis at the age of 14, he had made steady progress in social and emotional maturation. In the perception and appreciation of social relations his behavior suggested a considerable approximation to normality.

In spite of severe damage to the parts of the brain concerned with the control of tactile-muscular behavior and the consequent almost total physical disability, this child was nevertheless able to make a considerable social adjustment to the world in which he lived. This, most probably, he was able to achieve because of the great amount of loving attention which he received and which was mediated to him though his senses of vision and hearing, which had developed without any great impairment.[15]

The Case of Patty

As an example of the severe social damage which can be done to a child under anarchic socializing conditions, the case of Patty (here reported for the first time) is illuminating.

In the fall of 1948 Patty, aged three years, was brought to a New York hospital with a fractured elbow. The immediate disappearance of the mother and the child's frightful physical and psychological condition caused the authorities to institute inquiries, from which it transpired that Patty, the oldest of two children by different fathers, had been unbelievably maltreated. The mother, a prostitute, lived with the two children in one room of a four-room apartment occupied by another family. The remainder of the story is best told in the words of the nurse in whose charge Patty was placed on admission to the hospital.[16]

I was on duty the hectic morning that Patty K——— was admitted to the children's Ward of the N——— Hospital. Children were crying, nurses were hurrying to and fro and Patty looked terrified. Most children were frightened when they came to this new and strange place, but the remarkable difference about Patty was that she didn't cry but rather cringed from any person who approached her. Her mother had come to the ward with Patty but left immediately without even saying goodbye to the child.

It didn't take us long to discover that Patty didn't know how to eat. When given her tray of food, she would grab as much as she could hold in one hand (her broken arm had been set and put in a cast) and hide the food under the bedclothes. When she finally learned the food would not be taken from her she ate ravenously, as much as three traysfull per meal and anything given to her between meals. After one week of diligent training she learned to use a spoon and rarely slips from this practice now. Her capacity for food has greatly slackened so that she now eats a normal amount for a three year old.

Our greatest nursing problem with Patty was due to the fact that she was totally incontinent of urine and feces. After she had been with us about two weeks and had come to trust a few chosen people we attempted to toilet-train her. The first time I took her into the bathroom I didn't understand her screaming terror of the toilet. Later we learned she had been "toilet-trained" at home by being locked in the bathroom for two or three hours a day. The rest of the day she spent tied to a chair because she "stole food out of the icebox" according to her mother. At this point I might add that Patty is one of two illegitimate children by the same mother, each with a different father. The mother remains unmarried. After six weeks Patty is toilet trained to the extent that she goes into the bathroom willingly and daily has a bowel movement after breakfast and after lunch but not to the extent that she will tell us when she has to have an excretion. If any of us forget her for a few hours she is likely to have an accident. This is probably due (in part) to the fact that she is just learning to talk.

When Patty came to us she could say just three obscene words and the remainder of her vocabulary consisted of unintelligible mumblings. By this time Patty has learned a number of words and can say a few complete sentences. Her sentences are those frequently spoken by the nurses on the ward, such as "Here comes the Doctor." "Don't touch that," "I'll be right back," or "Stop it, Patty." The best feature is that Patty uses each sentence at the appropriate time.

For a long time we were perplexed as to what we could do about the child's constant denudative actions. Because she could not get the hospital gowns over her cast she just ripped them off. She would tear as many as five or six gowns a day. Finally we decided to buy some bright red overalls and a brightly colored shirt. It worked! She never has torn or taken off these clothes or the many others that have been given to her since. However, if made to stay in bed very long in the morning she invariably attracts attention by tearing off her hospital pajamas.

When Patty was first allowed out of bed to run about the ward her gait suggested propulsion. She would run headlong until she hit the wall or a door. She has overcome this, but her manner is still that of a child who has been so restrained that she runs wild when given freedom.

She has yet to learn how to play. It is a rare occasion for her to sit still as long as five minutes concentrating on one toy.

After eight weeks of a daily tub bath Patty is just now getting over her fear of the water. Plastic toys in the tub have helped us here. The child's mother has admitted that she didn't bathe Patty because "Patty doesn't like water." The numerous abscesses covering the little girl's legs and buttocks when she was brought to the hospital confirmed our guess that she hadn't been washed much.

Patty is beginning to have faith in more people. After the first week she started to come to us nurses of her own volition. Next she progressed to approaching anybody dressed in white, whether it be a lab technician, X-ray aide or nurse. Her greatest fear has been for any or all men, but she is slowly getting over that.

She had no idea of how to show affection. If she liked someone she tagged that person and continually butted them with her head. Now she can hug as well as the next child.

Since Patty has been with us, receiving a great deal of attention and affection, she has become extremely jealous of all the other children. The moment someone picks up a baby to cuddle, Patty is racing around the ward pulling linen from the beds, tearing up books and doing anything else that she knows will attract attention.

There is still a large amount of work to be done with this child and it will take someone with a great deal of patience and time to do it. We are hopeful that the little we have done will not be undone by sending her back to the home she came from, but rather that she can be placed in a good foster home.

Unfortunately it was not possible to follow the subsequent history of Patty.

It is evident that the social damage done to Patty was not as great as it would have been had she been completely isolated. What Patty was suffering from was extreme social neglect coupled with long-continued and massive frustrations, as evidenced by her importunate demands for love and her curiously aggressive behavior.

It is probable that Patty was born with, at least, normal intelligence potentialities. The poverty of the socializing stimuli to which she was exposed was such that she simply failed to develop as a normal social being. In other words, her development as a human being was largely determined and limited by the kind of social stimulation she received. Patty's history, as well as that of all the other isolated or quasi-isolated children cited in this chapter, suggests that the human organism develops as a person to the extent only to which it has received the adequate socially personalizing stimulations; in the absence of such stimulations it fails altogether to develop as a person, and its social competence is nonexistent.

With reference to all children, and with poignant reference to such children as Patty, this chapter may be concluded with the words of Alfred Adler:

> The child's inclination to co-operation is challenged from the very first day. The immense importance of the mother in this respect can be clearly recognized. She stands on the threshold of the development of social feeling. The biological heritage of social feeling is entrusted to her charge. She can strengthen or hinder contact by the help she gives the child in little things, in bathing him, in providing all that a helpless infant is in need of. Her relations with the child, her knowledge, and her aptitude are decisive factors. . . . It may be readily accepted that contact with the mother is of the highest importance for the development of human social feeling. . . . *We probably owe to the maternal sense of contact the largest part of human social feeling, and along with it the essential continuance of human civilization.*[17]

12 THE DIRECTION OF HUMAN DEVELOPMENT

In the long run the fate of a civilization depends not only on its political system, its economic structure, or its military might. Perhaps, indeed, all of these ultimately depend in turn upon the faith of the people, upon what we believe and feel about Man; about the possibilities of human nature; about our relation or lack of it to such intangibles as the meaning of morality or the true nature of Value.

—Joseph Wood Krutch*

Human Nature

What is a human being? That is the question this book set out to answer, though the question was phrased differently. We set out by inquiring into the nature of man's original nature and the manner in which that nature is influenced and conditioned to assume a socially functional form.

The kind of answer each person or society returns to the question: "What is a human being?" will largely determine the health of such persons and societies. What human beings and their societies *do* about human beings is determined by the inner attitudes motivating their outer acts.

In this last chapter let us recapitulate our main findings, and endeavor to draw the significant conclusions—conclusions which, in all humility, we hope may help humanity direct its own development toward the attainment of the optimum degree of health and happiness.

* Joseph Wood Krutch, "Speaking of Books," *New York Times Book Review*, August 16, 1953, p. 2.

The Need to Love

The infant not only needs to be loved, but quite as much as he needs to be loved he needs to love others. It is due to the poverty of our language, which faithfully reflects the inadequacies of our understanding of these matters, that we are forced to distinguish between the need to be loved and the need to love others. That need is unitary and is only arbitrarily divisible. The division may be convenient, but it should never be forgotten that it is arbitrary. It is not possible to want to be loved without wanting to love others.

When it is said, then, that the infant needs to be loved, it should concomitantly be understood that the infant also wants to love others. It is important to understand that the infant's need for love is not adequately satisfied unless it receives the necessary stimulations for the development of its capacity to love. It may, indeed, be said that the child's need for love is the most significant developer of its own capacity to love others. The child learns to love others by being loved.

There has been a tendency to regard the newborn and infant as a passive, utterly dependent creature who is entirely devoted to receiving without in any way giving. This view is wholly false, for from the very outset the child grows by striving to give, and it is biologically equipped to do so from the moment of birth.

The nursing couple, mother and infant, confer basic benefits upon one another—for when a baby is born, a mother is, or should be, also born. In the reciprocal relationship in which mother and child are involved it becomes increasingly evident that the gift they make to each other is their own selves—selves that are striving for fulfillment and development. The gift unaccompanied by the committal of the giver is arid, a mere thing unenriched by the human meaning to the recipient of the giver. The infant expects others to become involved with him, and he is profoundly involved in others. The less others are with him, the more he strives to be with them. We have already seen that those infants who are so isolated that they have no one with whom to be involved tend to become apathetic and waste away. The human situation is involvement with others in increasingly healthier relationships. And by health I mean the ability to love, the ability to work, the ability to serve.

The self grows by the increasing interactive involvement with others. Whether the self develops as an affectionate one or as more or less defective in that quality will depend largely, if not entirely, upon whether its experience of these qualities from others, especially the mother, has been of a loving kind.

Every neurosis has at its core the failure of healthy involvement, of relatedness to others. The foundations for this failure, as Freud pointed out, are laid within the first six years or so of life. This is but another way of saying that there has been a failure of the developing ego to receive adequate satisfactions.

The ego develops in health only when it receives an adequate regimen of satisfactions. The greatest of these is the opportunity afforded the developing human being to exercise his capacity for love. Never has this been better said than by George Chapman (1559-1634), the Tudor poet and playwright, who in his play *All Fools,* probably produced in 1599, writes,

> I tell thee, Love is Nature's second sun
> Causing a spring of virtues where he shines;
> And as without the sun, the world's great eye,
> All colours, beauties, both of Art and Nature,
> Are given in vain to men, so without love
> All beauties bred in women are in vain,
> All virtues born in men lie buried;
> For love informs them as the sun doth colours;
> And as the sun, reflecting his warm beams
> Against the earth, begets all fruits and flowers;
> So love, fair shining in the inward man,
> Brings forth in him the honourable fruits
> Of valour, wit, virtue, and haughty thoughts,
> Brave resolution, and divine discourse.—Act I, Scene I

The Child Is Born Good

The age-old view that the human being is born "a natural barbarian," "an animal," "not naturally 'good' according to any standards set by civilized society"; that "children are *naturally* hostile," "little anarchists," "aggressive," "braggadocious and cruel,"[1] arises from the misinterpretations of the doctrine of "the Fall" or of "original sin." The reinforcement which these views received from nineteenth-century evolutionary biology and psychoanalytic theory in the first half of the twentieth century almost succeeded in hardening this view of the nature of human nature into something resembling an incontrovertible fact, a Law of Nature. Happily, in recent years, as a consequence of studies influenced both by developments in evolutionary biology and psychoanalytic theory, evidence has become available which indicates that the traditional view of human nature is unsound and, what is worse, capable of being profoundly damaging to human beings and to their societies. For this evidence indicates that human beings are born good—"good" in the sense that there is no evil or hostility in them, but that at birth they are wholly prepared, equipped, to function as creatures who not only want and need to be loved by others but who also want and need to love others. The evidence for these statements has been cited at some length in these pages. Let those who know of any evidence which controverts these statements bring it forth. I do not believe that such evidence exists.

The belief is widely held by many students of human nature that human beings are born neither good nor evil but indifferent; that whether they become good or evil or both depends largely, if not entirely, upon the social conditioning they are made to undergo. This view sounds reasonable enough, but the evidence I believe, when critically examined proves this view to be as unsound as the traditional view alleging the inherent brattishness or hostility of human nature.

The evidence cited in the present book shows that the human organism at birth is a highly organized creature—*not* a disorganized, unready, unprepared, "wild" beast; that the newborn is highly organized to function as an increasingly growing-in-love harmonic bestower-of-benefits-upon-others, whose birthright, as an American philosopher has said, is development. The inner requirements of the infant are such as to cause him to want to be loved and to want to love others, and the basic needs of the infant are structured to function in this manner. The infant expects to have its needs satisfied, and when the infant's needs are satisfied it develops as a loving, cooperative, harmonic human being—that is, as a healthy human being. We have accepted the definition of health, attributed to Freud, as the ability to love and the ability to work. The infant is equipped with the potentialities to develop both capacities. How well a human being will develop his capacities to love and work will depend largely upon the kind of training he will have received during infancy and childhood. The evidence shows, beyond any doubt, that the development of all the organism's potentialities for being human is a matter, reduced to its simplest elements, of certain kinds of stimulation and response: the stimulation of other human beings.

This stimulation, we have learned, must be of a certain kind. It must, in the first place, minister to and satisfy the needs of the infant. In order to minister satisfactorily to the needs of the infant it is desirable to know and understand the nature of those needs. In order to understand the nature of humanity and the direction of development which humanity may in future successfully pursue, it is indispensably necessary to understand the nature of the basic needs of the organism; these needs, whatever changes they may undergo, remain at the core essentially the same throughout life, from birth to death.

The nature of these needs has been discussed, and we have found that needs must be satisfied within reasonably short intervals and with certain frequencies—that it is not enough to "love" an infant three or four or five times a day, but that he must be loved for the greater part of the day—all the day—until he has had those inner securities built up within him which will later render it unnecessary for him to be in any way anxious about those stimulations which at the outset of his postnatal career are so indispensably necessary for his development.

As human beings we are the creators of human beings, and we shall always have the kind of human beings among us that we make. The role of chromosomes and genes should not be underestimated in the making of human beings, but as we have earlier pointed out (pp. 85–86), the expression of the chromosomes and genes is to a certain extent under environmental control, and to the extent that we control the environment we control heredity, for heredity is the expression of the interaction of the genes with environment. We cannot get more out of genes than we put into them or, to phrase this more constructively, we can get more out of genes than would otherwise be possible by providing them with environments in which they may optimally express themselves. Genes determine the limits of development under all environments; environments should therefore be provided which enable the human being to attain his fullest development within those limits.[2]

Heredity, like constitution, is not as earlier generations thought it to be, the equivalent of predestination, but is the expression of that which is biologically given in interaction with that which is environmentally provided. Heredity should mean not Fate, but something about which we can, if we will, do a great deal. We shall not be able to substitute environment for genes, but we should always bear in mind that genes are not determiners of traits but of the responses of the developing organism to the environment. We can, therefore, always do something toward controlling the expression of those responses. It is good to know this, and it should serve to induce an optimistic mood. As E. L. Thorndike has remarked, "To the real work of man—the increase of achievement through improvement of the environment—the influence of heredity offers no barrier."

The making and molding of human beings as human beings is in our power as human beings. Since this is so, the direction of human development, of human evolution, is within our power as human beings—for good or evil. It is necessary, then, that we shall make quite certain that the direction of that development shall be good and neither evil nor confused.

What Is Good?

The evidence we have now considered tells us that "good" is whatever the person does that confers survival benefits upon others in a manner which contributes to their ability to love and to work—in other words, to their ability to do likewise to and for other human beings. Human welfare is whatever contributes to the maintenance and development of human health—the ability to love and the ability to work.

To the extent that any person departs in his behavior from the undeviating practice of his capacity for love and work, to that extent we would have reason to believe that forces inimical to his healthy functioning are at work in him. We should seek to understand those forces and remedy them by providing the person with those conditions of life which will most contribute toward his healthy functioning. It should be one of the functions of education to make human beings understand the nature of human goodness, and what it is that must be done to develop such goodness as has already been developed in one by one's educators. It should be the primary function of all human societies to provide those conditions which shall make it possible for as many human beings as possible to function as good human beings. This constitutes the answer to the question "Education for what?"[3]

What the human organism requires most for its development is a nutriment of love; the source of virtually all health is in the experience of love, especially within the first six years of life. No matter how well the needs of the human organism are physically satisfied, unless the physical satisfying of those needs is accompanied by love, the human organism will not develop satisfactorily, that is to say, it will not develop as an organism that has been so harmonically satisfied that its principal interest lies in satisfying others. After all, this is what most of us want most of all to do all our lives, however confusedly or not we may recognize it: to satisfy others. The tragedy is that so many of us have failed to learn, because we had not been properly taught, how to satisfy others. To be rejected at any age because those who have been responsible for us have failed to teach us how to love others is, perhaps, the most unkind of all the inhumanities which human beings commit against human beings.

The child that is unloved does not develop properly; it may even sicken and die principally as a consequence of insufficient love. Some children manage to survive under the most barren of human conditions—we do not yet know why. Some day we shall study such children and discover the answer, but it would appear that most, if not all, children suffer seriously crippling effects when exposed to an inadequate diet of love. There has here been cited but a fraction of the evidence supporting these statements. The material now available showing the fundamental importance of love for the healthy development of the human being is of considerable proportions.

From all this material it seems now clear that the main principle by which human beings must guide the future course of their development is love. It is, therefore, of the first importance that we be clear as to the meaning of love.

What Is Love?

Love is that form of behavior that contributes to the healthy development of both the lover and the loved. By healthy development is meant the increase in the capacity to function as a totally harmonic person who confers creatively enlarging benefits upon all with whom he comes into association. Love, it would seem, is the principal developer of the potentialities for being human, it is the chief stimulus to the development of social competence, and the only quality in the world capable of producing that sense of belongingness and relatedness to the world of humanity that every healthy human being desires and develops.

Love is creative, creative both for the receiver and the giver. Genuine love can never harm or inhibit, it can only benefit and create freedom and order. Love has a firmness and a discipline of its own for which there can be no substitute. No child can ever be spoiled by genuine love, and there are few if any human problems which cannot be most efficiently solved by its application.

We may tentatively set out below the qualities and characteristics of love, upon which most students of the subject seem to be agreed.

The Qualities and Characteristics of Love

1. *Love implies the possession of a feeling of deep involvement in another, and to love another means to communicate that feeling of involvement to them.* Essentially this means that while love begins as a subjective state, it must be activated and made objective, that is, it must be demonstrative if it is to be fully realized. Love is not passive, it is active, it means involvement.

2. *Love is unconditional, it makes no bargains and trades with no one for anything.* It is given freely and without any strings attached. It says, in effect, to the loved one: "I am for you because you are you—and not because you are going to be something I want or expect you to be, but simply because you are you as you now are."

3. *Love is supportive.* It conveys to the loved one that he can depend upon those who love him, that they will always be standing by to give him the support he most needs, with no questions asked, neither condemning nor condoning, but endeavoring sympathetically to understand, that no trust will be misused, that no faith will be broken; that he will never under any circumstances be failed in his needs.

4. *Love is firm.* Love is characterized by a firmness and integrity which not only conveys a feeling of security to the loved one, but serves also as a discipline in that it helps the loved one to respond in kind. But love continues even though we know that the loved one may never respond in kind. The firmness of love conveys to the loved one that both one's "Yea" and one's "Nay" are equally the firm evidence of one's love. The loved one, therefore, comes to incorporate this kind of firmness within himself.

> Let me not to the marriage of true minds
> Admit impediments. Love is not love
> Which alters when it alteration finds,

Or bends with the remover to remove:
O, no! it is an ever-fixèd mark,
That looks on tempests and is never shaken;
It is the star to every wandering bark,
Whose worth's unknown, although his height be taken.
Love's not Time's fool, though rosy lips and cheeks
Within his bending sickle's compass come;
Love alters not with his brief hours and weeks,
But bears it out even to the edge of doom.
If this be error and upon me prov'd,
I never writ, nor no man ever lov'd.

So wrote William Shakespeare.

5. *Love is most needed by the human organism from the moment of birth.* Our evidence indicates that love is the birthright of every human being, the birthright which is indispensably necessary for the optimum development of the person. It seems to be clear that the best environment, in which love is most efficiently and satisfactorily provided, is within the warm ambience of the bosom of the family. The pattern of love which the child learns within the family, if he learns it well, he will later extend to all human beings.

6. *Love is reciprocal in its effects, and is as beneficial to the giver as it is to the recipient.* To love another means to love oneself as well as the other; in this sense love is the highest form of selfishness as well as the highest form of unselfishness, the best of all forms of conduct for the development of the self, one's own self and the selves of others.

7. *Love is creative* in that it actively participates in the creative development of the loved one as well as contributing toward the further development of the lover.

8. *Love enlarges the capacities of those who are loved* and of those who love so that they become increasingly more sensitive in probably all areas of their being.

9. *Love continually elicits, by encouragement, the nascent capacities of the loved one.* In the absence of love those capacities will either fail altogether to be elicited or fail of healthy development. For example, the capacity to feel sensitively, to feel warmly toward others,

the capacity to perceive rapidly the changing character of a situation, the capacity to identify with others, the ability to adjust rapidly to rapidly changing conditions, and the like. In all these capacities the person who has been loved is more efficient than the person who has been inadequately loved.

10. *Love is tender,* with a tenderness that abjures every form of insensitivity and every form of violence.

11. *Love is joyful,* it is pleasure-giving, happiness-producing, it is goodness itself. This does not mean that love is necessarily associated with states of ecstasy or gaiety. Love may produce temporary states of nonpleasure or displeasure, as for example, in children and others who are forbidden some immediate satisfaction for their own "good." Prohibitions stemming from love contribute to the development of the capacity for love and mature character.

12. *Love is fearless.* Love has no element of fear in it,[4] and produces no fear in others. Love braves all conditions and situations in a security-producing manner; hence, love tends to reduce fear, allay suspicion, soften all harshness, and produce peacefulness.

13. *Love enables the person to treat life as an art* which the person, as artist, is continually seeking to improve and beautify in all its aspects.

14. *Love as an attitude of mind and as a form of behavior is adaptively the best and most efficient of all adjustive processes in enabling the human being to adapt himself to his environment.*

15. *For the person and for the species love is the form of behavior having the highest survival value.*[5]

Adequate love is necessary for the adequate physical growth and development of the human organism, as well as for its adequate psychical growth and development; and intelligence as well as mental health is furthered by the contributions which love makes to the developing person. In love, in short, we have discovered the touchstone and the compass by which man may guide his own most successful course through the shoals and reefs of this life, instead of being tossed about, as he has in the past, and as he is being at present, in a rudderless boat upon a mysterious and uncompassionate sea.

To live as if to live and love were one is not a new recommendation; what is new is that the meaning of love should have been rediscovered in the twentieth century by scientific means. Every people has its equivalent of the Sermon on the Mount, and our churches have constantly reminded us of the existence of love and enjoined us to practice it. This being so, it may well be asked why it is that we seem so monumentally to have failed to realize such injunctions? Why is it that there have been so many members of churches but so few lovers? Why is it that there are so many Christians but so few followers of Jesus?

The answer, it seems to me, is that we have been miseducated out of the capacity to be lovers of our fellow human beings, and that we have on the other hand been confusedly trained to keep our eye on the main chance. For the most part this has been the secular training of western man. We have tended to live by false values, and to transmit these values to the young. We have tended to make egotists of creatures that are biologically organized to function most efficiently as altruists. The evidence indicates that from birth onward the direction of the human being's drives is toward cooperation, and that healthy development consists principally in the encouragement of the optimum fruition of these drives. If, as in the western world we have largely been doing, we interfere with the development of those drives by opposing to them requirements that are antagonistic toward the development of cooperativeness, these drives tend to become deformed and weakened, while at the same time conflicts are engendered within the psyche which produce great personal and social disoperativeness.

It appears, then, that whatever contributes toward personal and social health and happiness is good and desirable for human beings, and that whatever contributes to the contrary is bad and undesirable for human beings. In short, whatever militates against or is opposed to the development of the tendencies toward cooperation in the person and in the society militates against and is opposed to the healthy development of the person and of the society. In essence this is to say that uncooperativeness or unlovingness is the worst of all the sins which one human being can commit against another.

In this volume we have, I hope, sufficiently explored the meaning and requirements of cooperation to be able to take for granted what it is that human beings must cooperate with. Perhaps it will bear repeating in a phrase: What human beings must cooperate with is the desire of other human beings to be loved—to be cooperated with. One cannot secure love by seeking it, but only by giving it. Having discussed and set out the criteria of love, of loving, there should be no difficulty in understanding what it is that requires to be done: Human beings must be satisfied in their need for love. The direction of human development lies in and through the course of love; all else is secondary to this. The primacy of love is unchallengeable—and unchallengeably clear as the first requirement of human development. All the agencies of socialization should be based upon the understanding of this fact. Since all agencies of socialization are educative, education constitutes the key to the solution of the ills of humanity, and the means by which all the potentialities of the organism for being human may be unlocked. Hence the importance of understanding the meaning of man for education and the meaning of education for man.

Education and Human Relations

In keeping with the general materialization of western man and the high value placed upon techniques, education has progressively degenerated into instruction. It is not unlikely that if, in the western world, we go on as we have been doing in the immediate past, in a generation or two scarcely anyone will remain who understands the difference between education and instruction. Instruction is the process of pumping information into the person, it literally means "to build into"; whereas education means the process of nourishing or rearing a child or young person, in the sense of the Latin word to which it is related, *educere,* to lead forth. We must recognize that today, in the western world, we have far too much instruction and all too little education. We are far too busy filling up the young with what we think they ought to know, to have much time left over for helping them become what they ought to be. There is, after all, a difference between *knowing* and *being*—it is better to be more than one seems and to be wise rather than knowledgeable. We pump in the information in the hope that somehow the recipients will know what to do with it or what it is for, and that somehow this procedure will make the beneficiaries of it realize their potentialities. By this means we naively suppose that human beings will learn how to distinguish the good from the bad and to act accordingly, that by this means they will learn how to use their minds and evaluate evidence critically, that by this means they will become better persons and better citizens. Never have we been more mistaken—as the record shows.

In the United States for the year ending in 1965 we find certifiable mental illness to exist in 1 out of every 4 families; we find that every two minutes someone was killed, maimed, robbed, or beaten with a gun. There was a murder every hour, a forcible rape every twenty-six minutes, an aggravated assault—that is, assault with intent to kill or inflict grievous bodily harm—every three minutes, a burglary every twenty-eight seconds, a robbery every five minutes, an auto theft every minute; and each year these rates rise.[6] What is perhaps worse than all this, if it could be worse, is that 1 out of every 43 children has a police record.[7] Juvenile delinquency, broken homes—1 out of every 3 marriages ends in divorce or separation[8]—these are all tragic evidences of the failure of education—education primarily in the home and secondarily in the school. This is perhaps not surprising in a land in which of our total national income 5 per cent was expended on alcoholic beverages as compared with approximately 3 per cent spent on education.[9]

Education—Teachers and Parents

We have made a fundamental error in distinguishing what goes on in the training of children in the home from what goes on in the training of the young in the schools. Education begins at birth, and the parents are the first educators, the mother usually being the principal of the parental educators. Because the first half dozen years of the child's life are so critically important for its development there can be little doubt that the parents, and in particular the mother, constitute the most important educators in the life of the person.[10] Hence, if any disinction is to be made between parental and school education it should be in terms of emphasis upon the supreme importance of the first six years of the child's life. This, however, in no way implies that the education of a human being is a discontinuous process, with a first part at home and a second part at school. On the other hand, education must be regarded as a continuous process, and it should be based upon a single and unitary viewpoint as to its nature and purposes in which everyone, parents and teachers, participate *together*.

Education is the process of teaching human beings to live in ways which contribute to the welfare of their fellow human beings. The theoretical background emerging out of the facts we have discussed in this book with respect to the meaning of "welfare" has already been examined at sufficient length. If the analysis of the facts is sound and the theory is likewise sound—as I believe it to be—then it is clear that the most important function of education is to draw out and develop the potentialities of the child for being a loving human being. The evidence suggests that to achieve the status of a loving human being is the most desirable and important that a human being can achieve. To produce loving human beings should be the primary purpose of education, and all else should be secondary to that purpose. Reading, writing, and arithmetic are but skills, techniques, means, which should be designed to assist the loving human being to realize to the optimum his potentialities for getting the most out of life by putting the most into it. Reading, writing and arithmetic are not ends in themselves but secondary means—means to the end of realizing the fullest richest life possible within the limits of the abilities of each human being. Such skills are secondary to the main purpose of living—which is life, a life that is worth living insofar as it realizes its highest form in the developed loving human being.

In our schools we pay lip-service to such an ideal of education, but in practice we teach *subjects,* we no longer teach human beings. Too much of our attention is devoted to problems of discipline, so that for many teachers their task has reduced itself to one of baby-sitting, for the original baby-sitters—the parents—who have failed to sit as they ought to have done. This problem has become so serious in the United States that in many high schools a permanent squad of police has been installed in order that some semblance of discipline shall be maintained! Perhaps these are extreme cases; in any event they are mentioned here in order to underscore, as it were, the kind of disciplinary problems with which the school is faced which under a reasonable system of education would never in the first place have arisen.

A patient, in searching for an explanation for his mental illness, remarked: "My mother's impulses never seemed to correspond to my needs."[11] This probably represents a sound statement of the origin of many mental diseases, and it may be profitably paraphrased in the statement that the impulses of many educators seem rarely to correspond to the needs of the young. This is not difficult to understand when one realizes that what the young want is principally to be stimulated in their need for human development, whereas too many teachers are engaged in filling them up with a number of subjects which to the child appear to be quite unrelated to his most fundamental needs. What is human learning if not the development of the needs for being human?

Almost all children find their lives in school puzzlingly unrelated to their lives at home. This should not be so. School should constitute a continuation and an enlargement of the experience which begins in the home and terminates in the world outside, only to be renewed again in the home and once more reinforced—as it should be—in the school, and so on until one's education is completed . . . if one's education ever is completed. The love which should and often does exist between parents and children—though it is more often found between mother and child—is the model and the pattern of the human relationship which should exist between all human beings. Lest there be misunderstanding as to my meaning, let me say that I mean exactly what these words imply, namely, that human beings should love each other as a mother loves her children, and that this should be possible for males as well as for females . . .

whether they have ever biologically engendered children or not.[12] But whether the male will learn to love as a parent, or in any other capacity, will depend largely upon his mother, for as La Barre points out, "The human male has no instincts, and no anatomy to teach him to love a child as such. If the male learns the pleasures of paternity as opposed to those of procreation, it is the result of the mother's teaching him."[13]

But how is it possible—to take but one instance—it may be asked, and indeed is it desirable, for members of the opposite sex to fall in love with one another, to love each other as a mother loves her child? The answer is that it is both possible and desirable. The love which should and can exist between male and female should consist in a developed form of maternal love in which all the elements of maternal love persist. A man should love a woman with the tenderness, respect, and care for her welfare with which a mother loves her child, but in addition he should be drawn to and love her for her qualities as a whole. Her external attractions, whatever their nature, may initiate the process but they should never constitute the *end* of it.

This is a different conception of love between the sexes from the romantic and prevailing erotic view. Contemporary love between the sexes is mainly sexual, the male being drawn toward the female principally through the stimulus-value of her curvilinear properties, the female, under the influence of selection pressure, generally settling for a male largely on the basis of his market value as a scarcity commodity, providing also he is someone who, with all his faults, one can like or learn to like.

Too many persons in our western cultures confuse a sexual attraction with love. As long as the opposite partner remains physically attractive the psychophysical disturbances the subject feels are equated with love. But such disturbances are no more akin to love than cupidity is to Cupid. Under such environmental conditions when the physical attractiveness ceases "love" also ceases. Such "love" is, of course, not love, but a crass sexuality. Such persons are sexual without being loving, whereas the loving person cannot be sexual without loving.

The essence of love between the sexes is the tender regard, respect, and care for the other person's welfare—and if it is not that, then whatever else it is, it is not love.

For a healthy human being it is possible to be as much interested in another's welfare as a mother is in her child's. There is a tender regard and involvement in such a person's interest in other human beings which has but to be experienced for it to be understood how well some persons have achieved this maternal capacity for love, even of the stranger.[14] It is in the development of this maternally based capacity for love that the future of humanity lies. Until this truth is fully understood and practiced, so far as the direction of human development is concerned almost all other activities will remain in comparison diversionary and stultifying. It must be the task of educators to awaken to this truth, and what it is that requires to be done to realize it.

The school, like the home, must become an experience in the growth and development of one's capacities for becoming a loving human being. But, in addition, the school has to provide the child with the necessary equipment, the technique and skills, with which it can the more satisfactorily realize—creatively realize—its potentialities for contributing to the welfare of its fellow human beings. The best equipment with which the teacher can provide the child is himself—the teacher's own being. A good teacher must mean something to himself if he is to mean anything to his pupils, and he can mean no more to his pupils than he means to himself. Hence, the value of a good teacher is exceeded by nothing, unless it be the value of a good parent. But when we truly understand the meaning of good teaching it is realized that the good parent is essentially a teacher, and that the good teacher is essentially a parent. How much of what is good in us do we not owe both to parents and to teachers? Where parents fail teachers often succeed. In a period when many of those who act as parents are not the biological genitors of their children it has become apparent that the complex feelings of parentage have no necessary connexion with biological parentage, that between persons who are biologically not kin the deepest feelings of kinship can develop.

There are some who have suggested that it would be a desirable thing to abolish social parentage.[15] This is silly. What we need to do is not to abolish social parentage but to deepen and extend our conception of it. Teachers should stand to their children *in loco parentis.* As the child's parents are its domestic parents, so at school the teacher should be to the child its school parents. I am suggesting that we deepen and extend the kinship system, not in terms of classificatory relationships, but in terms of changes in attitudes. All adults, particularly teachers of the young in the schools, should take a parental interest in the welfare of children. Unfortunately, in the past the attitude of the teacher to the child often resembled that of the company sergeant to the newly inducted private. We have seen that when the sergeant behaves as a reassuring parental figure to the men in his charge their mental health and their efficiency under battle conditions are greatly improved. It is not only schoolteachers, but teachers of every kind who have this lesson to learn: To teach well, one must love one's pupil as a mother loves her child. There have been some teachers who have grasped the truth of this principle, and they have unexceptionally been the great teachers; perhaps the greatest of them all was and is Heinrich Pestalozzi (1746–1827). It was Pestalozzi who said that "Love is the sole and everlasting foundation on which our nature can be trained to humaneness." And it was Pestalozzi who wrote: "The good instincts of mankind, in their pure state, are more than gifts of art or chance. Their fundamental qualities lie deeply buried in man's nature. All men feel the need to develop these powers and the paths along which Nature reveals them, must be kept clear and easy of access. To achieve wisdom and tranquility, the processes of human education must be kept simple and of universal application."[16]

It is through love that teachers of every kind, whether they be actual or derived parents, must seek to develop those fundamental qualities and powers, of which Pestalozzi speaks, along the paths which Nature reveals. We need to recall, in the words of Francis Bacon, that Nature in order to be commanded must be obeyed.

If, then, what has been adumbrated in this book as the nature of human nature, the requirements for the development of human nature, is sound it will be understood that learning and being loved are more closely interrelated conditions than has hitherto been clearly understood. This, perhaps, indicates a more intensive statement of the law of reinforcement. To live, to learn, and to love, these are the three great chords of being; to unify them into a harmonic series requires the skill of an artist. Life regarded as a public performance on the violin, during which one must learn the instrument as one goes along,[17] rarely results in anything more than an unhappy fiddler. A human being should be a work of art. He can be turned into a work of art by other human beings who are artists, and thus learn to become an artist himself, an artist who, in turn, works continually to improve himself and help others to improve themselves. Knowing what is to be done, how else can one better achieve what is to be realized than with the tenderness and loving care of a mother?

All of us are to some extent the product of the maternal principle. The next best thing to being a mother is to behave like one. And by behaving like a mother, we of course mean the possession of those attitudes of mind which condition one to behave toward others as a mother does toward her child. Perhaps the English, the Germans, and those Germans of the Orient, the Japanese, are the peoples who have most departed from this ideal, for that there has been a departure is suggested by the fact that many nonliterate peoples such as the Eskimo and the Australian aborigines—to name two of the most primitive—have pretty closely approximated to the realization of this ideal. Not all earlier men may have been cooperative and loving, but that many of them were there can be no reasonable doubt. The Italians[18] and the French[19] are somewhat more influenced, in their human relations, by the maternal principle, but these peoples are far from having learned the lesson completely. Indeed, their recent history indicates a significant deterioration. And yet to the extent that the Italians and the French retain their warmth they are warmer than the

English, the Germans, and the Japanese. It is no accident that these latter peoples make the most efficient soldiers. One of the kindest and most significant things one can say about any people is that they make poor fighters. It is not by fighting that any human problem will ever be solved, any more than any child will ever be improved by spanking, rather than by love and by the understanding which is love.

There burns a pure flame within us; that flame is love. It is the source from which we draw and convey our warmth to others. It is the light which guides us in relation to our fellow men; it is the flame before which we warm the hands of life, and without which we remain cold all our lives. It is the light of the world. The light which it casts enables us clearly and unambiguously, unfalteringly, to see our relation to our fellow men. It is the task of teachers to keep that flame alive, for if they fail to do that, there is a real danger that the light may go out of the world.

Our present educational and social failure to recognize the new bases of human relationships must change if we are to survive —nothing less than that. We must cease doing violence to human nature. By doing violence to human nature we have produced the unique paradox of the creature who, by nature capable of being the most loving and peaceful, has been turned into the most destructively violent on the face of the earth. Our shattered values have made the horrible, devastating threat of an atom-bomb world a reality. Clearly, we need to know at least as much about the maker as about the manufacture of atom-bombs.[20]

Human beings who are torn and distracted by internal insecurities and anxieties, who are conditioned to love their neighbors on Sundays and to compete with them on weekdays, cannot long survive. A nation of such persons must eventually founder on the reefs of its own false values. External defenses can never make up for the lack of internal controls. What needs to be done is to develop internal controls in human beings so that they can withstand external pressures and maintain internal equilibrium. This can never be achieved by doing violence to their nature. It can only be done by strengthening those basic needs with which all human beings are born—not by frustrating them. It is these basic needs that provide us with the basic values which human beings must seek to satisfy and fulfill if they are to live and function in optimum health and happiness.

Values, Ethics, Education, and the Good Life

A value is the judgment of the quality of an experience.[21] Such value judgments are biologically based in and originally constituted by the basic needs of the organism, and all other needs, secondary, tertiary, quaternary, and so on, are eventually built up upon the functioning of these needs. Values are in essence guides to need-gratifications. The experiences that will gratify my needs create my values, therefore the structure and functioning of my needs determine the range and limits of my values. I must have oxygen to gratify my need for air, but whether that oxygen comes to me in a tent, a house, a factory, a mine, or in a strato-liner, and whether it vary all the way from pure to polluted will depend upon accidental conditions which must neither fall below nor exceed certain limits. Within these limits, which my biological needs determine, I can adapt myself to any atmospheric conditions. And so it is for all other needs. The experiences that will not gratify my needs are negatively valued by me—these, too, are values. My judgment of the quality of these experiences and my acceptance of them or not will largely be determined by my organismal needs—needs which I share with all other human beings.

The supreme value is love, and if we use this as our touchstone of value we cannot possibly go wrong. Man is the evaluating animal, and he evaluates on the basis of his needs. Every human being is born a creature that evaluates all experience in terms of the desire to be loved and the desire to love. We at long last have thus arrived at an understanding that there do exist certain universal values, and that these are born with every human being. "What is right is what is right for human nature." It was Aristotle who declared that the important thing about the nature of man is not what he is born *as,* but what he is born *for.* In order to know what man is born *for* it is indispensably necessary to understand what he is born *as,* and when we understand what he is born *as* we will the better be enabled to assist him to realize what he is born *for.*

Since we now have some understanding of the basic structure of human nature, we are at least in a position to be able to test our theory. The basic needs are not logical inferences but factual phenomena; they *ought* to be satisfied if the organism is to survive or develop, and that *oughtness* is as much a fact and lies as much in the world of *is* as do the basic needs themselves. "Ought" is in this case merely a way of denoting a necessary response—which, again, falls within the world of *is.* As Arnold Brecht has so well put it, "Thus it is a factual statement rather than a logical inference when we say that feeling some specific requiredness as an *ought* is part of our human equipment. This urge, this demand, this *ought,* whatever its value and validity, is a factum, a datum, found in the world of *is.* It would be so even if only a part of mankind felt this *ought* as such. Here is the bridge, or one bridge, between *is* and *ought.*"[22] The nature of the basic needs conditions the oughtness of the responses; what ought to be is what the basic needs determine, and what they determine we are now for the first time able to decipher. In the nature of the basic needs we have the Rosetta Stone which translates for us into the vernacular what the direction of human development ought to be, what, indeed, it must be if the human race is to survive.

But much more than survival is involved. What is involved is the realization of the potentialities for goodness of all human beings everywhere for the greatest good of all humanity—the unbridgeable gap between *ought* and *is,* when we look at what *is* in terms of what we know the basic needs to determine, and at what *ought* to be if human beings are to develop in optimum health and happiness. To realize the good life in the person and behavior of each human being, our evidence indicates that each human being must be adequately loved, that is to say, he must have his needs adequately satisfied for being loved and loving others. Such human beings will create institutions and societies which will be the best that human beings can possibly create and, within whatever limitations those societies operate, they will remain infinitely perfectible. Utopia would not at once descend upon the earth, nor would all human problems immediately be solved. But under such conditions they would become more capable of solution than they have yet ever been.

The reciprocal adaptation which human beings make to one another in terms of love is the basic adaptation, the basic adaptation which binds, reproduces, and preserves the person and the group. This kind of adaptation has been called by Professor Hugh Miller "associative adaptation."[23] The behavior of human beings is either "good" or "bad" to the extent that it is better or worse associatively adapted. "Associative adaptation" is here but another name for love. It is to be noted that it is not said that a person is either "good" or "bad," but that his behavior may be good or bad in virtue of its quality of associative adaptation or love. Our assumption has been throughout that all human beings (with a few possible exceptions) are basically good, but by unfortunate conditioning they are frequently caused to function badly. "Goodness," then, is virtually equatable with "love," and "badness" with a failure of love.

Ethics, then, for us becomes both the art and the science of the reciprocal adaptation of human beings to each other in love—in loving attitudes of mind and in loving conduct. There is, of course, nothing new in this view of ethical conduct. What is new is the scientific validation which the discoveries made in recent years concerning the nature of human nature have brought to this view of ethics.[24] Our revised conception of human nature, as set out in the pages of this book, should have the profoundest influence upon religion and ethics, but it should be fairly clear that religion and ethics are basically taught not so much in the churches as in the home and in the school.[25] The churches should continue to develop and consolidate what has been taught in the home and in the school —if what has been there taught is sound and humane. If it is not, it does not seem to me that the church can do much to undo the damage that has been done. The churches should be the preservers not of inflexible orthodoxies but of the truths by which men must live and from which they must never depart—truths, however, which are infinitely perfectible. It is not with the institutionalization of the religious impulse, but with its education, that the church should be concerned, with the development of a religious attitude which embraces a sense of the possibilities of existence and a devotion to the cause of those possibilities. The church must become not merely the repository of the highest ideals of humanity, but an active participant in the educational process of helping human beings realize those ideals.

Christians believe that God is Love. Our inquiry in this book has amounted to the conclusion that Love is God. It is a distinction with a significance, the difference being that while most Christians accept the view that God is Love, and let it go at that, Jesus himself felt also that Love is God, that love of God was essential, but equally essential was the love of man for man. This seems to me to represent the great contribution of Jesus, the development of the seedling Old Testament injunction to love one's neighbor as oneself. Jesus not only sent men to God, but he also sent God to men, by sending men to men. He enjoined men to live a way of life with their fellow men which was the way of love—love for each other. This way of love I would call *philia,* distinguishing it from the Platonic and Old Testament "eros": love in which man seeks God in order to satisfy his spiritual hunger by the possession and enjoyment of the Divine perfection, and from the New Testament love of man for God, *agape,* which implies the whole-hearted surrender to God, placing one's entire faith in Him, and desiring only that His will should be done.[26]

For too many modern Christians *agape* has taken the form of a kind of apple-polishing of the Divine. The concept of love which we have here been developing most closely resembles *philia,* but is not identical with it, for our concept is best called by what it refers to, namely, *maternal love.*

It will fall principally to mothers and teachers to spread this gospel, and toward this end I would strongly urge that the nursery school be made part of the educational system of the land. In nursery school children between two and five years of age would, for a few hours, each day receive the benefits of mother and teacher working together on the complementary task of contributing toward the child's development. The nursery school would represent the principal agency through which the parents could be brought together with the school in the complementary task of developing the potentialities of the child. In nursery school parents, especially the mother, would be encouraged to help teachers and teachers would be encouraged to help parents in the joint enterprise of helping the child. The parents would contribute what the teachers ought to know, and the teachers would contribute what the parents ought to know, for the benefit of the child as well as for the benefit of all concerned. The teaching the child receives at home and the teaching it receives at school must be joined and unified. The teaching of the elementary skills of reading, writing, and arithmetic is important, but not nearly as important as the most important of all the skills—human relations.

A scientific approach to education must begin with the basic assumption that values must in the long run be tested by their capacity to contribute to the happiness and creativeness of human beings living together. If we have found a scientific basis *in fact* for what *should be,* we should at least be willing to give it a try.

Our schools need to be transformed into institutes for the study of the science (theory) and the art (practice) of loving human relations. Children in such schools will continue to be taught the theory and practice of human relations from their earliest years. It is in the nursery, kindergarten, and elementary school that the most fundamental learning will be done, and it is for this reason that we must learn to understand that the most important teachers in the human community, in addition to the parents, are the teachers of the young. College professors on this scheme of values, valuable as they are, are not as important as elementary school teachers. Our society, therefore, needs to undergo a fundamental change in its attitudes toward schoolteachers, to revalue them for what they are worth—as next to the parents the most important members of the community, for teachers are the unacknowledged legislators of the world, the midwives of humanity. We need, therefore, to elevate the status and increase the prestige of the profession of teaching the young, and to reward its votaries in such a manner as to encourage the finest persons among us to dedicate their lives to the high and significant task of helping human beings realize their potentialities.

The teaching of the three "R's" must be secondary and supplementary to the teaching of the primary skill of human relations, for what, indeed, is any instruction worth if it is not integrated into an understanding of man's responsibility to man? Whatever is learned should be learned primarily with reference to its significance for human relations, and always with the emphasis on cooperation, on adaptive association, on love, on shared relationships. Cracker-barrel human relations are not good enough. Children should be taught not how to become submissive echoes of their teachers and their traditions, but how to evaluate humanely, sympathetically, and critically the world in which they are living. They should be taught not only the overt but also the covert values of their society, and they should be taught not only what is right with their society but what is wrong with it, and that it is going to be their responsibility to put things right, and how they may be put right.

In this light education must be conceived to be the drawing out of the best that is within the person by making available to him all the encouragements and supports and stimulations which he requires, to enable him to become a loving, cooperative, non-conflictful person, who is not only aware of what is right with the world but is also equipped with the knowledge, the desire, and the wisdom necessary to bring it nearer that ideal of what it should and can be . . . a person who will not be a competitor, but a cooperator, a person for whom altruism will be a passion and selfishness a disorder; a person wise enough to know that

He who would love his fellow men
Must not expect too much of them . . .

a person who will want to improve the world as he finds it, and not accept things as they are; a person who will not risk wrecking the social machinery by exceeding the speed-limit of rational inquiry; who will not abolish anything, but merely render it necessary to discontinue it, dispelling fear by supplying facts and knowledge; who will recognize the strange necessity of beauty; who will have a sense of personal responsibility for decency and justice; who will never offer up the smoke of incense before an empty shrine, nor pretend to a creed he does not believe; a person, in short, who having had a loving order made within himself will make loving order in the world—

be to other souls
The cup of strength in some great agony,
Enkindle generous ardour, feed pure love
Beget the smiles that have no cruelty—
Be the sweet presence of a good diffused,
And in diffusion more intense.

—George Eliot

Survival and Fulfillment

Humanity today stands on the threshold of a possible new dispensation—the self-dispensing fulfillment of its evolutionary destiny. Until recent times humanity has been engaged in a struggle for existence, for survival. This struggle has for large masses of humanity been progressively decreased. The population of the world increases at an accelerating rate, a fact which since the days of Malthus has constituted cause for alarm to many students of humanity. Whether uncontrolled increase of population in the world or in any community is or is not desirable the fact of increase bears abundant testimony to the ability of large and increasingly large numbers of human beings to survive.[27]

The problem of physical survival has largely been solved. On the other hand, for the larger number of human beings the problem of psychological survival has not been solved. In the United States alone one out of every eighteen persons will spend some time in a mental hospital.[28] By psychological survival is meant survival, or better, fulfillment of one's potentialities for being a happy, creative, and cooperative human being. Julian Huxley has referred to this subject in the following words:

> Human life *is* a struggle—against frustration, ignorance, suffering, evil, the maddening inertia of things in general; but it is also a struggle *for* something, and for something which our experience tells us can be achieved in some measure, even if we personally find ourselves debarred from any measure that seems just or reasonable. And fulfillment seems to describe better than any other single word the positive side of human development and human evolution—the realization of inherent capacities by the individual and of new possibilities by the race; the satisfaction of needs, spiritual as well as material; the emergence of new qualities of experience to be enjoyed; the building of personalities. But it cannot be achieved without struggle, not merely struggle with external obstacles, but with the enemies within our own selves.[29]

The realization of inherent capacities by the person and of new possibilities by the race—that is what is meant by fulfillment. If human beings are enabled to fulfill themselves they will encounter no enemies within themselves. At the present time the greatest obstacle in the path of human progress is not the atom or hydrogen bomb or any other external obstacle, but the disordered selves of human beings. The self of a human being is the means through which he sees and evaluates the world. An imperfect means applied to the achievement of confused goals is not the best of auguries for a happy dénouement. A self that is organized to function in terms of love is different in its effects from one that is disorganized to function on the dual basis of some sort of relation to society in which there is, first, a religion in some way concerned with the doctrine of love, and second, a secular tradition which offers high rewards to the successful competitor. Man requires no supernatural sanctions for love. Love is a fact of nature, and it is the most important of all the facts about human nature. Love is and should be the most natural of religions for human beings. The person who has been brought up to be a loving human being will not be able to see the world in anything but loving terms. Violence will be as foreign to his nature as it is at present common to the acquired nature of most men of contemporary western civilizations. To most persons, conditioned as they are in the western world today, love and violence are not only not incompatible but are perfectly reconcilable forms of conduct, whereas in fact violence is not only contrary to man's basic nature but inimical to it.[30]

Man's self is the means of whatever ends he achieves, and the ends he seeks to achieve are largely determined by the nature of the self that has been built into him. Hence the pressing necessity of realizing that healthy human development and survival depends upon our ability to help human beings fulfill their potentialities and thus develop selves that are as much in harmony with their basic inner necessities as they are in harmony with those of all other healthy human beings. No man ever achieves his real self until he is his best self. We know something of the nature of those necessities, and we have good reason to believe that if we would but act upon that knowledge we will have taken the most important step in the right direction toward the fulfillment of humanity's promises.

Human nature is good. It is our present *human nurture* that is bad. We need to conform human nurture to the requirements of human nature. Our nurture must be based on basic human nature. Human beings and nations of human beings will solve their problems only when they have learned this lesson and applied it to themselves.

> Truth is within ourselves; it takes no rise
> From outward things, whate'er you may believe:
> There is an inmost centre in us all,
> Where truth abides in fulness; and around,
> Wall within wall, the gross flesh hems it in,
> Perfect and true perception—which is truth;
> A baffling and perverting carnal mesh
> Which binds it, and makes error: and, "*to know*"
> Rather consists in opening out a way
> Whence the imprison'd splendour may dart forth,
> Than in effecting entry for the light
> Supposed to be without.
>
> —BROWNING, *Paracelsus*

Appendix A LEARNING THEORY

We learn looking backward. We live looking forward.—ANON.

The need for love . . . provides the incentives and conditions for *learning* by experience and for accumulating knowledge from generation to generation and so of building up an immortal tradition. —IAN SUTTIE.*

The method is the message. —ANON.

We have been inquiring into the relationship between the manner in which the child is reared, and those mental configurations or habits which are formed in childhood and continue as a basic part of the motivational system of the person. The person, as a social being, may be regarded as a more or less stable system of adjustive habits capable of self-regulation and of change. These habits are mostly acquired by *learning* from other human beings. It may be of value, therefore, for the better understanding of the manner in which the organism becomes socialized to inquire into the elements of the learning process.

Most theories of learning are unavoidably oversimplified,[1] and this is true of the account of human social learning which will follow. We do not yet know enough about the physiology and psychology of learning to be able to give a thorough account of it, which is why the title of this appendix emphasizes theory. Much of the experimental work on learning has been done on rats (psychological rodentology), and some on monkeys, but we must always remember that culture is not a maze, nor human behavior comparable to that of a rat moving in a maze.[2] We shall miss our cue if we extrapolate from the findings on rats and monkeys to the conditions prevailing among human beings, and yet we should be in error were we altogether to neglect the findings of the rat psychologists, for in the absence of similar experimental knowledge for human beings we can, with caution, usefully consider these findings insofar as they may eventually lead to a better understanding of the learning process in man. It cannot, however, be too strongly emphasized that learning theory insofar as it relates to man is at the present time

* Ian Suttie, *The Origins of Love and Hate,* New York, Julian Press, 1943, p. 20.

in a somewhat primitive state. There are some who believe that learning theory constitutes nothing more than an elaborate system for labeling the obvious after the fact, having no analytic value whatever, nor in any way adding to our understanding of personality and culture.[3] While this may be true of the application of learning theory to socialization by some investigators, and while there may be a good deal of truth in this point of view generally, it is necessary to make a start at some point with a theory of learning, however inadequate, if we desire to attain some understanding of the manner in which the human being learns his culture. Labels may ultimately prove to be helpful in the analytic process involved in thinking more clearly about the nature of learning.

The Spontaneity Factor

Before proceeding with the exposition of learning theory it is necessary to make certain preliminary limiting statements. The first of these requires special emphasis because in the concentration on learning theory it may be neglected. This is the fact that there is some reason to believe that not all behavior is an expression of what is learned. When, for example, a person is confronted with a novel situation that lies outside the competence of his learned responses, his behavior may function upon an almost if not entirely purely, organic level. Fear, anger, curiosity, the flight reactions of embarrassment in a social situation are familiar forms of such behavior. In such circumstances the behavior exhibited may be wholly or almost wholly in terms of unlearned responses. Such responses have been attributed by Moreno to a *spontaneity factor*.

> . . . there is within the range of individual expression an independent area *between* heredity and environment, influenced but not determined by hereditary (genes) and social forces (tele). The *s* (spontaneity) factor would have in this area its topographical location. It is an area of relative freedom and independence from biological and social determinants, an area in which new combinatory acts and permutations, choices and decisions are formed, and from which human inventiveness and creativity emerges.[4]

Even when socially learned responses are made to novel situations it is probable that they are integrated in a matrix of unlearned responses. Indeed, this of necessity characterizes the greater part of the learning process of the infant. The distinction between *situation* and *response* so far as the infant is concerned is artificial. The situation is the response and the response is the situation for the infant, and it is in this relational situation-response world that he makes his unlearned attempts at behavior spontaneously.[5] From this relational universe he gradually learns by successful selection to make the most adequate responses to situations which become slowly but surely more differentiated for him, but until they are differentiated they are novel situations, and spontaneity is defined as the adequate response to a novel situation. It is these selective acts which the Morenos regard as creative. "He may create," they write, "as an individual actually very little—most of his acts resembling those of his peers, but the logic of the child in feeling creatively is justified by the *mode* of his experience, its status nascendi, rather than by the originality of his experience."[6]

Spontaneity, as conceived by the Morenos, is the inherent tendency of the person to experience as his own state a freedom or autonomy of action which is quite independent of any external influence, and free from any internal influence which he cannot control. Whether or not the spontaneity factor is a genuine or important element to be considered in the analysis of the learning process future research may reveal. It is a factor to be borne in mind. Meanwhile, it appears probable that many of the emotional relationships of the person to the environment are the outcome of integrative processes which are only indirectly related to the learning process.

Social Learning

All social learning takes place under social conditions, in social situations; therefore the proper evaluation of any learned act cannot be made in terms of learning principles alone. The social conditions, the immediate social situation, in which the learning occurred must also be known. Psychology describes the principles of learning, the social sciences describe the conditions. Those who are interested in understanding human behavior must acquaint themselves with both, and—as we have to some extent already seen—with something more: an understanding of the biological or organic bases of human behavior and the varying organization which these undergo in differing cultures. With an equipment based on such foundations there is more than a promise that the sciences of behavior will develop predictive powers which in the not too distant future will place them in the forefront of the applied sciences.[7]

By behavior is to be understood any act of a living organism. By social behavior is to be understood the acts of the organism which have been learned in the interactive process with other persons, the interactive process involving not only other persons but also things. The organism learns from experience, and learning is the profit which accrues from experience. Indeed, learning may be defined as the alteration in behavior that results from experience.[8] Purely organic behavior in a human social group is of minimal survival value. Derived needs in particular require derived responses, and these must be socially learned. What, then, is learning reduced to its simplest terms? In its simplest terms ***learning is*** *the process by which a stimulus becomes connected with a response.* Upon analysis learning is seen to assume two principal forms, as the strengthening of one out of a number of more or less distinct responses to a need, and the formation of new receptor-effector connections. The first is typical of simple selective learning, and the second of conditioned-reflex learning. A mixed form of learning also occurs in which new receptor-effector connections are set up at the same time that selective learning is taking place.

Selective Learning

Learning which of a number of random responses to a need will best satisfy the need is the process of *selective learning.*

Conditioning

Learning by conditioning means to set up new receptor-effector connections rather than to strengthen connections already strong enough in combination to evoke overt responses. For example, meat (the unconditioned stimulus) is presented to a dog; this is followed by salivation in the dog (the unconditioned response) while at the same time a buzzer (the conditioned stimulus) is sounded. After a number of such experiences the dog is exposed to the sound of the buzzer alone, to which it then responds by salivation (the conditioned response). A new receptor-effector connection has been established. The necessity of selecting one response from the varied responses normally evoked is eliminated. Such conditioning frequently occurs during the selective learning process in which the response comes to be made to any one of a number of stimuli associated with the original stimulus situation.

In all these processes the organism itself establishes or acquires automatically adaptive receptor-effector connections. Such acquisition is *learning.*[9]

Simple Conditioning

First Trial

Unconditioned stimulus ⟶ Unconditioned response
(Meat) (Salivation)
Neutral stimulus ⟶ Unconditioned response
(Buzzing) (Turning head or no response)

Later Trials

Conditioned stimulus ⟶ Conditioned response
(Buzzing) (Salivation)

Following Hull, the substance of the elementary learning process seems to be this: Stimulus energies produce a condition of need in a setting of receptor discharges. This combination of conditions activates numerous vaguely adaptive response potentials mediated by the unlearned receptor-effector organization of the organism. The relative strengths of these various response potentials vary from instant to instant (oscillation factor). The resulting spontaneous variability of the momentary unlearned behavior reaction potentials produces the randomness and variability of the unlearned behavior evoked under given conditions. Should one of these random responses, or a sequence of them, result in the reduction of a need dominant at the time, there follows as an indirect effect what is known as *reinforcement*. This is an important principle common to all forms of learning. This primary reinforcement consists, first, in a strengthening of the particular receptor-effector connections which originally mediated the reaction, and second, in a tendency for all receptor discharges occurring at about the same time to acquire new connections with the effectors mediating the given response.

The first effect is known as primitive trial-and-error learning; the second is known as conditioned-reflex learning. In most adaptive situations both processes occur concurrently. Hull points out that "very likely they are at bottom the same process, differing only in the accidental circumstance that the first begins with an appreciable strength, whereas the second sets out from zero. As a result, when the same need again arises in this or a similar situation, the stimuli will activate the same effectors more certainly, more promptly, and more vigorously than on the first occasion."[10]

Reinforcement

In the more complexly developed organism, and particularly in man, there are numerous situations in which learning occurs with no associated primary need reduction. Under such conditions analysis reveals that the reinforcing agent is a situation or event involving a stimulus aggregate or complex which has been closely and consistently associated with the need reduction. Such a situation or event is called a *secondary reinforcing agent,* and the strengthening of the receptor-effector connections which results from its action is known as *secondary reinforcement.*

The organization within the nervous system brought about by a particular reinforcement is called a *habit.*

For our purposes "the law of reinforcement" is best stated by Thorndike, who called it the *law of effect.*

Of several responses made to the same situation, those which are accompanied or closely followed by satisfaction to the animal will, other things being equal, be more firmly connected with the situation, so that when it recurs, they will be more likely to recur; those which are accompanied or closely followed by discomfort to the animal, other things being equal, will have their connection with that situation weakened, so that, when it recurs they will be less likely to occur. The greater the satisfaction or discomfort, the greater the strengthening or weakening of the bond.[11]

There have been many restatements of the "law of reinforcement," but it should in justice be pointed out that the credit for possibly its first and most succinct statement belongs to Shakespeare when, in *The Taming of the Shrew,* he makes Tranio say:

> No profit growes, where is no pleasure ta'en:
> In brief, sir, study what you most affect.

The "affect" or "effect" is the reinforcing agent, the degree of satisfaction, the "pleasure ta'en," the degree of complacency or of tension reduction, and in some cases increase in tension. In short, it is some form of what may perhaps best be described as *reward* which reinforces the connection between the originating stimulus and the adaptively most satisfactory response. Furthermore, under such rewarding conditions an increment of learning takes place, and when the stimulus is again repeated the same response is more likely to occur. This is another way of stating the law of effect, and this form of the law may be spoken of as *the law of reinforcement.* When a stimulus or drive is followed by an unsuccessful response, a response which produces no reward, any existing bond between the stimulus-energy and the response is weakened and in time finally suffers extinction so that the unrewarded response fails to occur on subsequent occasions.

Learning and Culture

The whole of human history can be described as a learning process, as a gradual—in large part—improvement in adjustment.[12] If we are to understand something of the nature of this adjustment it is of fundamental importance that we make these simple principles of learning our own, for they are of some significance for an understanding of the relation of learning to the development of culture and its maintenance. From the bare-bones point of view of learning theory a person is an organism that exhibits behavior which is constantly being reinforced, and the same may be said of culture—the behavior of social groups is a function of interacting persons in stimulus-response or motivation-reward situations. Thus, when we describe the learned behavior of a person, what we are really doing is to describe some segment of the cultural habits or learned ways of doing things peculiar to the group in which he has been socialized. In this sense a description of a culture is the description of the behavior of the persons comprising it.

It is with the process of the acquisition of learned cultural habits that we are primarily concerned in considering the social development of the individual, with the strengthening of cultural habits in persons by rewards or their weakening by the lack of them. With the description of this process we shall continue presently. Meanwhile let us proceed with our discussion of learning theory.[13]

The Process of Social Learning

In order to learn, four conditions must obtain. One must: (1) want something or be motivated; (2) do something or act; (3) notice something during the act; and (4) get something or gain satisfaction. In this series of events we have a statement of the four essential elements of learning, more briefly described by the terms *drive, response, cue,* and *reward* or *reinforcement.*

The *drive* is but another word for urge or need, and is usefully retained as a synonym because it emphasizes the motivational aspect of needs, just as "urge" emphasizes the aspect of tension. The term *drive* suggests activity leading to purposeful behavior. The drive, need, or urge is the motivation which stimulates the organism to act, and one could equally well use the term *motive* to describe this condition or aggregate of conditions. It is important to understand that by *drive* we mean not only the basic drives, but also the derived or socially emergent drives, and also the fact that any impulse, no matter in what way it arises, is capable of acting as a drive. Allport calls this the principle of *the functional autonomy of motives.* Allport regards "adult motives as infinitely varied, and as self-sustaining, contemporary systems, growing out of antecedent systems, but functionally independent of them."[14] It remains, however, an open question whether the satisfaction, however indirect, of some basic needs does not lie at the bottom of every autonomous act.

The *response* consists of purposeful acts calculated to bring about a reduction in the intensity of the drive. The response is what the organism does in relation to the drive. The response may be recognized as consisting of two series of acts: (1), the act immediately preceding the reward (the act closest in time to the reward), is the *goal response,* the response most strongly reinforced, and (2), *instrumental acts,* the acts leading up to the goal response. The instrumental acts are also strengthened increasingly in the order of their temporal relation to the reward, a fact which is subsumed in the concept of *the gradient of reward or reinforcement.*

The *cue* is a stimulus which is originally perceived during the response, and which, becoming associated with successful response, frequently provides the originating stimulus for the response. Cues may be provided by stimuli originating from outside the organism (exteroceptive stimuli), or by stimuli from within the organism (proprioceptive stimuli), or the combination of both. Cues are those stimuli which serve as guides in the performance of a response. They give direction and orientation to the response, they act as indicators. They indicate to the organism when, where, and how to respond. The drive motivates the response, the cue guides or directs the response along the appropriate channels. When the dominant character of a stimulus is its intensity it may be spoken of as a drive; when it functions primarily as a guide it may be referred to as a cue. The ability to notice a cue can be learned as a response. This is called learning to pay attention.

The *reward* is the reduction in the intensity of the drive. It is the event which satisfies the need. The reward signifies that the proper *adjustment* has been made by the organism, that the proper biologically or socially adaptive acts have been performed.

These four elements of learning apply to derived or acquired needs as well as to basic needs. Striving to attain social goals is satisfied by achieving them.

Social learning theory, reduced to its simplest terms, is for the most part the study of the circumstances in which cues become connected with responses. Such studies are conducted in a multidimensional matrix sandwiched in between need and reward situations. In fact all, or almost all, behavior is calculated to mediate between these two situations—those in which impulses are aroused and those in which they are satisfied. In the satisfaction of his basic and later his derived or acquired needs the person learns to make the proper responses to the cues originally accompanying them. A great number of cues are provided directly to the growing person by his culture as the conditions which must be followed by certain acts if the person is to achieve and earn the approbation of the group. The formula here is universal and follows the simple pattern of our learning process. The desire for social approbation or the avoidance of social disapprobation is the drive to which a response is made in the presence of cues provided by the situation, and the attainment of the goal, the reward of social approbation or the avoidance of social disapprobation, is secured and the intensity of the drive is satisfactorily reduced. This may be illustrated from a common experience of everyday life.

Arriving in the morning at his place of work Mr. Smith always greets his fellow workers with a hearty "Good morning." Why does he utter these words of greeting? They may have become automatic with him, and amount to no more than a formula completely devoid of affective content, in spite of the overt heartiness. Whether this be so or not, Mr. Smith had to learn how and when to use those particular words, either under conditions in which it was repeatedly explained to him, or by observation and imitation, or more usually by all three means: that it makes others feel happy—however slightly—to be greeted, that one feels happier for having done so and being greeted in return; that it is a mark of friendliness, a form of politeness which helps to make "the wheels of social intercourse go round more smoothly." A greeting is, of course, a form of social recognition. In urban areas Mr. Smith will have learned to greet in this way only those persons whom he knows, the rest he will pass by in silence. In rural areas he may greet everyone, even perfect strangers. In urban areas it is good form to behave in the first way and not customary to behave in the second way, while in some rural areas it is usual to behave in the second way and not customary to restrict one's greetings merely to persons whom one knows. Such urban-rural differences in behavior are due to many conditions, and are learned primarily through training or socialization. It might be well to remind ourselves here that fundamentally learning or training and socialization are closely intertwined with one another if they are not one and the same thing.

Mr. Smith has acquired the habit of saying "Good morning," that is to say, under certain conditions he utters certain sounds and does things with the muscles of expression of his face, the latter almost unconsciously. Why does Mr. Smith behave in this manner? The answer can most economically be given in one word: Security. He wishes to remain secure, to be undisturbed, not to be disapproved by his group, but to be approved, recognized. He is aware that in order to maintain the approval of his group he must not offend by failing to do those things which are socially required of him. In the morning he greets others because he feels an urge to do so, and having virtuously performed this social rite he may proceed upon the more or less even tenor of his way. In this type of behavior virtue is indeed its own reward. The reduction in the intensity of the urge is achieved by the utterance of the formula which is the proper response to the particular situation, and eliciting or not a greeting in return. The behavior may be broken down as follows:

Drive: Social obligation: The traditional way of behaving;
Cue: Under certain conditions: The learned conditions;
Response: To greet another person: The learned response;
Reward: And thus, with the consciousness of having made the socially approved response in the socially obligatory manner, reduce the intensity of the drive.

Under other conditions it will not be enough for Mr. Smith to make the greeting in order to secure reduction in drive. His greeting under such other conditions will have to be returned, and the returned greeting will then constitute the greater part if not the whole of his reward. Failure to receive the reward will be disturbing to him.

All social behavior, with few exceptions, can be analyzed in this elementary manner, and the ability to do so renders possible a more efficient understanding of the manner in which the individual becomes socialized.

Reward and Habit

Responses tend not to be repeated unless they are rewarded. In fact repetition of a response gives rise to fatigue, an urge to which the proper adjustive response is rest. Rest is incompatible with the repetition of an unrewarded response, and a conflict situation arises in which the restoration of energy, the reward of the response to the fatigue drive, inhibits these unrewarded responses. This is the pattern by which rewards attached to urges are, in social situations or conflict situations, made to compete with each other, and new habits antagonistic to old ones set up. The new habit must be stronger in virtue of the greater strength of its reward if the old one is to be inhibited and superseded. The old habit or response is not, however, dissolved into nothingness; it is merely superseded, inhibited, and weakened.

Learning and Inhibition

The likelihood that a given need will elicit a given response that can be *increased* is the type of behavior that is called *learning*. The likelihood that a given need will elicit a given response that can be *decreased* is called *inhibition*.

Inhibition, of course, forms a large part of the process of learning to become a social being, and the elements of the learning process already described apply with equal force to the analysis of inhibition as to learning. When, for example, a child desists from making the responses which it has been informed are extremely undesirable and has perhaps been severely punished for having made those responses, the cessation of such behavior is not due so much to the reprimand or the spanking, but rather to the fact that the child has become aware that the reward for not making such responses is greater than the reward for making them. This is the usually claimed rationale behind punishment. One more illustration: A child "fears" to enter a certain room because the reward for not entering it is greater than that for entering it. On the same principle some persons who actually fear to enter a certain room will nonetheless force themselves to do so in order to secure the reward of the excitement achieved by doing so and the anticipated relief which will accrue following the experience. Such behavior is well accounted for in terms of the principle of reward.

Stimulus Generalization

There are several other principles of learning which may be considered here. The first of these is the principle of *stimulus generalization.* The response involved in the original learning becomes connected, by associative reinforcement, with a considerable zone of stimuli other than, but adjacent to, the stimulus conventionally involved in the original learning: this is stimulus generalization. In fact, every energy impinging upon the organism's receptors, whether they be apperceptive or anatomical, in the zone of stimuli to which it is exposed is, under certain circumstances, capable of evoking the same response. Such stimuli are said to be functionally equivalent. This spreading of the results of learning to other stimuli is called *primary stimulus generalization.* The fact that many stimuli alike possess the potentiality of evoking the same response constitutes *primary stimulus equivalence.*[15]

It is not necessary for such stimuli to be present during learning. They need only be similar to or resemble the original stimulus to which the particular response was made. This fact renders possible the transfer of what is learned in one situation to other similar situations. Every situation falls into a class or pattern of situations, and since no two stimulus situations are ever exactly alike the person, willy-nilly, learns to respond to patterns of cues rather than to a specific cue, at least in social life. When, for example, a child learns that a given form of behavior yields rewards in his relations with his siblings, he is likely to try this behavior with other children, that is, he generalizes or transfers habits which have been learned in one situation to other more or less similar situations. The same principle of generalization applies to responses.

Response Generalization

Just as there is a degree of equivalence among stimuli so there is a degree of equivalence among responses. Thus, a stimulus which has come to be connected with a particular response may, under certain circumstances, elicit a different response without prior training. This is known as *response generalization*. The different response will, in some respects at least, resemble the original response, and will be equivalent to it. In other words, to bring about the reward different responses may be tried in the same situation. A child desiring food may make various muscular efforts to secure it on one occasion, upon another he will make gurgling sounds, on still another he will utter novel sounds expressing his desire, or he may cry, or perform any number of similar acts. In this way he learns that any one of a number of a certain class of acts will bring about the desired result.

Discrimination

On the other hand, the child also learns that many generalized responses are not rewarded, that particular stimuli call for specific responses, that discrimination of stimuli and of response is necessary. He learns to respond selectively by the discrimination of stimuli and the making of the properly differentiated response. Thus, the child in attempting to behave with other children as it does with its siblings may be severely rebuffed, and he learns that the same responses cannot be made to all persons. To the properly discriminated stimuli he learns to make the properly discriminated responses. In other words, by the reward of the response to one pattern of cues and the non-reward or punishment of the response to a somewhat different pattern of cues a *discrimination* is gradually established. The process of discrimination is the means by which the specificity of the cue-response connection is secured. In this manner, also, the child comes to learn the importance of cues and to be on the watch for them. By this means he learns to adapt his responses to a single drive in a multiplicity of different ways depending upon the differential cues associated with the drive. The cue, indeed, may be called the *adaptive stimulus,* since it enables the organism to make the correct discrimination which will lead to the most appropriate response.

The Gradient of Reward or Reinforcement

Immediate rewards are more effective than remote ones. When a number of different responses are made to a cue and the last of these responses is followed by reward, the connection between the last response and the cue will be strengthened the most, while the connection with each of the preceding responses will be strengthened by a progressively smaller amount. Where a series of responses are made to a cue or series of cues the connections more remote from the reward are strengthened less than those closer to the reward. That is to say, the effects of reward increase in a gradient, the closer the connections are to a reward the more they are strengthened. This is the principle of the *gradient of reward or reinforcement.* This principle accounts for the increased tendency to respond the nearer the goal is approached, simply because the connections between the cue and the goal-response have been most strengthened. The gradient of reward has the tendency to cause the subject to choose the shortest of alternative responses to a goal and to eliminate unnecessary responses from a sequence.

The effects of reward are not restricted to the particular cue-response sequence which is associated with the goal-response; they also strengthen the other cue-response connections leading up to the goal-response. There thus often exists a hierarchy of responses in which there is a graduated spread of reward in general determined by degree of proximate relation to the goal-response. The spread of the effects of reward has the function of strengthening the connections to responses which comprise the first steps of the sequence leading to reward. This function can be greatly reinforced if certain stimuli involved in the sequence acquire a sub-goal, or secondary rewarding value, by repeated association with the primary reward.

Anticipatory Response

Wherever possible responses near the stage of reward tend to occur before their original time in the response series, they tend to become anticipatory. Unnecessary or useless acts in the response sequence tend to be crowded out. Anticipatory responses enable the organism to adapt itself to a situation even before the actual drive has come into play, and by generalization even in the absence of the original cue eliciting the goal-response. For example:

> A child touches a hot radiator. The pain elicits an avoidance response, and the escape from pain rewards this response. Since the sight and muscular feel of the hand approaching the radiator are similar in certain respects to the sight and muscular feel of the hand touching the radiator, the strongly rewarded response of withdrawal will be expected to generalize from the latter situation to the former. After one or more trials, the child will reach out his hand toward the radiator and then withdraw it before touching the radiator. The withdrawal response will become anticipatory; it will occur before that of actually touching the radiator. This is obviously adaptive, since it enables the child to avoid getting burns.[16]

The tendency for responses to occur in a sequence does not necessarily depend upon the subject's insight into the adaptive value of the process.

Anticipatory Response and Conditioning

The mechanism of anticipatory response is clearly related to that of the conditioned reflex or response, the response made to a cue strongly associated with the original cue response. Mowrer and Kluckhohn have, however, correctly objected to the practice of many writers who equate conditioning and all learning on the ground that clarity is best served if the term *conditioning* is "restricted to that special sphere of learning in which an incidental stimulus becomes so strongly connected, by associative reinforcement, with a 'right' or 'goal' response that this stimulus can alone elicit the response," and they propose to make clear what they believe to be the essential difference by adding the words, *"in the absence of the original motive.* Such stimuli" they add "may be referred to as *signals,* in contradistinction to *cues.* Both, however, are properly called *signs,* to indicate that they both gain their significance, or *meaning,* from the same process, namely, associative reinforcement."[17]

Mowrer and Kluckhohn's definition of conditioning may be accepted with the proviso that it applies equally well to the processes of ordinary learning reinforcement, that at most, the conditioned reflex is, as Hull says, a special case of ordinary learning reinforcement. A distinction may certainly be made, but this does not apply to fundamentally different principles or laws, but only to the differences in the conditions under which the same principles or laws operate. Whereas selective learning involves the differential strengthening of one from a number of more or less distinct responses to a need, conditioned-reflex learning involves the formation of receptor-effector connections *de novo* in respect to one conspicuous act. The difference, if it is a difference, is that in selective learning such a conspicuous act may constitute one of a whole series of acts, and which one shall become the conspicuous conditioned response will depend upon the particular conditions prevailing in a given need situation. Since so much particularly of the emotional life of the person is developed by a process of elaboration of conditioned emotional responses we would do well to pay further attention to the nature of the conditioning process here.

While the goal-response and the cue which has directed the drive is reinforced most strongly there are, at the same time, other cues whose connections with the goal-response are also reinforced. The former is a primary and the latter a secondary or associative reinforcement. Under almost all conditions the original cue may elicit the secondary response. The primary response is the unconditioned response, the secondary response is the conditioned response, and as we have seen it may also be called the anticipatory response. Furthermore, the conditioned response is capable of being made equally well in the absence or the presence of the original cue or need situation. The importance, however, of the conditioned response lies in the fact that it is capable of being made in the absence of the original cue or motive (drive). This fact has the most important implications for the understanding of the social development of the person and of the group, for by its means the development of sign and symbolic behavior becomes possible, the development of a highly complex means of communication-language, the development of abstract thought, and the power to transmit and acquire the complex equipment necessary for social life. Spelt has shown that conditioned responses are capable of being developed in the fetus,[18] and Wenger has shown that the newborn is capable of conditioned responses.[19] In the case of the fetus the conditioned responses are to a buzzer originally associated with a loud noise, in the case of the newborn the response is with lid closure to the conditioned stimulus of a vibrator applied to the sole of the foot originally associated with an unconditioned flash of light. Thus, from the moment of birth, and possibly even before, the human organism is capable of learning, and by a pattern which the conditioned response almost perfectly illustrates. It is desirable, therefore, that the conditioning process be fully understood.

In the simplest form of conditioning the organism responds to a stimulus while another stimulus is also presented; for example, a light is flashed and the eyelids close, at the same time the sole of the foot is stroked; later the stroking of the sole of the foot leads directly to response.

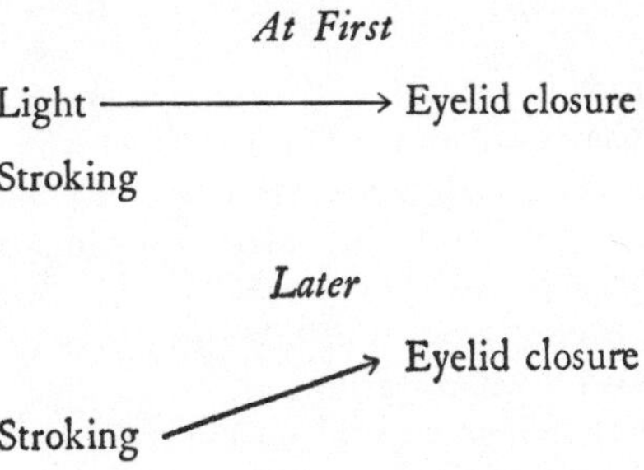

A child frightened by the loud sound made by the fall of a window shade, responded thereafter to the sight of a window shade with fear, though she appears to have originally responded to the sound of a falling window shade. She was freed of this fear by simple reconditioning. In pleasant circumstances over the course of several afternoons, with a reasonable supply of candy at hand, it was gradually demonstrated to her that quite a variety of amusing games could be played with a well-trained window shade. In other words, her conditioned response to the window shade was reconditioned. Under more rewarding conditions the child learned to respond to the window shade with interest rather than fear. The connection between pleasure and window shade was now stronger than the connection between fear and shade, so that the latter connection became weakened and finally extinguished.

At First

(Unconditioned stimulus) Loud noise ⟶ Fear (Unconditioned response)

(Conditioned stimulus) Window shade ⟶ Turning (Unconditioned response)

Later

(Conditioned stimulus) Window shade - - → Fear (Conditioned response)

Under Reconditioning the following processes occur:

(Conditioned stimulus) Window shade → Fear (Conditioned response)
(Reconditioned stimulus) Window shade → Reward (Reconditioned response)

The reward now associated with the window shade becomes biologically more dominant than the fear associated with it; there is a reinforcement of the biologically more rewarding response, and in time an extinction of the earlier conditioned, less rewarding response. This has been called the principle of *dominance* (Razran; Murphy, Murphy, and Newcomb), but is clearly an illustration of the principle of reward or reinforcement. Much human learning follows this pattern of a new cue-response connection being built up on the basis of old cues with new responses, or old responses with new cues. In terms of everyday language, old habits are sloughed off and new ones formed.

Conditioning and reconditioning are processes constantly proceeding during the socialization of the child. Cues which once served to produce a particular response come to produce another response, and the same responses come to be made to different cues. Responses are made to signs which stand for significant conditions or situations, though the condition or situation is not present to the senses. We respond to things even though the actual thing is no longer there, that is, we respond to the sign of the thing as if we were responding to the actual thing of which it is a sign. All human beings are well stocked with such tendencies to respond, and in daily life we draw upon these to make the necessary adjustments called forth by the signs which impinge upon us.

The ability to delay and regulate one's responses, the capacity to live, as it were, in the future, and to plan responses to stimuli not present to sense are frequently exhibited aspects of conditioning in daily life. Delayed reaction experiences illustrate the manner in which these processes work. A person whose behavior is motivated by a particular stimulus will generally continue to respond to anything which is capable of acting as the sign of that stimulus after the original stimulus has disappeared. Thus, the presence of a light may be noted in connection with a goal, and though the light which is a considerable distance away is extinguished the goal is nevertheless reached without difficulty by keeping the position where the light was in mind. This represents the pattern of much human behavoir.

Second and higher order conditioning, in which a conditioned response may be built upon the foundation of another, and a third and a fourth upon these, very probably plays an important part in socially learned behavior. It is generally found that the secondary or higher order stimuli have the effect of attenuating or extinguishing the connection between the lower order stimuli and the response. This finding has the most important significance for learning theory, since it is obvious that, first, it can be utilized in a practical way for the attenuation or extinction of habit, and second in explaining the acquisition of new habits. Second and higher order conditioning are specific forms of reconditioning.

In the process of social development the individual becomes conditioned to complicated patterns of stimuli rather than to purely discrete stimuli. A significant item of such a pattern may, by generalization, evoke the response called for by the pattern; a part stands for the whole. This is a type of learned behavior which is most common to social man.

An immense amount of conditioning takes place during the social development of the person without his being aware of it. Music, for example, which has been heard during meals is usually rated more highly than when it is heard unaccompanied by an enjoyable meal.

Subliminal Conditioning

One may make all sorts of responses in certain situations and yet be unable to give any good reason for making them. Murphy, Murphy, and Newcomb refer to negative conditioning of this sort where words which were regularly followed by electric shocks later aroused withdrawing movements and also inner disturbances shown by the galvanic skin reflex.

Although the subject may not remember that the word was followed by shock, the word produces the inner disturbance. (Indeed, the disturbance is *greater* in those instances in which the subject's memory fails him. There is here something like the blocking or repression to which psychoanalysts have called attention.) One has learned at the visceral level what he has not learned on the verbal level. Social learning of this sort may be of great importance in the tension-fear-prejudice situation, though its nature never becomes clear to the learner.[20]

Rationalizations will be offered to explain these responses while the true causes remain hidden from the person himself. The same mechanism is at work in the posthypnotic state with respect to posthypnotic suggestions.[21] And, indeed, much that transpires in the psychotherapeutic situation falls into the class of subliminal as well as liminal conditioning.[22]

Subliminal stimuli or stimuli which do not enter consciousness at all may become conditioned and modify social behavior. Murphy, Murphy, and Newcomb give an account of a reaction-time experiment, in which the subject was asked to lift his hand from the telegraph key the moment a light was shown. With practice the subject reduced his reaction time to 0.2 second.

But the experimenter inserted in the external ear a tiny cylinder containing a wire which could be made to hum as soon as the switch was thrown. The experimenter made sure in all cases that the humming was truly subliminal. No subject could tell when it started or stopped. In the next series of reaction-time experiments the switch was thrown a small fraction of a second before the stimulus light was flashed. The result, after practice with the method, was a reduction of the apparent reaction time in some cases to less than 100 one-thousandths of a second. The subject had been conditioned to the subliminal sound of the humming in the cylinder.[23]

Subliminal cues play a considerable role in conditioning, and there is some evidence that this type of conditioning is operative from the moment of birth and probably even before. In Chapter VIII (p. 163) we saw that the fetus at the thirty-first week will respond with vigorous movement to the sound of a doorbell buzzer when this is placed over the fetal head, these responses increasing in vigor as the fetus nears term. The fetal heartbeat will increase in rate when a vibrating tuning fork is placed on the mother's abdomen. Similar increases in fetal heart rate have been recorded after loud sharp noises have occurred near the mother. As early as the fifth month the fetus may hiccough. The fetus may suck its thumb or fingers, it swallows, excretes urine, and sometimes passes stool. It is quite possible that in respect of some of these forms of behavior the fetus is capable of being conditioned. Reference has already several times been made to Spelt's conditioning of a fetus to sound. It has also been suggested that such conditioning may play an important role in the subsequent personal development of the person. May it not be that occupational differences in pregnant women, through the externally originating stimuli to which they expose the fetus, cause certain responses to be made by the fetus which influence the later development of the person? Greenacre, as we saw in Chapter V (p. 92) suggests that fetal responses to unpleasant stimuli may even give rise, on the organic level, to a predisposition to anxiety which might prove an important determinant in producing the severity of any neurosis.

These are at the present time nothing but suggestions. We must await the findings of future research on fetal and infant behavior along these lines before we can come to any definite conclusions.

The newborn would certainly appear to respond to stimuli of a subtle nature, as is witnessed by the fact that it is soon able to perceive the difference between being wanted and not being wanted. The stimuli which enable the newborn to perceive this difference would, at the adult level, be described as of a subliminal nature, but it appears certain that such "subliminal" stimuli are in some way sharply discriminated by the newborn, even though they may not be cognitively evaluated—they certainly are organismically evaluated. We have seen that the newborn is capable of being conditioned to such stimuli.

In the course of his development the person learns to make considerable use of such subliminal cues, and the strong tendency of adults to judge other persons or situations by "instinct" or "intuition" is in large measure based on such subliminal conditioning.

> I do not like thee Doctor Fell,
> The reason why I cannot tell.
> But this I know, and know full well,
> I do not like thee, Doctor Fell.

This venerable quatrain may now, at long last, be explained as the expression of an attitude which was subliminally conditioned.

As Murphy, Murphy, and Newcomb put it, "We learn day by day the meaning of gestures, facial expression, tone of voice; but a great deal that we learn functions beneath the level of consciousness, or may be above the threshold of consciousness today and function just as well when below it tomorrow."[24]

Helene Deutsch has suggested that woman's intuition is due to the necessity for that greater inner alertness which a masculine society thrusts upon her, a sort of acute "listening in the dark." "Woman's understanding of other people's minds," she writes, "her intuition, is the result of an unconscious process through which the subjective experience of another person is made one's own by association and thus is immediately understood. The other person's subjective experience manifests itself in an external happening that is sometimes barely perceptible, but that in an intuitive person evokes by quick association a definite inner state."[25]

In other words, woman undergoes a better training in the interpretation of subliminal cues than man. The wit who remarked that woman's intuition is merely man's transparency was speaking wiser than he knew and at the same time exhibiting his own opacity.

The conditioned response is a preparatory or anticipatory response, a function of organic readiness or preparation for tension-reduction; it is, in brief, a redirected drive.[26]

Imitation

Imitation is the most fundamental of all the forms of social learning. In all societies and at all ages of the developing person it is socially most highly rewarded. It is the principal way in which the developing person learns to behave and learns to modify his behavior. The importance of imitation in the socialization process has long been understood in every society, and in our own is given recognition in the saying that the child learns not by precept but by example.

As Piaget points out, the child learns to imitate, it is not born with a hereditary drive which causes it to imitate. The act by which a model is reproduced is imitation. Piaget has shown that imitation or the precursors of imitation begin quite early in the infancy of the person.[27] It is not a correct assumption that the child begins to imitate in the second half of the second year.

Imitation may be of the conditioned-response type, or imitation after a trial-and-error period, or deliberate imitation. Miller and Dollard have offered a convenient classification of the sub-mechanism involved in imitation which we shall here follow. The classification is threefold: (1) *same* behavior, (2) *matched-dependent* behavior, and (3) *copying.*

To imitate is to behave like another. In *same* behavior we are dealing with behavior which may be learned with or without imitative aids, it is of the trial-and-error variety. What is involved is the sameness of the cue to which but a single patterned response must be made if the reward is to be secured, and this results in a sameness of behavior which different individuals arrive at independently. Two persons follow the same route because they read the same route numbers leading to their destination.

Copying involves the act of one person learning to model his behavior on that of another. The copier must know when his behavior is the same, and he must have criteria for the sameness and difference of the acts he performs.

Matched-dependent behavior is important in social life. It arises pre-eminently in the dependent situation, wherever one person is older, shrewder, or more skilled than another. Children must perforce follow their elders, they must learn by reliance upon others to do what is required of them. In the process of socialization children match behavior with their elders and are dependent on them for cues as to what to do. Here is a simple illustration of matched-dependent behavior given by Miller and Dollard. Two children, Jim aged five and Bobby aged two, were playing in their bedroom which was adjacent to the family kitchen.

> The kitchen opened upon a back stairway. It was six o'clock in the evening, the hour when father usually returned home, bearing candy for the two children. While playing in the bedroom, Jim heard a footfall on the stairs; it was the familiar sound of father's return. The younger child, however, had not identified this critical cue. Jim ran to the kitchen to be on hand when father came in the back door. Bobby happened on this occasion to be running in the direction of the kitchen and behind Jim. On many other occasions, probably many hundreds, he had not happened to run when Jim did. He had, for instance, remained sitting, continued playing with his toys, run to the window instead of the door, and the like; but on this occasion, he was running behind his brother. Upon reaching the kitchen, Jim got his candy and Bobby his.
>
> On subsequent nights with similar conditions, the younger child ran more frequently at the mere sight of his brother running. When he ran, he received candy. Eventually, the behavior, under pressure of continued reward, became highly stabilized, and the younger child would run when the older ran, not only in this situation but in many others where time and place stimuli were different. He had learned in this one respect to *imitate* his older brother, but he had not learned to run at the sound of his father's footfall.[28]

Analysis of the behavior of these two children may be broken down into the following elements:

Leader

Drive: Appetite for candy
Cue: Father's footfall
Response: Running
Reward: Eating candy

Imitator

Drive: Appetite for candy
Cue: Leg-twinkle of brother
Response: Running
Reward: Eating candy

These acts of leader and imitator can be put together in one diagram:

	Leader		*Imitator*
Drive:	Appetite for candy		Appetite for candy
Cue:	Father's footfall	dependent – →	Leg-twinkle of leader
Response:	Running – – – –	matched – – →	Running
Reward:	Eating candy		Eating candy

The responses are *matched*. When the older brother runs, the younger does likewise; in other words, the response of the imitator is elicited by cues from the act of the leader. This type of situation and this way of meeting it is of very common occurrence in human society. It should be clear that it actually represents a simple illustration of the conditioned response. A diagram will make this clear.

Leader:	UCS = Father's footfall	UCR = Running	Reward eat up candy
Imitator:	CS = Leader's leg-twinkle	CR = Running	

Here the diagram is made with reference to the imitator. Actually the leader's response is quite as conditioned as the imitator's; there is simply a difference of cues involved. For the leader the father's footfall is the conditioned stimulus (CS) which starts as the sign for candy which motivates the response of running to secure it as the reward. In the case of the imitator, father's footfall has not yet been discriminated as a cue, but the brother's leg-twinkle has, and this, under certain conditions, becomes the sign for candy and motivates the running which leads to the candy reward. In diagrammatic form this is then properly represented as follows:

UCS = Candy — UCR = Running and eating candy
CS = Leader's leg-twinkle — CR = Running and eating candy

This becomes under conditioning:

CS = Leader's leg-twinkle → CR = Running and eating candy

The real stimulus is the candy eaten after the first experience; later, the leader's leg-twinkle becomes associated as a sign of the candy and running as the proper response to secure it.

This is one of the commonest patterns of imitation which occurs in social life at every age level.

The social conditions under which imitative behavior normally occurs are those of hierarchy or rank with respect to specific skills and social statuses.

There are at least four classes of persons who are imitated by others. They are: (1) superiors in an age-grade hierarchy, (2) superiors in a hierarchy of social status, (3) superiors in an intelligence ranking system, and (4) superior technicians in any field.

Age-Grade Superiors

The fact that persons within any society are graded in age-groups provides the basic means by which imitation can take place. In our own society we recognize age-grading in such terms as "infant," "child," "adolescent," "college student," "grown man," "man in the prime of life," and "old man." These terms imply that a certain type of behavior may be expected from the persons they define. In the process of socialization the person makes the transition from one age-grade to another by learning the responses which are peculiar to each age-grade. It is important at this point to note that it is not always age or size which determines one's age-grade status in a particular community, but rather one's social readiness for the role of a person of a particular age-grade. Among the Australian aborigines a youth will not be initiated until he is considered socially developed or mature enough to be admitted to the first or second stages of initiation.[29] Among ourselves we tend to treat many persons as belonging to a much younger age-grade than their chronological age would suggest. We respond to such persons on the basis of their behavior. If they behave like young people we tend to regard them as belonging to the "young people" age-grade. Furthermore, in our society a single person can actually belong to several age-grades. In one group of that society such a person may be regarded as a youth, in another group as an adult, depending upon his behavior or the behavior that is thrust upon him by each group. A youth who can successfully imitate the behavior of a mature adult in one group will be accepted as such, whereas in another group, his home community group, he will be more diffident about acting as an adult and will tend to adhere to the behavior characteristics of his own particular age-grade.

The rewards held out by the higher age-grades are obvious: Greater freedom, more privileges and prestige. Consequently, children in all societies desire to enter the superordinal age-grades as soon as possible. Long trousers in early teen-agers and a cigarette carelessly depending from the lips of middle teen-agers are familiar evidences of this desire in our own society, and they are obvious examples of the deliberate imitation process. As Miller and Dollard point out, an age-grade system constitutes an approximate skill and prestige hierarchy.

> Up to a point (perhaps old age), freedom and privilege increase with the advancement through different phases of the age cycle. As children moving up in the age-cycle are allowed or taught to make the responses of those in the next age-grade above them, and find that these responses lead to reward (for example, being permitted to stay up later and play longer), those above them acquire prestige—that is, they become leaders and models for matched-dependent and copying responses of wide range and variety. Rewarded matching or copying of particular responses institutes a tendency to match the behavior of superordinate persons over a wide range of responses. The tendency to match behavior with a superordinate person or group does not need to be conscious, willful or intentional. It can occur, and does frequently occur, automatically and without verbal aids. The imitative response is directly connected to the cue of the other person's behavior without intermediate mental links of response.[30]

It is unnecessary here to enter into all the ramifications of the imitative process in relation to age-grading; most readers will be familiar with this from their own experience. It will be clear that the age-grade limits imitation, that a member of one age-grade may do many things which are done in the superordinate age-grades but may not do others which are limited to the superordinate age-grades. Thus a child may imitate the table manners of his older brother but may not stay up as late as he does. An older person may be solemn, a younger person rarely. In young children the forbidden superior age-grade behavior finds expression in play imitating the behavior of adults.

In nonliterate societies age-grade differences in behavior are much more sharply drawn than in our own society. The age-grades are organized into a clear hierarchy, with definite privileges and obligations pertaining to membership in each. Definite ceremonies mark the entry into and the exit from each group.

It remains to be said that imitation is not a basic drive, but a socially acquired drive which occurs only under specific conditions and in response to definite rewarding goals. Finally, it must be remembered that imitation is efficient only insofar as it possesses meaning and functional significance for the imitator.

Social-status and Intelligence Superiors

Imitation of superiors in social status and imitation of the intelligent are obvious processes which need not detain us here. A few words may be said concerning *imitation of technicians.* Every society has its specialized divisions of labor, and no one person generally participates as a specialist in all of them. The more technologically complex a society is the more restricted is this participation. The category of technicians cuts across age-grading, social class, and intelligence hierarchies. Older persons may learn from younger, and upper class persons from lower class persons. Men in one field of techniques may learn from men in other fields. Children learn specialized techniques such as the three "R's" from their school teachers. College students learn from their professors. A surgeon may learn various useful devices from a plumber, and so on. We imitate technicians whenever we find it rewarding to do so.

Non-imitation

Learning not to imitate others under certain conditions is also an important process in socialization. When with reference to certain behavior non-imitation is rewarded negative imitation will occur. In this way perception of difference can become a secondary reward. This is the case when an upper class person compares himself with a social inferior, or when a cultivated person compares himself with an uncultivated one. Children learn not to behave like other children whose behavior is disapproved. The opposite behavior is approved; it will therefore tend to be adopted because it is rewarded.

Identification

A somewhat neglected and important factor in learning is what Freud described as the process of unconscious molding of a person's ego on a model. "First," writes Freud, "identification is the original form of emotional tie with an object. Secondly, in a regressive way it becomes a substitute for a libidinal object tie, as it were by means of the introjection of the object into the ego; and thirdly, it may arise with every new perception of a common quality shared with some other person who is not an object of the sexual instinct."[31] And again, "Our ego becomes like another, one which results in the first ego behaving itself in certain respects in the same way as the second; it imitates it, and as it were takes it into itself."[32]

Identification is not to be confused with imitation, even though Seward has recently defined identification as "a generalized disposition to imitate the behavior of a model."[33] Identification always involves some imitation, but whereas imitation is mostly conscious, identification is largely unconscious. As Alexander says, "Identification is the basis of all learning which is not acquired independently by trial and error. It is the most important mechanism in the development of the mature ego."[34] Children tend to take an active part in the development of their own ego by identifying themselves with parental figures, whom they endeavor to be like. It is because of the social stimuli that these figures as models provide that children strive to make something of themselves.[35] As Balint points out ". . . in relation to parents, love and identification are so much intermingled that any clear differentiation between the two seems hopeless." "A child can only become fond of something unknown . . . if he can succeed in identifying it with something known. The common basis of loving and of understanding is identification, and without it both would be impossible."[36]

Emotions

In learning the emotions play a significant role, for in the process of conditioning any emotion which has been aroused may itself come to serve as a motive and source of reinforcement for new trial-and-error learning, generalization, discrimination, and even further (higher order) conditioning. Depending upon its strength an emotion may serve either as a cue or as a drive, or both. A strong emotion has drive value and a reduction in its strength acts as a reward. To the extent that an emotion is distinctive it has cue value. This, of course, illustrates a general principle which is true of any stimulus, whether originating externally or self-induced.

All the emotions are themselves subject to the laws of learning, and their connections with various cues and drives are practically entirely the result of prior training, contrary to the belief which prevailed but a short time ago that there existed an inherited disposition for particular instincts to be accompanied by particular emotions. The *mechanism* of the emotions is innate; their capacity to get attached to particular cues is acquired (or acquirable), and it is from this standpoint that emotions may be spoken of, in any social context, as acquirable drives. Thus, anxiety is one of the innate responses of pain, but "the physiological reactions producing the sensation of anxiety can easily be learned as responses to new situations, while those producing the original pain cannot. Therefore the anxiety is referred to as an acquirable drive and the pain as a primary drive."[37]

One of the ways in which acquired drives differ from innate or primary drives is that the former are much more difficult to define and specify. The fact that it is possible to attach different stimulus-producing responses to the same cue, so that both fear and anger may be aroused in the same situation, that different proportions of two or more stimulus-producing responses may be attached to different cues, so that one situation may make a person very angry and slightly anxious, whereas another may make him slightly angry and very anxious, and that different individuals may learn to respond to the same cue with different mixtures of stimulus-producing responses, so that one individual may be angry, disgusted, and afraid while another is only afraid, are some of the factors which make the definition of acquired drives difficult.

Rewards which are the goals of acquired drives can likewise vary. Another way in which acquired drives and rewards differ from innate drives and rewards is that acquired drives and rewards are much more changeable.

Canalization

Up to as late as the twelfth postnatal month many of the child's drives are not clearly directed upon specific objects. A wide variety of stimuli even in the young child are capable of arousing many of his drives. But with the passage of time drives become attached to specific objects or aspects of experience which have frequently satisfied those drives, and such stimuli become more and more adequate initiators of the proper responses. In this process we see the mechanism for acquired tastes. In this process a direct relationship between the satisfying experience and the drive becomes established. In this way individual preferences and general cultural preferences develop by a process of fixation. The drive is channeled or *canalized* in a specific direction characteristic of the person and his culture. It is important to distinguish between canalization as a social process and conditioning. In canalization the object first eliciting a drive response, the original or unconditional response, remains the adequate direct cue; there is no entry of a substitute cue or associative reinforcement. In the conditioned response a new and often accidental stimulus, occurring while an adequate unconditioned stimulus is at work, acquires the power to call out a response. It is often relatively easy to extinguish the connection between a cue-response in simple conditioning, but much harder to produce such extinction in a canalized response.

The process of canalization is of great importance for learning theory, for a large proportion of our social motives are canalized drives. Indeed, it has been suggested by Murphy, Murphy, and Newcomb that "there is enormously less conditioning and more canalization in social life than most writers have recognized."[38] As these authors point out, a taste for beer or olives, for golf or politics, is not acquired solely through conditioning.

> We start with an interest in food, or tone, or strenuous activity, or the interchange of gestures or facial expressions with our fellows; and these needs, supplemented by many others and guided by cultural processes, give us in time a specific craving for our game of golf or our political argument. We think it worth while to stress that the rudiments of response to tone, taste, smell, and the forms and features of people in the child's immediate world are clearly present and canalized by social experience until they become fairly definite and fixed.[39]

While conditioning is one of the processes which produce similar stabilization of habits, it is not the sole process by which such responses to given cues are produced. Canalization is at least an equally important means of securing such responses. The frequency and intensity of certain stimuli in rewarding situations is a fact which is alone sufficient to produce a connection between them and a drive; so that one can depend upon such cues to evoke the proper drive-response.

But while canalization plays an important role in the acquisition of social habits, that role is a minimal one in infancy compared with the part it plays later. For example, during early infancy the mother ministering to the child's needs is not specifically perceived as an independent object; what is perceived are the satisfactions which she provides in response to the infant's needs, in the form of food and care. These satisfactions are elicited by a large number of unconditioned stimuli that, as the child develops the image of the mother, gradually become associated with the satisfying situation. By associative reinforcement she becomes a symbol of present and anticipated satisfactions; by her presence she may serve to satisfy a number of drives. She, as an object, has become a satisfying substitute stimulus, she has become a conditioned stimulus producing satisfying responses. Though she cannot satisfy all drives by the fact of her presence alone, it is more than doubtful whether the infant sees it that way. What he comes to know is that when this object (the mother) is present, needs are satisfied. It is probable that this is the pattern of most of the learning of the infant, and that canalization does not really begin to take effect until the period of childhood has been reached. It is not by canalization but by conditioning that the mother becomes the object of love. The preference for certain foods, however, becomes established by sheer force of their repeated direct satisfying value, that is, by canalization.

Learning and Values

When the process of canalization is complete, so that the person is prepared to satisfy a need with a definite response, a value has been established. In this sense a value may be defined as the maintenance of a set toward the attainment of a goal.[40] The person learns to want many goals. When these goals are remote and are strived for, value obtains. When the person blindly gropes for some undefined goal in a random manner, value does not obtain. Some definitely known goal must be held in view. This last statement implies that a value takes its existential form from the fact that a goal is being contemplated or approached, rather than from the actual achievement of the goal. The latter is the *reward,* the former the *value.* Thus, stimuli which act as cues and even drives, as well as the goal itself, may all become values. Value itself is not a reward; it is best regarded as a *potential rewarder.* We often strive for things we do not have, and may never have. That we value what we strive to attain is exhibited in the striving, not in the attainment.

An attitude and a value are ultimately one and the same thing. The distinction which is usually made between them is quite arbitrary, being based on the degree of verbalization involved: where verbalization is high we speak of an attitude, where it is low, of a value.

In the process of socialization the values of the person undergo integration, and it is this integration, indeed, which constitutes the basis of the integration of personality: the organization of values into a system derived from the history of the individual's own experience.

The conflicts between values constitute, in the social situation, important factors in the social development of the person. The resolution or nonresolution of these conflicts, the confusion of values, in terms of the social definition of goals, are processes which have very important influences upon the developing personality. Since by far the larger number of the person's values are learned, it is of the first order of importance for human beings to learn what values they should live by.

Appendix B THE EFFECTS UPON THE MOTHER OF REMOVAL OF THE INFANT IMMEDIATELY AFTER BIRTH

To the solid ground
Of Nature, trusts the mind which builds for aye. —WORDSWORTH

Experimental data on the effects upon the mother of separating the infant from her immediately after birth are not many. The following observations are, therefore, extremely valuable, and are for this reason here reprinted by courtesy of the author, Betsy Marvin McKinney, and *Child-Family Digest*. It is to be hoped that Mrs. McKinney's interesting observations will prompt the further study, under experimental conditions, of the relationships she reports.

A CANINE DEMONSTRATION*

About four weeks ago our beloved collie, Jeanie, produced eight pups. The experience proved so interesting (in its implications) I thought you might like to hear about it. Theoretically she belongs to the three children, and since some of Jeanie's pups were whelped in the daytime hours before the children's bedtime, they were able to be on hand to watch, utterly fascinated, of course.

She began having them so fast and was also so fatigued trying to catch up with the cleaning and decording of each puppy before the next was on the way that I removed them one by one to a nearby box lined with soft flannel as soon as she had occupied that part of her maternal duties, thinking to help her and give her a rest, as well as to prevent her possible rolling on an earlier pup when she gave birth to a later one. She's such a trusting soul where we are concerned that she permitted this human interference without too much anxiety, and continued with her whelping until all eight had arrived. When it seemed that no more pups would be forthcoming, I returned them to her for a few seconds for reassurance purposes, and then removed them all again, this time for an hour or so, to give her a "real rest." She was very tired, and had been working hard for some hours.

* Reprinted by permission of the author, Betsy Marvin McKinney, and *Child-Family Digest,* vol. 10, 1954, pp. 63–65.

Last year, as soon as the fourth and last pup of her first litter was born, she was eager to leave her whelping box for an airing and needed no urging, but this time she wouldn't budge. She would *not* get out and seemed, moreover, to be getting more and more anxious about her squirming little pups. So I put them back beside her, whereupon they began to root around and nuzzle and in very short order, to nurse. I suddenly realized that this was the first real opportunity I'd given her puppies to nurse her despite the fact that several hours had elapsed since the first birth.

I stayed with her a few hours more in case any more. pups might still arrive (went to bed around dawn that day!) and when at the end of that time and despite all the wiles I knew I *still* couldn't get that listless dog out of her whelping box for the relief I knew she must need by then, the full impact of what I had done began to dawn.

Finally, by means of really stern scolding, I forced her to go outdoors for a few necessary seconds, after which she returned to her box to stay there, nursing those pups, *for over 24 hours!*

It was a shock to realize with shame and abashment that I had performed on Jeanie the same type of cultural deprivation and damage that is performed on many human mothers when their babies are taken away from them at birth without permitting the immediate nursing that is an instinctive urge of the newborn.

As for Jeanie, that poor animal was in bad internal shape, and I am afraid it was all due to me. She *had* to stay there hours longer than she'd otherwise have needed to, to be nursed back into reasonable internal health by her puppies. She was in a bad way, hemorrhaged during the night, and I could have kicked myself for being so stupid. As it was, it took our Jeanie a pretty long time to come back to normal—and in all probability because I'd deprived her of the immediate therapeutic suckling which would have pulled her together when she needed it most—directly following the birth and clean-up of each puppy!

You know I wonder sometimes if this same situation occurs without anyone realizing it, in the case of human mothers; if there is any tie-in between slow recoveries from childbirth and the removal, sometimes for long periods, of the new mother's baby? I wonder if the standard injection of pituitrin routinely used to contract the uterus following delivery could, despite its possible need in many cases, have the long-term effect that immediate and continued nursing has, wherein the baby and mother answer each other's needs at exactly the tempo and to the exact extent that both require, over an extended period of time? It is almost symbiotic, that early relationship, the mother giving her baby security along with the stimulus to nourishment while the baby serves her as a therapeutic agent speeding her recovery from her own recent tiring labors in bringing her baby forth.

At any rate, Jeanie certainly demonstrated this principle in an unmistakable way and I felt very badly at my own share in her discomfort.

Appendix C REFERENCES

Chapter 1. Introduction

1. C. Kluckhohn and H. R. Murray, "A conception of personality," in *Personality in Nature, Society, and Culture,* 2d ed., New York, A. A. Knopf, 1953, p. 43.

2. R. Linton, *The Cultural Background of Personality,* New York, Appleton-Century, 1945, p. 18.

3. E. R. Hilgard and D. G. Marquis, *Conditioning and Learning,* New York, Appleton-Century, 1940, p. 347.

4. J. Deese, *Psychology of Learning,* New York, McGraw-Hill, 1952, p. 342.

5. E. R. Guthrie, "Conditioning: A theory of learning in terms of stimulus, response and association," *Forty-First Yearbook of the National Society for the Study of Education,* Part II, Bloomington, Illinois, Public School Publishing Company, 1942, chap. I, p. 17.

6. Deese, *op. cit.*

7. Ives Hendrick, "Early development of the ego," *Psychoanalytic Quarterly,* vol. 20, 1951, pp. 41–61.

8. Kimball Young, *Personality and Problems of Adjustment,* New York, Crofts & Co., 1940, p. 124.

9. L. O. Kattsoff, *The Design of Human Behavior,* St. Louis, Mo., Educational Publishers, 1953, p. 28.

10. See B. F. Skinner, *Science and Human Behavior,* New York, Macmillan, 1953; A. F. C. Wallace, "A science of human behaviour," *Explorations,* no. 3, 1954, pp. 127–136.

11. For an excellent discussion of law from this point of view see Felix Kaufmann, *Methodology of the Social Sciences,* New York, Oxford University Press, 1944; also chapter 4, "Sociological law," in George A. Lundberg's *Foundations of Sociology,* New York, Macmillan, 1939, pp. 133, *et seq.;* see also P. Sorokin, *Sociocultural Causality, Space, Time,* Durham, North Carolina, Duke University Press, 1943; Douglas G. Haring, "Science and social phenomena," *American Scientist,* vol. 35, 1947, pp. 351–363; Lewis W. Beck, "The 'Natural Science Ideal' in the social sciences," *Scientific Monthly,* vol. 48, 1949, pp. 386–394; E. W. Leaver and J. J. Brown, "The need for general laws in the social sciences," *Science,* vol. 114, 1951, pp. 339–382; Florian Znaniecki, *Cultural Sciences,* Urbana, University of Illinois Press, 1952.

12. Similar phenomena have been observed among numerous other animals. In fishes, for example, it has been observed that in overpopulated aquaria infanticide increases in direct proportion to crowding, and a population suited to the volume of water is thus maintained (C. M. Brader and C. W. Coates, "A preliminary study of population stability and sex ratio of *Lebistes,*" *Copeia,* no. 3, pp. 147–155, 1932). See also J. B. Calhoun, "The social aspects of population dynamics," *Journal of*

Mammalogy, vol. 33, 1952, pp. 129–159; M. F. Ashley Montagu, *Coming Into Being Among the Australian Aborigines,* London, Routledge, 1937.

13. See G. P. Murdock, *Social Structure,* New York, Macmillan, 1949; and S. F. Nadel, *The Foundations of Social Anthropology,* Glencoe, Illinois, Free Press, 1951. For a contrary view see E E. Evans-Pritchard, *Social Anthropology,* Glencoe, Illinois, Free Press, 1951.

14. See P. F. Lazarsfeld, *Mathematical Thinking in the Social Sciences,* Glencoe, Illinois, Free Press, 1954; S. C. Dodd, *The Dimensions of Society,* New York, Macmillan, 1942; and N. Rashevsky, *Mathematical Biology of Social Behavior,* Chicago, University of Chicago Press, 1951. See the writings of W. R. Ashby, "Effect of controls on stability," *Nature,* vol. 155, 1945, p. 242; "Dynamics of the cerebral cortex: The behavioral problems of systems in equilibrium," *American Journal of Psychology,* vol. 59, 1946, pp. 682–685; *Design For a Brain,* New York, John Wiley, 1952. See also E. F. Haskell, "A natural classification of societies," *Transactions of the New York Academy of Sciences,* Ser. II, vol. 9, 1947, pp. 186–196.

15. E. G. Miller, Jr., "Scientific method and social problems," *Science,* vol. 109, 1949, pp. 290–291.

16. D. L. Watson, *The Study of Human Nature,* Yellow Springs, Ohio, Antioch Press, 1953, p. 109.

17. P. W. Bridgman, "The prospect for intelligence," in *Reflections of a Physicist,* New York, Philosophical Library, 1950, pp. 342–368.

18. Gerald Holton, "On the duality and growth of physical science," *American Scientist,* vol. 41, 1953, pp. 89–99.

19. R. H. Seashore, "Physiological psychology," in *Annual Review of Physiology,* vol. 8, 1946, pp. 515–534.

20. See Hans Vaihinger, *The Philosophy of "As If,"* New York, Harcourt, Brace & Co., 1924.

21. Richard Hofstadter, *Social Darwinism in American Thought 1860–1905,* Philadelphia, University of Pennsylvania Press, 1944, p. 176.

22. Whether one refers to the duplicated organisms as maternal and daughter or sister cells depends upon the school of philosophy in these matters to which one belongs. It makes not the least difference what terminology one adopts. The problem is perhaps best resolved in the limerick:

> An ameba named Sam and his brother
> Were drinking a toast to each other;
> In the midst of their quaffing
> They split themselves laughing
> And now each of them is a mother.

23. W. M. Wheeler, *Social Life Among Insects,* New York, Harcourt, Brace, 1923.

24. T. C. Schneirla, "The 'levels' concept in the study of the social organization of animals," in J. H. Rohrer and M. Sherif (editors), *Social Psychology at the Crossroads,* New York, Harper, 1951, p. 89. See also J. B. Calhoun, "The social aspects of population dynamics," *Journal of Mammalogy,* vol. 33, 1952, pp. 139–159.

25. W. C. Allee, *Cooperation Among Animals,* New York, Henry Schuman, 1951, p. 21.

26. "There is something fundamentally social in living things, and closer scrutiny shows that this must be a characteristic of all life, since every organism is, at least temporarily, associated with other organisms, even if only with members of the opposite sex and with its parents. . . . This statement holds good even of such supposedly unsocial creatures as lions, eagles, sharks, tiger-beetles, and spiders. There are,

in fact, no truly solitary organisms. We may say, therefore, that the social is a correlate as well as an emergent of all life in the sense in which Morgan speaks of the mind as being both a correlate and an emergent of life. . . . Indeed, the correlations of the social—using the term in its most general sense—even extend down through the non-living to the very atom with its organization of component electrons." (William M. Wheeler, "Emergent evolution and the development of societies," in *Essays in Philosophical Biology,* Cambridge, Harvard University Press, 1939, pp. 158–159.)

27. T. Dobzhansky, *Genetics and the Origin of Species,* 3d ed., New York, Columbia University Press, 1951, pp. 78–79.

28. G. G. Simpson, *Life of the Past,* New Haven, Yale University Press, 1953, p. 56.

29. J. P. Scott, "Social behavior, organization and leadership in a small flock of domestic sheep," *Comparative Psychology Monographs,* vol. 18, 1945, pp. 1–29.

30. C. F. Jacobsen, M. M. Jacobsen, and J. G. Yoshioka, "Development of an infant chimpanzee during her first year," *Comparative Psychology Monographs,* vol. 9, 1932, pp. 1–94.

31. Personal communication from Dr. J. A. Reyniers, November 10, 1951.

32. Charles H. Cooley, *The Social Process,* New York, Scribner's, 1918, p. 28.

33. T. Dobzhansky and M. F. Ashley Montagu, "Natural selection and the mental capacities of mankind," *Science,* vol. 105, 1947, pp. 587–590; N. C. Tappen, "A mechanistic theory of human evolution," *American Anthropologist,* vol. 55, 1953, pp. 605–607; M. F. Ashley Montagu, "Cultural and physical evolution," *American Anthropologist,* vol. 56, 1954, p. 290; W. Etkin, "Social behavior and the evolution of man's mental faculties," *American Naturalist,* vol. 88, 1954, pp. 129–142.

Chapter 2. The Biological Basis of Cooperation

1. N. Tinbergen, *Social Behaviour in Animals,* New York, Wiley, 1953, p. 53; W. C. Allee, *Cooperation Among Animals,* New York, Henry Schuman, 1951.

2. N. R. F. Maier and T. C. Schneirla, *Principles of Animal Psychology,* New York, McGraw-Hill, 1935, pp. 1–7. See also L. K. Frank, *Nature and Human Nature,* New Brunswick, New Jersey, Rutgers University Press, 1951.

3. E. S. Russell, *The Directiveness of Organic Activities,* New York, Cambridge University Press, 1945, p. 191.

4. N. Tinbergen, *op. cit.,* p. 2.

5. For critical surveys of this literature see the references in footnotes 20 and 25.

6. H. V. Wilson, "Development of sponges from dissociated tissue cells," *Bulletin of U. S. Bureau of Fisheries,* vol. 39, 1910, pp. 1–30; P. S. Galtsoff, "Regeneration after dissociation," *Journal of Experimental Zoology,* vol. 42, 1925, pp. 183–251.

7. C. M. Child, "Axial development in aggregates of dissociated cells from *Corymorpha,*" *Physiological Zoology,* vol. 1, 1928, pp. 419–461.

8. I. E. Wallin, *Symbionticism and the Origin of Species,* Baltimore, Williams & Wilkins, 1927. See particularly H. S. Jennings, *The Behavior of Lower Organisms,* New York, Columbia University Press, 1906.

9. P. Deegener, "Soziologische beobachtungen an *Hyponomeuta cognatellus,*" *Hb. Biol. Centralbl.,* vol. 42, 1922, pp. 241–253.

10. See R. Redfield (editor), "Levels of integration in biological and social systems," *Biological Symposia,* vol. 8, Lancaster, Pennsylvania, Jaques Cattell Press, 1942.

11. J. T. Bonner, *Morphogenesis,* Princeton, Princeton University Press, 1952, pp. 173 *et seq.*

12. For a survey of the literature see W. C. Allee, *op. cit.;* W. C. Allee, *Animal Aggregations,* Chicago, University of Chicago Press, 1931; W. C. Allee, *et al., Principles of Animal Ecology,* Philadelphia, Saunders, 1949. See also the references quoted in footnotes 20 and 25.

13. W. S. Allee, *Cooperation Among Animals, loc. cit.*

14. W. C. Allee, K. P. Schmidt, and R. Hesse, *Ecological Animal Geography,* New York, Wiley, 1951.

15. W. C. Allee, *Cooperation Among Animals, loc. cit.,* p. 35.

16. *Ibid.,* pp. 106–107; J. B. Calhoun, "The social aspects of population dynamics," *Journal of Mammalogy,* vol. 33, 1952, pp. 139–159; N. Tinbergen, *op. cit.*

17. E. Fraser Darling, *Bird Flocks and the Breeding Cycle,* New York, Cambridge University Press, 1938.

18. T. Brailsford Robertson, "Experimental studies on cellular multiplication: II. The influence of mutual contiguity upon reproductive rate and the part played therein by the 'x-substance' in bacterised infusions which stimulate the multiplication of infusoria," *Biochemical Journal,* vol. 15, 1921, pp. 612–619.

19. In *The Origin of Species* (1859) Darwin wrote: "I should premise that I use the term Struggle for Existence in a large and metaphorical sense, including dependence of one being on another, and including (which is more important) not only the life of the individual, but success in leaving progeny" (chap. III, p. 62). Having mentioned "dependence" here Darwin thereafter neglects to develop the notion. In *The Descent of Man* (1871), however, he to some extent made up for this neglect. See Ashley Montagu " 'Social instincts,' " *Scientific American,* vol. 182, 1950, pp. 54–56.

20. For a discussion of this subject see M. F. Ashley Montagu, *Darwin, Competition, and Cooperation,* New York, Schuman, 1952.

21. A. V. Espinas, *Des Sociétés Animales,* Paris, Librairie Ballière, 1878, 3d ed., 1924; Kessler, "Mutual aid as a law of nature and the chief factor of evolution," *Memoirs (Trudy) of the St. Petersburg Society of Naturalists,* vol. 9, 1880, a lecture delivered at the annual meeting of the St. Petersburg Society of Naturalists, January 8, 1880, noticed in *Nature,* London, January 21, 1880; J. M. A. Lanessan, "La lutte pour l'existence et l'association pour la lutte," *Bibliotheque Biologique,* Paris, 1881; L. Büchner, *Liebe und Liebes-Leben in der Thierwelt,* Berlin, 1883; P. Geddes and A. Thomson, *The Evolution of Sex,* London, Scott, 1889; Menzbir, *Darwinism in Biology* (in Russian); J. Novikoff, *Les Luttes Entre Sociétés Humaines et Leur Phases Successives,* Paris, 1893, 2d ed., 1896. See also Novikoff's *La Guerre et ses Prétendus Bienfaits,* Paris, 1894.

22. T. H. Huxley, "The struggle for existence: a programme," *Nineteenth Century,* vol. 23, 1888, pp. 161–180.

23. Many times reprinted, but now out of print.

24. Henry George, *Progress and Poverty,* New York, 1897, book X, chap. III.

25. C. C. Coe, *Nature Versus Natural Selection,* London, 1895; J. M. A. Lanessan, *La Lutte Pour l'Existence et l'Evolution des Sociétés,* Paris, Alcan, 1903; J. W. L. Jones, "Sociality and sympathy," *Psychological Review,* vol. 5, 1903, pp. 1–98; L. M. Keasbey, "Co-operation, coercion and competition," *Science,* vol. 17, 1903, pp. 922 *et seq.;* C. Bouglé, "Darwinism and sociology," in *Darwin and Modern Science* (edited by A. C. Seward), Cambridge, at the University Press, 1909, pp. 465–476; Henry M. Bernard, *Some Neglected Factors in Evolution,* New York, Putnam, 1911; Patrick

Geddes and J. Arthur Thomson, *Sex,* London, Williams & Norgate, 1911; Yves Delage and Marie Goldsmith, *The Theories of Evolution,* New York, Huebsch, 1912; Hermann Reinheimer, *Evolution by Co-operation: A Study of Bioeconomics,* London, Kegan Paul, 1913; A. Cresson, *L'Espèce et Son Serviteur,* Paris, 1913; William Patten, "Co-operation as a factor in evolution," *Proceedings of the American Philosophical Society,* vol. 55, 1916, pp. 505–532; George Nasmyth, *Social Progress and the Darwinian Theory,* New York, Putnam, 1916; P. Deegener, *Die Formen der Vergesellschaftung im Tier-reiche,* Leipzig, Veit, 1918; John M. Macfarlane, *The Causes and Course of Evolution,* New York, Macmillan, 1918; William Patten, *The Grand Strategy of Evolution,* Boston, Richard Badger, 1920; Hermann Reinheimer, *Symbiosis: A Socio-Physiological Study of Evolution,* London, Headley Bros., 1920; William M. Wheeler, *Social Life Among Insects,* New York, Harcourt, Brace & Co., 1923; Robert W. Gibson, *The Morality of Nature,* New York, Putnam, 1923; Leo S. Berg, *Nomogenesis, or Evolution Determined by Law,* London, Constable, 1926; William M. Wheeler, "Social evolution," in *Human Biology and Racial Welfare* (edited by Edmund V. Cowdry), New York, Hoeber, 1930; Herbert F. Standing, *Spirit in Evolution,* London, Allen & Unwin, 1930; W. E. Allee, *Animal Aggregations, loc. cit.;* W. C. Allee, *The Social Life of Animals,* New York, W. W. Norton, 1938; Christopher Caudwell, "Love," in *Studies in a Dying Culture,* London, Bodley Head, 1938; William Galt, "The principle of cooperation in behavior," *Quarterly Review of Biology,* vol. 15, 1940, pp. 401–410; Robert Redfield (editor), "Levels of integration in biological and social systems," *loc. cit.;* Charles Sherrington, *Man on His Nature,* New York, Cambridge University Press, 1941; Alfred E. Emerson, "Basic comparisons of human and insect societies," in *Biological Symposia,* vol. 8, 1942, pp. 163–177; R. Gerard, "Higer levels of integration," in *Biological Symposia,* vol. 8, 1942, pp. 67–87; W. C. Allee, "Where Angels Fear to Tread," *Science,* vol. 97, 1943, pp. 518–525; Ralph Lillie, *General Biology and Philosophy of the Organism,* Chicago, University of Chicago Press, 1945; John Hewetson, *Mutual Aid and Social Evolution,* London, Freedom Press, 1946; Alfred E. Emerson, "The biological basis of social cooperation," *Illinois Academy of Science Transactions,* vol. 39, 1946, pp. 9–18; L. R. Wheeler, *Harmony of Nature: A Study of Co-operation for Existence,* New York, Longmans, 1947; Thomas H. Huxley and Julian S. Huxley, *Touchstone For Ethics,* New York, Harper, 1947; Henry G. Maurice, *Ask Now the Beasts,* London, Society for the Preservation of the Fauna of the Empire, 1948; L. L. Whyte, *Everyman Looks Forward,* New York, Holt, 1948; Samuel J. Holmes, *Life and Morals,* New York, Macmillan, 1948; M. F. Ashley Montagu, "The origin and nature of social life and the biological basis of cooperation," *Journal of Social Psychology,* vol. 29, 1949, pp. 267–283; Hugh Miller, *The Community of Man,* New York, Macmillan, 1949; E. Morton Miller, "A look at the anatomy and physiology of groups," *Bios.,* vol. 20, 1949, pp. 24–31; W. C. Allee, *et al., Principles of Animal Ecology, loc. cit.;* George G. Simpson, *The Meaning of Evolution,* New Haven, Yale University Press, 1949; Herman J. Muller, "Genetics in the scheme of things," *Hereditas,* supplementary volume, 1949, pp. 96–127; F. J. Trembley, "Evolution and human affairs," *Proceedings of the Pennsylvania Academy of Science,* vol. 23, 1949, pp. 181–195; Alfred Korzybski, *Manhood of Humanity,* Lakeville, Connecticut, Institute of General Semantics, 1950; Ashley Montagu, *On Being Human,* New York, Schuman, 1950; Ashley Montagu, " 'Social instincts,' " *loc. cit.;* Michael Graham, *Human Needs,* London, Cresset Press, 1951; Ashley Montagu, *Darwin, Competition, and Cooperation, loc. cit.;* Vera Daniel, "Physical principles in human co-operation," *Sociological Review* (London), vol. 44, 1952, pp. 107–134; R. A. M.

Bergman, "The biological foundations of society," *Civilizations,* vol 2, 1952, pp. 1–15; Alfred E. Emerson, "The supraorganismic aspects of the society," *Colloques Internationaux du Centre National de la Recherche Scientifique,* vol. 34, 1952, pp. 333–353; A. Campbell Garnett, *The Moral Nature of Man,* New York, Ronald Press, 1952; Julian Huxley, *Evolution in Action,* New York, Harper, 1953; Edmund W. Sinnott, *Two Roads to Truth,* New York, Viking, 1953; Louis O. Kattsoff, *The Design of Human Behavior,* St. Louis, Educational Publishers, 1953; Alfred E. Emerson, "Dynamic homeostasis: A unifying principle in organic, social, and ethical evolution," *Scientific Monthly,* vol. 78, 1954, pp. 67–85; Edmund W. Sinnott, "Biology and teleology," *Bios,* vol. 25, 1954, pp. 35–43; Pitirim A. Sorokin, *The Ways and Power of Love,* Boston, Beacon Press, 1954; Umberto D'Ancona, *The Struggle For Existence,* Leiden, Brill, 1954; T. A. Goudge, "The concept of evolution," *Mind,* vol. 43, 1954, pp. 16–25; T. A. Goudge, "Some philosophical aspects of the theory of evolution," *University of Toronto Quarterly,* vol. 8, 1954, pp. 386–401; Max Scheler, *The Nature of Sympathy,* New Haven, Yale University Press, 1954; G. Witt, "Primary love therapy," *Psychoanalysis,* vol. 3, 1954, pp. 63–73; R. Kourilsky, A. Soulairac, and P. Grapin (editors), *Adaptation et Aggressivité,* Paris, 1913.

26. W. C. Allee, "Where angels fear to tread: A contribution from general sociology to human ethics," *Science,* vol. 97, 1943, p. 521.

27. *Ibid.,* p. 520.

28. J. B. Calhoun, *op. cit.*

29. T. C. Schneirla, "Problems in the biopsychology of social organization," *Journal of Abnormal and Social Psychology,* vol. 41, 1946, pp. 385–402.

30. C. D. Leake, "Ethicogenesis," *Scientific Monthly,* vol. 60, 1945, pp. 245–253. See also a revision of this article in *Studies and Essays in the History of Science and Learning* (edited by M. F. Ashley Montagu), New York, Schuman, 1946, pp. 261–275. A further reprinting of this article together with a criticism and discussion of it will be found in C. D. Leake and P. Romanell, *Can We Agree?* Austin, University of Texas Press, 1950.

31. P. R. Burkholder, "Cooperation and conflict among primitive organisms," *American Scientist,* vol. 40, 1952, p. 603. See also C. L. Birch, "Experimental background to the study of the distribution and abundance of insects," *Evolution,* vol, 7, 1953, pp. 136–144.

32. T. Dobzhansky and M. F. Ashley Montagu, "Natural selection and the mental capacities of mankind," *Science,* vol. 105, 1947, pp. 587–590.

33. Robert W. Gibson, *op. cit.,* p. 30.

34. *Ibid.,* p. 95.

35. A. E. Emerson, "The biological basis of social cooperation," *loc. cit.,* pp. 8–18. See also W. C. Allee, "Biology and international relations," *New Republic,* vol. 112, 1945, pp. 816–817.

36. "The care of the eggs might be called social behaviour, for from the time of being laid the eggs are individuals. Usually we do not consider such one-sided relations as really social, but we must not forget that the egg, although not moving, does give special stimuli which have a profound influence on the parent bird," N. Tinbergen, *op. cit.,* p. 6.

37. Ralph Linton, "Culture, society, and the individual," *Journal of Abnormal and Social Psychology,* vol. 33, 1938, pp. 425–436.

38. Carl J. Warden, *The Emergence of Human Culture,* New York, Macmillan, 1936.

39. This account of the hunting habits of lions is taken from Ralph Linton's *The Study of Man*, New York, (Appleton-Century, 1936, p. 78). Desiring to check on the accuracy of this account I wrote to Dr. L. S. B. Leakey, Director of the Coryndon Museum, at Nairobi, Kenya Colony. Dr. Leakey was born and brought up in Kenya Colony and has always had a keen interest in its natural history, and his reply—for which I am much indebted to him—raises more than a doubt as to the accuracy of the alleged change in lions' habit of hunting. However, the possibility does exist that the way of hunting referred to was adaptively devised by the lions, at some earlier time, to meet the appropriate conditions. Under date of November 2, 1953, Dr. Leakey writes: "I do not think there is any question of lion having altered their traditional way of hunting. So far as I can tell you lions have always had several different methods of hunting. One of which was the hunting solo or in pairs, and the other the hunting by a 'pride' of lion, in which some of the lion remained hidden while the other lions quite openly walked towards the game and edged them towards the hidden member of the 'pride.' I am practically certain records of both methods of hunting can be found, even in the earliest literature dealing with lions in Africa."

40. Zing Y. Kuo, "Genesis of cat's responses to the rat," *Journal of Comparative Psychology*, vol. 11, 1931, pp. 1–35.

41. *Ibid.*, p. 35.

42. Loh Seng Tsai, "Peace and cooperation among natural enemies," reported at the St. Louis, December 30, 1952, meeting of the American Association for the Advancement of Science.

43. J. Fisher and R. A. Hinde, "The opening of milk bottles by birds," *British Birds*, vol. 42, 1949, pp. 347–357; see also T. H. Hawkins, "Opening of milk bottles by birds," *Nature*, vol. 165, 1950, pp. 435–436.

44. R. A. Hinde and J. Fisher, "Further observations on the opening of milk bottles by birds," *British Birds*, vol. 44, 1952, pp. 392–396. In Sweden the spotted woodpecker *(Dendrocopus major)* has been observed opening milk bottles, and in the *Seattle Times*, June 7, 1937, there is a photograph of Steller's jay *(Cyanocitta stelleri)* opening a milk bottle.

45. W. H. Thorpe, "The learning abilities of birds," *Ibis*, vol. 93, 1951, pp. 1–52, 252–296; W. H. Thorpe, "The definition of some terms in animal behavior studies," *Bulletin of Animal Behavior*, vol. 9, 1951, pp. 34–40; Konrad Z. Lorenz, *King Solomon's Ring*, New York, Crowell, 1952, pp. 140, 144–145.

46. W. E. D. Scott, "Data on song in birds," *Science*, n. s., vol. 14, 1901, pp. 522–526.

47. E. Conradi, "Song and call-notes of English sparrows when reared by canaries," *American Journal of Psychology*, vol. 16, 1905, pp. 190–199.

48. See M. Metfessel, "Relationships of heredity and environment in behavior," *Journal of Psychology*, vol. 10, 1940, pp. 177–198.

49. Konrad Z. Lorenz, *op. cit.*, p. 140.

50. Robert M. Yerkes, *Chimpanzees*, New Haven, Yale University Press, 1943, p. 52.

51. The scientist-compeer of St. Francis, Professor Konrad Z. Lorenz, has given us a profound insight into the nature of the "beast" in his delightful book *King Solomon's Ring*, (*loc. cit.*). See also H. G. Maurice, *op. cit.*, and Ruth C. Noble, *The Nature of the Beast*, New York, Doubleday, 1946.

52. T. H. Langlois, "A Study of the small-mouth bass, *Micropterus dolomieu* (Lacepede) in rearing ponds in Ohio," *Ohio Biological Survey, Ohio State University*

Studies. Bulletin No. 33, vol. 6, 1936; T. H. Langlois, "Sociological succession," *Ecology,* vol. 18, 1937, pp. 458–461.

53. E. Fredericson, "Competition: the effects of infantile experience upon adult behavior," *Journal of Abnormal and Social Psychology,* vol. 46, 1951, pp. 406–409.

54. J. B. Calhoun, *op. cit.,* p. 143.

55. T. C. Schneirla, "Levels in the psychological capacities of animals," in *Philosophy For the Future* (R. W. Sellars *et al.,* editors), New York, Macmillan, 1949, pp. 243–286.

56. T. Dobzhansky and M. F. Ashley Montagu, *op. cit.* See also P. R. David and L. H. Snyder, "Genetic variability and human behavior," in *Social Psychology at the Crossroads* (edited by J. H. Rohrer and M. Sherif), New York, Harper, 1951, pp. 53–82. In the same volume see also T. C. Schneirla, "The 'levels' concept in the study of social organization in animals," pp. 83–120.

57. See K. Lorenz, *op. cit.,* and N. Tinbergen, *op. cit.*

58. Leslie A. White, *The Science of Culture,* New York, Farrar Straus, 1949, p. 27.

59. Ernst Cassirer, *An Essay on Man,* New Haven, Yale University Press, 1944, p. 32.

60. See J. Ruesch and G. Bateson, *Communication,* New York, Norton, 1951; T. C. Schneirla, "Comparative psychology," *Encyclopedia Britannica,* vol. 17, 1948, pp. 690–708; Karl Deutsch, "Mechanism, teleology, and mind," *Philosophy and Phenomenological Research,* vol. 12, 1951, pp, 185–222.

61. Robert M. Yerkes and Henry W. Nissen, "Pre-linguistic sign behavior in chimpanzee," *Science,* vol. 89, 1939, pp. 585–587.

62. Clifford T. Morgan, *Physiological Psychology,* New York, McGraw-Hill, 1943, p. 551; James Deese, *The Psychology of Learning,* New York, McGraw-Hill, 1953, pp. 254–259.

63. Leslie A. White, "The symbol: The origin and basis of human behavior," *Philosophy of Science,* vol. 8, 1940, pp. 451–463; reprinted in the same author's *The Science of Culture, loc. cit.,* pp. 22–39.

64. Cathy Hayes, *The Ape in the House,* New York, Harper, 1951.

65. For a brilliant discussion of this subject see G. H. Mead, *Mind, Self, and Society,* Chicago, University of Chicago Press, 1944, pp. 32–134.

66. George Kelemen, "The anatomical basis of phonation in the chimpanzee," *Journal of Morphology,* vol. 82, 1948, pp. 229–256. Students have long been puzzled by the apes' inability to talk. The suggestion most often made is that cerebrally these animals are not developed sufficiently to be able to talk, and this is probably true. Kelemen has, however, stated on the basis of a study of the larynx in a chimpanzee that "even with the help of the high grade of intelligence of this animal every attempt to make him utter human voice and speech must fail on the basis of anatomy. An imaginary being equipped with a human brain and the larynx of the chimpanzee could not produce any other phonetic effect than this animal actually does" (p. 254). Much earlier see Peter Camper, "Account of the organs of speech of the Orang-Outang," *Philosophical Transactions,* vol. 69, 1779, pp. 135–159. "Having dissected the whole organ of voice in the Orang, in apes, and several monkies, I have a right to conclude, that Orangs and apes are not made to modulate the voice like men: for the air passing by the *rima glottidis* is immediately lost in the ventricles or ventricle of the neck, as in apes and monkies, and must consequently return from thence without force and melody within the throat and mouth of these creatures: and this seems to me the most evident proof of the in-

capacity of Orangs, apes and monkies, to utter any modulated voice, as indeed they have never been observed to do" (pp. 155–156).

67. G. H. Mead, *op. cit.*, p. 50.

68. Ernst Cassirer, *op. cit.*

69. Howard Becker, "Science, culture, and society," *Philosophy of Science*, vol. 19, 1952, pp. 282–283.

70. Konrad Z. Lorenz, *op. cit.*

71. Wolfgang Koehler, *The Mentality of the Apes*, New York, Harcourt, Brace, 1925, p. 317.

72. Clifford T. Morgan, *op. cit.*, p. 531.

73. Kurt Goldstein, *Human Nature in the Light of Psychopathology*, Cambridge, Harvard University Press, 1940.

74. John F. Markey, *The Symbolic Process and Its Integration in Children*, New York, Harcourt, Brace, 1928, p. 156.

75. John B. Watson, *Behaviorism*, 2d ed., Philadelphia, Lippincott, 1930.

76. See D. O. Hebb, *The Organization of Behavior*, New York, Wiley, 1949, p. 117, for a pointed discussion of the conditioned reflex theory of language.

77. See Edward Sapir, *Language*, New York, Harcourt, Brace, 1921; *Selected Writings of Edward Sapir* (David Mandelbaum, editor), Berkeley, University of California Press, 1949; L. Bloomfield, *Language*, New York, Holt, 1933; Franz Boas, *Language*, in F. Boas (editor), *General Anthropology*, Boston, Heath, 1938. See also W. M. Urban, *Language and Reality*, New York, Macmillan, 1939.

78. "Who knows not foreign languages, knows not his own."

79. Bronislaw Malinowski, *Coral Gardens and Their Magic*, New York, American Book Co., 1935, vol. 2, p. 7. See Malinowski "The problem of meaning in primitive languages," in C. K. Ogden and I. A. Richards, *The Meaning of Meaning*, New York, Harcourt, Brace, 1923, pp. 451–510.

80. Carl J. Warden, *op. cit.*, p. 7.

81. B. Malinowski, *Coral Gardens and Their Magic*, *op. cit.*, p. 52.

82. K. J. W. Craig, *The Nature of Explanation*, New York, Cambridge University Press, 1943.

83. James Deese, *op. cit.*, p. 254.

84. *Ibid.*, p. 259.

85. A. L. Kroeber, "Culture, events, and individuals," in *The Nature of Culture*, Chicago, University of Chicago Press, 1952, p. 104.

86. The mores are the more explicitly defined and emphasized moral standards and customs of the group as compared with the implicit spontaneous unpremeditated ways (folkways) of doing things such as greeting, eating three meals a day, manner of dress, courtship, and the like.

87. This description of culture is based on that given by A. L. Kroeber and C. Kluckhohn in their joint work "Culture," *Papers of the Peabody Museum* (Cambridge), vol. 47, 1952, p. 181.

88. O. K. Moore, "Nominal definitions of 'culture,'" *Philosophy of Science*, vol. 19, 1952, pp. 245–256.

89. J. L. Myres, *Political Ideas of the Greeks*, New York, Abingdon Press, 1927, p. 16.

Chapter 3. The Meaning of Man's Nervous System

1. See G. L. Freeman, *Physiological Psychology*, New York, Van Nostrand, 1948.
2. L. Monné, "Structure and function of neurones in relation to mental activity,"

Biological Reviews, vol. 24, 1949, pp. 297–315. See also Edmund W. Sinnott, *Cell and Psyche,* Chapel Hill, University of North Carolina Press, 1950, p. 60: "In any living system one cannot separate the processes of growth which lead to the development of the body from those by which the life of the body is maintained." Or, as von Bonin puts it: "structure should be understood as an enduring order impressed upon a flow of energy." Gerhardt von Bonin, *Essay on the Cerebral Cortex,* Springfield, Illinois, Thomas, 1950, p. ix.

3. C. Judson Herrick, *Brains of Rats and Men,* Chicago, University of Chicago, Press, 1926, p. 4.

4. J. C. Eccles, "Hypotheses relating to the brain-mind problem," *Nature,* vol. 168, 1951, p. 3.

5. Ralph Gerard, "Neurophysiology in relation to behavior," in Roy Grinker (editor), *Mid-Century Psychiatry,* Springfield, Ill., Thomas, 1954, pp. 23–32.

6. Paul Weiss (editor), *Genetic Neurology,* Chicago, University of Chicago Press, 1950.

7. S. H. Gasser, "The classification of nerve fibers," *Ohio Journal of Science,* vol. 41, 1941, pp. 145–149.

8. O. S. English and G. H. J. Pearson, *Emotional Problems of Living,* New York, Norton, 1945, p. 45.

9. A. W. Angulo y Gonzalez, "Is myelinogeny an absolute index of behavioral capability?" *Journal of Comparative Neurology,* vol. 48, 1929, pp. 459–464.

10. Hans Held, "Die Lehre von den Neuronen," *Fortschritte der Naturwissenschaftlichen Forschung, n.f.,* vol. 8, 1929, pp. 41–44.

11. Walter B. Cannon, *The Wisdom of the Body,* New York, Norton, 1939.

12. G. von Bonin, *op. cit.,* p. 124. See Nina Bull, "Toward a clarification of the concept of emotion," *Psychosomatic Medicine,* vol. 7, 1945, pp. 210–214. See also Stanley Cobb, *Emotions and Clinical Medicine,* New York, Norton, 1950.

13. Kurt Goldstein, "On emotions considered from the organismic point of view," *Journal of Psychology,* vol. 31, 1951, pp. 37–49.

14. Russell Myers, "Semantic dilemmas in neurology, psychology, and general semantics," *General Semantics Bulletin,* nos. 10 and 11, 1952/53, p. 49.

15. H. R. Miller, *Central Autonomic Regulations in Health and Disease,* New York, Grune & Stratton, 1942, p. 21; J. S. Bockoven, "Social behavior and autonomic physiology in long-standing mental illness: Its relation to the problem of altruism," in P. Sorokin (editor), *Forms and Techniques of Altruistic and Spiritual Growth,* Boston, Beacon Press, 1954, pp. 283–289.

16. R. A. Cleghorn, "The hypothalamic-endocrine system," *Psychosomatic Medicine,* vol. 17, 1955, pp. 367–376; J. H. Masserman, "The hypothalamus in psychiatry," *American Journal of Psychiatry,* vol. 98, 1942, pp. 633–637.

17. James C. White and Reginald Smithwick, *The Autonomic Nervous System,* 2d ed., New York, Macmillan, 1941, pp. 62–76.

18. H. Selye, *Stress,* Montreal, Acta Endocrinologica, 1950; H. G. Wolff *et al* (editors), *Life Stress and Bodily Disease,* Baltimore, Williams & Wilkins, 1950; H. G. Wolff, *Stress and Disease,* Springfield, Illinois, Thomas, 1954; N. B. Talbot *et al., Functional Endocrinology,* Cambridge, Harvard University Press, 1952.

19. M. F. Ashley Montagu, "Constitutional and prenatal factors in infant and child health," in M. J. E. Senn (editor), *The Healthy Personality,* New York, Josiah Macy Jr. Foundation, 1950, pp. 148–210.

20. R. A. Spitz, "Infantile depression and the general adaptation syndrome," *Proceedings of the 42nd Annual Meeting American Psychopathological Association,* 1953, pp. 93–108.

21. Judson Herrick, *op. cit.,* pp. 146–147.

22. For an admirable critical discussion of this subject see Russell Myers, *op. cit.*, pp. 35–51.

23. J. W. Macfarlane, "The guidance study," *Sociometry*, vol. 2, 1939, pp. 1–33.

24. H. E. Jones, "The galvanic skin reflex," *Child Development*, vol. 1, 1930, pp. 106–110.

25. O. H. Mowrer, *Learning Theory and Personality Dynamics*, New York, Ronald Press, 1950, p. 240.

26. L. S. Kubie, "The ontogeny of anxiety," *Psychoanalytic Review*, vol. 28, 1941, p. 81.

27. Karl S. Lashley, "The problem of serial order in behavior," in *Cerebral Mechanisms of Behavior* (L. A. Jeffress, editor), New York, Wiley, 1951, pp. 71, 131.

28. W. Grey Walter, *The Living Brain*, New York, Norton, 1953.

29. Herrick, *op. cit.*, pp. 264–265.

30. L. Monné, *op. cit.*, pp. 297–315.

31. *Ibid.*, p. 311.

32. Ward C. Halstead (editor), "Brain and behavior: A symposium," *Comparative Psychology Monographs*, vol. 20, 1950; W. C. Halstead, "Brain and intelligence," in *Cerebral Mechanisms in Behavior* (L. A. Jeffress, editor), New York, Wiley, 1951, pp. 244–288.

33. H. Hydén and H. Hartelius, "Stimulation of nucleoprotein production in the nerve cell by malononitrile, and its effect on psychic functions in mental disorder," *Acta Psychiatrica et Neurologica*, Supplement 47, 1948, pp. 1–117. See also J. Mendelson, *et al.*, "Stability and absorption spectrum of malononitrile," *Science*, vol. 120, 1954, pp. 266–269.

34. Percival Bailey, "Concerning the organization of the cerebral cortex," *Texas Reports on Biology and Medicine*, vol. 6, 1948, pp. 34–56; Percival Bailey, "Cortex and mind," in R. Grinker (editor), *Mid-Century Psychiatry*, Springfield, Ill., 1953, pp. 8–22.

35. L. S. Kubie, "Instincts and homeostasis," *Psychosomatic Medicine*, vol. 10, 1948, pp. 15–30.

36. Gerhardt von Bonin, *op. cit.*, pp. 131–132.

37. A. Tustin, "Feedback," *Scientific American*, vol. 187, 1952, pp. 48–54.

38. Gardner B. Murphy, *Personality*, New York, Harper, 1947, p. 84.

Chapter 4. Heredity and Environment

1. By other methods other observers have arrived at very similar estimates: See J. N. Spuhler, "On the number of genes in man," *Science*, vol. 108, 1948, p. 279, and R. D. Evans, "Quantitative inferences concerning the genetic effects of radiation on human beings," *Science*, vol. 109, 1949, pp. 299–304.

2. G. W. Beadle, "Genes and biological enigmas," in *Science in Progress*, 6th Series (edited by G. Baitsell), New Haven, Yale University Press, 1949, pp. 184–249; M. Demerec, "What makes genes mutate?" *Proceedings American Philosophical Society*, vol. 98, 1954, pp. 318–322; L. J. Stadler, "The gene," *Science*, vol. 120, 1954, pp. 811–819; H. J. Muller, "Life," *Science*, vol. 121, 1955, pp. 1–9.

3. See Sir Charles Sherrington, *Man On His Nature*, 2d ed., New York, Cambridge University Press, 1951, p. 103: "Each gene in the egg-cell embodies a unit 'character' in the make-up of the individual springing from the ovum."

4. Carl von Naegeli, *Mechanische-physiologische Theorie der abstammungslehre*, Munich and Leipzig, 1884. J. Clausen, D. D. Keck, and W. M. Hiesy, *Experimental*

Studies on the Nature of Species, Carnegie Institution of Washington, D.C., 1940, 1945.

5. R. S. Lillie, "Directive action and life," *Philosophy of Science,* vol. 4, 1939, pp. 202–226.

6. "Heredity . . . may be defined as the influence on the individuals of the materials which they receive from their parents at the beginning of their lives." Herbert S. Jennings, *Genetics,* New York, Norton, 1935, p. 4.

7. See pp. 249–266.

8. T. Dobzhansky, "What is heredity?" *Science,* vol. 100, p. 406.

9. M. F. Ashley Montagu, "Our changing concept of human nature," *Impact of Science on Society* (Unesco, Paris), vol. 3, 1952, pp. 219–232.

10. Beautifully stated by John Donne in *Love's Deity,* where he speaks of "that vice-nature, custom."

11. J. B. Scott, "The magnification of differences by a threshold," *Science,* vol. 100, 1944, pp. 569–570; J. P. Scott and M. S. Charles, "Genetic differences in the behavior of dogs: a case of magnification by thresholds and by habit formation," *Journal of Genetic Psychology,* vol. 84, 1954, pp. 175–188; John Fuller and J. P. Scott, "Genetic factors affecting intelligence," *Eugenics Quarterly,* vol. 1, 1954, pp. 28–43.

12. M. F. Ashley Montagu, *Man's Most Dangerous Myth: The Fallacy of Race,* 4th ed., New York & Cleveland, World Publishing Co., 1964.

Chapter 5. Life in the Womb and the Trauma of Birth

1. George W. Corner, *Ourselves Unborn,* New Haven, Yale University Press, 1944, pp. 51–55; William F. Windle, *Physiology of the Fetus,* Philadelphia, Saunders, 1940, p. 206.

2. L. W. Sontag and T. W. Richards, "Studies in fetal behavior," *Monographs of the Society for Research in Child Development,* vol. 3, no. 4, 1938.

3. For a good summary of the whole subject of prenatal behavior see Leonard Carmichael, "The onset and early development of behavior," in *Manual of Child Psychology* (edited by Leonard Carmichael), New York, Wiley, 1954, pp. 60–185; M. F. Ashley Montagu, "Constitutional and prenatal factors in infant and child health," in *The Healthy Personality* (edited by M. J. E. Senn), New York, Josiah Macy, Jr., Foundation, 1950, pp. 148–210.

4. H. S. and H. B. Forbes, "Fetal sense reaction: hearing," *Journal of Camparative Psychology,* vol. 7, 1927, pp. 353–355.

5. L. W. Sontag and T. W. Richards, *op. cit.,* pp. 49–60.

6. Jack Bernard and L. W. Sontag, "Fetal reactivity to tonal stimulation: a preliminary report," *Journal of Genetic Psychology,* vol. 70, 1947, pp. 205–210.

7. L. W. Sontag and R. F. Wallace, "Study of fetal activity," *American Journal of Diseases of Children,* vol. 48, 1934, pp. 1050–1057; L. W. Sontag, "Differences in modifiability of fetal behavior and physiology," *Psychosomatic Medicine,* vol. 6, 1944, pp. 151–154.

8. L. W. Sontag, "The significance of fetal environmental differences," *American Journal of Obstetrics and Gynecology,* vol. 42, 1941, pp. 996–1003.

9. L. W. Sontag, "War and the fetal maternal relationship," *Marriage and Family Living,* vol. 6, 1944, pp. 1–5.

10. J. L. Halliday, *Psychosocial Medicine,* New York, Norton, 1948, p. 91.

11. Phyllis Greenacre, "The predisposition to anxiety," *Psychoanalytic Quarterly*, vol. 10, 1941, pp. 610–638.

12. Samuel Taylor Coleridge, *Miscellanies, Aesthetic and Literary* (collected and arranged by Thomas Ashe), London, Bohn Standard Library, 1885, p. 301.

13. Otto Rank, *The Trauma of Birth*, New York, Robert Brunner, 1952. This work was originally published in German in 1924 and in English translation in 1929. A good summary of the theory will be found in Patrick Mullahy, *Oedipus Myth and Complex*, New York, Hermitage Press, 1948, pp. 162–168, and also in Rollo May, *The Meaning of Anxiety*, New York, Ronald Press, 1950, pp. 128–131.

14. Sigmund Freud, *The Problem of Anxiety*, London, Hogarth Press, 1936.

15. Stanley Cobb, *Borderlands of Psychiatry*, Cambridge, Harvard University Press, 1944, p. 88.

16. W. E. Le Gros Clark, "Ignorances in the anatomical field," *Prospects In Psychiatric Research* (edited by J. M. Tanner), Oxford, Blackwell, 1953, pp. 5–29.

17. Nandor Fodor, *In Search of the Beloved: A Clinical Investigation of the Trauma of Birth and Pre-Natal Conditioning*, New York, Hermitage Press, 1949, p. 383.

18. Margaret Ribble, *The Right of Infants*, New York, Columbia University Press, 1943, p. 15.

19. M. Kenworthy, "The pre-natal and early post-natal phenomena of consciousness," in E. Dummer (editor), *The Unconscious*, New York, Knopf, 1927, p. 181. In this remarkably prescient study Kenworthy states that "The interesting comparative studies of the emotional and nervous reactions of the new-born babies of Caesarian section and those born through the birth canal of primiparous and multiparous mothers indicates the relative effects of such births." I have not been able to trace such studies.

20. Mary Shirley, "A behavior syndrome characterizing prematurely-born children," *Child Development*, vol. 10, 1939, pp. 115–128.

21. Mary C. Drillien, "Studies in prematurity, stillbirth and neonatal death, factors affecting birth-weight and outcome, delivery, and its hazards," *Journal of Obstetrics and Gynaecology of the British Empire*, vol. 54, 1947, pp. 300–323, 443–468; Mary C. Drillien, "Studies in prematurity; development and progress of prematurely born children in pre-school period," *Archives of the Diseases of Childhood*, vol. 23, 1948, pp. 69–83.

22. Philip J. Howard and Calier H. Worrell, "Premature infants in later life," *Pediatrics*, vol. 9, 1952, pp. 577–584; B. Beskow, "Mental disturbances in premature children of school age," *Acta Pediatrica*, vol. 37, 1949, pp. 125–130; Julius H. Hess, "Experiences gained in a thirty year study of prematurely born infants," *Pediatrics*, vol. 11, 1953, pp. 425–434.

23. Sigmund Freud, *Inhibitions, Symptoms and Anxiety*, London, Hogarth Press, 1936.

24. Otto Rank, *op. cit.*, p. 11.

25. *Ibid.*, p. 212.

26. For another interpretation see Ernest Jones, *Nightmare, Witches, and Devils*, New York, Norton, 1931.

27. Denys E. R. Kelsey, "Phantasies of birth and prenatal experiences recovered from patients undergoing hypnoanalysis," *Journal of Mental Science* (London), vol. 99, 1953, pp. 212–223.

28. M. L. Peerbolte, *Prenatal Dynamics*, Leyden, Sijthoff, 1954.

29. L. W. Sontag, "Evidences of disturbed prenatal and neonatal growth in bones of infants at one month," *American Journal of Diseases of Children*, vol. 53, 1938,

p. 1248; L. W. Sontag and L. M. Harris, "Evidences of disturbed prenatal and neonatal growth in bones of infants aged one month," *American Journal of Diseases of Children,* vol. 56, 1938, pp. 1248–1255.

30. Ira S. Wile and R. Davis, "The relation of birth to behavior," *American Journal of Orthopsychiatry,* vol. 11, 1941, pp. 320–324.

31. Phyllis Greenacre, "The biological economy of birth," in *Psychoanalytic Study of the Family,* vol. 1, pp. 31–51, New York, International Universities Press, 1945.

32. P. L. Schroeder, "Behavior difficulties in children associated with the results of birth trauma," *Journal of the American Medical Association,* vol. 92, 1929, pp. 100–104.

33. J. L. Despert, "Anxiety, phobias, and fears in young children," *The Nervous Child,* vol. 5, 1946, pp. 8–24.

34. J. L. Boland, "Type of birth as related to stuttering," *Journal of Speech and Hearing Disorders,* vol. 16, 1951, pp. 40–43.

35. O. Hobart Mowrer, *Learning Theory and Personality Dynamics,* New York, Ronald Press, 1950, p. 559.

Chapter 6. The Basic and Acquired Needs

1. Bronislaw Malinowski, *A Scientific Theory of Culture and Other Essays,* Chapel Hill, University of North Carolina Press, 1944, p. 74.

2. *Ibid.,* p. 75.

3. Frank A. Beach, *Hormones and Behavior,* New York, Hoeber, 1948.

4. Otto Klineberg, *Social Psychology,* 2d ed., New York, Holt, 1954, p. 69.

5. For a stimulating though quite different discussion of needs and drives—the author preferring the noncommittal *drives*—see B. F. Skinner, *Science and Human Behavior,* New York, Macmillan, 1953, pp. 143–159.

6. Lawrence S. Kubie, "Instincts and homeostasis," *Psychosomatic Medicine,* vol. 10, 1948, pp. 15–30.

7. G. L. Freeman, *The Energetics of Human Behavior,* Ithaca, Cornell University Press, 1948, pp. 49–50.

8. Walter B. Cannon, *The Wisdom of the Body,* New York, Norton, 1939, p. 24.

9. For a valuable criticism and clarification of the concept of homeostasis, see J. R. Maze, "On some corruptions of the doctrine of homeostasis," *Psychological Review,* vol. 60, 1953, pp. 405–412.

10. C. A. Mace, "Homeostasis, needs and values," *British Journal of Psychology,* vol. 44, 1953, pp. 200–210.

11. L. S. Kubie, *op. cit.,* pp. 19–20.

12. *Ibid.,* p. 20.

13. K. S. Lashley, "Experimental analysis of instinctive behavior," *Psychological Reviews,* vol. 46, 1928, p. 445.

14. L. S. Kubie, *op. cit.,* pp. 21–23.

15. L. S. Kubie, "A physiological approach to the concept of anxiety," *Psychosomatic Medicine,* vol. 3, 1941, pp. 263–267.

16. L. S. Kubie, "Instincts and homeostasis," *loc. cit.,* pp. 21–22.

17. R. Stagner, "Homeostasis as a unifying concept in personality theory," *Psychological Review,* vol. 58, 1951, pp. 5–17.

18. L. S. Kubie, "Instincts and Homeostasis," *loc. cit.,* p. 23.

19. Sigmund Freud, *An Outline of Psychoanalysis,* New York, Norton, 1949, p. 19.

20. For what it may be worth it is interesting in passing to note that the consonant (really partially vowel—"em") sound "m" followed by a vowel forms the first letters of the word for "mother" in many languages. These sounds are incorporative, internalizing ones, akin to the "mmmm" sound that one often makes while consuming a particularly tasty dish. On the other hand the word for father usually commences with an externalizing rejecting "fricative" "f" or plosive "p" or "b." The word "mamma," meaning "mother" and the Latin word for breast "mamma," may here afford a clue to a very ancient connection.

21. Ian D. Suttie, *The Origins of Love and Hate,* New York, Julian Press, 1953, p. 35.

22. R. Linton, *The Cultural Background of Personality,* New York, Appleton-Century, 1945, p. 8.

23. Davenport Hooker, "Reflex activities in the human fetus," in *Child Behavior and Development* (edited by R. G. Barker, *et al.*), New York, McGraw-Hill, 1943, pp. 17–28. See W. F. Windle, *Physiology of the Fetus,* Philadelphia, Saunders, 1940, p. 185.

24. It would seem that some, at least, of the aquatic mammals are equally fond of cutaneous stimulation. McBride and Kritzler of the Duke University Marine Laboratory at Beaufort, North Carolina, write that "Dolphins are very fond of rubbing their bodies on various objects, so a backscratcher, constructed of three stout sweeper's brushes fixed to a slab of rock with the bristles directed upward, was installed in the tank. The young dolphins took to rubbing themselves on these brushes as soon as the adults discovered their purpose. The 1947 female, at the age of two years, became so fond of being caressed by the observer that she would frequently rear cautiously out of the water to rub her chin on the knuckles of his clenched fist." A. F. McBride and H. Kritzler, "Observations on pregnancy, parturition, and post-natal behavior in the Bottlenose Dolphin," *Journal of Mammalogy,* vol. 32, 1951, p. 261, pp. 251–266.

25. It is well known among experts and dairy farmers that hand-milked cows give more, and richer, terminal milk than machine-milked cows.

26. This seems to happen particularly frequently among chihuahua dogs, the mothers often making little or no attempt to lick their young. Hence their high mortality rate unless some substitute for maternal licking, such as stroking by the human hand, in introduced.

27. These experiments are reported in "Germ-free life studies," *Lobund Reports,* no. 1, 1946, and no. 2, 1949, University of Notre Dame.

28. *Ibid.,* no. 1, p. 20.

29. Personal communication from Professor Reyniers, November 10, 1950.

30. See Larry Rhine, "One little kitten and how it grew," *McCall's Magazine,* vol. 80, July, 1953, pp. 4–6: "The A.S.P.C.A. woman said, 'Your problem is not with the eating. You see, a kitten's first eliminations are stimulated by the mother cat. Now, if you'd like to try to do the same with a cotton swab dipped in warm water you might be able to . . .' "

31. W. F. Windle, *op. cit.*

32. Frederick S. Hammet, "Studies of the thyroid apparatus," *Endocrinology,* vol. 4, 1922, pp. 221–229.

33. M. J. Greenman and F. L. Duhring, *Breeding and Care of the Albino Rat for Research Purposes,* 2d ed., Philadelphia, Wistar Institute, 1931.

34. Otto Weininger, "Physiological damage under emotional stress as a function of early experience," *Science,* vol. 119, 1954, pp. 285–286; Otto Weininger *et al.,* "Gentling and weight gain in the albino rat." *Canadian Journal of Psychology,* vol. 8, 1954, pp. 147–151. See pp. 199–223 this book.

35. Sir William Osler, *Aphorisms* (collected by R. B. Bean and edited by W. B. Bean), New York, Schuman, 1950, p. 126.

36. On the allergic relationships between the skin and breathing see Bret Ratner, C. Collins-Williams, and S. Untracht, "Allergic-dermal respiratory syndrome in children," *American Journal of Diseases of Children,* vol. 82, 1951, pp. 666–676.

37. Mary Drillien, "Studies in prematurity. Part 4: Development and progress of the prematurely born child in the pre-school period," *Archives of the Diseases of Childhood,* vol. 23, 1948, pp. 69–83.

38. Mary Shirley, "A behavior syndrome characterizing prematurely-born children," *Child Development,* vol. 10, 1939, pp. 115–128.

39. Margaret A. Ribble, "Disorganizing factors of infant personality," *American Journal of Psychiatry,* vol. 98, 1941, pp. 459–463.

40. For a graphic and significant account of the same phenomenon in dogs, see B. M. McKinney, "A canine demonstration," *Child Family Digest,* vol. 10, 1954, pp. 63–65. Reprinted in this volume, pp. 346–348.

41. S. Lóránd and J. Asbót, "Ueber die durch Reizüng der Brustwarze angeregten reflektorischen Uteruskontraktionen," *Zentralblatt für Gynäkologie,* vol. 74, 1952, pp. 345–352.

42. Toward the end of the eighteenth century Erasmus Darwin pointed out that our fondness for rolling hills and gently undulating landscapes was probably derived from our conditioning upon the cushion of our mother's breasts. *Zoonomia, or the Laws of Organic Life,* Part I, London, J. Johnson, 1794. This also recalls the lines from Psalm 121, "I will lift up mine eyes unto the hills, from whence cometh my help."

43. It is interesting to note that female fish will not spawn unless they are repeatedly touched—usually by the male. See N. Tinbergen, *Social Behaviour in Animals,* New York, Wiley, 1953, pp. 29, 83.

44. However, Tinbergen tells us that "In many higher animals, particularly land animals, fertilization involves mating, or copulation. This requires more than mere synchronization. It means bodily contact. This is a thing most animals avoid. This avoidance is an adaptation, part of their defence against predators. Being touched usually means being captured." Tinbergen, *op. cit.,* p. 22.

45. O. Spurgeon English, "Sex and human love," in *About the Kinsey Report* (edited by Donald P. Geddes and E. Curie,) New York, New American Library, 1948, pp. 101–102.

46. Charlotte Wolff, *A Psychology of Gesture,* London, Methuen, 1948, p. 49.

47. M. F. Ashley Montagu, "The sensory influences of the skin," *Texas Reports on Biology and Medicine,* vol. 11, 1953, pp. 291–301.

Chapter 7. Needs, Culture, and Values

1. In many nonliterate societies "no very clear-cut line is drawn between social service and economic service." See Raymond Firth, *Elements of Social Organization,* London, Watts, 1951, p. 193.

2. Bronislaw Malinowski, *A Scientific Theory of Culture,* Chapel Hill, University of North Carolina, 1944, p. 38.

3. Ralph Linton, "Culture, society and the individual," *Journal of Abnormal and Social Psychology*, vol. 33, 1938, pp. 425–436.

4. David B. Dill, *Life, Heat, and Altitude*, Cambridge, Harvard University Press, 1938.

5. Bronislaw Malinowski, *op. cit.*, p. 86.

6. S. Rosenzweig, "Babies are taught to cry: A hypothesis," *Mental Hygiene*, vol. 38, 1954, pp. 81–84.

7. H. D. Renner, *The Origin of Food Habits*, London, Faber and Faber, 1944.

8. Alfred C. Kinsey, *et al.*, *Sexual Behavior in the Human Female*, Philadelphia, Saunders, 1953; M. F. Ashley Montagu, *The Natural Superiority of Women*, New York, Macmillan, 1953.

9. N. Tinbergen, *Social Behaviour In Animals*, New York, Wiley, 1953, p. 22.

10. Geoffrey May, *Social Control of Sex Expression*, New York, Morrow, 1931; Clellan S. Ford and Frank A. Beach, *Patterns of Sexual Behavior*, New York, Harper, 1951.

11. See M. F. Ashley Montagu, *Coming Into Being Among the Australian Aborigines*, London, Routledge, 1937; M. F. Ashley Montagu, *Adolescent Sterility*, Springfield, Illinois, Thomas, 1946.

12. W. H. R. Rivers (editor), *Essays on the Depopulation of Melanesia*, Cambridge, Cambridge University Press, 1922.

13. A. Lommell, "Modern culture influences on Australian Aborigines," *Oceania*, vol. 21, 1950, pp. 14–24; R. M. Berndt, "Influence of European culture on Australian Aborigines," *Oceania*, vol. 21, 1951, pp. 229–235; B. B. Rubenstein, "An emotional factor in infertility," *Fertility and Sterility*, vol. 2, 1951, pp. 80–86.

14. H. Schuermann, "Ueber die Zuhnahme männlicher Fertilitätsstorungen und ueber die Bedeutung psychischer Einflüsse für zentralnervöse Regulation der Spermiogenese," *Medizinische Klinik*, vol. 43, 1948, pp. 366–368; W. H. Gantt, "Disturbances in sexual functions during periods of stress," in *Life Stress and Bodily Disease* (edited by H. G. Wolff, *et al.*), Baltimore, Williams & Wilkins, 1950, pp. 1030–1050; W. R. Miles, "The sex expression of men living on a lowered nutritional level," *Journal of Nervous and Mental Disorders*, vol. 49, 1919, pp. 208–224. Under conditions of stress or starvation the functions of the pituitary gland are disturbed and it fails to produce its hormones, as a result the sex glands, the thyroid, and the adrenal glands show decreased activity. See W. H. Perloff *et al.*, "The starvation state and functional hypopituitarism," *Journal of the American Medical Association*, vol. 155, 1954, pp. 1307–1313.

15. Walter B. Cannon, "'Voodoo' death," *American Anthropoligist*, vol. 44, 1942, pp. 169–181. See also the symposium volume *Life Stress and Bodily Disease*, *loc. cit.*

16. Hans Selye, *Stress*, Montreal, Acta Endocrinologica, 1950; Hans Selye, "The general adaptation syndrome and the diseases of adaptation," *Journal of Clinical Endocrinology*, vol. 6, 1946, pp. 117–230; Hans Selye, *Textbook of Endocrinology*, Montreal, Acta Endocrinologica, 1947, pp. 837–867; Hans Selye, *The Stress of Life*, New York, McGraw-Hill, 1956; O. Weininger, "Mortality of albino rats under stress as a function of early handling," *Canadian Journal of Psychology*, vol. 7, 1953, pp. 111–114; H. G. Wolff, *Stress and Disease*, Springfield, Illinois, Thomas, 1954; E. W. Bovard, "A theory to account for the effects of early handling on viability of the albino rat," *Science*, vol. 120, 1954, p. 187.

17. There now exists a very large amount of experimental evidence to support this statement. See H. S. Liddell, "Conditioned reflex method and experimental neurosis," in *Personality and the Behavior Disorders* (edited by J. McV. Hunt), vol. 1, pp. 389–412, New York, Ronald, 1944.

18. "It seems that neuroses are only acquired during early childhood (up to the age of six), even though their symptoms may not make their appearance until much later," Sigmund Freud, *An Outline of Psychoanalysis,* New York, Norton, 1949, p. 83.

19. "Clinical data indicate that it is always more physiologically relaxing to react to frustration as directly as the situation will allow. This includes talking back politely to the boss rather than raving about mistreatment to friends, taking up a job that has to be redone rather than crying over it, and concentrating upon improving upon a necessary skill rather than to get in another person to help out," G. L. Freeman, *The Energetics of Human Behavior,* Ithaca, Cornell University Press, 1948, p. 125.

20. Henry A. Murray, *Explorations in Personality,* New York, Oxford University Press, 1938, p. 130.

21. Flanders Dunbar, *Psychosomatic Diagnosis,* New York, Hoeber, 1944; Flanders Dunbar, *Emotions and Bodily Changes,* 5th ed., New York, Columbia University Press, 1955.

22. An innovation has been defined as "any thought, behavior, or thing that is new because it is qualitatively different from existing forms. Strictly speaking an innovation is an idea, or a constellation of ideas," which may or may not be given overt or tangible expression. See H. G. Barnett, *Innovation: The Basis of Cultural Change,* New York, McGraw-Hill, 1953, p. 7.

23. David Bidney, *Theoretical Anthropology,* New York, Columbia University Press, 1953, p. 17.

24. See Edmund Burgler, "The gambler: a misunderstood neurotic," *Journal of Criminal Psychopathology,* vol. 4, 1943, pp. 379–393. See also Robert Lindner, "The psychodynamics of gambling," in R. Lindner (editor), *Explorations in Psychoanalysis,* New York, Julian Press, 1953, pp. 197–217.

25. See *The Diary of Dostoyevsky's Wife* (edited by R. Fülöp-Miller and Fr. Eckstein), New York, Macmillan, 1928, pp. 232–241. Madame Dostoyevsky remarks: "It was a habit of Fyodor's [Dostoyevsky] to make one feel first terrified and then delighted" (p. 257). He would, as it were, prolong the pain in order to heighten the pleasure. See also Dostoyevsky's very revealing short novel *The Gambler,* New York, Dutton, 1948.

26. Margaret Mead (editor), *Competition and Cooperation Among Primitive Peoples,* New York, McGraw-Hill, 1937; Ruth Benedict, *Patterns of Culture,* New York, Mentor Books, 1946; John J. Honigmann, *Culture and Personality,* New York, Harper, 1954.

27. Ralph Linton, *The Cultural Background of Personality,* New York, Appleton-Century, 1945, pp. 7–10.

28. Abraham H. Maslow, "Some theoretical consequences of basic-need gratification," *Journal of Personality,* vol. 16, 1948, pp. 402–416.

29. Abraham H. Maslow, "'Higher' and 'lower' needs," *Journal of Psychology,* vol. 25, 1948, pp. 433–436. Reprinted in the same author's *Motivation and Personality,* New York, Harper, 1954, pp. 146–154.

30. Hadley Cantril, "Toward a scientific morality," *Journal of Psychology,* vol. 27, 1949, pp. 363–376.

31. Maslow, *op. cit.,* p. 150.

32. John Dewey, *Problems of Men,* New York, Philosophical Library, 1946, p. 258.

33. Julian Huxley, *Evolution in Action,* New York, Harper, 1953, p. 150.

34. See Wolfgang Kohler, *The Place of Value in a World of Facts,* New York, Liveright, 1938, pp. 31 *et seq.,* for a discussion of "intrinsic requiredness."

35. Samuel Alexander, *Beauty and Other Forms of Values,* New York, Macmillan, 1933, p. 10; K. G. Collier, "The inheritance of values," *Sociological Review* (London), vol. 40, 1948, pp. 97–112; Dorothy D. Lee, "Are basic needs ultimate?" *Journal of Abnormal and Social Psychology,* vol. 43, 1948, pp. 391–395; Nina Bull, "The biological basis of value," *Scientific Monthly,* vol. 53, 1941, pp. 170–174; Sol W. Ginsburg, "Values and the psychiatrist," *American Journal of Orthopsychiatry,* vol. 20, 1950, pp. 466–478; Bronislaw Malinowski, "Value and derived needs," in his *Freedom and Civilization,* New York, Roy Publishers, 1944, pp. 124–137; Hadley Cantril, *The "Why" of Human Experience,* New York, Macmillan, 1950; C. A. Mace, "Homeostasis, needs and values," *British Journal of Psychology,* vol. 44, 1953, pp. 200–210.

36. Professor L. O. Kattsoff has independently arrived at a precisely similar conclusion. "The concept of health," he writes, "is the absolute criterion for the evaluation of modes of behavior." See his *The Design of Human Behavior,* St. Louis, Educational Publishers, 1953, p. 115.

37. Abraham H. Maslow, "The instinctoid nature of basic needs," *Journal of Personality,* vol. 22, 1954, pp. 326–347.

38. L .O. Kattsoff, *op. cit.,* p. 69.

39. Samuel L. Hart, *Treatise on Values,* New York, Philosophical Library, 1949, p. 56.

40. Abraham H. Maslow, "Our maligned human nature," *Journal of Psychology,* vol. 28, 1949, p. 273.

41. Trygve Braatøy, *Fundamentals of Psychoanalytic Technique,* New York, John Wiley, 1954, p. 49. See particularly the admirable first chapter "Love—the basis of personal psychotherapy."

42. Sol. W. Ginsburg, *op. cit.,* p. 478.

43. E. W. Fellows, "Science and values: A survey of current points of view," *Scientific Monthly,* vol. 73, 1951, pp. 111–113.

44. Henry Margenau, "Scientific basis of ethics," *Main Currents in Modern Thought,* vol. 9, 1952, pp. 82–83.

Chapter 8. Dependency, Interdependency, and Love

1. See M. F. Ashley Montagu, "Constitutional and prenatal factors in infant and child health," in *The Healthy Personality* (edited by M. J. E. Senn), New York, Josiah Macy, Jr., Foundation, 1952, pp. 148–210. Reprinted in W. E. Martin and C. B. Stendler, *Readings in Child Development,* New York, Harcourt Brace, 1954, pp. 15–29.

2. M. A. Wenger, "An investigation of conditioned responses in human infants," in M. A. Wenger, J. M. Smith, and O. C. Irwin, "Studies in infant behavior," *University of Iowa Studies in Child Welfare,* vol. 12, 1936, pp. 7–90. See also Karl C. Pratt, "The neonate," in *Manual of Child Psychology* (edited by Leonard Carmichael), New York, Wiley, 1954, pp. 216–217, N. L. Munn, "Learning in children," same volume, pp. 374–458.

3. See Karl C. Pratt, *op. cit.,* pp. 215–291. See also, P. F. Durham Seitz, "Psychocutaneous conditioning during the first two weeks of life," *Psychosomatic Medicine,* vol. 12, 1950, pp. 187–188.

4. David K. Spelt, "The conditioning of the human fetus *in utero,*" *Journal of Experimental Psychology,* vol. 38, 1948, pp. 338–346.

5. See Phyllis Greenacre, *Trauma, Growth and Personality,* New York, Norton, 1952; Rollo May, *The Meaning of Anxiety,* New York, Ronald Press, 1950.

6. See pp. 88–104.
7. Otto Rank, *The Trauma of Birth,* New York, Brunner, 1952, pp. 11–12.
8. S. Freud, *Three Contributions to the Theory of Sex,* Nervous and Mental Diseases Publishing Co., New York, 1910.
9. Rank, *op. cit.,* p. 17.
10. For a good account of the neonate see Karl C. Pratt, *op. cit.,* pp. 215–291.
11. See M. F. Ashley Montagu, "Some factors in family cohesion," *Psychiatry,* vol. 7, 1944, pp. 349–352; M. F. Ashley Montagu, "The sensory influences of the skin," *Texas Reports on Biology and Medicine,* vol. 11, 1953, pp. 291–301.
12. *Time,* August 12, 1954, p. 46.
13. See Grantly Dick Read, *Childbirth Without Fear,* New York, Harper, 1953, pp. 199–200. For detailed evidence see Betsy McKinney, "A canine demonstration," *Child Family Digest,* vol. 16, 1954, pp. 63–65, and the present book, pp. 346–348.
14. M. Bevan-Brown, *The Sources of Love and Fear,* New York, Vanguard Press, 1950, p. 15.
15. Alfred Adler, *Social Interest: A Challenge to Mankind,* New York, Putnam, 1938, p. 214.
16. *Ibid.,* pp. 220-221.
17. M. Bevan-Brown, *op. cit.*
18. *Ibid.,* p. 10.
19. See L. L. Lemak, "Roentgenological manifestations of gastrointestinal ulceration in the newborn," *American Journal of Roentgenology,* vol. 66, 1951, pp. 191–199; E. Kezur, F. T. Kapp, and M. Rosenbaum, "Psychological factors in women with ulcers," *American Journal of Psychiatry,* vol. 108, 1951, pp. 368–373; B. R. Girdany, "Peptic ulcer in childhood," *Pediatrics,* vol. 12, 1953, pp. 56–61.
20. Franz Alexander, "Psychogenic factors in bronchial asthma," Part I, *Psychosomatic Medicine Monograph,* No. 4, 1941, p. 58; I. D. Harris, L. Rapoport, M. A. Rynerson, and Samter, M., "Observations on asthmatic children," *American Journal of Orthopsychiatry,* vol. 20, 1950, pp. 490–505.
21. E. Kezur, F. T. Kapp and M. Rosenbaum, *op. cit.,* pp. 368–373. See also O. Spurgeon English and Florence Foster, *Fathers Are Parents Too,* New York, Putnam, 1951.
22. For a discussion of the organ neuroses, see Otto Fenichel, *The Psychoanalytic Theory of the Neuroses,* New York, Norton, 1945, pp. 236–267; also the same author's *The Collected Papers of Otto Fenichel,* First Series, New York, Norton, 1953, Second Series, New York, Norton, 1954; Irving D. Harris, "Mood, anger and somatic dysfunction," *Journal of Nervous and Mental Disease,* vol. 113, 1951, pp. 152–158; Joseph J. Michaels, "A psychiatric adventure in comparative patho-physiology of the infant and adult," *Journal of Nervous and Mental Disease,* vol. 100, 1944, pp. 49–63.
23. Irving D. Harris, *op. cit.,* H. Hartmann, E. Kris, and R. M. Loewenstein, "Notes on the theory of aggression," in *The Psychoanalytic Study of the Child,* vol. 3/4, New York, International Universities Press, 1949, pp. 9–42.
24. B. Bettelheim and Emmy Sylvester, "Physical symptoms in emotionally disturbed children," *The Psychoanalytic Study of the Child, loc. cit.,* pp. 353–368.
25. Emory S. Bogardus (discussion), in Floyd H. Allport, "The group fallacy in relation to social science," *American Journal of Sociology,* vol. 29, 1924, p. 704.
26. Harry S. Sullivan, "The illusion of personal individuality," *Psychiatry,* vol. 13, 1950, p. 329.
27. A. N. Whitehead, *Adventures of Ideas,* New York, Cambridge University Press, p. 137.

28. E. Gutkind, *Choose Life,* New York, Schuman, 1952, p. 134.

29. C. M. Child, "The beginnings of unity and order in living things," in E. Dummer (editor), *The Unconscious,* New York, Knopf, 1927, p. 37.

30. This, it may be recalled, is the theme of Stephen Crane's famous story *The Red Badge of Courage,* which during 1951–52 was widely seen in its admirable movie version.

31. Albert J. Glass, "Combat exhaustion," *United States Armed Forces Medical Journal,* vol. 2, 1951, pp. 1471–1478.

32. See M. F. Ashley Montagu (editor), *The Meaning of Love,* New York, Julian Press, 1953.

33. Nelson N. Foote, "Love," *Psychiatry,* vol. 16, 1953, pp. 245–251.

34. Harry S. Sullivan, *Conceptions of Modern Psychiatry,* Washington, D.C., William Alanson White Psychiatric Foundation, 1947, p. 20.

35. Erich Fromm, *Man For Himself,* New York, Rinehart, 1947, pp. 98–101.

36. Ian D. Suttie, *The Origins of Love and Hate,* New York, Julian Press, 1953, p. 36.

37. Leo Loeb, *The Biological Basis of Individuality,* Springfield, Illinois, Thomas, 1944, pp. 651–652.

38. Sir Charles Sherrington, *Man On His Nature,* 2d ed., New York, Cambridge University Press, 1951, pp. 382–383.

39. What could be achieved this way and by what means has been extremely though not impossibly set out in two novels, the earlier by Aldous Huxley, *Brave New World,* New York, Harper, 1932; the more recent by George Orwell, *Nineteen Eighty-Four,* New York, New American Library, 1948. See also Ray Bradbury, *Fahrenheit 451,* New York, Ballantine Books, 1953.

40. See pp. 105–131.

41. See G. Scott Williamson and I. H. Pearse, *Biologists in Search of Material,* London, Faber & Faber, 1947.

42. A neurosis has been defined as the process of making the best of your frustrations in an unsatisfactory sort of way.

43. Erich Fromm, *Escape From Freedom,* New York, Rinehart, 1941; Erich Fromm, *Man For Himself, loc. cit.;* Rollo May, *The Meaning of Anxiety, loc cit.;* Rollo May, *Man in Search of Himself,* New York, Norton, 1952; W. H. Auden, *The Age of Anxiety,* New York, Random House, 1947; M. W. Childs and D. Cater, *Ethics in a Business Society,* New York, Mentor Books, 1954.

44. James C. Moloney, "Psychiatric observations in Okinawa Shima," *Psychiatry,* vol. 8, 1945, pp. 391–401; James C. Moloney, *The Battle For Mental Health,* New York, Philosophical Library, 1952; James C. Moloney, *The Magic Cloak,* Wakefield, Massachusetts, Montrose Press, 1949, pp. 299–314.

45. During 1951 while on a visit to the Southwest I learned of a group of investigators who had arrived to study mental illness among American Indians. Not being able to discover a single mentally ill Indian they packed their bags and departed! It occurred to no one, apparently, to inquire why there were no mentally ill Indians. For an interesting discussion bearing on this subject see P. M. Yap, "Mental diseases peculiar to certain cultures," *Journal of Mental Science,* vol. 97, 1951, pp. 313–327; Erik H. Erikson, *Childhood and Society,* New York, Norton, 1950; John W. M. Whiting and Irving Child, *Child Training and Personality,* New Haven, Yale University Press, 1953; Douglas G. Haring (editor), *Personal Character and Cultural Milieu,* Syracuse, New York, Syracuse University Press, 1949; S.

Sargent and M. Smith (editors), *Culture and Personality,* New York, Viking Fund, 1949.

46. John E. Boodin, *The Social Mind,* New York, Macmillan, 1939, p. 155.

47. Otto Rank, *Modern Education,* New York, Knopf, 1932, p. 99.

48. Erich Fromm, *Ecsape From Freedom, loc. cit.,* pp. 21–22.

49. See, for example, Geza Roheim's interesting work, *The Origin and Function of Culture,* Nervous and Mental Diseases Monographs, No. 69, New York, 1943.

50. For an illuminating discussion of this subject see Cathy Hayes, *The Ape in Our House,* New York, Harper, 1951.

51. For a discussion of this subject see Margaret M. Wood, *Paths of Loneliness,* New York, Columbia University Press, 1953. Paul Halmos, *Solitude and Privacy,* New York, Philosophical Library, 1953.

52. André Gide, *The Journals of André Gide,* vol. 1, New York, Knopf, 1947.

53. John Donne, *Complete Poetry and Selected Prose* (edited by John Hayward), New York, Random House, 1929, p. 538.

54. Sigmund Freud, "Psychoanalysis," *Encyclopaedia Britannica,* 14th ed. Chicago, 1929.

55. Harry S. Sullivan, "Psychiatry: Introduction to the study of interpersonal relations," *Psychiatry,* vol. 1, 1938, pp. 121–134.

56. For a criticism of the Freudian conception of "Narcissism" see Ian D. Suttie, *op. cit.,* p. 32. For a beautiful proof of the statement in the text see P. F. D. Seitz, "Psychocutaneous conditioning during the first two weeks of life," *Psychosomatic Medicine,* vol. 12, 1950, pp. 187–188.

57. Alfred Adler, *op. cit.,* pp. 282–283 and 284.

58. William Galt, "The principle of cooperation in behavior," *Quarterly Review of Biology,* vol. 15, 1940, pp. 401–410.

59. Kathleen Nott, "The topographical illusion," *Horizon* (London), vol. 19. 1949, pp. 367–371.

60. Beata Rank, "Aggression," *The Psychoanalytic Study of the Child, loc. cit.,* pp. 43–48.

61. René A. Spitz, "The role of ecological factors in emotional development in infancy," *Child Development,* vol. 20, 1949, pp. 145–155; René A. Spitz, "Autoerotism," *The Psychoanalytic Study of the Child, loc. cit.,* pp. 85–120.

62. David Beres and Samuel J. Obers, "The effects of extreme deprivation in infancy on psychic structure in adolescence: A study in ego development," *The Psychoanalytic Study of the Child,* vol. 5, New York, International Universities Press, 1950, pp. 212–235.

63. H. Hartmann, E. Kris, and R. M. Loewenstein, "Comments on the formation of psychic structure," *The Psychoanalytic Study of the Child,* vol. 3/4, *loc. cit.,* pp. 11–38; H. Hartmann, "Comments on the psychoanalytic theory of the ego," *The Psychoanalytic Study of the Child,* vol. 5, *loc. cit.,* pp. 74–96; Beata Rank and Dorothy Macnaughton, "A clinical contribution to early ego development," *ibid.,* pp. 53–65.

64. René A. Spitz, "Relevancy of direct infant observation," *The Psychoanalytic Study of the Child,* vol. 5, *loc. cit.,* pp. 66–73.

65. Edith Jacobson, "Contribution to the metapsychology of cyclothymic depression," in *Affective Disorders* (edited by Phyllis Greenacre), New York, International Universities Press, 1953, pp. 49–83.

66. Galt, *op. cit.,* p. 405.

67. *Ibid.,* p. 407.

68. Trigant Burrow, "The social neurosis: A Study in 'clinical anthropology,'"

Philosophy of Science, vol. 16, 1949, pp. 25–40. For a more extended treatment see Trigant Burrow, *The Neurosis of Man,* New York, Philosophical Library, 1953.

69. Alfred Adler, *op. cit.,* p. 110.

70. Trigant Burrow, "The social neurosis: A study in 'clinical anthropology,'" *loc. cit.,* p. 40.

71. Alfred Adler, *op. cit.,* p. 285.

72. The term "savage" was dropped when we learned that "savages" are, in fact, not "savage" or "wild." The term "primitive" is falling into disuse because we now know that the only things primitive about "primitive" peoples is their technological development—but then only by *unfair* comparison with our own. The term "nonliterate" refers more accurately and with less prejudice to such peoples.

73. Charlotte Buhler, "Die Ersten Sozialen Verhaltungsweisen des Kindes," in *Soziologische und Psychologische Studien über das Erste Lebensjahr,* Jena, Fischer, 1927; Charlotte Buhler, "Spontaneous reactions of children in the first two years," *Proceedings and Papers of the 9th International Congress of Psychology,* 1929, pp. 99–100.

74. M. J. Muste and D. F. Sharpe, "Some influential factors in the determination of aggressive behavior in preschool children," *Child Development,* vol. 18, 1947, pp. 11–28; K. Lewin, R. Lippitt, and R. K. White, "Patterns of aggressive behavior," *Journal of Social Psychology,* vol. 10, 1939, pp. 271–299; M. E. Bonney, "A sociometric study," *Sociometry,* vol. 9, 1946, pp. 21–47; M. D. Fite, "Aggressive behavior in young children," *Genetic Psychology Monographs,* vol. 22, 1940, pp. 151–319; L. Bender, S. Keiser, and P. Schilder, "Studies in aggressiveness," II, *Genetic Psychology Monographs,* vol. 18, 1938, pp. 546–564; R. R. Sears, J. W. M. Whiting, V. Nowlis, and P. S. Sears, "Some child-rearing antecedents of aggression and dependency in young children," *Genetic Psychology Monographs,* vol. 47, 1953, pp. 135–234.

75. Lauretta Bender, "The genesis of hostility in children," *American Journal of Psychiatry,* vol. 105, 1948, pp. 241–245; Lauretta Bender, *Aggression, Hostility and Anxiety in Children,* Springfield, Illinois, Thomas, 1953.

76. A. H. Maslow, "Our maligned animal nature," *Journal of Psychology,* vol. 28, 1949, pp. 273–278.

77. Katherine M. Banham, "The development of affectionate behavior in infancy," *Journal of Genetic Psychology,* vol. 76, 1950, pp. 283–289.

78. Beata Rank, *op. cit.,* pp. 43–48.

79. This notion, of course, draws its character from Freud's conception of the Id. See p. 260.

80. M. E. Harding, *Psychic Energy,* New York, Pantheon Books, 1947, p. 1.

81. For an extreme expression of this point of view, see Richard M. Brickner, "Normal vertebrate behavior as a cause of human trouble," *American Journal of Psychiatry,* vol. 108, 1952, pp. 801–812.

82. Charles R. Knight, *Prehistoric Man,* New York, Appleton-Century, 1949.

83. This fact is aptly enshrined in a contemporary quatrain:

> What a crazy world
> Its wonders never cease
> All the civilized at war
> All the savages at peace!

84. See Roy H. Pearce, *The Savages of America,* Baltimore, Johns Hopkins Press, 1953; C. Turnbull, *Black War,* Melbourne, Cheshire, 1948; J. G. Paton, *Missionary to the New Hebrides,* New York, Revell, 1907.

85. In a personal communication dated October 30, 1953, a scientific colleague, after visiting the people of the coral atoll Ifaluk in the southern Pacific, writes "It was the most completely non-aggressive society imaginable. They had heard about Christianity and were asking about it—we told them that they were closer to the Christian ethic than any people we had ever heard of, and that we couldn't see why they should change this!" And this is Admiral Peary on the Eskimos of West Coast Greenland: "They are savages, but they are not savage; they are without government, but they are not lawless; they are utterly uneducated according to our standard, yet they exhibit a remarkable degree of intelligence. In temperament like children, with all a child's delight in little things, they are nevertheless enduring as the most mature of civilized men and women, and the best of them are faithful unto death. Without religion and having no idea of God, they will share their last meal with anyone who is hungry, while the aged and the helpless among them are taken care of as a matter of course. They are healthy and pure-blooded; they have no vices, no intoxicants, and no bad habits—not even gambling. Altogether they are a people unique upon the face of the earth. A friend of mine well calls them the philosophic anarchists of the north. . . . To Christianize them would be quite impossible; but the cardinal graces of faith, hope, and charity they seem to have already, for without them they would never survive the six-months' night and the many rigors of their home." Robert E. Peary, *The North Pole,* New York, Doubleday, 1910, pp. 46–48.

86. Henry G. Maurice, *Ask Now the Beasts,* Occasional Paper No. 9, Society for the Preservation of the Fauna of the Empire (London), 1948. See also J. H. Moore, *The Universal Kinship,* Chicago, Kerr, 1905; Alfred E. Emerson, "Dynamic homeostasis: a unifying principle in organic social and ethical evolution," *Scientific Monthly,* vol. 78, 1954, pp. 67–85.

87. A. I. Good, "Gorilla-Land," *Natural History* (New York), vol. 56, 1947, pp. 36-46. The Rev. A. I. Good was born and brought up in the Cameroons, and has been a missionary there for over forty years. He writes (pp. 45–46), "In the sections in which gorillas are most common, the natives seem not to be afraid of them and pay little attention to them. Of course, they see them almost every day. They tell me, and I have heard this over and over, that occasionally a big male gorilla will make a pretense of attacking, but that it is a bluff. He will approach to perhaps 20 or 25 feet, act threateningly, roar fiercely, stamp on the ground, turn his rear on you in a disgusting manner while watching you over his shoulder, but will not push the attack home if you stand up to him. He does not like to have you around and evidently wants to scare you off his premises, but if you don't scare, he will finally go away." For a similar account see C. R. Joy (editor), *The Animal World of Albert Schweitzer,* Boston, Beacon Press, 1950, pp. 97–102.

88. A. H. Maslow, *op. cit.,* p. 274.

89. See Belle J. Benchley, *My Friends the Apes,* Boston, Little, Brown, 1944; Gertrude D. Lintz, *Animals Are My Hobby,* London, Museum Press, 1945. Every reader of the present volume should read this book for the moving and illuminating account of the life history of the gorilla which subsequently became known as "Gargantua," as well as for the commentary it provides upon western man. Dr. George B. Schaller, a field-observer of the mountain gorilla in its native habitat, writes that "the gorilla is the most amiable of creatures," and only attacks when it is harassed. "The Mountain Gorilla," *New Scientist,* vol. 13, 1962, pp. 16–18. See also the same author's *The Mountain Gorilla,* Chicago, University of Chicago Press, 1963, and *The Year of the Gorilla,* Chicago, University of Chicago Press, 1964.

90. See G. V. Childe, *Man Makes Himself,* New York, Mentor Books, 1951; G.

V. Childe, *What Happened in History,* New York, Mentor Books, 1943; Grahame Clark, *From Savagery to Civilization,* New York, Schuman, 1946; G. V. Childe, *Social Evolution,* New York, Schuman, 1952; Ronald Latham, *In Quest of Civilization,* London, Jarrolds, 1946; Erich Kahler, *Man The Measure,* New York, Pantheon Books, 1950.

91. F. A. Hayek (editor), *John Stuart Mill and Harriet Taylor,* Chicago, University of Chicago Press, 1951, p. 279.

Chapter 9. Love and the Privation of Love

1. James Plant, *Personality and the Cultural Pattern,* New York, The Commonwealth Fund, 1937, p. 267.

2. In a report on ten different cities in the United States Dr. Henry Chapin, in 1915, found that in all but one institution every infant under two years of age died (H. D. Chapin, "A Plea for Accurate Statistics in Infants' Institutions," *Transactions of the American Pediatric Society,* vol. 27, 1915, p. 180). The various discussants of Dr. Chapin's paper fully corroborated his findings from their own experience, Dr. R. Hamil remarking with grim irony, "I had the honor to be connected with an institution in this city of Philadelphia in which the mortality among infants under one year of age, when admitted to the institution and retained there for any length of time, was 100 per cent." Dr. R. T. Southworth added, "I can give an instance from an institution in New York City that no longer exists in which, on account of the very considerable mortality among the infants admitted, it was customary to enter the condition of every infant on the admission card as hopeless. That covered all subsequent happenings." Finally, Dr. J. H. M. Knox described a study he had made in Baltimore. Of two hundred infants admitted to various institutions almost 90 per cent did within a year. The 10 per cent that survived, he stated, did so apparently because they were taken from institutions for short times and placed in the care of foster parents or relatives.

3. Ruth M. Bakwin and Harry Bakwin, *Psychologic Care During Infancy and Childhood,* New York, Appleton-Century, 1942, p. 295.

4. Margaret Ribble, *The Rights of Infants,* New York, Columbia University Press, 1943, pp. 4–7.

5. See John Bowlby, *Maternal Care and Mental Health,* New York, Columbia University Press, 1951.

6. Lawson G. Lowrey, "Personality distortion and early institutional care," *American Journal of Orthopsychiatry,* vol. 10, 1940, pp. 576–585.

7. For an important series of research findings on the personality of the institutionalized child see William Goldfarb, "The effects of early institutional care on adolescent personality," *Journal of Experimental Education,* vol. 12, 1943, pp. 106–129; also the following papers by the same author, "Infant rearing and problem behavior," *American Journal of Orthopsychiatry,* vol. 13, 1943, pp. 249–265; "The effects of early institutional care on adolescent personality (graphic Rorschach data)," *Child Development,* vol. 14, 1943, pp. 213–223; "Infant rearing as a factor in foster home replacement," *American Journal of Orthopsychiatry,* vol. 14, 1944, pp. 162–166; (with Bruno Klopfer) "Rorschach characteristics of 'Institution Children,'" *Rorschach Research Exchange,* vol. 8, 1944, pp. 92–100; "Psychological privation in infancy and subsequent adjustment," *American Journal of Orthopsychiatry,* vol. 15, 1945, pp. 247–255; "Effects of psychological deprivation in infancy and subsequent stimulation," *American Journal of Psychiatry,* vol. 102, 1945, pp. 18–33.

8. F. Bodman, *et al.*, "The social adaptation of institution children," *Lancet*, vol. 258, 1950, pp. 173–176; M. Castle, "Institution and non-institution children at school," *Human Relations*, vol. 7, 1954, pp. 349–366.

9. William Goldfarb, "The effects of early institutional care on adolescent personality," *loc. cit.*, p. 128.

10. David M. Levy, "Primary affect hunger," *American Journal of Psychiatry*, vol. 94, 1937, pp. 643–652.

11. William Goldfarb, "Psychological privation in infancy and subsequent adjustment," *loc. cit.*, p. 254.

12. René A. Spitz, "The role of ecological factors in emotional development," *Child Development*, vol. 20, 1949, pp. 145–155; René A. Spitz, "Hospitalism," *The Psychoanalytic Study of the Child*, vol. 1, New York, International Universities Press, 1945, pp. 53–74; René A. Spitz, "Hospitalism: A follow-up report," *The Psychoanalytic Study of the Child*, vol. 2, New York, International Universities Press, 1947, pp. 113–117; René A. Spitz, "Are parents necessary?" in *The March of Medicine, 1947*, New York, Columbia University Press, 1948, pp. 37–53; René A. Spitz, "Anaclitic depression," *The Psychoanalytic Study of the Child*, vol. 2, *loc. cit.*, pp. 313–342; René A. Spitz, "Autoerotism," *The Psychoanalytic Study of the Child*, vol. 3/4, New York, International Universities Press, 1949, pp. 85–120.

13. René A. Spitz, "Anaclitic depression," *loc. cit.*, p. 331.

14. See R. A. Spitz, "The psychogenic diseases of infancy," *The Psychoanalytic Study of the Child*, vol. 6, New York, International Universities Press, 1951, pp. 255–275. See also L. Bender and H. Yarnell, "An observation nursery: A study of 250 children in the Psychiatric Division of Bellevue Hospital," *American Journal of Psychiatry*, vol. 97, 1941, pp. 1158–1174; Harry Bakwin, "Loneliness in infants," *American Journal of Diseases of Children*, vol. 63, 1942, pp. 30–40; H. Edelston, "Separation anxiety in young children," *Genetic Psychology Monographs*, vol. 28, 1943, pp. 3–95; Harry Bakwin, "Emotional deprivation in infants," *Journal of Pediatrics*, vol. 35, 1949, pp. 512–521; Adrian H. Vander Veer, "The unwanted child," Publication of the Illinois League for Planned Parenthood, April 10, 1940, pp. 3–12; Eustace Chesser, *Unwanted Child*, London, Rich & Cowan, 1948; Percival M. Symonds, *The Dynamics of Parent-Child Relationships*, New York, Bureau of Publications, Columbia University, 1949.

15. August Aichorn, *Wayward Youth*, New York, Viking Press, 1935.

16. David Beres and Samuel J. Obers, "The effects of extreme deprivation in infancy on psychic structure in adolescence: A study in ego development," *The Psychoanalytic Study of the Child*, vol. 5, New York, International Universities Press, 1950, pp. 212–235.

17. Along these lines see Beata Rank and Dorothy Macnaughton, "A clinical contribution to early ego development," *The Psychoanalytic Study of the Child*, vol. 5, *loc. cit.*, pp. 53–73.

18. Portia Holman, "Some factors in the aetiology of maladjustment in children," *Journal of Mental Science*, vol. 99, 1953, pp. 654–688; see also Leo Bartmeier, "The contribution of the father to the mental health of the family," *American Journal of Psychiatry*, vol. 110, 1953, pp. 277–280; O. Spurgeon English and Florence Foster, *Fathers Are Parents Too*, New York, Putnam, 1951.

19. M. Bevan-Brown, *The Sources of Love and Fear*, New York, Vanguard Press, 1950, p. 40.

20. See George W. Corner, *Ourselves Unborn*, New Haven, Yale University Press, 1944, pp. 102–107.

21. See J. P. Scott and Mary-'Vesta Marston, "Critical periods affecting the development of normal and mal-adjustive social behavior in puppies," *Journal of Genetic Psychology,* vol. 77, 1950, pp. 25–60; J. P. Scott, "The relative importance of social and hereditary factors in producing disturbances in life adjustment during periods of stress in laboratory animals," in *Life Stress and Bodily Disease* (edited by H. G. Wolff, *et al.*), Baltimore, Williams & Wilkins, 1950, pp. 61–71; J. P. Scott, "The process of socialization in higher animals," in *Interrelations Between the Social Environment and Psychiatric Disorders,* New York, Milbank Memorial Fund, 1954, pp. 82–102.

22. John Bowlby, "Some pathological processes set in train by early mother-child separation," *Journal of Mental Science,* vol. 159, 1953, pp. 265–272.

23. For descriptive cases see Dorothy Burlingham and Anna Freud, *Infants Without Families,* London, Allen & Unwin, 1944; Anna Freud and Dorothy Burlingham, *War and Children*, New York, International Universities Press, 1943.

24. J. Robertson and J. Bowlby, "Observations of the sequences of responses of children aged 18 to 24 months during the course of separation," *Courier of the International Children's Centre,* vol. 2, 1952, pp. 132–142; J. Roudinesco, M. David, and J. Nicolas, "Observation of children aged 12 to 17 months recently separated from their families and living in an institution," *ibid.*, pp. 66–78; J. Roudinesco, "Severe maternal deprivation and personality development in early childhood," *Understanding the Child,* vol. 21, 1952, pp. 104–108; Mary D. Ainsworth and John Bowlby, "Research strategy in the study of mother-child separation, "*Courier of the International Children's Centre,* vol. 4, 1954, pp. 1–47.

25. D. Rosenbluth, J. Bowlby, and J. Roudinesco, "Separation from the mother as a traumatic experience for the child: Some notes on obtaining a relevant history," *Courier of the International Children's Centre,* vol. 2, 1952, pp. 1–8.

26. H. D. Chapin, "A plan of dealing with atrophic infants and children," *Archives of Pediatrics,* vol. 25, 1908, p. 491.

27. H. D. Chapin, "Are institutions for children necessary?" *Journal of the American Medical Association,* vol. 64, January 2, 1915.

28. J. Brennemann, "The infant ward," *American Journal of Diseases of Children,* vol. 43 (March) 1932, p. 577.

29. Salimbene in J. B. Ross and M. M. McLaughlin (editors), *A Portable Medieval Reader,* New York, Viking Press, 1949, p. 366.

30. It is now believed that retrolental fibroplasia, first recognized in 1942 as a disease of premature infants (characterized by the appearance of a fibrous band behind the lens which draws upon and detaches the retina, thus causing permanent blindness), is related to the excess oxygen given premature babies during their first two weeks while in hospital. See J. T. Lanman *et al.*, "Retrolental fibroplasia and oxygen therapy," *Journal of the American Medical Association,* vol. 155, 1954, pp. 223–226; Leona Zacharias, "Progress in the study of retrolental fibroplasia," *The Sight Saving Review,* (Summer) 1953. Reprinted in *Child Family Digest,* vol. 9, 1953, pp. 47–52.

31. Philip J. Howard and Calier H. Worrell, "Premature infants in later life," *Pediatrics,* vol. 9, 1952, pp. 577–584.

32. Julius H. Hess, "Experiences gained in a thirty year study of prematurely born infants," *Pediatrics,* vol. 11, 1953, pp. 425–434.

33. A. R. Gilliland, "Socio-economic status and race as factors in infant intelligence test scores," *Child Development,* vol. 22, 1951, pp. 271–273. See also the same author's "Environmental influence on infant intelligence test scores," *Harvard Educational Review,* vol. 19, 1949, pp. 142–146.

34. See pp. 205–209.

35. Ralph Fried and M. F. Mayer, "Socio-emotional factors accounting for growth failure of children living in an institution," *Journal of Pediatrics,* vol. 33, 1948, pp. 444–456. E. M. Widdowson, "Mental contentment and physical growth," *The Lancet,* vol. 1, 1951, pp. 1316–1318.

36. Griffith Binning, "Peace be on thy house," *Health,* March/April, 1948, pp. 6–7, 28, 30.

37. *Ibid.,* p. 30.

38. H. Durffee and K. M. Wolf, "Anstaltspflege und Entwickling im ersten Lebensjahrs," *Zeitschrift für Kinderforschung,* vol. 42/3, 1933, pp. 273–320.

39. René A. Spitz, "Hospitalism: A follow-up report," *loc. cit.,* pp. 113–117. See also H. Hetzer and R. Ripin, "Fruehestes Lernen des Saeuglings in der Ernaehrungs-Situation," *Zeikschrift für Psychologie,* vol. 118, 1930, pp. 82–127.

40. N. B. Talbot, E. H. Sobel, B. S. Burke, E. Lindemann, and S. S. Kaufman, "Dwarfism in healthy children: Its possible relation to emotional disturbances," *New England Journal of Medicine,* vol. 236, 1947, pp. 783–793.

41. H. Lihn, K. Menninger, and M. Mayman, "Personality factors in osteo-arthritis," in H. G. Wolff, *et al.* (editors), *Life Stress and Bodily Disease, loc. cit.,* pp. 744–749.

42. Hans Selye, *The Physiology and Pathology of Exposure to Stress,* Montreal, Acta, 1950, p. 103; E. W. Bovard, Jr., "A theory to account for the effects of early handling on viability of the albino rat," *Science,* vol. 120, 1954, p. 187; W. R. Ruegamer, *et. al.,* "Growth, food utilization, and thyroid activity in the albino rat as a function of extra handling," *Science,* vol. 120, 1954, pp. 184–185; H. D. Kruse, "The interplay of noxious agents, stress, and deprivation in the etiology of disease," in I. Galdston (editor), *Beyond the Germ Theory,* New York, Health Education Council, 1954, pp. 17–38; H. D. Kruse, "The ratios of health and disease—how the presence, excess, deficit, or absence of conditions evokes disease," *ibid.,* pp. 39–52; H. R. Schaeffer, "Behavior under stress: a neurophysiological hypothesis," *Psychological Review,* vol. 61, 1954, pp. 323–332.

43. Selye, *op. cit.,* p. 12.

44. R. A. Spitz, "Infantile depression and the general adaptation syndrome," in *Depression: Proceedings of the 42nd Annual Meeting American Psychological Association,* 1953, pp. 93–108.

45. Celia Burns Stendler, "Critical periods in socialization and overdependency," *Child Development,* vol. 23, 1952, pp. 2–12.

46. O. H. Mowrer, *Learning Theory and Personality Dynamics,* New York, Ronald Press, 1950.

47. M. F. Ashley Montagu, "Some factors in family cohesion," *Psychiatry,* vol. 7, 1944, pp. 349–352; Herbert Thoms, E. B. Jackson, L. M. Stowe, and F. W. Goodrich, Jr., "The rooming-in plan for mothers and infants," *American Journal of Obstetrics and Gynecology,* vol. 56, 1948, pp. 707–711; E. B. Jackson, *et al.* "A hospital rooming-in unit for four newborn infants and their mothers," *Pediatrics,* vol. 1, 1948, pp. 28–43.

48. Ruth M. Bakwin and Harry Bakwin, *op. cit.,* p. 294.

49. M. F. Ashley Montagu, "Some factors in family cohesion," *loc. cit.,* pp. 349–352.

50. John Bowlby, *Maternal Care and Mental Health, loc. cit.,* p. 55.

51. Lauretta Bender, "Psychopathic behavior disorders in children," in *Handbook of Correctional Psychology* (edited by R. M. Lindner and R. V. Seliger), New York, Philosophical Library, 1947.

52. William Goldfarb, "Variations in adolescent adjustment of institutionally reared children," *American Journal of Orthopsychiatry,* vol. 17, 1947, pp. 449–457.

53. Dorothy Burlingham and Anna Freud, *Monthly Report of Hampstead Nurseries,* May, 1944 (unpublished), quoted by Bowlby, *op. cit.*, p. 21.

54. M. F. Ashley Montagu, "Social time: A functional and methodological analysis," *American Journal of Sociology,* vol. 44, 1938, pp. 282–284.

55. John Bowlby, *Maternal Care and Mental Health, loc. cit.*, pp. 27–28.

56. These observations have been fully confirmed by other investigators. See, for example, Fritz Redl and David Wineman, *Children Who Hate,* Glencoe, Illinois, Free Press, 1951, and the same authors' *Controls From Within,* Glencoe, Illinois, Free Press, 1952; Portia Holman, *op. cit.* See also Frank J. Cohen, *Children In Trouble,* New York, Norton, 1952.

57. *Identification* is the process of molding by the person of his own ego after some aspect or the whole of one which has been taken for a model.

58. *Introjection* is the process of finding or incorporating within the self motives or qualities which are those of another person or object.

59. John Bowlby, "Forty-four juvenile thieves: Their characters and home life," *International Journal of Psycho-Analysis,* vol. 25, 1944, pp. 19–53, 122, 154–178.

60. The *libido* consists of all those energies which comprise the dependency love drives, which may broadly be resumed under the term "love," love including not only sexual love, but self-love, love for parents and children, friendship, love for humanity in general, and even devotion to concrete objects and to abstract ideas.

61. The *pleasure-principle* may be defined as the tendency for mental life and the development of the personality to be shaped primarily according to the pleasure-pain aspects of inner and also of outer stimuli.

62. The *reality-principle* defines the tendency to shape mental life according to the requirements of external necessity, forced upon the person by the need for adaptation to his environment.

63. These ideas are beautifully developed by August Aichorn in *Wayward Youth, loc. cit.*, pp. 187–210. See also Kate Friedlander, "Formation of the antisocial character," in *The Psychoanalytic Study of the Child,* vol. 1, New York, International Universities Press, 1945, pp. 189–203; Erik H. Erikson, *Childhood and Society,* New York, Norton, 1951; Frank J. Cohen, *op. cit.*, Bruno Bettelheim, *Love Is Not Enough,* Glencoe, Illinois, Free Press, 1950.

64. John Bowlby, "Critical phases in the development of social responses in man and other animals," in *Prospects In Psychiatric Research* (edited by J. M. Tanner), Oxford, Blackwell Scientific Publications, 1953, pp. 80–85. Reprinted in *New Biology,* No. 14 (edited by M. L. Johnson and M. Abercrombie), New York, Penguin Books, 1953, pp. 25–32.

65. Konrad Z. Lorenz, *King Solomon's Ring,* New York, Crowell, 1952, pp. 40–42.

66. Konrad Z. Lorenz, "Die angeborenen Formen möglicher Erfahrung," *Zeitschrift für Tierpsychologie,* vol. 5, 1943, pp. 235–409.

67. René A. Spitz and K. M. Wolf, "The smiling response: a contribution to the ontogenesis of social relations," *Genetic Psychology Monographs,* vol. 34, 1946, pp. 57–125.

68. W. Grey Walter, *The Living Brain,* New York, Norton, 1953, p. 91.

69. Quoted in W. Healy, A. F. Bronner, and A. M. Bowers, *The Structure and Meaning of Psychoanalysis,* New York, Knopf 1930, p. 117. See also N. Tinbergen, *Social Behaviour in Animals,* New York, Wiley, 1953; N. Tinbergen, *The Study of Instinct,* New York, Oxford University Press, 1952.

70. For a critical examination of the Lorenz-Tinbergen studies see A. Ginsberg, "A reconstructive analysis of the concept of 'instinct,'" *Journal of Psychology,* vol. 33, 1952, pp. 235–277; D. S. Lehrman, "A critique of Konrad Lorenz's theory of instinctive behavior," *Quarterly Review of Biology,* vol. 28, 1953, pp. 337–363; Rex Knight, "Animal behaviour," *Nature,* vol. 174, 1954, pp. 857–859.

71. Dorothy Burlingham and Anna Freud, *op. cit.*

72. M. F. Ashley Montagu, "The premaxilla in man," *Journal of the American Dental Association,* vol. 23, pp. 2043–2057, 1936.

73. Joseph Needham, *Morphogenesis and Embryology,* New York, Cambridge University Press, 1942.

74. B. M. Spinley, *The Deprived and the Privileged: Personality Development in English Society,* London, Routledge, 1953; M. L. Farber, "English and Americans: values in the socialization process," *Journal of Psychology,* vol. 36, 1953, pp. 243–250; M. L. Farber, "English and Americans: a study in national character." *Journal of Psychology,* vol. 32, 1951, pp. 241–249; M. C. Erickson, "Social status and child-rearing practices," in T. M. Newcomb and E. Hartley (editors), *Readings in Social Psychology,* New York, Holt, 1947, pp. 494–501; Allison Davis, "American status systems and the socialization of the child," *American Sociological Review,* vol. 6, 1941, pp. 345–356; Allison Davis, "Child training and social class," in R. G. Barker *et al* (editors), *Child Behavior and Development,* New York, McGraw-Hill, 1943; Allison Davis and R. J. Havighurst, *Father of the Man,* Boston, Houghton Mifflin, 1947; A. B. Hollinshead, *Elmtown's Youth,* New York, Wiley, 1949; C. B. Stendler, "The learning of certain secondary drives by Parisian and American middle class children," *Marriage and Family Living,* vol. 16, 1954, pp. 192–200.

75. These observations have been thoroughly confirmed by the first study on English personality types to be published, B. M. Spinley's *The Deprived and the Privileged,* London, Routledge, 1953; see also Geoffrey Gorer, *Exploring English Character,* Cresset Press, London, 1955.

76. E. M. Forster, *Abinger Harvest,* New York, Harcourt, Brace, 1947.

77. For an excellent and rare example of "sudden illumination," the discovery of the warmth and humanity and utter difference of the Italian personality from the American, by an American, see the late John Horne Burns' remarkable novel, *The Gallery,* New York, Harper, 1948.

78. An American Lady, *Change For the American Notes,* 1843, quoted in Yvonne-ffrench, *Transatlantic Exchanges,* New York, Library Publishers, 1952, p. 128.

79. T. W. Adorno, Else Frenkel-Brunswik, D. J. Levinson, and R. Nevitt Sanford, *The Authoritarian Personality,* New York, Harper, 1950.

80. *Ibid.,* p. 975.

81. David Levy, "Anti-Nazis: criteria of differentiation," in Alfred H. Stanton and Stewart E. Perry, *Personality and Political Crisis,* Glencoe, Illinois, Free Press, 1951, pp. 151–227.

82. David Levy, *Maternal Overprotection,* New York, Columbia University Press, 1943.

83. René A. Spitz, "Hospitalism," *loc. cit.,* pp. 53–14; René A. Spitz, "Hospitalism: a follow-up, II," *loc. cit.,* pp. 113–117. René A. Spitz, "Are parents necessary?" in *Medicine in the Postwar World,* New York, Columbia University Press, 1948, p. 46. René A. Spitz, "Anaclitic depression," *loc. cit.,* pp. 313–342.

84. Ian D. Suttie, *op. cit.,* p. 16.

85. Ralph S. Lillie, *General Biology and Philosophy of Organism,* Chicago, University of Chicago Press, 1945, pp. 208–209.

86. There have been no special studies on this subject for the Australian

aborigines, the evidence is largely of a casual observational kind, and in a sense is therefore perhaps all the more valuable; the following works contain important material: Baldwin Spencer and Frank J. Gillen, *The Arunta,* 2 vols., New York, Macmillan, 1927; Baldwin Spencer, *Wanderings In Wild Australia,* 2 vols., New York, Macmillan, 1928; J. R. B. Love, *Stone Age Bushmen of Today,* London, Blackie, 1936; Jack McLaren, *My Crowded Solitude,* London, Newnes, 1926; Charles P. Mountford, *Brown Men and Red Sand,* New York, Philosophical Library, 1948.

87. V. Stefansson, *My Life With The Eskimo,* New York, Macmillan, 1913; V. Stefansson, *The Friendly Arctic,* New York, Macmillan, 1944; Robert Marshall, *Arctic Village,* New York, Literary Guild, 1933; Gontran De Poncins, *Kabloona,* New York, Reynal & Hitchcock, 1941.

88. Margaret Mead, *Sex and Temperament in Three Primitive Societies,* New York, Mentor Books, 1950; Margaret Mead, *From The South Seas,* New York, Morrow, 1939; Hortense Powdermaker, *Life in Lesu,* New York, Norton, 1933.

89. Alice Joseph and Veronica F. Murray, *Chamorros and Carolinians of Saipan,* Cambridge, Harvard University Press, 1951.

90. Cora Du Bois, *The People of Alor,* Minneapolis, University of Minnesota Press, 1944; Margaret Mead and Gregory Bateson, *Balinese Character,* New York, New York Academy of Sciences, 1942; Margaret Mead and F. C. Macgregor, *Growth and Culture,* New York, Putnam, 1951.

91. Ruth Benedict, *The Chrysanthemum and the Sword,* Boston, Massachusetts, Houghton Mifflin, 1946; Geoffrey Gorer, "Japanese character structure," New York, Institute for Intercultural Studies, 1942; John Embree, *The Japanese Nation,* New York, Farrar & Rinehart, 1945. John Embree, *A Japanese Village, Suye Mura,* London, Kegan Paul, 1946; James C. Moloney, *Understanding the Japanese Mind,* New York, Philosophical Library, 1954; Douglas Haring, "Japanese national character," *Yale Review,* vol. 42, 1953, pp. 375–392; Jean Stoetzl, *Without the Chrysanthemum and the Sword,* London, Heinemann, 1954.

92. M. C. Yang, *A Chinese Village,* New York, Columbia University Press, 1945; Olga Lang, *Chinese Family and Society,* New Haven, Yale University Press, 1946; F. L. K. Hsu, *Under the Ancestor's Shadow,* New York, Columbia University Press, 1948; F. L. K. Hsu, *Chinese and Americans,* New York, Schuman, 1953.

93. Geoffrey Gorer, "Burmese personaliy," New York, Institute for Intercultural Studies, 1945.

94. Wayne Dennis, *The Hopi Child,* New York, Appleton-Century, 1940; Laura Thompson and Alice Joseph, *The Hopi Way,* Chicago, University of Chicago Press, 1945; Gordon Macgregor, *Warriors Without Weapons,* Chicago, University of Chicago Press, 1946; Dorothea Leighton and Clyde Kluckhohn, *Children of the People* [the Navaho], Cambridge, Harvard University Press, 1947; Clyde Kluckhohn and Dorothea Leighton, *The Navaho,* Cambridge, Harvard University Press, 1946; Erik H. Erikson, *Childhood and Society,* New York, Norton, 1950; Laura Thompson, *Culture in Crisis,* New York, Harper, 1950; Victor Barnow, "Acculturation and personality among the Wisconsin Chippewa," Memoir No. 72, *American Anthropologist,* vol. 52, 1950, pp. 1–152; Alice Joseph, Rosamund B. Spicer, and Jane Chesky, *The Desert People: A Study of the Papago Indians,* Chicago, University of Chicago Press, 1950; John J. Honigmann, "Culture and ethos of Kaska society," *Yale University Publications in Anthropology,* New Haven, Yale University Press, 1949, pp. 1–365.

95. Margaret Mead, *And Keep Your Powder Dry,* New York, Morrow, 1942; Geoffrey Gorer, *The American People,* New York, Norton, 1948; James West, *Plainville, U.S.A.,* New York, Columbia University Press, 1945; W. Lloyd Warner, *American Life,* Chicago, University of Chicago Press, 1953; Conrad M. Arensberg, *The*

Irish Countryman, New York, Macmillan, 1937; David Rodnick, *Postwar Germans,* New Haven, Yale University Press, 1948; Bertram Schaffner, *Father Land,* New York, Columbia University Press, 1948; A. W. Davis, and R. J. Havighurst, *Father of the Man,* Boston, Houghton Mifflin, 1947; R. J. Havighurst and H. Taba, *Adolescent Character and Personality,* New York, Wiley, 1949; A. B. Hollinshead, *Elmtown's Youth,* New York, Wiley, 1949; Claudia Lewis, *Children of the Cumberland,* New York, Columbia University Press, 1946; David Levy, "Anti-Nazis: criteria of differentiation," *Psychiatry,* vol. 11, 1948, pp. 125–167; Ruth Benedict, "Child rearing in certain European countries," *American Journal of Orthopsychiatry,* vol. 19, 1949, pp. 342–350; Geoffrey Gorer and John Rickman, *The People of Great Russia,* New York, Chanticleer Press, 1950; David Riesman, *The Lonely Crowd,* New Haven, Yale University Press, 1950; Ruth Métraux and Margaret Mead, *Themes in French Culture,* Stanford, Calif., Stanford University Press, 1954; Margaret Mead and Ruth Métraux, *The Study of Culture at a Distance,* Chicago, University of Chicago Press, 1953; Geoffrey Gorer, *Exploring English Character,* London, Cresset Press, 1955.

For general and special readings in the field see Clyde Kluckhohn and Henry A. Murray (editors), *Personality: In Nature, Society and Culture,* 2d ed., New York, Knopf, 1953; Douglas G. Haring (editor), *Personal Character and Cultural Milieu,* Syracuse, New York, Syracuse University Press, 1949; S. S. Sargent and Marian W. Smith (editors), *Culture and Personality,* New York, Viking Fund, 1949; Patrick Mullahy (editor), *A Study of Interpersonal Relations,* New York, Heritage Press, 1949; Howard Brand (editor), *The Study of Personality,* New York, Wiley, 1954; J. S. Slotkin, *Personality Development,* New York, Harper, 1952; John J. Honigmann, *Culture and Personality,* New York, Harper, 1954; A. H. Stanton and S. E. Perry, *Personality and Political Crisis,* Glencoe, Illinois, Free Press, 1951; Harold Orlansky, "Infant care and personalty," *Psychological Bulletin,* vol. 46, 1949, pp. 1–48, abridged in W. E. Martin and C. B. Stendler, *Readings in Child Development,* New York, Harcourt, Brace, 1954, pp. 321–336.

96. James C. Moloney, *The Magic Cloak,* Wakefield, Massachusetts, The Montrose Press, 1949, pp. 299–323.

97. C. P. Mountford, *op. cit.,* p. 21.

98. Julian Huxley, *Evolution In Action,* New York, Harper, 1953.

99. Edmund B. Sinnott, *Cell and Psyche,* Chapel Hill, University of North Carolina Press, 1950.

Chapter 10. Experience, Culture, and Personality

1. See R. E. Money-Kyrle, *Psychoanalysis and Politics,* London, Duckworth, 1951.

2. J. McV. Hunt, "The effects of infant feeding frustration upon adult hoarding in the albino rat," *Journal of Abnormal and Social Psychology,* vol. 36, 1941, pp. 338–360.

3. Emil Fredericson, "Competition: The effects of infantile experience upon adult behavior," *Journal of Abnormal and Social Psychology,* vol. 46, 1951, pp. 406–409.

4. Emil Fredericson, "The effects of food deprivation upon competitive and spontaneous combat in C57 black mice," *Journal of Psychology,* vol. 29, 1950, pp. 89–100.

5. M. W. Kahn, "The effect of severe defeat at various age levels on the aggressive behavior of mice, *Journal of Genetic Psychology,* vol. 79, 1951, pp. 117–130

6. J. P. Scott and Mary-'Vesta Marston, "Nonadaptive behavior resulting from a series of defeats in fighting mice," *Journal of Abnormal and Social Psychology,* vol. 48, 1953, pp. 417–428.

7. M. W. Kahn, "Infantile experience and mature aggressive behavior of mice: some maternal influences," *Journal of Genetic Psychology,* vol. 84, 1944, pp. 65–75.

8. J. A. King and N. L. Gurney, "Effect of early social experience on adult aggressive behavior in C57BL/10 mice," *Journal of Comparative and Physiological Psychology,* vol. 47, 1954, pp. 326–330.

9. David M. Levy, "Experiments on the sucking reflex and social behavior in dogs," *American Journal of Orthopsychiatry,* vol. 4, 1934, pp. 203–224.

10. S. Ross, "Sucking behavior in neonate dogs," *Journal of Abnormal and Social Psychology,* vol. 46, 1951, pp. 142–149.

11. David M. Levy, "Instinct satiation, an experiment on the pecking behavior of chickens," *Journal of Genetic Psychology,* vol. 18, 1938, pp. 327–348.

12. B. Hymovitch, "The effects of experimental variations on problem-solving in the rat," *Journal of Comparative Physiological Psychology,* vol. 45, 1952, pp. 313–321

13. Frederick S. Hammett, "Studies of the thyroid apparatus: I," *American Journal of Physiology,* vol. 56, 1921, pp. 196–204.

14. Frederick S. Hammett, "Studies of the thyroid apparatus: V," *Endocrinology,* vol. 6, 1922, pp. 221–229.

15. Walter Freeman and James W. Watts, *Psychosurgery,* Springfield, Illinois, Thomas, 1951; John F. Fulton, *Frontal Lobotomy and Affective Behavior,* New York, Norton, 1951; Phyllis Greenacre (editor), *Affective Disorders,* New York, International Universities Press, 1953.

16. R. E. Money-Kyrle, *Superstition and Society,* London, Hogarth, 1939, p. 126.

17. Margaret A. Ribble, "Infantile experience in relation to personality development," in J. McV. Hunt (editor), *Personality and the Behavior Disorders,* vol. 2, New York, Ronald, 1944, pp. 621–651; Margaret Ribble, *The Rights of Infants,* New York, Columbia University Press, 1943; "The significance of infantile sucking for the psychic development of the individual," and "Disorganizing factors in infant personality," in Silvan Tomkins (editor), *Contemporary Psychopathology,* Cambridge, Harvard University Press, 1943, pp. 1–8, 9–15.

18. For an excellent brief survey see Margaret W. Gerard, "Emotional disorders of childhood," in Franz Alexander (editor), *Dynamic Psychiatry,* Chicago, University of Chicago Press, 1952, pp. 165–210.

19. Edward Bibring, "The mechanism of depression," in Phyllis Greenacre (editor), *op. cit.,* pp. 36–37.

20. Katherine M. Banham, "The development of affectionate behavior in infancy," *Journal of Genetic Psychology,* vol. 76, 1950, pp. 283–289.

21. O. H. Mowrer and Clyde Kluckhohn, "Dynamic theory of personality," in J. McV. Hunt (editor), *Personality and the Behavior Disorders, loc. cit.,* p. 89.

22. Margaret Mead, *And Keep Your Powder Dry,* New York, Morrow, 1942.

23. Gardner Murphy, Lois B. Murphy, and Theodore M. Newcomb, *Experimental Social Psychology,* New York, Harper, 1937, p. 555.

24. For provocative discussions of consciousness in these terms see Karl W. Deutsch, "Mechanism, teleology, and mind," *Philosophy and Phenomenological Research,* vol. 12, 1951, pp. 185–222; and Talcott Parsons, "Consciousness and symbolic processes," in Harold Abramson (editor), *Problems of Consciousness,* New York, Josiah Macy, Jr., Foundation, 1954, pp. 47–58. For an early proponent of

these ideas see Robert Briffault, "Consciousness as a social product," in his *Psyche's Lamp,* London, Allen & Unwin, 1921, pp. 203–216.

25. Lawrence K. Frank, "Cultural coercion and individual distortion," *Psychiatry,* vol. 2, 1939, p. 14.

26. Alfred Baeumler, "Race: a basic concept in education," *World Educaion,* vol. 4, 1939, pp. 506–509 (translated from the German article in the *Internazionale Zeitschrift für Erziehung,* vol. 8, 1939). For a similar point of view see Cyril Darlington, *The Facts of Life,* London, Allen & Unwin, 1953.

27. George E. Simpson and J. M. Yinger *Racial and Cultural Minorities,* New York, Harper, 1953; M. F. Ashley Montagu, *Man's Most Dangerous Myth: The Fallacy of Race,* 3rd ed., New York, Harper, 1952.

28. Romanzo C. Adams, *Interracial Marriage in Hawaii,* New York, Macmillan, 1937; Edwin G. Barrows, *Hawaiian Americans,* New Haven, Yale University Press, 1947.

29. Erwin H. Ackerknecht, "White Indians," *Bulletin of the History of Medicine,* vol. 15, 1944, pp. 15–35. See also Howard H. Peckham, *Captured By Indians,* New Brunswick, N. J., Rutgers University Press, 1954.

Chapter 11. Isolation versus Socialization

1. For Laura Bridgman see Maud Howe Elliott and Florence Howe Hall, *Laura Bridgman,* Boston, Little, Brown, 1903; Mary Swift Lamson, *Life and Education of Laura Dewey Bridgman,* Boston, Houghton Mifflin, 1881. For Helen Keller see Helen Keller, *The Story of My Life,* New York, Doubleday, 1903, 1954.

2. J. A. L. Singh and Robert M. Zingg, *Wolf-Children and Feral Man,* New York, Harper, 1942.

3. J. G. Speed, "Sweat glands of the dog," *Veterinary Journal,* vol. 97, 1941, pp. 252–256; T. Aoki and M. Wada, "Functional activity of the sweat glands in the hairy skin of the dog," *Science,* vol. 114, 1951, pp. 123–124.

4. For this information I am indebted to Dr. Edmund Spaeth, Professor of Ophthalmology at the University of Pennsylvania Medical School.

5. These have been entertainingly discussed in the chapter "Wolf! Wolf!" in Bergen Evans, *The Natural History of Nonsense,* New York, Knopf, 1946, pp. 86–99. Additional relevant material will be found in Wayne Dennis, "The significance of feral man," *American Journal of Psychology,* vol. 54, 1941, pp. 425–432; David G. Mandelbaum, "Wolf-child histories from India," *Journal of Social Psychology,* vol. 17, 1943, pp. 25–44; M. F. Ashley Montagu, "Wolf-children and feral man," *American Anthropologist,* vol. 45, 1943, pp. 468–472.

6. Kingsley Davis, "Extreme social isolation of a child," *American Journal of Sociology,* vol. 45, 1940, pp. 554–565; Kingsley Davis, "Final note on a case of extreme isolation," *American Journal of Sociology,* vol. 52, 1947, pp. 432–437.

7. Many of these accounts will be found in J. R. M. Singh and R. M. Zingg, *op. cit.*

8. A. F. Tredgold, *Mental Deficiency,* 7th ed. Baltimore, William Wood, 1947, pp. 153–154.

9. For further discussion of this subject see, W. Dennis, "The significance of feral man," *loc. cit.,* R. M. Zingg, "Reply to Professor Dennis," *American Journal of Psychology,* vol. 54, 1941, pp. 432–435; Anne Anastasi and John P. Foley, Jr.,

Differential Psychology, New York, Macmillan, 1949, pp. 182–192; W. Dennis, "A further analysis of reports of wild children," *Child Development,* vol. 22, 1951, pp. 153–158; L. J. Stone, "A critique of studies of infant isolation, *Child Development,* vol. 25, 1954, pp. 9–20.

10. G. E. Coghill, *Anatomy and the Problem of Behaviour,* New York, Cambridge University Press, 1929, p. 104.

11. *Ibid.,* p. 105.

12. *Ibid.,* p. 107.

13. *Ibid.,* p. 110.

14. Marie K. Mason, "Learning to speak after six and one half years," *Journal of Speech Disorders,* vol. 7, 1942, pp. 295–304; Kingsley Davis, "Final note on a case of extreme isolation," *loc. cit.,* pp. 432–437.

15. Arnold Gesell and Harry M. Zimmerman, "Correlations of behavior and neuropathology in a case of cerebral palsy from birth injury," *American Journal of Psychiatry,* vol. 94, 1937, pp. 505–536.

16. I am obliged to Nurse Russell and to Dr. R. Schopbach for making the history of this case available to me.

17. Alfred Adler, *Social Interest: A Challenge to Mankind,* New York, Putnam, 1938, pp. 220–221.

Chapter 12. The Direction of Human Development

1. All these allegations, and more, are made about children by no less an authority than Miss Dorothy Thompson in an article entitled "I remember me," in *The Ladies' Home Journal,* February, 1954 and reprinted in *The Reader's Digest,* May, 1954.

2. H. S. Jennings, *Prometheus or Biology and the Advancement of Man,* New York, Dutton, 1925. Jennings' little book should be required reading, once a year at least, for every social scientist and for all biologists. See also, T. Dobzhansky, "What is heredity?" *Science,* vol. 100, 1944, p. 406; P. R. David and L. H. Snyder, "Genetic variability and human behavior," in J. H. Rohrer and M. Sherif (editors), *Psychology at the Crossroads,* New York, Harper, 1951, pp. 53–82.

3. See Robert S. Lynd, *Knowledge For What?* Princeton, Princeton University Press, 1939; George Norlin, *Things in the Saddle,* Cambridge, Harvard University Press, 1940; W. Macneile Dixon, *The Human Situation,* New York, Longmans, 1939; Earl C. Kelley, *Education For What is Real,* New York, Harper, 1947; Marie I. Rasey, *Toward Maturity,* New York, Hinds, Hayden & Eldridge, 1947.

4. Jealousy is a *disorder* of love.

5. For further discussions of love along these lines see Ashley Montagu (editor), *The Meaning of Love,* New York, Julian Press, 1953; Christopher Caudwell, "Love," in the same author's *Studies In A Dying Culture,* London, John Lane, 1938, pp. 129–157; Daniel A. Prescott, "Role of love in human development," *Journal of Home Economics,* vol. 44, 1952, pp. 173–176; Erich Fromm, *Man For Himself,* New York, Rinehart, 1947; Nelson N. Foote, "Love," *Psychiatry,* vol. 16, 1953, pp. 245–251; Ian D. Suttie, *The Origins of Love and Hate,* New York, Julian Press, 1953; Vladimir Solovyev, *The Meaning of Love,* New York, International Universities Press, 1945; Walter De La Mare, *Love,* New York, Knopf, 1943.

6. F. B. I. Report for 1953, *The New York Times,* April 25, 1954.

7. Marjorie Rittwagen, "Child criminals are my job," *Saturday Evening Post,*

March 27, 1954, p. 19; M. L. Barron, *The Juvenile in Delinquent Society,* New York, Knopf, 1954.

8. J. Louise Despert, *Children of Divorce,* New York, Doubleday, 1953.

9. H. A. Bloch, *Disorganization,* New York, Knopf, 1952, p. 4.

10. J. C. Flugel, *The Psycho-Analytic Study of the Family,* London, Hogarth Press, 1921; Fritz Wittels, *Set the Children Free,* London, Allen & Unwin, 1932; Alfred Adler, *Social Interest: A Challenge to Mankind,* New York, Putnam, 1938; Anne L. Kuhn, *The Mother's Role in Childhood Education: New England Concepts,* New Haven, Yale University Press, 1947; Percival M. Symonds, *The Dynamics of Parent-Child Relationships,* New York, Bureau of Publications, Teachers College, 1949; James H. Bossard, *Parent and Child,* Philadelphia, University of Pennsylvania Press, 1953.

11. Quoted to me by Dr. John Rosen of New York City and Doylestown, Pa.

12. See, for example, John LaFarge, *The Manner Is Ordinary,* New York, Harcourt Brace, 1954, p. 166, who writes, "a priest's celibacy is a true fatherhood, as that of a woman dedicated to life in a religious community is a genuine motherhood." See also P. A. Sorokin, *Altruistic Love,* Boston, Beacon Press, 1950.

13. Weston La Barre, *The Human Animal,* Chicago, University of Chicago Press, 1954, p. 210.

14. It is of interest to note that the first word which a human being is most likely to utter is "mother"—it is also the last word which men are likely to utter. The last word, however, that a woman utters is likely to be some unselfish thought for another.

15. Plato, *The Republic,* Bk. V, 461—and numerous others.

16. Heinrich Pestalozzi, *Aphorisms,* New York, Philosophical Library, 1947, pp. 4–5.

17. E. M. Forster, *A Room with a View,* New York, Knopf, 1954, p. 306.

18. J. H. Burns, *The Gallery,* New York, Harper, 1948; H. Kubly, *American in Italy,* New York, Simon & Schuster, 1955.

19. R. Métraux and M. Mead, *Themes in French Culture,* Stanford, California, Standford University Press, 1954.

20. On this subject see W. A. R. Leys, "Human values in the atomic age," *Annals of the American Academy of Political and Social Science,* vol. 1, 1953, pp. 127–133; M. F. Ashley Montagu, "Living in an atom-bomb world," *Technology Review,* vol. 52, 1950, pp. 205–228; see also the film, made by the author of this book, "One World or None," obtainable from the National Committee on Atomic Information, Washington, D.C.

21. For an illuminating discussion of value from this point of view see Hadley Cantril, *The "Why" of Human Experience,* New York, Macmillan, 1950. For useful works on value theory see Ray Lepley (editor), *Value: A Cooperative Inquiry,* New York, Columbia University Press, 1939; Clyde Kluckhohn, "Values and value orientations in the theory of action: Explorations in definition and classification," in T. Parsons and E. A. Shils (editors), *Toward A General Theory of Action,* Cambridge, Harvard University Press, 1951, pp. 388–433; W. C. Trow, "The value concept in educational psychology," *Journal of Educational Psychology,* vol. 44, 1953, pp. 449–462; Abraham Edel, "Concept of values in contemporary philosophical value theory," *Philosophy of Science,* vol. 20, 1953, pp. 198–207.

22. Arnold Brecht, "The myth of 'is' and 'ought.'" *The Political Philosophy of Arnold Brecht,* New York, The New School for Social Research, 1954, pp. 115–116.

23. Hugh Miller, *The Community of Man,* New York, Macmillan, 1949, a book

which I regard as one of the most brilliant and important published in our time, but which has received far too little attention.

24. For a close approach to the ethical point of view arrived at in these pages see the works of three philosophers: Hugh Miller mentioned above; A. Campbell Garnett (*The Moral Nature of Man,* New York, Ronald Press, 1952); and W. T. Stace (*What Are Our Values?* Lincoln, University of Nebraska, 1950). See also Walter A. Weisskopf, "The ethical role of psychodynamics," *Ethics,* vol. 62, 1952, pp. 184–190.

25. See M. F. Ashley Montagu, *Helping Children Develop Moral Values,* Chicago, Science Research Associates, 1953.

26. See further on this subject, Anders Nygren, *Agape and Eros,* London, S.P.C.K., 1953; J. Burnaby, *Amor Dei,* London, 1938; M. C. D'Arcy, *The Mind and Heart of Love: A Study of Eros and Agape,* London, Faber, 1945; Paul Tillich, *Love, Power, and Justice,* New York, Oxford University Press, 1954.

27. On this subject see Josué de Castro, *The Geography of Hunger,* Boston, Little Brown, 1952; Harcourt Brown, *The Challenge of Man's Future,* New York, Viking, 1954; F. Le Gros Clark and N. W. Pirie, *Four Thousand Million Mouths,* New York, Oxford University Press, 1951; but above all read Murray D. Lincoln, *Plenty—Pattern for Peace,* Columbus, Ohio, Farm Bureau Insurance Companies, 1952.

28. O. Spurgeon English and Stuart M. Finch, *Introduction to Psychiatry,* New York, Norton, 1954, p. 11.

29. Julian Huxley, *Evolution In Action,* New York, Harper, 1953, pp. 162–163.

30. In this connection see the little-known book by Leo Tolstoy, *The Law of Love and the Law of Violence,* New York, Rudolph Field, 1948.

Appendix A Learning Theory

1. For a survey of learning theories see E. R. Hilgard, *Theories of Learning,* New York, Appleton-Century-Crofts, 1948. See also W. K. Estes *et al., Modern Learning Theory,* New York, Appleton-Century-Crofts, 1954; Kentucky Symposium, *Learning Theory, Personality Theory and Clinical Research,* New York, Wiley, 1954.

2. A rat psychologist has been defined as one who is always pulling habits out of rats.

3. See especially Dorrian Apple, "Learning theory and socialization," *American Sociological Review,* vol. 16, 1951, pp. 23–27. See also B. F. Skinner, "Are theories of learning necessary?" *Psychological Review,* vol. 57, 1950, pp. 193–216.

4. J. L. Moreno and F. B. Moreno, *Spontaneity Theory of Child Development,* New York, Beacon House, 1944, p. 9. For an extensive treatment of "spontaneity," see J. L. Moreno, *Who Shall Survive?* 2d ed., New York, Beacon House, 1953.

5. Jean Piaget, *Play, Dreams and Imitation in Childhood,* New York, Norton, 1953, p. 148.

6. J. L. Moreno and F. B. Moreno, *op. cit.,* p. 41.

7. For a discussion along these lines see Clark L. Hull, *A Behavior System,* New Haven, Yale University Press, 1952, p. 327, *et seq.*

8. E. R. Guthrie, "Conditioning; a theory of learning in terms of stimulus, response, and association," *Forty-First Yearbook of the National Society for the Study of Education,* Part 2, Bloomington, Illinois, Public School Publishing Co., 1942, p. 17.

9. Clark L. Hull, *Principles of Behavior,* New York, Appleton-Century-Crofts, 1943.

10. *Ibid.*, p. 386.

11. Edward L. Thorndike, *Animal Intelligence,* New York, Macmillan, 1911, p. 244.

12. Lawrence E. Cole, *Human Behavior,* New York, World, 1953, p. 264.

13. This discussion owes most to the following workers: Neal E. Miller and John Dollard, *Social Learning and Imitation,* New Haven, Yale University Press, 1941; John Dollard and Neal E. Miller, *Personality and Psychotherapy,* New York, McGraw-Hill, 1950; Clellan S. Ford, "Culture and human behavior," Scientific *Monthly,* vol. 55, 1942, pp. 546–557; O. H. Mowrer, *Learning Theory and Personality Dynamics,* New York, Ronald Press, 1950; Gardner Murphy, *Personality,* New York, Harper, 1947; J. W. Tilton, *An Educational Psychology of Learning,* New York, Macmillan, 1951.

14. G. W. Allport, *Personality,* New York, Holt, 1937, pp. 191–207, especially p. 194.

15. Clark L. Hull, *Principles of Behavior, loc. cit.,* p. 197; E. R. Hilgard and D. G. Marquis, *Conditioning and Learning,* New York, Appleton-Century-Crofts, 1940, p. 176.

16. N. E. Miller and John Dollard, *op. cit.,* pp. 49–50.

17. O. H. Mowrer and Clyde Kluckhohn, "Dynamic theory of personality," in *Personality And The Behavior Disorders* (edited by J. McV. Hunt), New York, Ronald Press, 1944, p. 82.

18. D. K. Spelt, "The conditioning of the human fetus *in utero,*" *Journal of Experimental Psychology,* vol. 38, 1948, pp. 338–346.

19. M. A. Wenger, "Conditioned responses in human infants," in *Child Behavior and Development* (edited by R. G. Barker, J. S. Kounin, and H. F. Wright), New York, McGraw-Hill, 1943, pp. 67–86.

20. G. Murphy, L. B. Murphy, and T. Newcomb, *Experimental Social Psychology,* New York, Harper, 1937, pp. 162–163.

21. For an excellent demonstration of this see Milton H. Erikson, "Experimental demonstrations of the psychopathology of everyday life," in Silvan S. Tomkins (editor), *Contemporary Psychopathology,* Cambridge, Harvard University Press, 1943, pp. 517–528.

22. M. F. Ashley Montagu, "Conditioning and reconditioning in the psychotherapeutic situation," *American Journal of Psychology,* vol. 58, 1945, pp. 391–392.

23. G. Murphy, L. B. Murphy, and T. Newcomb, *op. cit.,* p. 163.

24. *Ibid.,* p. 164.

25. Helene Deutsch, *Psychology of Women,* New York, Grune and Stratton, 1944, vol. 1, 1936.

26. Gardner Murphy, *op. cit.,* pp. 193–194.

27. Jean Piaget, *op. cit.*

28. N. E. Miller and John Dollard, *op. cit.,* pp. 94–95.

29. M. F. Ashley Montagu, *Coming Into Being Among the Australian Aborigines,* London, Routledge, 1937.

30. N. E. Miller and J. Dollard, *op. cit.,* pp. 184–185.

31. S. Freud, *Group Psychology and the Analysis of the Ego,* London, Hogarth Press, 1922, pp. 60–80.

32. S. Freud, *New Introductory Lectures on Psychoanalysis,* New York, Garden City, 1933

33. J. P. Seward, "Learning theory and identification, II. The role of punishment," *Journal of Genetic Psychology,* vol. 84, 1954, pp. 201–210.

34. F. Alexander, *Fundamentals of Psychoanalysis,* New York, Norton, 1948, p. 92.

35. O. H. Mowrer, "Learning theory and identification. I. Introduction," *Journal of Genetic Psychology,* vol. 84, 1954, pp. 197–199.

36. A. Balint, "Identification," in S. Lorand (editor), *The Yearbook of Psychoanalysis,* New York, International Universities Press, p. 321, p. 326. See also Ives Hendrick, "Early development of the ego: identification in infancy," *Psychoanalytic Quarterly,* vol. 20, 1954, pp. 44–61.; Edmund Burgler, "The 'leading' and 'misleading' basic identifications," *Psychoanalytic Review,* vol. 32, 1954, pp. 263–295.

37. Neal E. Miller and John Dollard, *op. cit.,* p. 61.

38. G. Murphy, L. B. Murphy, and T. M. Newcomb, *op. cit.,* p. 192.

39. *Ibid.*

40. *Ibid.,* p. 199.

INDEX